Scott Whitfield

Volume I

QUANTUM THEORY OF
ATOMIC STRUCTURE

The late F. K. Richtmyer was Consulting Editor of the series from its inception in 1929 to his death in 1939. Lee A. DuBridge was Consulting Editor from 1939 to 1946; and G. P. Harnwell from 1947 to 1954.

QUANTUM THEORY OF
ATOMIC STRUCTURE

VOLUME I

JOHN C. SLATER

Institute Professor
Massachusetts Institute of Technology

McGRAW-HILL BOOK COMPANY, INC.

New York   Toronto   London   1960

QUANTUM THEORY OF ATOMIC STRUCTURE   VOLUME I

THE MAPLE PRESS COMPANY, YORK, PA.

Preface

This two-volume work is the first of a series of books which I hope to write, covering the field of the application of quantum mechanics to the structure of atoms, molecules, and solids and to the theory of the physical and chemical properties of matter. Ever since the development of wave mechanics in 1926, it has been clear that we had the theoretical basis for the study of matter; but the theory has been difficult enough so that progress in working it out has been slow. Nevertheless, even in the first ten years following 1926, the general outlines of the theory began to be clear, and by now a great many of the details have been worked out, though there is still a great deal to be done. The subject has grown enormously and is constantly developing. This expansion, in a sense, is mirrored in a sequence of books which I have already written. In 1933 Professor Frank and I, in "Introduction to Theoretical Physics," included about 200 pages on the quantum theory and its applications to the study of matter. In 1951, in "Quantum Theory of Matter," I enlarged this material to a full-length book of some 500 pages. Now I am taking two volumes to go over the material on atoms which is treated in the first 200 pages of "Quantum Theory of Matter." And I hope that there are a number of volumes still to come.

I have here followed the same general plan which was used in those two earlier books; that is, to start with the principles of wave mechanics, then to use these to discuss the hydrogen atom, the central-field problem, and more complicated atoms. Since some of the same ground was covered in the earlier books, I have not hesitated to use material from them when it seemed appropriate, and the reader will find that in the first volume of the present work, essentially all the topics are covered which are taken up in the first seven chapters of "Quantum Theory of Matter." But it is obvious, from the increased length, that there is much more besides, and I hope that the presentation is significantly improved. The second volume of the present work is almost entirely new material, which was not covered at all in either of the earlier books.

It has been my aim to write the two volumes of the present work on rather different levels of difficulty. The first volume starts with the beginning of wave mechanics, and I believe that it can well be used as an introductory text in quantum mechanics, as well as in atomic structure. It uses only the more elementary methods to discuss the structure of atoms and yet gets far enough so that the two final chapters of the volume give a rather complete survey of present work on the structure of some of the more important of the atoms. It is my view that everything in this volume is really needed by anyone who expects to go on to the study of quantum chemistry, or the theory of solids, or any aspect of the theory of matter. With the needs of the fairly elementary student in mind (that is, of perhaps a first-year graduate student) I have included problems, appendixes covering such topics as the parts of classical mechanics needed to discuss quantum mechanics, and enough references to enable the student to get started studying the literature.

The second volume, on the other hand, is on a level which will probably make it mostly used as a reference work in the more advanced aspects of the theory of atomic structure. In its appendixes it includes considerable tabular material which would be valuable to the professional student of atomic theory. It contains a rather full bibliography of the major papers relating to the development both of wave mechanics and of atomic structure. Many of the topics taken up in this second volume are as essential as those in the first volume for those going on with chemical or solid-state theory; some other parts, such as Racah's methods, for example, have so far found fewer applications outside the field of atomic structure but are likely to prove more useful in the future, and I believe it very desirable for the student to have them available, even though he may not study them in his graduate work. This second volume carries the subject in most respects as far as the excellent and well-known work of Condon and Shortley, "Theory of Atomic Spectra" (Cambridge University Press, 1935), and in many respects it goes further, since there have been many advances in the field since that book was written. I must acknowledge here my debt to that book and my respect for its pioneering effort in the field.

As I mentioned at the beginning of this Preface, it is my hope to follow this book with further ones, on more or less the same level, treating the theory of molecules and of solids. These later books will make use of the present one to give the fundamental grounding which they require; for practically all the more advanced methods of molecular and solid-state theory are the outgrowths of problems which are already met in the study of atomic structure.

In the present state of science the study of atomic structure is needed by many persons other than the theoretical physicist. The chemist, the metallurgist, the electrical engineer, all are meeting problems of the application of quantum theory to the study of matter as very essential parts of their subjects.   Often these other workers have not had as thorough a grounding in quantum mechanics and its applications as they need to handle their subjects properly.   I have had them in mind, just as much as the professional physicist, in writing this book and shall continue to keep them in mind in the further books in this series.   I believe that it is a mistake to think that a chemist or an engineer who wishes to study the application of quantum mechanics to his field can be satisfied with a more superficial treatment than a physicist can.   In other words, I do not think that the present two volumes go too far for these workers.   But since they often have a restricted background in theoretical physics, I have tried to make this book as complete as possible, so that it can be read without the need of consulting other texts, aside from those on mathematics, with which in these days most engineers are well acquainted.

There is one other comment which I might make concerning the theoretical physicist.   In these days physics has become divided very sharply into two categories: nuclear and nonnuclear physics, the latter including the topics taken up in the present series of books.   The training of nuclear physicists is often deficient in the study of chemical and solid-state physics.   I hope that the present series of books may help remedy this deficiency.   I feel, specifically, that there is nothing in the present two volumes which is not as essential to a nuclear physicist as to a chemical or solid-state physicist.   Many of the topics coming into nuclear theory, such as multiplet theory, vector coupling, and so on, are taken over rather directly from ordinary atomic theory.   It may well be that the present work will prove to be a useful introduction to these topics, for nuclear physicists.

Finally I should like to acknowledge the great stimulation, in the writing of this book and of the others which I hope will follow it, of the members of the Solid-State and Molecular Theory Group at the Massachusetts Institute of Technology, and in particular of Professor G. F. Koster of that group.   The chance of talking over the various problems of the quantum theory of matter with the members of the group, over the past eight years or more, has been as helpful to me as I hope it has been to the members of the group.   I should also like to acknowledge the helpfulness of the Office of Naval Research, and of the Lincoln Laboratory, in extending the financial support which has made that group possible.

John C. Slater

Contents

1

The Historical Development of Modern
Physics, from 1900 to Bohr's Theory

1-1. Introduction. The first half of the present century has been one of the most fruitful periods in the development of physics. It has seen the theory of relativity, the quantum theory, and modern ideas of the structure of atoms, molecules, and solids come into existence. There have been several other very exciting times in the history of physics. One came with the development of classical mechanics, by Galileo, Huygens, Kepler, and Newton, in the seventeenth century. Another was the development of the wave theory of light, by Young and Fresnel, at the beginning of the nineteenth century. Still another was the development of our ideas of electromagnetism, starting with Oersted, Faraday, and others, and culminating in the theoretical work of Maxwell, showing that electromagnetic waves and light were identical; this was a product of the middle of the nineteenth century. A later nineteenth-century development was the theory of heat, leading to the kinetic theory of gases and the theory of statistical mechanics, by Clausius, Boltzmann, and Gibbs. All these great advances in the science were essentially complete by 1900, and the stage was set for another and different development, along atomic lines. The present century has seen this development, and it deserves to rank with the others in importance, if it does not in fact overshadow them. Perhaps the leading names to be attached to these twentieth-century discoveries are Planck,[1] Einstein,[2] Rutherford,[3] Bohr,[4] Heisenberg,[5] and Schrödinger.[6] They rank with the great physicists of history.

[1] M. Planck, *Ann. Physik,* **4**:553 (1901).
[2] A. Einstein, *Ann. Physik,* **17**:891 (1905); **18**:639 (1905).
[3] E. Rutherford, *Phil. Mag.,* **21**:669 (1911).
[4] N. Bohr, *Phil. Mag.,* **26**(1):476 (1913).
[5] W. Heisenberg, *Z. Physik,* **33**:879 (1925).
[6] E. Schrödinger, *Ann. Physik,* **79**:361, 489, 734; **80**:437, **81**:109 (1926).

The layman has become better acquainted with the name of Einstein and his theory of relativity than with any of the other results of twentieth-century physics. His famous equation $E = mc^2$, where m is a mass, c the velocity of light, and where the equation states that this mass is equivalent to an energy E, is familiar to everyone, along with its application to nuclear physics and the development of nuclear energy. In contrast, Rutherford, who made the discovery of the nuclear atom, and Planck, Bohr, Heisenberg, and Schrödinger, who developed the quantum theory and its application to atomic structure, are less well known. The physicist ranks them as equally significant, however. They will concern us in our work more than Einstein and the theory of relativity. That theory is particularly important when we are dealing with very high energies, very great velocities approaching the velocity of light. Such questions concern us when we are dealing with the atomic nucleus. But one of the facts emerging from our present knowledge of the atom is that there is a very clear-cut distinction between the phenomena of the atomic nucleus and those of the outer part of the atom. All ordinary effects of heat, light, electricity and magnetism, chemistry, metallurgy, and so on, arise entirely from the outer part of the atom. They are not concerned with very great energies; and, for them, relativity plays the part of a minor correction to classical mechanics. On the contrary, it is for just such problems relating to very small systems, on an atomic scale, that the quantum theory is needed. Our task in this volume will be to review the present theory of these phenomena which arise from the outer parts of atoms; we shall omit the nuclear phenomena, not because they are not important but because to include them would make an impracticably large book. Hence we shall use relativity only incidentally, but the quantum theory must be our principal topic.

The development of the quantum theory stretched over 25 years, and there are three vital dates to remember in connection with it, at the beginning, the middle, and the end of the period. In 1901 Planck made the first suggestion of the quantum theory. In 1913 Bohr found how to apply it to the theory of the hydrogen atom, making the first real advance in our understanding of the dynamics of the particles in the atom. And in 1926 Schrödinger discovered the equation which bears his name, which furnished the real mathematical basis of the theory, a basis which was partly foreshadowed in the preceding year, 1925, in a different but equivalent form, by Heisenberg. Since 1926, we have been engaged in working out the consequences of Schrödinger's formulation of the theory, which is known as wave mechanics, and in applying it to the many problems of atomic, molecular, and solid-state structure. We feel that the theory, as now formulated, provides the precise mathematical foundation for all these phenomena, just as Newton's laws provide the foundation for classical mechanics and Maxwell's equations that for electromagnetism. Unfortunately, wave mechanics is a much more difficult branch of mathematics than either of these others, and we are still far from having worked out all the consequences of the theoretical discoveries made in 1926. But the progress has been great, and we can now give a very convincing picture of the structure of atoms and of their behavior under all sorts of external conditions. This is the topic of our book.

In the major part of the present work, we shall assume the principles of wave mechanics as the foundation of our treatment, just as a text on classical mechanics assumes Newton's law or one on electromagnetism assumes Maxwell's equations, and we shall proceed from these principles in a deductive way, to try to explain the behavior of matter. But the reader will not appreciate the subject properly if he is not familiar with the processes of discovery which had to be passed through in the period from 1901 to 1926, to develop these laws. Such an inductive period in science is in some ways more stimulating than a deductive period, in which one is merely working out the consequences of principles which everyone admits are true. To give the reader a little of this appreciation, we present in the first two chapters a short sketch of the historical development of physics, during the momentous quarter century from 1901 to 1926.

1-2. The Electron and the Nuclear Atom.   A number of observations during the nineteenth century had indicated that atoms had some sort of internal structure, of an electrical nature. One type of information came from Faraday's experiments on electrolysis. Faraday found that, when electric current passed through an ionic solution, material was deposited on the electrodes. But, furthermore, he observed that the amount deposited was always proportional to the amount of charge transferred by the current. It was as if each ion that had passed through the electrolytic tank had carried just so much charge. If there had been a good measurement of the mass of an atom in those days, Faraday from his experiments could have said just how big this charge was. Crude estimates of atomic masses were available, and hence crude guesses as to this charge were possible. We know now that the charge, for a monovalent ion, is just one electronic charge; and, in the way indicated, there were rough estimates of this quantity by the end of the nineteenth century. The name electron, for this unit of charge, was invented by the Englishman Stoney, in the 1880s.

Before the end of the century, the electron had been discovered as an isolated particle. Crookes, J. J. Thomson, and many others had been making experiments on electrical discharges in gases. They found very good evidence that charged particles, carrying both positive and negative charges, existed in these discharges. They deflected those particles in electric and magnetic fields, just about at the close of the century, and from their dynamics made estimates of the ratio of their charge to mass. From this information it was found that some of the negatively charged particles had a mass small compared with an atomic mass; it was assumed that these particles were the electrons themselves. The positively charged particles, however, called ions, proved to have masses of atomic size.

There was evidence that atoms contained not only electrons but building blocks of other types as well. One could not fail to observe, as Prout had noticed fairly early in the nineteenth century, that the atomic weights of many of the elements proved to be surprisingly close to integers; and Prout had suggested that they were made out of fundamental particles, perhaps hydrogen atoms, all alike. This hypothesis of course came up against the obvious obstacle that some of the atomic weights were very far from integers, and it remained for the discovery of isotopes in the present century to remove this difficulty and show that Prout's hypothesis really had foundation.

Finally, during the last years of the century, two new discoveries greatly excited the physicists. Röntgen, in 1895, discovered the X rays, or roentgen rays. These rays, capable of passing through matter, were completely different from anything observed before. Their discovery was followed almost immediately by Becquerel's discovery of radioactivity, from the observation that uranium emitted rays which, like the X rays, could pass through matter and in fact could blacken a photographic plate even if it were wrapped up in an opaque covering. It was discovered that in radioactive disintegrations several types of radiation were emitted, and by 1900 J. J. Thomson, the Curies, Crookes, Rutherford, and Soddy were all working actively on the problem of finding what they were. Soon, also, the chemical separation of radium from uranium by the Curies, and other similar experiments, had shown that a number of elements were radioactive.

It did not take long to establish the nature of the types of radiation emitted by radioactive atoms, which Rutherford called alpha, beta, and gamma radiation. It was shown that the alpha and beta rays were deflected by electric and magnetic fields, so that they consisted of streams of charged particles, while the gamma rays were not deflected. By experiments on the deflection, it was shown that the beta rays were electrons, with the same ratio e/m, or ratio of charge to mass, which the electrons had already been found to have by J. J. Thomson. The alpha particles, however, were found to be positively charged, rather than negatively as the electrons were, and to have a value of e/m indicating that their mass was in the neighborhood of atomic masses, much greater than the electronic mass. By comparison with e/m experiments on other positive ions, it appeared that they were helium ions with a charge equal to twice the electronic charge. As for the gamma rays, which could not be deflected, it was soon shown that they were identical in nature with X rays, which had been shown to be electromagnetic waves like light; the X rays, however, had wavelengths much shorter than ordinary light, and the gamma rays had still shorter wavelengths.

The next question which arose was: How did these radiations come to be emitted from the radioactive atoms? This question was closely connected with another one, which at first seemed very puzzling: when a sample of radioactive material was examined, its properties often changed with time, in complicated ways, as if its composition were not staying constant. Rutherford and Soddy, in 1903, proposed an explanation which has proved to be correct and which tied together all the known facts about radioactivity. This explanation suggested that radioactive atoms could spontaneously explode, transforming themselves into other atoms, and that such explosions were going on all the time, so that in a given time interval a certain fraction of the atoms would blow up, quite independent of outside influences. If we have a number of atoms of which a fixed fraction is destroyed per second, this means that the number remaining at any time will decrease exponentially with the time (provided there are no new atoms being produced), and the length of time required for the number to be reduced to half its original value is called the half-life. Rutherford and Soddy found elements with all sorts of half-lives, from short ones of a few minutes to long ones of thousands or millions or billions of years.

The theory of Rutherford and Soddy went much further than this simple hypothesis of explosion, for they also were able to find out what were the products of one of the explosions. If an atom when it explodes transforms itself into another, then the number of atoms of this other type will gradually increase with time, unless an equilibrium is established by a subsequent explosion of the new type of atoms. By an elaborate series of tests, Rutherford and Soddy were able to show which atoms were transformed radioactively into which others, with the half-lives of each type. They were able to set up simultaneous differential equations for the numbers of atoms of the various types as functions of time, to solve these equations, and to show that they gave a complete explanation of the complicated effects which they had observed as to the time dependence of radioactivity. The case they made out for the transformation hypothesis was so convincing that it has never been questioned.

They found extremely interesting correlations between the chemical properties of the various radioactive elements which they discovered and the types of radiations which they emitted. They found that, when an atom emitted an alpha particle, the resulting atomic species showed chemical properties which would place it two units before the parent atom in the periodic table of the elements, while if it emitted a beta particle, its chemical properties would indicate that it should be one unit beyond the parent atom. This suggested an extremely important generalization, which is in a way the foundation of our whole present understanding of the periodic system of the elements: it suggested that the ordinal number of an atom in the periodic table of the elements, starting with hydrogen 1, helium 2, lithium 3, and so on, which we now call the atomic number, represented in some way the number of units of positive charge in the atom. For if this were the case, the emission of an alpha particle, which has two units of positive charge, should decrease the atomic number by 2, while the emission of a beta particle, with one unit of negative charge, should increase the atomic number by unity. Many sorts of subsequent evidence have verified the correctness of this hypothesis. A corollary of the hypothesis is obvious: since an atom as a whole is uncharged, a neutral atom must contain a number of electrons equal numerically to its atomic number.

One of the early verifications of this corollary regarding the number of electrons came from the so-called Thomson scattering formula for X rays. Thomson, assuming that X rays were simply electromagnetic rays of short wavelength, investigated the law of scattering by matter containing electrons. His formula showed that the scattering should be proportional to the number of electrons per unit volume. It was later shown that X-ray scattering is really much more complicated than this, on account of crystal diffraction; but there are important cases where Thomson's scattering formula holds, and it was shown experimentally by Barkla and others that the scattering was approximately in agreement with the hypothesis that the number of scattering electrons per atom was equal to the atomic number.

Rutherford and Soddy could draw definite conclusions regarding atomic masses, or atomic weights. The helium atom, or alpha particle, has four units of atomic weight. Hence it is clear that, if an atom emits an alpha particle, the new atom resulting from it must have an atomic weight which is less by four units. The electron, or beta particle, on the other hand, has practically no mass compared with the mass of an atom, so that, if an atom emits a beta particle, its atomic weight should not change. There were a number of cases where these hypotheses could be verified. In particular, the radioactive series of elements terminated in lead as a final product, and the atomic weight of this lead could be determined from certain minerals whose lead content apparently resulted as an end product of radioactive disintegration; its atomic weight had the predicted value, as found from the uranium or thorium which was the original element from which the lead was descended. Furthermore, the atomic weight of this lead was different from that of ordinary lead, a fact which seemed very remarkable to the chemists of that time but which became clear soon afterward with the discovery of isotopes. Thus radium disintegrates into lead of atomic weight 206, thorium into lead of atomic weight 208, while ordinary lead has an atomic weight of about 207.

The atomic weight of helium is almost exactly 4, so that, in a series of radioactive elements in which one is produced from another by the emission of an alpha or a beta particle, the atomic weights of successive elements differ almost exactly by four units.   These atomic weights were found to be very close to integers.   As a result, the physicists of the time began to take very seriously Prout's hypothesis that the true atomic weights of all atoms are integers, and the current explanation was that they were made up out of protons and electrons.   We now know that this explanation was not complete. We now understand the nuclear nature of the atom, which was not known until Rutherford proved it in 1911, and we know that the nuclei are built up out of protons, hydrogen nuclei with a unit positive charge and a unit mass or atomic weight, and neutrons, uncharged particles with a mass almost the same as that of the proton.   The alpha particle consists of two neutrons and two protons, accounting for its charge of 2 (from the charges on the two protons) and its atomic weight of 4 (from the four particles).   We also know that a stable nucleus contains approximately equal numbers of protons and neutrons, as the alpha particle does; this explains the empirical fact that atomic weights are approximately twice the atomic numbers.   The number of neutrons is, in fact, somewhat greater than the number of protons, for the heavier elements, so that the atomic weight is somewhat more than twice the atomic number.

We also know now that artificially radioactive atoms can be formed, in which there are too many neutrons, or too many protons, for the ideal composition corresponding to stability.   These atoms can disintegrate by emission of various types of particles, with the release of various amounts of energy.   We know, furthermore, that, on account of Einstein's relation $E = mc^2$, the release of a certain amount of energy makes a corresponding change in the mass.   The mass equivalent of the energy released is small compared with a unit of atomic weight; and the net result of this is that the atomic weights of the various atoms are almost integers, but not quite.   As we say, we now understand these matters relating to the masses of the various atoms quite thoroughly, but they were not understood in the period around 1911 of which we are writing. The first observation of artificial radioactivity came in 1919, when Rutherford produced the artificial disintegration of an atom, bombarding a nitrogen atom with an alpha particle, and knocking off a proton.   It was not until 1932 that Chadwick, in studying the disintegration of beryllium by alpha particles, knocked off a neutral particle which came to be known as the neutron. Until this discovery of the neutron in 1932 it was believed that the nucleus was made of protons and electrons. But we are getting ahead of our story: in the period around 1911, it was surmised that true atomic weights were integers, as Prout had supposed a hundred years earlier, but it was not even known that the nucleus of the atom existed. It was popular, following ideas of Thomson, to think of the positive charge in the atom as being spread throughout the volume of the atom, perhaps in a uniformly charged sphere. Let us return to this period and consider the discoveries which led to the understanding of the nuclear atom.

There was, in the first place, an obvious experimental objection to Prout's hypothesis: the existence of chemical elements, like chlorine with its atomic weight of 35.46, whose atomic weights were not integral. The number of elements with integral atomic weights was far too large to be explained by chance, but how could one explain these nonintegral values? A solution was immediately suggested by Rutherford and Soddy's explanation of radioactive disintegration. They found in a number of cases that there were several elements of the same atomic number, but of different atomic weight, arising in various stages of radioactive disintegrations; the case of lead, which we have already mentioned, was an obvious one. Their hypothesis indicated that the chemical properties of the element depended only on the atomic number. Hence these elements should be chemically identical, and in fact, as far as chemical tests showed, they were. It was very natural to assume that the same thing might be going on among the nonradioactive elements: that many of our ordinary elements might be mixtures of a number of different nuclear species, all with the same atomic number, but with different atomic weights. The elements whose atomic weights were known to be integral would be assumed to consist of only one such nuclear species, whereas those, like chlorine, which obviously had fractional atomic weights would have to be mixtures.

This hypothesis was soon verified, in a brilliant way, by the work of Aston with his mass spectrograph, following up the pioneer work of Thomson. Thomson and Aston examined ordinary elements, neon being one of the very early ones worked on, found the values of e/m for the ions, and hence found the masses of the atoms. And they found that in many cases the elements as they existed in nature did in fact consist of mixtures of atoms of different atomic weights and that these atomic weights were integers, as accurately as they could tell at the time. Soddy had invented the name isotopes, to represent the different atoms with the same atomic number, and hence chemical behavior, but different atomic weight. Continuation of this work of Aston into the 1920s and later has disclosed the isotopic constitution of all the elements and has shown that the chemical atomic weights are nothing but a suitably weighted mean of the atomic weights of the various isotopes. The fact that the chemical atomic weight is found to be the same in almost all natural samples of a given element shows that the matter composing the earth must have been once well mixed, presumably while the earth was still molten, so that all chlorine, for instance, is made up from the original mixture having definite ratios of its various isotopes. The only observed cases where natural atomic weights vary are in those elements which have been produced by radioactive disintegration since the earth solidified.

The measurements we have been discussing are those of e/m, the ratio of charge to mass of the ion. In addition to these, measurements of the electronic charge e were necessary, which, by means of the measured e/m, led to absolute determinations of the masses of the atoms, and hence of Avogadro's number, the number of atoms in a gram-molecular weight. Rough estimates of the charge of positive nuclei had been made early in the study of radioactivity; since atoms are electrically neutral, the positive ions must carry numerically the same charge as an electron or a multiple of it. In radioactive disintegrations, where charged particles are thrown off by nuclei, the number of disintegrations could be estimated by observing nuclear processes by scintillation methods. By allowing the particles to impinge on a luminescent screen, each nuclear disintegration became visible and could be seen with a microscope. The total amount of charge released in such disintegrations could be measured by electrical methods. From these two pieces of information, the charge involved in a single disintegration could be found. Measurements of this type were not accurate, however; and it was not until the development of Millikan's well-known oil-drop experiment in 1911, refining a method used earlier by Townsend in a cruder form, that we had really good measurements of the electronic charge. This brought with it, as we see, a determination of the masses both of the electron and of atoms, and consequently of Avogadro's number.

We have now sketched the main outlines of the arguments that went into the elucidation of the relations between atomic number, atomic weight, and chemical properties. The next great step was that taken by Rutherford in 1911, when his experiments on the scattering of alpha particles by matter led to the hypothesis of the nuclear atom. Rutherford allowed a beam of alpha particles to pass through matter and observed that most of the particles showed very slight deviations from a straight path. However, occasional particles showed deflections through very large angles, and calculation of the dynamics of a collision between an alpha particle and an electron showed that such a deflection could not result from such a collision, under any circumstances; the electron is too light to be able to deflect a heavy particle that much, no matter how close the collision is.   This mathematical analysis showed that such a sharp deflection could come only from a collision of a heavy particle with another of comparable mass and at such a small distance that the electrical force of attraction or repulsion was extremely great.

Such an observation was completely incomprehensible if the positive charge in the atom was spread out over the whole atom, as Thomson had assumed.   The only sort of explanation which could be given was that the positive charge was very concentrated, in a minute nucleus, carrying almost all the mass, and yet so small that two nuclei could approach to a distance very small compared with atomic dimensions.   Rutherford therefore concluded that the alpha particle, and the nuclei, must be essentially point particles, containing almost the whole mass of the atom, and with positive charges equal numerically to the atomic number times the electronic charge, so that the alpha particle would have a charge of two units.   He used the theory of scattering, assuming that the particles repelled each other according to the Coulomb law of electrostatics, with a force inversely proportional to the square of the distance between and proportional to the product of the charges, and predicting how many alpha particles should be scattered through each angle.   When this formula was compared with the experimental results, it checked very satisfactorily, verifying the assumption that the charges on the nuclei were given by the atomic numbers and that they acted electrostatically on each other.

This experiment, then, furnished the experimental proof of the nuclear atom.   Rutherford at once was able to give a general picture of an atom. It consisted of a very minute nucleus, containing practically all the mass of the atom, with a positive charge equal to the atomic number times the magnitude of the electronic charge.   For electrical neutrality, the nucleus would have to be surrounded by a number of electrons equal to the atomic number.   The forces exerted between two nuclei were shown to be given by the Coulomb, or inverse-square, law, down at least to a very small distance, of the order of a small multiple of 10^{-12} cm; for the largest deflections of alpha particles were shown to come from encounters at a distance of this order of magnitude, and the scattering law, derived on the basis of the Coulomb law, held for these deflections.   This deduction of the nuclear nature of the atom formed one of the most important discoveries of the century in the field of atomic structure.

Two consequences of this postulate were obvious.   In the first place, the atom as a whole must have some analogy to the solar system.   There was a very heavy but concentrated nucleus, attracting the electrons according to the inverse-square law.   They had a very much smaller mass and would have to be assumed to be at a comparatively large distance from the nucleus.   Thus, we have seen that the nucleus cannot be of dimensions larger than the order of 10^{-12} cm.   On the other hand, atomic dimensions, as one can tell from a great variety of evidence, are of the order of magnitude of 10^{-8} cm.   This evidence comes from many independent sources.   For instance, from the kinetic theory of gases, it is possible to estimate the radii of molecules from measurements of the viscosity and thermal conductivity of gases, which depend on the mean free paths of molecules.   The study of the properties of imperfect gases also leads to values of molecular dimensions.   Much more direct evidence is available, however; in a liquid or solid, we may merely assume that the atoms fill up most of the space, and since we know how many atoms or molecules there are in a given volume, from Avogadro's number and the density, we can immediately compute the molecular volumes.   All these types of evidence agree in leading to atomic dimensions of the order of magnitude of 10^{-8} cm, as we have stated.

With such a small nucleus and such a comparatively large atom, the resemblance to the planets moving round the sun is obvious.   Since the nucleus is so heavy compared with the electrons, it must remain approximately fixed as the electron moves round it in its orbit; therefore its mass will be unimportant in the dynamics of the electrons, and only its charge, which produces the attraction between nucleus and electrons and holds them in their orbits, will be significant in determining their motion. Hence, we see how the motion of the electrons is determined by the atomic number but not the atomic weight of the atom, so that we understand how it is that different isotopes can have the same chemical properties.

The other deduction is that the study of atomic structure can be divided into two quite separate parts: the structure of the nucleus, and that of the outer electronic system.   This separation has persisted and has led to an almost complete separation of atomic physics into two parts, nuclear and nonnuclear physics.   The reason is the great difference in size between the nucleus and the rest of the atom.   Nuclear phenomena— radioactive disintegration, artificial radioactivity, and so on—go on in the very small volume of the nucleus, of dimensions 10^{-12} cm, and are concerned with very high energies.   They are almost completely unaffected by the behavior of the outer electrons of the atom.   On the other hand, the behavior of the outer electrons is determined almost completely by only one property of the nucleus, its charge, or atomic number.   It is the outer electrons which determine the ordinary properties of the atom with which we are familiar: its spectrum, its chemical properties, the behavior of the molecules and solids which it can form.   Thus it can come about that one can treat these outer electrons almost without reference to any other nuclear properties than the charge, and this is what we shall do in the larger part of our treatment.

There are finer details, however, in which other properties of the nucleus affect the motion of the outer electrons. The nuclear masses come in to a slight extent: though the nuclei are very heavy compared with the electrons, still they move slightly along with the electronic motion and this produces minor corrections in the theory, which can be used to check the nuclear masses. In addition, the nuclei prove to have magnetic moments, and these produce appreciable, though very small, effects on the motion of the outer electrons, observed in the form of hyperfine structure and nuclear magnetic resonance. These interconnections between nuclear and electronic behavior are of great theoretical interest, and we shall take them up later; but when we consider them in comparison with the fundamental fact that most properties of the electronic motion depend only on the nuclear charge, we see that they are comparatively unimportant in the study of matter in bulk.

Rutherford's discovery of the nuclear nature of the atom came in 1911; the striking progress in atomic structure in the years following this was in the study of the outer electronic structure of the atom. Bohr's theory of the structure of the hydrogen atom came in 1913, only 2 years after Rutherford's discovery of the nuclear atom. The discovery of X-ray diffraction, and its application to the nature of crystals, as well as to the X-ray spectra of the atoms, came at the same time. These led to Bohr's explanation of the periodic system of the elements, to the interpretation of atomic spectra, and finally to the discovery of wave mechanics by Schrödinger in 1926. But Bohr's theory was based only partially on the nuclear nature of the atom. Its other foundation was the quantum theory, which as we have stated had been suggested first in 1901. We must now go back to look into its history, so as to understand the sort of dynamical concepts which Bohr had to deal with in his attempt to explain atomic structure.

1-3. The Development of the Quantum Theory from 1901 to 1913. The quantum theory had its origin in a somewhat involved problem: the theory of black-body radiation. Toward the latter part of the nineteenth century, it had been proved that the radiation inside a totally enclosed cavity, such as a furnace, maintained at a constant temperature, was a function of the temperature only and was identical with the radiation which would be emitted by a perfectly black body at the same temperature. This radiation had been investigated experimentally. At a moderately low temperature it is of course invisible, lying entirely in the infrared part of the spectrum; but as the temperature rises, the body begins to emit visible radiation, as it becomes first red-hot, then white-hot. It was found that, at a given temperature, the intensity rose to a peak at a certain wavelength, falling both at lower and at higher wavelengths. Two empirical laws regarding the radiation had been verified by theory based on fundamental thermodynamics: Wien's displacement law, stating that the wavelength corresponding to the maximum intensity was inversely proportional to the absolute temperature, and the Stefan-Boltzmann law, stating that the total intensity emitted in all wavelengths was proportional to the fourth power of the absolute temperature. But all efforts to derive an equation giving the intensity as a function of wavelength had failed. Wien had attempted a derivation, getting something in rough agreement with experiment, but it was believed, with good reason, that there were flaws in his derivation. A more fundamental approach was made by Rayleigh and Jeans, and the law which they derived, and which we are now convinced represents the authentic prediction of classical thermodynamics and mechanics, was absurdly incorrect: it predicted that, at any temperature, the intensity would increase continuously with decreasing wavelength, so that there would be no maximum but instead an infinitely high intensity in the X-ray part of the spectrum. This was an extremely puzzling discrepancy, for the assumptions leading to the derivation were fundamental to classical theory, and there was no way to see how they could be altered.

The problem of black-body radiation is rather complicated, and we shall postpone its details until Chap. 6, where we shall take it up from the point of view of wave mechanics. We can state here, however, that the place where the difficulty in the derivation seemed to lie was in the principle of equipartition of energy. This is the principle, fundamental in classical statistical mechanics, according to which the mean kinetic energy of each coordinate, or degree of freedom, at a given temperature, equals $\frac{1}{2}kT$, where k is Boltzmann's constant, T the absolute temperature. In a linear oscillator—a particle held to a position of equilibrium by a force proportional to the displacement, so that it oscillates sinusoidally with a frequency ν—the mean potential energy, by simple principles of mechanics, equals the mean kinetic energy, so that the total energy equals kT. The Rayleigh-Jeans law predicted that the intensity at a given frequency should vary proportionally to T, and this proportionality could be traced back to the law of equipartition; the law was

$$\rho_\nu = \frac{8\pi\nu^2}{c^3}\, kT \qquad (1\text{-}1)$$

where $\rho_\nu\, d\nu$ represents the energy per unit volume in the frequency range $d\nu$, where c is the velocity of light, and where the term kT comes from equipartition. We see in Eq. (1-1) the way in which the intensity increases indefinitely with frequency at constant temperature. The other aspect of it, according to which the intensity is proportional to temperature at a given frequency, is equally in complete contradiction to experiment. If we consider, for instance, a frequency in the visible part of the spectrum, we know that a hot body emits no radiation at this frequency until it is heated enough to glow; thereafter the radiation increases rapidly. The intensity, in other words, follows a law which starts out at zero when $T = 0$, hardly becomes appreciable at all until quite a high temperature is reached, but then rises very rapidly. This is completely different from equipartition.

It was at this point that Planck made his revolutionary proposal of 1901, leading to the quantum theory. Planck had the insight to realize that equipartition could not be circumvented except by a complete departure from classical mechanics, and he could see the type of departure which was required. He proposed that an oscillator of frequency ν, instead of being able to take on all possible energy values, could have only one of an equally spaced set of values of energy equal to zero, $h\nu$, $2h\nu$, . . . , or in general $nh\nu$, where n is an integer, and where h is a constant, which is now known as Planck's constant. The unit $h\nu$ of energy of an oscillator, which cannot be subdivided according to this proposal, was called a quantum by Planck, leading to the name of the theory.

If one makes Planck's assumption, it is then possible to show that there would be a departure of just the proper sort from equipartition. We can, in fact, reproduce his argument very simply. According to fundamental thermodynamic principles, the probability of finding a system with an energy E, at temperature T, is proportional to the so-called Boltzmann factor, $e^{-E/kT}$. If the probability of finding the oscillator with an energy $nh\nu$ is proportional to $e^{-nh\nu/kT}$, the average energy of the oscillator is

$$\frac{\displaystyle\sum_{n=0}^{\infty} nh\nu e^{-nh\nu/kT}}{\displaystyle\sum_{n=0}^{\infty} e^{-nh\nu/kT}} = \frac{h\nu}{e^{h\nu/kT} - 1} \tag{1-2}$$

We shall go further into the derivation of this formula in Chap. 6. This function of Eq. (1-2) has just the desired type of deviation from equipartition. At low temperatures, where $e^{h\nu/kT} \gg 1$, it approaches $h\nu e^{-h\nu/kT}$ and is exceedingly small. At high temperatures, where we can expand the exponential in the form $e^{h\nu/kT} = 1 + h\nu/kT + \cdots$, the function approaches the classical value kT.

When Planck inserted Eq. (1-2) into the theory of black-body radiation, his formula for the intensity at frequency ν was

$$\rho_\nu = \frac{8\pi\nu^2}{c^3} \frac{h\nu}{e^{h\nu/kT} - 1} \tag{1-3}$$

in place of the Rayleigh-Jeans law of Eq. (1-1). Planck's law proved to be in perfect agreement with experiment; and as a result, his revolutionary assumption about the energy of a linear oscillator had to be accepted by every physicist, and the quantum theory was born. The value of h was found, with very considerable accuracy, by fitting Eq. (1-3) to the already rather accurate experiments on black-body radiation.

Planck's hypothesis soon received support from another quarter, the theory of the specific heat of solids. If we have a monatomic crystal, containing N atoms, each of these will be capable of vibration in each of the three coordinate directions. We can handle the x, y, and z motions separately, and if equipartition is assumed, we shall find an average energy of kT for each of these, or of $3NkT$ for the whole crystal. The heat capacity, the derivative of the energy with respect to the temperature, is then $3Nk$. This law had been known experimentally since the early nineteenth century, when it was discovered empirically by Dulong and Petit. But by the early years of the present century, it had been found experimentally that though the law of Dulong and Petit held at moderately high temperatures, such as room temperature or above, the specific heat actually fell to zero at the absolute zero of temperature. Einstein,[1] in 1906, proposed an explanation of this fact. He suggested that the oscillating atoms of the crystal behaved just as Planck had assumed, having energies which were integral multiples of the quantum $h\nu$, and hence having an average energy at temperature T as given by Eq. (1-2). If we assume that the vibrational energy equals $3N$ times the expression of Eq. (1-2), then at high temperatures it equals $3NkT$, so that the Dulong-Petit law follows at these temperatures; but at temperatures so low that kT is small compared with $h\nu$, the energy becomes almost independent of temperature, and the specific heat falls to zero. Thus Einstein's suggestion explained qualitatively the behavior of the specific heat. Debye, in 1912, improved the theory, by taking account of the fact that actually a solid has many modes of elastic vibration of different frequency, and he worked out a theory of specific heat which agrees well quantitatively, as well as qualitatively, with experiment. It was clear from this work that Planck's suggestion about the quantization of the energy of an oscillator had to be taken very seriously.

Both these applications of the quantum theory, to black-body radiation and the specific heat of solids, were based on rather involved thermodynamics. In contrast, another suggestion of Einstein,[2] this one in 1905, made an application of the quantum theory which was so straightforward that it appealed to every one and showed what a revolutionary theory it really was. This was to the theory of the photo-

[1] A. Einstein, *Ann. Physik*, **22**:180 (1906).
[2] A. Einstein, *Ann. Physik*, **17**:132 (1905).

electric effect.   It had been known for some time that light, falling on a metallic surface, caused electrons to be ejected from the surface.   There was nothing very remarkable about this, at first sight; it was known that electrons could be ejected thermionically, if the temperature were high enough.   Obviously, the light falling on the surface carried energy, this energy could be absorbed by the electrons, and they could thus acquire energy just as they could from thermal agitation and so be able to escape the potential barrier which would keep slow electrons from leaving the metal.

It was only when the laws of photoelectric emission began to be examined quantitatively that its truly remarkable behavior was discovered.   The German physicist Lenard made some of the first studies of these laws; later Millikan made the results more quantitative.   Lenard found that, when the intensity of the impinging light was changed, without changing its spectral distribution, the energy of the ejected electrons did not change, but only their number.   We know now that this continues, as the light gets weaker and weaker, until the rate of emission can be so small that only a few electrons per second are ejected.   Each of these few, however, has a large energy, which can well be several electron volts.   Millikan established just what this energy was, by studying photoelectric emission in case the impinging light was monochromatic. He found that the energy of the electrons was distributed through a range of energies, up to a maximum limit, which equaled $h\nu - e\phi$, where h was the same Planck's constant which we have mentioned earlier, ν was the frequency of the light, e was the magnitude of the electronic charge, and ϕ the work function, which was known from the work of Richardson on thermionic emission, and which represented the difference in electrical potential between the interior of the metal and empty space outside.

These results looked exactly as if each electron liberated inside the metal by the action of the light were initially given an energy $h\nu$, of which it then lost an amount $e\phi$ in getting through the surface, and a further arbitrary amount in its collisions with the atoms on the way out, so that the ejected electrons would have an energy anywhere from $h\nu - e\phi$ on down, the maximum representing the case where no energy was lost on collision.   But this result seemed almost inconceivable, when one looked at the case of light of weak intensity, in which electrons were ejected only occasionally.   One could compute the energy in the light wave falling on the sample and compare it with the energy of the ejected electrons.   On the average, things came out all right; the impinging energy was greater than the energy of the electrons.   But it seemed as if, in the case of weak light, almost all the light falling on the whole sample for an appreciable fraction of a second would have to be concentrated in one single electron, to give it the required energy.   How could this possibly happen?

It was to explain this fact, known qualitatively from the work of Lenard, though Millikan had not yet performed his more accurate experiments, that Einstein made the bold hypothesis which really put the quantum theory on its feet.   He assumed that the energy in the radiation field really existed in discrete particles, quanta (now called photons), each of amount $h\nu$, and that it was not continuously distributed through the field at all, as classical electrodynamics would suggest.   In that case, the photoelectric results no longer seemed queer.   In a weak light, there were very few photons per second; but when one of these photons struck the sample, it could convey all its energy to a single electron with which it collided, and the electron would then behave just as Lenard and Millikan had found that it did.   A change in the intensity of light would mean merely a change in the number of photons per second, and hence in the number of ejected electrons.   But so long as the frequency stayed the same, each photon would still have the same energy.   Of course, there was an obvious difficulty with this proposal: it seemed to contradict the wave nature of light, and yet interference and diffraction provided indisputable proof of the correctness of the wave theory.   We shall come in Sec. 2-2 to the type of compromise which finally satisfied people as an explanation of this paradox: essentially a coexistence of the two types of theories, the energy being carried in photons, but with a wave field to guide them.   It was only with the development of wave mechanics in 1926, when it appeared that the same sort of duality occured in mechanics too, that physicists felt satisfied with this state of things.

1-4. The State of Atomic Spectroscopy in 1913.   We have now sketched the main points of the nuclear nature of the atom, and of the quantum theory, as they were known in 1913, when Bohr produced his theory of the hydrogen atom.   To put his theory into proper perspective, we need to know a third thing: the nature of the spectrum of hydrogen, and of atoms in general.   Experimental spectroscopy had been studied since the middle of the nineteenth century, and it was known that atomic spectra consisted of sharp lines of definite frequency.   Some atoms had very complicated spectra, though that of hydrogen was simple. The spectroscopists Balmer and Rydberg had been able to fit the frequencies of hydrogen, and of some of the simpler spectra, with very accurate empirical formulas.   Balmer's formula for hydrogen was

$$\text{Frequency} = R\left(\frac{1}{4} - \frac{1}{n^2}\right) \tag{1-4}$$

where R is a constant and n is an integer, equal to 3, 4, ...   This

Balmer formula was similar to Rydberg's formula, which worked for the alkali metals and some other cases. Rydberg's formula was

$$\text{Frequency} = R \left[\text{constant} - \frac{1}{(n-d)^2} \right] \qquad (1\text{-}5)$$

where n again is an integer, d is a constant, and R is, remarkably enough, the same constant found in Balmer's formula. This constant, called the Rydberg frequency, equal approximately to 3.29×10^{15} cycles/sec, pointed to a far-reaching relation between the spectra of different chemical elements.

In both Balmer's formula, Eq. (1-4), and Rydberg's formula, Eq. (1-5), the frequency appears as the difference of two quantities. Ritz, another spectroscopist, showed in 1908 that these were special cases of a more general principle, which is now called Ritz's combination principle. He showed experimentally that, in any atomic spectrum, we could set up tables of quantities, which he called terms, of the dimensions of frequencies, such that the observed frequencies could be written as the differences between two term values. Thus, in Balmer's case, the quantity $R/4$ would be one term, and the values R/n^2 would be other terms; similarly, in Eq. (1-5), the quantity $R(\text{constant})$ is a term, and $R/(n-d)^2$ are other terms. The spectroscopists found that, if one made up tables of terms and tried taking differences of all possible term values, some of these differences would appear in the observed spectra, while others would not; and there appeared to be a principle, which was called a selection rule, specifying which pairs of terms could lead to observed spectrum lines. It was natural, in the hydrogenic case, to assume that the complete set of terms was given by the set of numbers R/n^2, where n could have any integral value. The first term in Balmer's formula, Eq. (1-4), is that with $n = 2$. It was natural to suspect the existence of a term for $n = 1$. In 1906 such a term was in fact found by Lyman; he found a series of lines in the hydrogen spectrum, in the far ultraviolet, known as the Lyman series, with frequencies given by the formula

$$\text{Frequency} = R \left(1 - \frac{1}{n^2} \right) \qquad n = 2, 3, 4, \ldots \qquad (1\text{-}6)$$

And in 1908 Paschen found a series in the infrared given by the formula

$$\text{Frequency} = R \left(\frac{1}{3^2} - \frac{1}{n^2} \right) \qquad n = 4, 5, \ldots \qquad (1\text{-}7)$$

Ritz's combination principle therefore seemed to imply, in hydrogen, that the difference of any two terms could lead to an observed spectrum line.

We see, then, the type of spectroscopic information which Bohr had at his disposal. But this spectroscopic information seemed to be in violent disagreement with the implications of Rutherford's nuclear atom. If one studies the motion of a charged particle, like the electron, moving according to classical mechanics in an inverse-square field such as the nucleus must provide, one finds that the electron continually radiates energy, of a frequency equal to its rotational frequency about the nucleus. By studying the dynamics of a particle moving according to an inverse-square attraction, we easily find that the orbit becomes smaller, and the frequency of rotation in the orbit greater, as the energy decreases. If, then, an electron rotating in such an orbit radiates energy away, it will move into orbits of successively smaller radii, successively higher frequency of rotation, and will continue to radiate more and more energy, of higher and higher frequency, until it falls into the nucleus. This catastrophe would have to happen to a classically constructed atom consisting of a nucleus and electrons. It clearly cannot be happening with the atoms of our experience; they radiate fixed frequencies, sharp spectral lines, and have a permanent existence. What prevents the catastrophe? It was this problem which Bohr undertook to solve.

1-5. The Postulates of Bohr's Theory of Atomic Structure. Bohr used in his theory a most ingenious combination of the ideas about the quantum theory which had been developed up to 1913. His assumptions seemed contradictory, and yet they worked. These postulates, supplemented by certain clarifying developments suggested by Sommerfeld[1] and Einstein[2] in 1916 and 1917, were the following:

1. An atomic system cannot exist with any arbitrary energy, but only with certain discrete energies, called energy levels, which can be denoted by the values $E_1, E_2, \ldots, E_i, \ldots$. These energies are determined by a modification of the classical mechanics, which in Bohr's theory took the form of superposing certain conditions, called quantum conditions, onto classical mechanics, so that only those solutions of Newton's laws of motion which simultaneously satisfied the quantum conditions could really exist. The most convenient form of the quantum conditions was suggested by Sommerfeld in 1916, essentially equivalent to proposals made by Bohr in 1913. These quantized states were described by certain quantum numbers, one or more integers whose value determined the energy level considered, so that the subscript i on an energy value E_i really stands for all the various quantum numbers required to describe the state.

2. In the absence of any interaction with radiation, the atomic system would continue to exist permanently in one of the energy levels, which

[1] A. Sommerfeld, *Ann. Physik*, **51**:1 (1916).
[2] A. Einstein, *Physik. Z.*, **18**:121 (1917).

for that reason are called stationary states. However, under actual conditions, the system has a certain probability of having a transition from the stationary state E_i which it happens to be in to any other state E_j. This transition is brought about by interaction with external radiation. If the energy of the state E_j is less than E_i, then the transition is accompanied by the loss of energy $E_i - E_j$ by the atomic system. This energy appears as energy in the radiation field, and the frequency of the emitted radiation is given by Bohr's frequency condition

$$E_i - E_j = h\nu \qquad (1\text{-}8)$$

where h is Planck's constant. The energy which appears in the radiation field forms a photon, which according to Einstein's hypothesis concerning the photoelectric effect has many of the characteristics of a material particle. If on the contrary the energy of the state E_j is greater than E_i, so that the energy of the atom is increased in the transition, a photon is absorbed by the atom in the process, its frequency again being given by Bohr's frequency condition, which in this case would be $E_j - E_i = h\nu$.

3. The probabilities of transition of the sort described in the preceding paragraph are given by a hypothesis of Einstein, stated in 1917, in the following way: Let ρ_ν be the energy density of external radiation of frequency ν, where ν is given by Bohr's frequency condition. By energy density, which we have met earlier in Sec. 1-3, we mean the following: We can imagine electromagnetic radiation—thermal radiation, microwave or radio-frequency radiation, visible radiation, etc.—to be localized in space, so that there is a certain amount per unit volume. This radiation will have a spectrum of frequencies, and the energy per unit volume, in the frequency range between ν and $\nu + d\nu$, is defined to be $\rho_\nu \, d\nu$. Then, in terms of this definition of energy density, Einstein assumed that the probability of transition of a system in state E_i to a lower energy level E_j, with emission of a photon of radiation of frequency given by Bohr's frequency condition, is

$$\text{Probability of radiation} = A + B\rho_\nu \qquad (1\text{-}9)$$

where A and B are constants characteristic of the transition. Here the term A is called the probability of spontaneous emission, since it occurs whether or not there is external radiation present, and the term $B\rho_\nu$ is called the probability of induced emission, since it is proportional to the external energy density. For a transition from a state E_i to a higher energy level E_j, with absorption of a photon of radiation, the probability of absorption according to Einstein is

$$\text{Probability of absorption} = B\rho_\nu \qquad (1\text{-}10)$$

Einstein showed that these probabilities of transition would satisfy the laws of thermodynamics only if A and B were related by the equation

$$\frac{A}{B} = \frac{8\pi h \nu^3}{c^3} \tag{1-11}$$

In these definitions, when we speak of the probability of transition, we mean that, if at time t_0 there are N systems in the energy level E_i, then in time dt following this time a number $N(A + B\rho_\nu)\,dt$ or $NB\rho_\nu\,dt$, respectively, will have had transitions to the state E_j, so that the number of systems in state E_i will have decreased by this number, there being a compensating increase in the number of systems in state E_j.

From these principles, we can calculate the average number of systems found in any state E_i in thermal equilibrium at temperature T, for which the energy density ρ_ν is given by Planck's law of black-body radiation, Eq. (1-3). We find that the number of systems in state E_i under these conditions is proportional to $e^{-E_i/kT}$, where k is Boltzmann's constant. This is the Boltzmann relation which we have mentioned earlier, and which holds both in classical and in quantum statistics. We notice that, as we go to low temperatures, the Boltzmann factors $e^{-E_i/kT}$ for states of low energies are much greater than those for high energies, and as T approaches the absolute zero, the factor for the very lowest energy level is indefinitely greater than for any other, so that, at the absolute zero, all systems will be found in this lowest energy level, which is known as the ground state. Higher states will be reached by thermal excitation at higher temperatures, or by absorption of external radiation, and are called excited states.

The first consequence of Bohr's postulates was an explanation of the existence of spectral terms, and the Ritz combination principle. For Eq. (1-8) states that the frequencies are differences of quantities E/h. These, then, must be the spectral terms; and the experimental work of the spectroscopists in deducing these terms from the observed spectra immediately provides one with an experimental table of the energy levels of the atom. Bohr was able to set up quantum conditions for hydrogen, which led to a prediction of the spectral terms R/n^2 which we have already seen exist for that atom. But before we go on to describe his quantum conditions, we should note that his hypotheses explained many other observations as well. For example, it is clear from his theory why the frequencies of emission and absorption lines are observed to be the same. We can also understand why not all emission lines are observed in absorption: in a cold gas, the atoms will all be found in their ground states, and therefore only those frequencies can be absorbed which correspond to transitions from the ground state up to some excited state.

The general idea of stationary states also suggested a quite different type of experiment. It is known that a gas is rendered luminous when it forms an electric arc. In this arc, there are electrons wandering round with a considerable energy. The mechanism of excitation seems clear. An electron strikes an atom in its ground state. If the electron has enough energy, it can raise the atom to one of its excited states; to do this, the electron must have an energy at least equal to the difference of energy between the ground state and the excited state, an amount called the excitation energy. The excited atom then can radiate and return to its ground state. Clearly, for example, for hydrogen, there will be a variety of excitation energies, given by the frequencies $R(1 - 1/n^2)$, where n is any integer greater than 1, multiplied by h. Larger and larger values of n will correspond to higher and higher excited states, with the electron in larger and larger orbits. There is obviously a limit, when n becomes infinite; we shall see shortly that this corresponds to an infinitely large orbit, or a case in which the electron is entirely removed from the nucleus, or the atom is ionized. This limiting value R then corresponds to the ionization potential of the hydrogen atom, the energy required for an electron to ionize it. Measured in electron volts, it is about 13.6 ev.

The suggested experiment, then, is one in which a gas, say atomic hydrogen, is bombarded by electrons of carefully controlled energy. If the energy is too small, no transitions of the atoms will be possible. The bombarding electrons cannot lose energy and will have what we call an elastic collision; the gas will emit no radiation. As the energy is increased to become equal to the first excitation energy, many electrons will collide with atoms, losing just enough energy to raise them to the first excited states. We shall have what are called inelastic collisions; the bombarding electrons come away from the collisions with reduced energies, reduced by just the amount which they have lost in exciting the atoms. At the same time, the atoms will start to radiate the line associated with the transition from the lowest excited state to the ground state. If the electron energy is raised still further, some bombarding electrons may be able to raise atoms to higher excited states. With still greater bombarding energy, electrons can ionize the gas, and we can measure an ionization potential, the minimum energy with which ionization is possible. Franck and Hertz started experiments of this sort immediately after Bohr's explanation of the nature of stationary states, in 1913. Their experiments resulted in a complete confirmation of these ideas, and a great deal of subsequent work of the same sort, by many physicists, has completely verified the idea of stationary states and of the transitions between them.

1-6. The Quantum Condition, and Bohr's Theory of Hydrogen. We now turn to Bohr's main problem, that of finding the stationary states of the hydrogen atom. This atom consists of an electron of charge $-e$

(we shall use e for the magnitude of the electronic charge) and mass m_0 (we shall call the electronic mass m_0, to distinguish it from a quantum number m which we shall introduce), moving about a proton of charge e and of mass so large that it can be considered infinite in a first approximation, under the action of the inverse-square electrostatic attraction between the opposite charges. The orbit of the electron in the general case is an ellipse, as in planetary motion; for simplicity, we shall treat only the special case where it is a circle, taking up the more general elliptical case in Appendix 1, where we also discuss the case where the finite mass of the proton must be taken into account. For the circular motion, where the electron moves with linear velocity v in a circle of radius r, the centripetal acceleration is v^2/r, by elementary mechanics. There must then be a force m_0v^2/r pulling it to the center, and this must be the electrostatic attraction, which in the rationalized mks system of units is $e^2/4\pi\epsilon_0r^2$, where ϵ_0 is the permittivity of free space, or in the nonrationalized cgs units it is e^2/r^2. We then have

$$\frac{m_0v^2}{r} = \frac{e^2}{4\pi\epsilon_0r^2}$$

for mks units; the corresponding formula in cgs units is obtained by omitting the factor $4\pi\epsilon_0$. Let us compute various mechanical quantities which we shall want for our discussion. We have

$$\text{Kinetic energy} = \tfrac{1}{2}m_0v^2 = \frac{1}{2}\frac{e^2}{4\pi\epsilon_0r} \qquad (1\text{-}12)$$

$$\text{Potential energy} = -\frac{e^2}{4\pi\epsilon_0r} = -2 \times \text{kinetic energy} \qquad (1\text{-}13)$$

$$\text{Total energy} = -\frac{1}{2}\frac{e^2}{4\pi\epsilon_0r} = -\text{kinetic energy} \qquad (1\text{-}14)$$

$$\text{Angular momentum} = m_0vr = \sqrt{\frac{e^2m_0r}{4\pi\epsilon_0}} \qquad (1\text{-}15)$$

The results which we have just given are those resulting from classical mechanics, for the circular orbits. Next we must consider the quantum condition; we have stated that the most useful form is the Sommerfeld quantum condition. This condition is stated most simply for a particle moving in one-dimensional motion. Thus let the particle have a coordinate q, a mass m_0, velocity v, and momentum $p = m_0v$. Let it oscillate back and forth along q periodically under the action of some type of force capable of producing such an oscillation classically (it is only for such periodic motions that the quantum condition can be applied). Then let us calculate what is called the phase integral $\oint p\,dq$. Here we are to find the momentum p at every point of the path and integrate p with respect to q from a particular starting point round the complete path of the particle, first to its extreme displacement in one direction, then back to its extreme displacement in the other direction (when the particle is going back, both p and dq will be negative, so that the contribution to the integral here will be positive, as it is when the particle travels forward), and finally back to the starting point. The integral sign $\oint$ indicates that the integral is to be taken round a complete cycle. Then Sommerfeld's quantum condition is that the phase integral must be an integral multiple of Planck's constant h,

$$\oint p \, dq = nh \tag{1-16}$$

This condition, superposed on classical mechanics, leads to the stationary states of Bohr's theory.

In our case, we have the motion of a particle in three dimensions, rather than in one dimension as in the case just described. Sommerfeld's quantum condition for this case takes a simple form: to find the phase integral, we must integrate the momentum with respect to the distance round the circumference of the circular orbit; that is, we multiply the constant momentum m_0v by the circumference $2\pi r$. We then have

$$\oint p \, dq = 2\pi m_0 vr = 2\pi \times \text{angular momentum} = nh$$
$$\text{Angular momentum} = \frac{nh}{2\pi} \tag{1-17}$$

We may then combine Eqs. (1-15) and (1-17) to find the radii of the orbits, insert these radii in Eq. (1-14), and find the energies. Thus we find

$$\text{Energy} = -\frac{2\pi^2 m_0 e^4}{(4\pi\epsilon_0)^2 h^2}\frac{1}{n^2} \tag{1-18}$$

$$\text{Radius} = n^2 \frac{h^2(4\pi\epsilon_0)}{4\pi^2 m_0 e^2} \tag{1-19}$$

In Eq. (1-18) we have the energy levels, proportional to $1/n^2$, in agreement with experiment; in Eq. (1-19) we have the corresponding radii of the orbits. The potential and kinetic energy can be found from Eqs. (1-13) and (1-14).

It is the energy levels of Eq. (1-18) which Bohr found to agree with experiment. To check this agreement, we need not only the proportionality with $1/n^2$, but also the absolute value of the constant factor, which should lead to the Rydberg. Let us therefore insert numerical values in the expression. We use the best modern values of the various constants, rather than the somewhat less accurate values available in 1913. We have

$$c = 2.9973 \times 10^8 \text{ m/sec}$$
$$= 2.9973 \times 10^{10} \text{ cm/sec}$$
$$\epsilon_0 = 8.8542 \times 10^{-12} \text{ farad/m}$$
$$h = 6.625 \times 10^{-34} \text{ joule-sec}$$
$$= 6.625 \times 10^{-27} \text{ erg-sec} \tag{1-20}$$
$$e = 1.6021 \times 10^{-19} \text{ coulomb}$$
$$= 4.8029 \times 10^{-10} \text{ esu}$$
$$m_0 = 9.1085 \times 10^{-31} \text{ kg}$$
$$= 9.1085 \times 10^{-28} \text{ g}$$

The calculations are simple in the mks units. It is not usually of interest to find the Rydberg, $2\pi^2 m_0 e^4/(4\pi\epsilon_0)^2 h^2$, in energy units. Instead, we wish the corresponding frequency, related to the energy by the equation $E = h\nu$; or the energy in electron volts, given by $E = eV$, where V is the voltage; or the wave number, the reciprocal of the wavelength, given by $E = hc(1/\lambda)$, where $1/\lambda$ represents the wave number. Then we have

$$
\begin{aligned}
\text{Rydberg frequency} &= \frac{2\pi^2 m_0 e^4}{(4\pi\epsilon_0)^2 h^3} \\
&= \frac{2\pi^2 \times 9.1085 \times 10^{-31} \times (1.6021 \times 10^{-19})^4}{(4\pi \times 8.8542 \times 10^{-12})^2 (6.625 \times 10^{-34})^3} \\
&= 3.290 \times 10^{15} \text{ cycles/sec} \tag{1-21}
\end{aligned}
$$

$$
\begin{aligned}
\text{Rydberg energy (ev)} &= \frac{2\pi^2 m_0 e^3}{(4\pi\epsilon_0)^2 h^2} \\
&= 13.605 \text{ ev} \tag{1-22}
\end{aligned}
$$

$$
\begin{aligned}
\text{Rydberg number (cm}^{-1}\text{)} &= \frac{2\pi^2 m_0 e^4}{(4\pi\epsilon_0)^2 h^3 c} \times 10^{-2} \\
&= \frac{3.290 \times 10^{15}}{2.9973 \times 10^8} \times 10^{-2} \\
&= 109,737 \text{ cm}^{-1} \tag{1-23}
\end{aligned}
$$

This latter number, the Rydberg number, is carried to more decimal places than would be warranted from the constants which go into it; unlike the other constants, it can be determined with spectroscopic accuracy, so that the number given is the experimental value, correct to the last significant figure. It agrees with the calculated value to within the error of the various constants going into it. We see, then, that the value of the Rydberg predicted by Bohr's theory is in perfect agreement with experiment, verifying the correctness of the theory. Finally, we find that the radius of the first Bohr orbit is

$$
\begin{aligned}
a_0 &= \frac{h^2 (4\pi\epsilon_0)}{4\pi^2 m_0 e^2} \\
&= 0.5292 \times 10^{-10} \text{ m} \\
&= 0.5292 \text{ angstrom} \tag{1-24}
\end{aligned}
$$

1-7. Elliptic Orbits, Space Quantization, and Zeeman Effect in Hydrogen. In the preceding section, we have treated only the circular orbits, but we show in Appendix 1 how to extend the process to the elliptic orbits. The situation proves to be the following: There is a quantum number, called the principal quantum number n, in terms of which the energy even of the elliptical orbits is given by the formula of Eq. (1-18). This quantum number also determines the major axis of the elliptical orbit, the major axis being the same as the diameter of the circular orbit, equal to twice the radius given in Eq. (1-19). There is another quantum number, which in the Bohr theory was called k, which determines the angular momentum: the angular momentum is $kh/2\pi$, rather than $nh/2\pi$ as in the circular orbit. The integer k can take on the integral values from the maximum value n down to unity. Thus the state for $n = 1$ has only $k = 1$, that for $n = 2$ has $k = 2$ or 1, and so on. The integer k, called the azimuthal quantum number, also determines the eccentricity, or minor axis, of the elliptical orbit: the ratio of minor to major axis is k/n. At the same time k determines the area of the orbit, which is $\pi/4$ times the product of major and minor axes. A third quantum number is generally called m, a magnetic quantum number (on account of its importance in the theory of the Zeeman effect, the effect of a magnetic field on the spectral lines). This is connected with a phenomenon called space quantization. The numbers n, k refer to shape and size of the orbit in a plane; but so far the plane of the orbit is not determined. It now proves to be the case that if there is a preferred direction in space, such as the direction of an applied magnetic field, only certain orientations of the plane of the orbit with respect to this direction are allowed. In particular, we remember that k measures the angular momentum in units of $h/2\pi$. We consider this to be a vector, at right angles to the plane of the orbit. The quantum condition relating to the magnetic quantum number then states that the component of this angular momentum along the preferred direction must be an integral multiple of $h/2\pi$. This component is given as $mh/2\pi$. Thus m can take on all integral values from k to $-k$. The orientations thus allowed in space, with their discrete values, are referred to as space quantization. They are illustrated by Fig. 1-1.

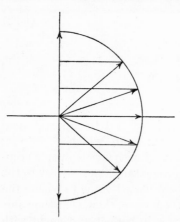

FIG. 1-1. Orientations of the angular momentum allowed by space quantization. Case illustrated is $k = 3$, $m = 3, 2, 1, 0, -1, -2, -3$.

The relation of space quantization to the magnetic problem is simple. It can be shown by electromagnetic theory (see Appendix 1) that associated with an orbit of a given angular momentum is a given magnetic moment. This arises because the electron rotating in its orbit has the characteristics of a current circulating in a loop, or a solenoid. This magnetic moment, furthermore, is proportional to the angular momentum, being equal to $-e/2m_0$ times the angular momentum in the mks system of units, or $-e/2m_0c$ times the angular momentum in the Gaussian system, where $-e$ is the electronic charge, m_0 its mass (not to be confused with the quantum number m), and c the velocity of light. There is then a natural unit of magnetic moment, $eh/4\pi m_0$ or $eh/4\pi m_0c$ in mks and Gaussian units, respectively, called the Bohr magneton and often denoted as μ_B. We then see that m, the magnetic quantum number, measures the negative of the component of magnetic moment along the axis in units of Bohr magnetons. In a magnetic field B along the axis, the energy of the magnetic moment will be $m\mu_B B$, the product of magnetic field and the component of moment along the field, the energy being a minimum when the magnetic moment points along the field. Thus there will be a modification of the energy levels, produced by the magnetic field, and proportional to it; this effect on the spectrum is called the Zeeman effect.

There are many further interesting points connected with the hydrogen spectrum, and with other atomic spectra, which were attacked by Bohr's theory; we have given enough, however, to indicate the sort of results which it obtained. It will be well to state here that many, but not all, of its results were correct and are taken over into wave mechanics. The principal modifications relate to space quantization, the Zeeman effect, and related subjects. There the general idea is correct; but in details there have to be modifications. In particular, complications arise between use of the integer k and of another integer l one unit smaller; and there are further complications on account of the existence of an intrinsic angular momentum and magnetic moment of the electron itself, generally called the electron spin, the angular momentum having the magnitude $\frac{1}{2}(h/2\pi)$, and the magnetic moment 1 Bohr magneton. We mention these matters now, though they will not become clear until later, only to put the reader on his guard, and to indicate that there were enough difficulties with the Bohr theory, before the advent of wave mechanics, to show that it needed modification.

1-8. Sommerfeld's Quantum Condition for the Linear Oscillator. Bohr's theory and Sommerfeld's quantum condition were by no means limited to the hydrogen atom. They provided a system of dynamics which could be applied to a wide range of problems, and a particularly interesting one is the linear oscillator, on account of the importance which it had in the development of the quantum theory, in the hands of Planck. Let us carry through this case. We have a particle of mass m, held to a position of equilibrium by a force F which equals $-kq$, where k is a constant, q the displacement from the equilibrium position. The potential energy is $kq^2/2$, whose negative derivative gives the force. The classical equation of motion is

$$m \frac{d^2q}{dt^2} = -kq \qquad (1\text{-}25)$$

whose solution is a sinusoidal oscillation with a frequency ν, where

$$\nu = \frac{1}{2\pi} \sqrt{\frac{k}{m}} \qquad (1\text{-}26)$$

We now wish to apply the quantum condition, Eq. (1-16), to see what energies are allowed in Bohr's form of the quantum theory.

To carry out the integration of Eq. (1-16), we must know the momentum p, as a function of the coordinate q. We can do this from the conservation of energy. If the total energy is E, we can express the law of conservation of energy in the form

$$E = \tfrac{1}{2}mv^2 + \tfrac{1}{2}kq^2$$
$$= \frac{p^2}{2m} + \tfrac{1}{2}kq^2 \qquad (1\text{-}27)$$

where $p = mv$ is the momentum. In Eq. (1-27) we have a relation between p and q, which we may write

$$\frac{p^2}{2mE} + \frac{kq^2}{2E} = 1 \qquad (1\text{-}28)$$

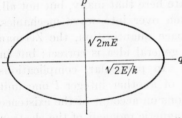

FIG. 1-2. Phase space for linear oscillator, with line of constant energy E.

We can solve this equation for p, substitute in Eq. (1-16), and carry out the integration directly; we leave this direct approach for a problem and show that we can get the quantum condition in an alternative way, using a coordinate space in which q is plotted as abscissa, p as ordinate.

Such a space, in which momentum is plotted against coordinate, is called a phase space and is of great use in statistical mechanics. In this phase space, Eq. (1-28) is the equation of an ellipse, of semiaxis $\sqrt{2E/k}$ along the abscissa, $\sqrt{2mE}$ along the ordinate, as shown in Fig. 1-2. To find the momentum corresponding to any coordinate, we need only look up the value of p on this curve corresponding to the given q. The two possible values (positive and negative) correspond to the two cases in which the particle is moving in the direction of increasing q or in the opposite direction.   In either case, the point representing the particle, called the representative point, is rotating in a clockwise direction around the ellipse.   The amplitude of oscillation is $\sqrt{2E/k}$; for this value of q, the momentum, and hence the velocity, reduces to zero, and the particle reverses its motion.

We can now carry out the calculation of the integral $\oint p\,dq$ by elementary methods.   If we travel round our ellipse in the clockwise direction, which is the direction in which the representative point would traverse it, the whole integral $\oint p\,dq$ is seen to be simply the area of the ellipse.   But the area of an ellipse is π times the product of the two semi-axes; thus our quantum condition becomes $2\pi E\,\sqrt{m/k} = nh$.   This can be written in another form, by using Eq. (1-26) for the frequency; it is equivalent to

$$E = nh\nu \tag{1-29}$$

Hence we have derived from the Bohr-Sommerfeld form of quantum theory the energy levels of a linear oscillator, agreeing with Planck's hypothesis, which we discussed in Sec. 1-3.   Here, as in the case of hydrogen, the Bohr theory, though near the truth, proves not to agree exactly with the results of wave mechanics; we shall find later that Eq. (1-29) has to be modified to the form $E = (n + \frac{1}{2})h\nu$, when we take up wave mechanics.

PROBLEMS

1. A Thomson atom consists of a charge of total amount e, uniformly distributed over the volume of a sphere of radius R_0, and an electron of charge $-e$ oscillating inside the sphere of positive charge.   Show that the electron will oscillate with simple harmonic motion, and find the frequency of oscillation.   *Hint:* Note that, when the electron is at a distance r from the center of the sphere $(r < R_0)$, the force on the electron can be found by principles of electrostatics, by assuming all the positive charge located in the sphere of radius r to be located at the origin, and by disregarding the positive charge outside this sphere.

2. Use the results of Prob. 1 to find the frequency of oscillation of an electron in a Thomson atom whose radius R_0 equals a_0, the radius of the first Bohr orbit for hydrogen, as given in Eq. (1-24).   Express the result as a multiple of the Rydberg frequency, given in Eq. (1-21).

3. Two experimental laws of black-body radiation, known before the Planck law was discovered, are known as Wien's displacement law and the Stefan-Boltzmann law.   Wien's displacement law states that the frequency in the spectrum for which the energy density ρ_ν is a maximum, at a given temperature, is proportional to the temperature.   The Stefan-Boltzmann law states that the total energy per unit volume in black-body radiation, integrated over all frequencies, is proportional to T^4.   Show that both these laws follow from Planck's law, Eq. (1-3).

4. If atoms are surrounded by black-body radiation at temperature T, obeying Planck's law, show that the probability $B\rho_\nu$ of absorption or induced emission is small compared with the probability A of spontaneous emission, provided the frequency ν

is large compared with the frequency for which the Planck distribution ρ_ν has its maximum value, but that the reverse is the case if the frequency is low compared with that for which ρ_ν has its maximum.

5. Prove that, for a given azimuthal quantum number k, the closest approach of an elliptical hydrogen orbit to the nucleus approaches $a_0 k^2/2$ as n becomes large.

6. An electron in a Bohr atom in a magnetic field can have a transition in which only its quantum number m changes, the other quantum numbers n and k remaining unchanged. Find the emitted frequency, and compare it with the frequency of classical rotation of a free electron in the same magnetic field.

7. Use the results of Appendix 1 to find the frequency of rotation of an electron in an elliptical Bohr orbit. Show that this frequency is independent of the azimuthal quantum number k and depends only on the principal quantum number n.

8. If you average the classical frequency of rotation, as given in Prob. 7, with respect to the principal quantum number n, from a given n to $n + 1$, prove that the resulting average frequency equals the emission frequency which would be found in quantum theory for the transition from the state with quantum number $n + 1$ to that with n.

9. Check the formula of Eq. (1-29) for the energy levels of a linear oscillator by direct evalution of the integral $\oint p \, dq$, expressing p in terms of q by Eq. (1-27).

2
Modern Physics from Bohr's Theory to Wave Mechanics

2-1. Introduction. During the period from 1913 (or 1916, if we recall that Sommerfeld's contributions to Bohr's theory came in that year) to 1926, or from Bohr's theory of hydrogen to Schrödinger's proposal of wave mechanics, there was extremely active development of physics, essentially along two separate lines. First, a great deal of thought was devoted to trying to remove the paradoxes of Bohr's theory, to reconcile wave theories with the discontinuities involved in quantum jumps and with the existence of photons. It was this line of thought which resulted directly in the discovery of wave mechanics. Second, there was an effort to extend the methods which Bohr had applied so successfully to hydrogen, the simplest atom, to more complicated atoms and to molecules. These attempts to explain atomic structure on the basis of Bohr's theory progressed fairly far, but it became clear that there were places where the theory was deficient and incapable by any minor modification of being applied to the real problems. Even more in molecular structure, no success at all was achieved by using Bohr's methods. This work on atomic and molecular theory helped to convince physicists that the theory in the simple form of Bohr and Sommerfeld could not be completely correct and made them ready to accept wave mechanics when it arrived.

Our object in the present book is to investigate the structure of atoms, rather than to follow history. Consequently we shall not take up these partially successful applications of Bohr's method to problems in atomic structure; we shall rather wait to discuss these problems until we have presented wave mechanics, which furnishes the really successful method of attacking them. Therefore at the moment we shall skip over many topics—the discovery of X-ray diffraction and its application both to crystal structure and X-ray spectra, the explanation given by Bohr of the periodic system of the elements, the explanation of atomic spectra, both simple and complex, the Pauli exclusion principle, the electron spin—

31

which were the major concern of most physicists during the years we are discussing. We shall take up all these topics later in great detail, but from the point of view of wave mechanics, and shall now proceed to the line of argument which led directly to the development of wave mechanics. We mention these other topics here only to warn the reader that we are rather doing violence to historical order; many of the problems which we shall discuss by means of wave mechanics had been treated, with very considerable success, by the older Bohr theory, and their study had contributed greatly to the ideas which stimulated wave mechanics.

2-2. Waves and Photons in Optics. In Sec. 1-3, in discussing the quantum theory and its application to the photoelectric effect, we pointed out the paradoxical situation according to which the photon theory seems to apply to light and yet seems completely contrary to wave theory. The truth of wave theory of course is shown by classical experiments on interference and diffraction, dating back to the beginning of the nineteenth century. But the reality of photons was shown not only by Einstein's theory of the photoelectric effect, but more particularly by the Compton effect, discovered in 1923. Compton[1] found that, when X rays are scattered by matter, some of the scattered radiation has a longer wavelength than the incident rays. He measured the amount of the shift and produced a theory which explained the experiments perfectly. He assumed that the incident radiation consisted of photons, which had momentum as well as energy. From the theory of relativity, one can find the relation between momentum and energy, and if the energy of a photon is $h\nu$, one can show that the momentum must be h/λ, where λ is the wavelength. We note that, since $\lambda\nu = c$, the velocity of light, this means that the momentum must be $h\nu/c$, which is reasonable for the following reason: From Einstein's relation between mass and energy, a photon of energy $h\nu$ must be equivalent to a mass $h\nu/c^2$ (since the energy of any mass equals the mass times c^2). Then the momentum of this mass, if it moved with the velocity of light, should be c times the mass, or $h\nu/c$, as we have just assumed.

Compton treated the collision of a photon of energy $h\nu$, momentum $h\nu/c$, colliding with a free electron initially at rest, as if he were dealing with a collision of ordinary material particles. The electron will recoil, in order to satisfy simultaneously the laws of conservation of energy and of momentum, and the photon will be scattered in some definite direction. Since the electron after recoil has some kinetic energy, it is clear that the photon will have lost some energy, to satisfy conservation of energy. Since its energy equals $h\nu$, it is obvious that its frequency after scattering will be less than the original frequency. Compton worked out the details

[1] A. H. Compton, *Phys. Rev.*, **22**:409 (1923).

of the collision and found a formula for the frequency of the scattered radiation which exactly agreed with experiment.

This experiment, more than anything else, convinced physicists of the reality of photons and of the necessity of bringing together the wave theory and the corpuscular theory. Gradually a feeling grew up that maybe the two theories were not contradictory; perhaps each one expressed some of the properties of light, and perhaps both theories were simultaneously right. We can understand the nature of the situation if we think, for instance, about the optical problem of the formation of interference fringes with extremely weak light. Let us suppose that we have a beam of parallel light falling on a screen in which there are two slits. We know by classical wave optics that interference fringes will be formed on the far side of the slits. Let us suppose that the light is so weak that photons come through the slits only infrequently. We may detect the photons by means of counters; present techniques make it easily possible to count each photon as it comes along. Let us assume that the counter is provided with an input window of very small aperture, so that it will detect only the photons falling on this small area. We can then perform experiments with the counter in different parts of the interference pattern and see what we get. Similar experiments are actually carried out every day in the X-ray part of the spectrum, where diffraction patterns produced by crystals are measured by means of counters.

The result of such an experiment is then found to be as follows: If the counter is placed at a position where the wave theory tells us that there should be strong intensity, we shall find many photons per second coming along. If it is at a place where wave theory indicates only weak intensity, few photons will be found. If a quantitative study is made of the number of photons per second crossing unit area at a given point in the pattern, the result will be proportional to the intensity of radiation which wave theory would predict at that point. This of course is subject to certain fluctuations; if we are measuring the number of photons per second and counting only a finite number of photons, there are inherent errors in the experiment on account of the finite number we are dealing with, a type of error encountered in any counter experiments. But subject to this inevitable error, which can be decreased in its proportional effect by counting many particles, the results of the wave theory check the number of counts actually measured.

It seems, then, as if the purpose of the wave theory were to provide statistical information about the motion of the photons: the intensity of radiation, calculated by wave theory, tells us how many photons will cross unit area per second. Or, expressed somewhat differently, the density of radiation, or the energy per unit volume, as calculated by wave theory, tells us how many photons per unit volume we may expect to find in the radiation field.   Einstein,[1] in a very interesting and little-known paper, showed that we can go even further with the wave theory. From fundamental statistical mechanics, we can find, from the wave theory, how much fluctuation there will be in the energy in a small element of volume.   This fluctuation proves to depend on the expression we use for the distribution of energy density, and if we insert the value given by Planck's law, for black-body radiation, we find a term in the fluctuation which is just what would be expected if the energy in the small element of volume consisted of N photons each of energy $h\nu$.   We know that, the smaller N is, the greater is the proportional fluctuation, and Einstein's deduction from Planck's law reproduced this phenomenon exactly.

It began to be supposed, then, that there was a statistical connection of the type we have sketched between waves and photons.   Naturally physicists asked: Is there a more precise law governing the motion of photons?   Is there some way of telling either theoretically or experimentally exactly what path a given photon has followed?   For instance, in the case of two slits, can we determine which of the two slits a given photon has gone through?   The conclusion to which the physicists came was that there is no indication of such a more precise law, and in fact it is not obvious how an experiment would be made to test it.   For example, if we want to make an observation on only those photons which have come through one of the slits, we can surely do it by closing the other slit and studying the photons which still emerge on the other side of the screen.   But by doing so we have destroyed the interference pattern, which exists only when both slits are open. Similar difficulties arise when we try to think through any type of experiment for investigating the laws of the motion of photons more precisely.

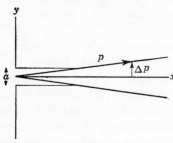

FIG. 2-1. Diffraction through an aperture.

As another example of a case where we cannot set up an experiment to give precise information about the motion of photons, let us consider diffraction through a single slit as in Fig. 2-1.   Here we show a very simple optical experiment, in which a parallel beam of light falls on an aperture and is spread on the far side by diffraction.   The reader who has studied diffraction will recall that the diffraction effect is quite different at small and at large distances from the aperture.   At large distances, we have what is called Fraunhofer diffraction, in which a beam spreads out

[1] A. Einstein, *Physik. Z.*, **10**:185, 817 (1909).

with an angular aperture of the order of magnitude of λ/a, where λ is the wavelength of the light, a the diameter of the aperture. This type of diffraction takes over at distances large enough so that the spreading beam, indicated in the figure, has a width of a or greater. At smaller distances, we have Fresnel diffraction, in which we have the beam of approximate width a, but with gradually developing fringes along its sides.

Now let the pattern fall on a screen whose distance from the aperture is great enough so that we are in the range of Fraunhofer diffraction. Let us consider a photon falling on one particular point of this screen, say toward the side of the Fraunhofer pattern. Let us ask what part of the aperture this photon has come through. The only way we can think of answering this question is to block off part of the aperture and see whether the photons passing through the smaller aperture that is left open will reach the point on the screen which we are investigating. But, by doing so, we defeat our purpose; for if the aperture a is reduced to a smaller value a', the Fraunhofer pattern will be spread more, to an angular aperture λ/a', and the whole problem is changed. Any attempt to limit the position in the aperture which the photon has passed through automatically spreads out the Fraunhofer beam and leads to an increased uncertainty about the precise direction in which the photon has traveled since leaving the aperture.

Consideration of such experiments as this gradually convinced physicists that it made no sense to ask for laws of motion of the photons more precise than the statistical statement that the intensity of the wave determined the probability of finding photons at the point in question. It was in this sense that the apparent conflict between a wave and a corpuscular theory of optics came to be reconciled: both are right, but we lack any means of setting up a precise and determined theory of the motion of photons. We cannot determine the path of an individual photon in such a problem as is illustrated in Fig. 2-1; we cannot do more than say that the photon will be found in the illuminated region, as deduced from wave theory, and is more likely to be found at bright spots in the pattern than in dark ones.

2-3. The Wave Hypothesis of de Broglie. The sketch which we have just given of the state of the theory of light, in the period just before 1926, will show that physicists were beginning to get used to the idea of a duality between waves and particles, with only a statistical relationship between them. But the decisive step to be taken was not in the theory of optics, but in mechanics. In his thesis in Paris in 1924, published in 1925, the physicist L. de Broglie[1] made the new suggestion that a duality between waves and particles existed in mechanics as well as in

[1] L. de Broglie, *Ann. phys.*, **3**:22 (1925).

optics. He suggested that waves somehow accompanied electrons and other particles, just as they seemed to accompany photons; and, by making this hypothesis, he was able to give the first plausible explanation as to why the quantum conditions existed. His idea was very simple. Suppose we have an electron moving round its orbit. If a wave accompanies it, going round and round, we shall have something like a standing wave. The condition of stability of a standing wave is that there be a whole number of wavelengths in the complete circuit, from one point back to the same point again, so that the wave can interfere constructively with itself. Why should not such a condition apply in mechanics, and why should not the quantum condition merely be a statement of the integral number of whole wavelengths demanded for this interference?

This argument was carried further by de Broglie, using rather complicated language on account of the fact that he used relativistic mechanics. Since then, it has been found that one can give just as convincing a form of the argument using classical mechanics, and we shall do so. Suppose, reversing the argument which we used in connection with the Compton effect, that we assume that the wavelength connected with a wave accompanying a particle of given momentum is found by the relation that the momentum equals h/λ. (De Broglie went through the justification of this assumption, in terms of the theory of relativity.) Suppose the wave circulates round the orbit of the particle. Then the number of waves in a small interval dq of distance round the orbit is equal to dq/λ, so that the total number of waves in the orbit is $\oint dq/\lambda$, where the integral is taken round the orbit. This, according to de Broglie's hypothesis, should be an integer. But $1/\lambda = p/h$, where p is the momentum, according to the hypothesis we have just described. Hence the condition for constructive interference of the waves is

$$\oint p \, dq = nh \tag{2-1}$$

or just the Sommerfeld quantum condition.

This simple explanation of the quantum condition was not carried further by de Broglie; it remained for Schrödinger, in 1926, to supply the additional suggestion needed to turn it into a complete theory. Justification for the hypothesis of de Broglie regarding waves accompanying particles, however, came very soon from a quite different source. It was noticed, soon after de Broglie's paper, that, if he were correct, particles such as electrons should show diffraction effects. It was possible immediately to find the wavelengths of the waves accompanying electrons of moderate energies, and it was evident that these wavelengths were of the same order of magnitude as X-ray wavelengths, so that one might expect to get electron diffraction by crystal lattices, just as it was known to be possible to get X-ray diffraction. This prediction was soon verified, in a very striking way, by Davisson and Germer and by G. P. Thomson, who observed electron-diffraction effects of precisely the type predicted by de Broglie's theory.

It was clear, then, that de Broglie's hypothesis had two strong confirmations: it predicted the quantum condition, and it explained the newly discovered phenomenon of electron diffraction. This was not enough, however: if it proposed to furnish a substitute for classical mechanics, it had to reduce to the ordinary Newtonian mechanics in the limit where that theory was known to apply. Let us therefore consider the application of de Broglie's waves to problems on a large scale and show, as he did, that the theory reduced to Newtonian mechanics. Then let us consider the limitations of classical mechanics and show that these limitations are imposed by the phenomenon of diffraction and lead to what is called the principle of uncertainty.

2-4. Newtonian Mechanics as a Limit of de Broglie's Wave Hypothesis. The characteristic of Newtonian mechanics is that we can define precisely the position of the particle at all values of the time. The associated de Broglie wave must then be one whose intensity is zero except where the particle is known to be; it is very large at that point. Such a wave is called a wave packet. We can set up a wave packet in the case of electromagnetic theory, and it helps us in understanding the de Broglie case if we consider this electromagnetic wave packet. The first step in setting up such a wave packet is to set up a ray of light; we let a parallel wave fall on a pinhole, and what comes through is a narrow bundle of radiation, or a ray. Next we equip the pinhole with a shutter and allow this to open only for an exceedingly small length of time, so short that the light comes through in a sort of puff, traveling along the ray like a particle. The result is a wave packet. It will go in a straight line in a medium of constant index of refraction, and its velocity will be the velocity of light. The situation is different if the index of refraction changes from point to point, as it does in heated air in the well-known phenomenon of the mirage. There the ray is curved, the velocity of the wave changes from point to point, and the result is a packet traveling with variable velocity, called the group velocity, along a curved path.

The law giving the path of the ray, in a medium where the index of refraction changes from point to point, is known as Fermat's principle, or the principle of least time. If one takes a ray starting at a point P_1 and passing through a point P_2 and computes the time taken for the light to pass from P_1 to P_2, traveling along the ray with the velocity v, one finds

$$\int_{P_1}^{P_2} \frac{ds}{v}$$

where ds is an element of distance along the path. Fermat's principle states that this time, computed for the true ray, is shorter than for any other path joining P_1 and P_2. This can be stated in another and more informing way. The velocity v equals $\lambda\nu$, the product of the wavelength and frequency. The frequency remains constant along the ray, even in a medium whose index of refraction varies from point to point; it is the wavelength λ which varies with position. The integral $\int ds/v$ appearing in Fermat's principle then equals $(1/\nu)\int ds/\lambda$. Since ν remains constant, we can state Fermat's principle in the form that

$$\int_{P_1}^{P_2} \frac{ds}{\lambda}$$

is shorter for the true path than for any other curve connecting P_1 and P_2. Here the wavelength is assumed to be a known function of position: at each point, we know the index of refraction, and hence the wavelength, for light of the particular frequency ν we are considering. Fermat's principle can be proved in several different ways, but the most informing proof is based on interference theory. We note that $\int ds/\lambda$ measures the number of wavelengths in the path. Fermat's principle states that this number, being a minimum for the true path, is stationary, or varies by only a small amount of higher order, if we go from the true path to a neighboring one. In other words, light traveling along neighboring paths can interfere constructively along the ray. A treatment by means of interference theory proves that the ray is just that path along which light can interfere constructively in this way.

In classical mechanics there is a principle, very similar to Fermat's principle, determining the path of a particle. It is called the principle of least action and is stated in the following way: At each point of space, we find the momentum p which a particle would have if it were located there. In doing this, we use the equation of conservation of energy, $p^2/2m + V = E$, where $p^2/2m$ is the kinetic energy, V the potential energy (a known function of position), and E the total energy. Thus, if the total energy is determined, we have $p = \sqrt{2m(E - V)}$. If we take the path of a particle traveling from point P_1 to P_2, with the energy E, and compute

$$\int_{P_1}^{P_2} p \, ds$$

from P_1 to P_2, where p is computed at each point of the path and we are extending the integral along the path, then we find that this integral is smaller for the true path of the particle than for any other path. The integral is called the action, and the principle is the principle of least action. By the calculus of variations, we can show that the principle of least action leads to Lagrange's equations, or to Newton's equations of motion, as the equations giving the motion of a particle which obeys the principle. This principle, or a closely related one called Hamilton's principle, stated in similar language, is often considered a fundamental formulation of the whole of mechanics, more fundamental than Newton's laws of motion. We discuss it in Appendix 2.

But now we see that, if we use Fermat's principle, a fundamental result of any wave theory, and combine it with de Broglie's assumption regarding the relation between momentum and wavelength, we are led at once to the principle of least action. For de Broglie assumed that $p = h/\lambda$. Hence with this assumption, Fermat's principle, the statement that

$$\int_{P_1}^{P_2} \frac{ds}{\lambda}$$

is a minimum becomes the statement that

$$\frac{1}{h} \int_{P_1}^{P_2} p\, ds$$

is a minimum. In other words, if we use de Broglie's assumptions, the two principles are identical and a proof of Fermat's principle from general wave theory leads to the proof that a wave packet of de Broglie waves will follow the path prescribed by Newtonian mechanics. It is a remarkable fact that Hamilton, in setting up the equations of motion which are known by his name, over 100 years before Schrödinger, was guided by an optical analogy of just the sort we have been describing. Hamilton realized that it was mathematically possible to set up a wave motion such that the rays associated with this wave were the trajectories of particles, according to Newtonian mechanics. The whole mathematical background of Hamiltonian mechanics is based on an analogy with geometrical optics in a medium of variable index of refraction. Hamilton thus, in a very real sense, anticipated de Broglie and Schrödinger by 100 years, for Hamilton's waves and de Broglie's were in many ways equivalent. But Hamilton, of course, knew nothing of quantum effects or of the other features which now lead us to use wave mechanics for handling phenomena on an atomic scale.

To complete our demonstration of the relation between wave mechanics and Newtonian mechanics, we should show that the wave packet moves along the ray with the correct velocity. It is a familiar fact of wave motion that a packet does not move with the phase velocity $\lambda\nu$ but with the group velocity $v_g = d\nu/d(1/\lambda)$. (See Appendix 3 for a discussion.) If we have propagation in three-dimensional space, the quantity $1/\lambda$ becomes a vector function of position, its direction being the direction of the wave normal, its magnitude the magnitude of $1/\lambda$. In that case, if we call the three components β_x, β_y, β_z, we have the vector relation of which the x component is $(v_g)_x = \partial \nu/\partial \beta_x$, with similar expressions for the other components. Now in our case we have $\nu = E/h$, $1/\lambda = p/h$; the vector quantity related to $1/\lambda$ is obviously a vector of magnitude p/h, pointing along the direction of the momentum. The energy E is to be expressed as a function of coordinates and of either the wavelength or p. But the energy, as expressed in terms of the coordinates and components of momentum, is known as the Hamiltonian function, denoted by H. Thus our expression for group velocity leads to the result

$$(v_g)_x = \frac{\partial H}{\partial p_x} \qquad (v_g)_y = \frac{\partial H}{\partial p_y} \qquad (v_g)_z = \frac{\partial H}{\partial p_z} \qquad (2\text{-}2)$$

The reader familiar with Hamilton's equations (see Appendix 4) will recognize these as three of Hamilton's equations for this particular problem, stating that v_g is in fact the velocity of the particle. To understand this, we need only take the explicit formula for H,

$$H = \frac{p_x^2 + p_y^2 + p_z^2}{2m} + V$$

where V is the potential energy. Then we have $\partial H/\partial p_x = p_x/m$, which certainly should be v_x according to classical mechanics.

As a result of this derivation, we must be on our guard to distinguish properly between the group velocity, given by Eq. (2-2), which is the velocity of the classical particle or of the wave packet, and the phase velocity, given by $\lambda \nu = E/p$. This phase velocity has no direct interpretation in classical mechanics. It is, however, the quantity v which appears in our discussion of Fermat's principle.

The derivation we have given in the present section shows that wave mechanics reduces properly to classical mechanics in the limit where we can neglect the size of the wavelength. In Chap. 4 and Appendix 3 we shall be able to give an even simpler derivation, proving straightforwardly that the center of gravity of a wave packet moves precisely according to the Hamiltonian equations of motion, or in accordance with Newton's laws. We are thus justified in using classical mechanics in any problem in which a wave packet can be set up which does not spread appreciably. Next we shall consider the limitation on classical mechanics imposed by diffraction.

2-5. Wave Packets and the Uncertainty Principle. We have seen that a wave packet constructed of de Broglie waves moves according to classical Newtonian mechanics. We must remember, however, that the existence of a wave theory of this type imposes a fundamental limitation on mechanics. Just as with optics, we assume that the intensity of the wave gives the probability of finding the particle at a given point and that there are no more precise laws determining the position of the particle. We cannot localize a particle more closely than to say that it lies within the wave packet. We are led to ask, then: How small can the wave packet be? A first, very crude answer to this question is that it must be at least as great as a wavelength in each of its dimensions, so that a particle cannot be localized more precisely than this. By studying diffraction more carefully, however, we can state the limitation in a more definite form, and in this form it becomes Heisenberg's principle of uncertainty,[1] stating the limitations on the accuracy of determining the position and momentum of a particle, on account of the fundamental fact that its motion is determined by a wave theory.

Let us consider the diffraction experiment described in Fig. 2-1. Here, if the aperture has a dimension a, and if y is along the direction in the plane of the aperture, we see that the fact that a particle has gone through the aperture fixes its y coordinate, at the instant that it went through, with an error, or uncertainty, of a. We may call this Δy. At the same time, on account of Fraunhofer diffraction, we do not know precisely the direction in which the particle is traveling after passing through the aperture. We know only that it lies within the diffracted ray, which is a spreading wave, the wave normals making angles up to about λ/a with the x axis. Thus, if we use de Broglie's assumption that the momentum equals h/λ, there will be a component of momentum along the y axis, in the diffracted beam, which will equal p times the sine of the angle between the momentum and the x axis, or anything up to approximately $p\lambda/a = h/a$. In other words, there is an uncertainty in the y component of momentum, which we may call Δp_y, of about this amount. Hence we have

$$\Delta y \, \Delta p_y = \frac{ah}{a} = h \qquad (2\text{-}3)$$

This is an example of the uncertainty principle, concerning the amount of uncertainty inherent in the description of the motion of particles by the wave theory. More generally, it proves to be the case that, when any coordinate x is specified with an uncertainty Δx, a corresponding uncertainty Δp_x appears in the momentum associated with it, of amount given equally for any wave theory, and hence equally for optics or for mechanics.

A similar relation holds between energy and time. Suppose we have a shutter over our hole and open it and close it very rapidly, so as to allow light, or particles, to pass through for only a very short interval of time Δt. Then the wave on the far side is an interrupted sinusoidal

---

[1] W. Heisenberg, *Z. Physik*, **43**:172 (1927).

train of waves, and if we analyze this train by Fourier analysis, we find that the frequency is no longer a definitely determined value but is spread out through a frequency band of breadth $\Delta\nu$, given by

$$\Delta\nu/\nu = 1/(\text{number of waves in train})$$

(see Appendix 3 for discussion). Now the number of waves in the train is $\nu\,\Delta t$, so that we have

$$\Delta\nu\,\Delta t = 1 \tag{2-4}$$

If we use the expression $E = h\nu$, this gives

$$\Delta E\,\Delta t = h \tag{2-5}$$

which is an uncertainty relation between E and t, showing that energy and time are equivalent to momentum and coordinate; if we try to measure exactly when particles go through the hole, their energy becomes correspondingly indeterminate.

From the uncertainty principle of Eq. (2-3), we can get back to our cruder form of statement, namely, that we cannot localize a particle more accurately than a wavelength. Thus, let the momentum be so poorly defined that we allow a variation Δp comparable with p itself. Then Eq. (2-3) states that the uncertainty Δq in the corresponding coordinate still will be at least as great as h/p, or the wavelength. It is now interesting to consider numerical values and ask what sort of practical limitation is placed on the application of classical mechanics by the uncertainty principle.

We find that classical mechanics forms a correct treatment of a problem in which the wavelengths of the particles are very small compared with any significant dimension of the problem, while quantum theory must be used if the wavelengths are comparable with other dimensions. In optics, we know that the case where the effect of finite wavelength must be considered leads to the phenomena of physical optics, while if the wavelength is so small that it can be neglected, we have geometrical optics. Hence geometrical optics is analogous to classical mechanics, and physical optics to quantum mechanics. If a significant dimension is called q and the momentum p, so that the wavelength is h/p, we then find that the number of wavelengths in this dimension is pq/h or, if p depends on q, it is $\int p\,dq/h$, which is Sommerfeld's quantum number. In other words, we expect that classical mechanics will be an adequate description if the quantum number is large, or if pq/h is large, where q is a significant dimension of the problem.

As a first illustration, let us consider problems on a large scale, such as we meet in everyday life. If masses are of the order of a gram, velocities of the order of centimeters per second, dimensions of the order of centimeters, pq will be of the order of magnitude of erg-seconds, enormously large compared with h, which is 6.63×10^{-27} erg-sec. Thus in such problems classical mechanics is completely adequate, and this holds even more in such problems as astronomical motions, where the masses, velocities, and dimensions are much greater. It is clear that, to get situations where we must use quantum mechanics, we must reduce greatly the momentum, the coordinate, or both. We know that in atomic and molecular processes we ordinarily meet rather large velocities; thus it is in the reduction of the masses and dimensions that we look for an approach to a region of applicability of quantum mechanics.

For atoms, we are dealing with electrons of mass approximately 9×10^{-28} g, moving with velocities about 10^9 cm/sec, in dimensions of the order of magnitude of 10^{-8} cm. Hence we have pq equal approximately to $9 \times 10^{-28} \times 10^9 \times 10^{-8} = 9 \times 10^{-27}$ erg-sec, just of the same order of magnitude as h. In other words, the electrons in the atom must be handled by quantum mechanics. This of course is no accident; it is, in fact, precisely the way in which the magnitude of atomic dimensions is fixed. The electrons are in states of very low quantum numbers.

For the vibrations of atoms as a whole, in molecules and crystals, one finds that the quantum numbers are quite small if the vibrations have the energies corresponding to thermal excitation at temperatures small compared with room temperature. However, if they go to temperatures considerably above room temperature, the quantum numbers become large enough so that we may use classical theory to a good approximation. Here the energy is $nh\nu$, where ν is the frequency of vibration. At a temperature T, according to thermodynamics, the average energy is approximately kT. Consequently the quantum number is of the order of magnitude of $kT/h\nu$. The vibrational frequencies of atoms in molecules and crystals are of the order of magnitude of 10^{13} cycles/sec. If we ask for a corresponding temperature, by the equation $kT = h\nu$, where ν is given this value, we find a temperature of about $500°K$, so that we must have a temperature considerably above this value, for vibrators of this frequency, before a classical treatment becomes approximately correct.

For different frequencies of oscillation, the dividing point comes at different temperatures. A heavy atom tends to vibrate with lower frequency than a light one, since the restoring forces do not vary greatly with the mass of the atom and the frequency of a classical vibrator varies as the square root of the elastic constant divided by the mass. Thus for a heavy atom the transition temperature comes at low temperatures compared with room temperatures. In a solid this temperature is closely related to the Debye temperature, which occurs in the theory of specific heats. Above the Debye temperature, the specific heat of a solid is given with good accuracy by classical mechanics and statistics; below the Debye temperature, characteristic quantum effects come into play. And, as a general rule, Debye temperatures tend to be well below room temperature for solids composed of heavy atoms, whereas for very light atoms these temperatures can be comparable with room temperature or even higher.

2-6. Schrödinger's Equation. We have now seen some of the consequences of de Broglie's proposal of waves accompanying particles, which he made in 1924. De Broglie's arguments had been largely qualitative, of the sort outlined in the preceding sections, though buttressed by more use of relativistic mechanics than we employed. Schrödinger, however, was a mathematical physicist well acquainted with the mathematics of vibrating media, and he was in the habit of expressing such problems by means of wave equations. With this background, when he considered de Broglie's hypothesis, he was led quite unambiguously and simply to the equation which bears his name;[1] and when he started to solve it, he found that the results of Bohr's theory of the hydrogen atom, the theory of the linear oscillator, and the other problems of quantum mechanics to which he applied it came out as simple and elegant results. His equation has been tested by problems of successively greater and greater difficulty, and it has emerged successfully for each such test. We seem to be justified in concluding that Schrödinger's formulation of wave mechanics in terms of a wave equation forms a fundamental law of nature, applying with great generality to quantum mechanics (and, by a passage to the limit, to classical mechanics) in the same sort of general way in which Newton's laws of motion form the fundamental laws of classical mechanics or Maxwell's equations those for electromagnetism. Most of the rest of our study, in fact, will consist of the application of Schrödinger's method to special problems.

To understand Schrödinger's argument, we must be familiar with wave equations in general. The simplest wave equation which we meet in physics arises from the problem of the vibrating string. Let the transverse displacement of a string from its undisplaced position be ψ, a function of x (the distance along the string) and t (the time). Then we consider an element of length of the string dx and apply Newton's equation $f = ma$ to this element, where f is the force, m the mass, a the acceleration. The force arises on account of the fact that the tension T in the string will be acting in different directions on the two ends of the element dx. Thus the transverse component of the tension force is approximately $T \, \partial\psi/\partial x$, as shown in Fig. 2-2. At the point $x + dx$, this component is $T \, \partial\psi/\partial x$ as computed at the point $x + dx$; but at the point x there is a force of the opposite sign, $-T \, \partial\psi/\partial x$, where the derivative is

[1] E. Schrödinger, *Ann. Physik,* **79**:361, 489, 734; **80**:437; **81**:109 (1926).

now to be computed at the point x.   The sum of these two gives a total transverse force, and it can be written approximately as $T(\partial^2\psi/\partial x^2)\,dx$. This force must be equal to the mass times the acceleration.   If μ is the mass per unit length, the mass of the element dx is $\mu\,dx$.   The acceleration is $\partial^2\psi/\partial t^2$.   Thus we have the equation

$$T\,\frac{\partial^2\psi}{\partial x^2} = \mu\,\frac{\partial^2\psi}{\partial t^2} \tag{2-6}$$

This is the wave equation for the vibrating string.

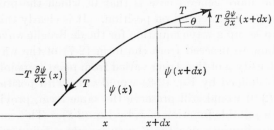

FIG. 2-2. Tensions on an element of string.   Vertical component at $x + dx$ is $T \sin \theta$. If we approximate $\sin \theta$ by $\tan \theta$, this is $T\,\partial\psi/\partial x$, computed at $x + dx$.   Similarly, at x the vertical component is $-T\,\partial\psi/\partial x$, computed at x.

Ordinarily we are interested in solutions of Eq. (2-6) which vary sinusoidally with the time, so that ψ depends on time through a factor $\sin \omega t$, where ω is an angular frequency; thus let $\psi = u(x) \sin \omega t$, where μ gives the dependence on x.   In this case $\partial^2\psi/\partial t^2$ equals $-\omega^2\psi$, and Eq. (2-6) may be rewritten, canceling out the time dependence, in the form

$$\frac{d^2u}{dx^2} + \omega^2\,\frac{\mu}{T}\,u = 0 \tag{2-7}$$

Equation (2-7) is now the equation for a sinusoidal oscillation,

$$u = \sin \frac{2\pi x}{\lambda}$$

where λ is the wavelength, given by

$$\frac{2\pi}{\lambda} = \omega \sqrt{\frac{\mu}{T}} \tag{2-8}$$

Thus we may rewrite Eq. (2-7) in the form

$$\frac{d^2u}{dx^2} + \left(\frac{2\pi}{\lambda}\right)^2 u = 0 \tag{2-9}$$

This is a standard form of the wave equation with the time eliminated. Similar equations hold in many other branches of physics: in problems of wave propagation in electrical lines, in acoustics, and in the vibrations of membranes, solids, electromagnetic cavities, and so on. In cases where the medium extends through two or three dimensions, as a membrane or a solid, u is a function of x and y, or of x, y, and z, and the second derivative d^2u/dx^2 has to be replaced by the sum of the two or three partial derivatives of u with respect to x, y, and z, symbolized by the expression $\nabla^2 u$, called the Laplacian of u.

The wave equation (2-9) is the simple case holding when the properties of the string, or, more generally, of the medium, do not vary from point to point. The more general case is that in which the properties, and hence the wavelength, depend on position. It is clearly this case which we must use to set up a wave equation for the de Broglie waves. We find a hint as to how to proceed from the form (2-7) of the wave equation. Suppose the density μ of the string varied from point to point. Then the wavelength as defined by Eq. (2-8) would vary with position. But we see that Eq. (2-9) would still preserve the same form, provided only we define λ to be a suitable function of x, by Eq. (2-8). This same equation, then, is the appropriate one for a wavelength varying with position; but then λ can be any arbitrary function of x, and it becomes a differential equation of much greater mathematical difficulty, an equation which can be solved analytically only in certain specially simple cases. It is this general form, however, which we encounter in setting up Schrödinger's equation.

We have now enough mathematical background to be able to retrace the path, really a very simple one, by which Schrödinger was led to his wave equation. Suppose we have a particle of mass m, moving along the x axis subject to a force whose potential energy is $V(x)$. We can then proceed, just as we did in the discussion of the linear oscillator in Sec. 1-8, to find the momentum, and hence the wavelength, at every point of the path, by use of the energy equation. The conservation of energy states that E, the total energy, equals $mv^2/2 + V$, or $p^2/2m + V$. Thus we have

$$p = \sqrt{2m(E - V)} \tag{2-10}$$

But by de Broglie's hypothesis $p = h/\lambda$, and we thus have the wavelength which must be substituted in Eq. (2-9) to get the wave equation. Substituting (2-10) in (2-9), we have at once

$$\frac{d^2u}{dx^2} + \frac{8\pi^2 m}{h^2}(E - V)u = 0 \tag{2-11}$$

Equation (2-11), where V is an appropriate function of x (different of course for each problem), is Schrödinger's equation. In case the particle is capable of moving in three dimensions rather than one, as of course is usually the case, Eq. (2-11) is to be replaced by

$$\nabla^2 u + \frac{8\pi^2 m}{h^2}(E - V)u = 0 \qquad (2\text{-}12)$$

where the Laplacian $\nabla^2 u$ is as defined above, and where V is now a function of x, y, and z. Such an equation, with an arbitrary V, is a partial differential equation of a type which is very hard indeed to solve, though some general properties can be stated. Nevertheless we have in Eq. (2-12) a general formulation of the motion of a particle, according to wave mechanics.

Schrödinger in his series of papers in 1926 proposing the wave mechanics went far beyond the mere statement of his equation and its solution in special cases, such as the linear oscillator and the hydrogen atom. He also gave a general formulation of wave mechanics, starting with the general Hamiltonian method of classical mechanics, setting up the wave equation for a general dynamical system, and proposing methods of great generality for getting information about the statistical behavior of a system in wave mechanics. This furnishes a set of postulates, suggested not only by the line of argument we have sketched but also by knowledge of Hamiltonian mechanics, which may be taken as the fundamental basis of wave mechanics. We are led in this way to the existence of stationary states, to the way of calculating properties of atoms, to the interpretation of Bohr's frequency condition, to the understanding of interaction with radiation and transitions between stationary states. Beginning with the next chapter, we shall state these postulates and explore their consequences, assuming that they are correct and that the properties of nature are to be deduced from them. This is quite a different type of argument from what we have followed so far, where we have been studying the processes which led up to the great generalization of wave mechanics. The correctness of wave mechanics is proved only by the fact that the consequences which we derive from it are in agreement with experiment. The rest of our study will be devoted to exploring those consequences and comparing them with experiment.

2-7. Suggested References on Atomic Physics and Quantum Mechanics. This is an appropriate point, where we have finished our sketch of the development of atomic physics up to the formulation of Schrödinger's equation, to pause and suggest certain books to the student who wishes to go more into detail than we do in this volume. Accordingly we list below a number of books of various types. Some of them are modern textbooks of atomic physics and quantum mechanics. Others, however, are particularly interesting for their historical role in the development of the subject. They are partly books by the physicists who developed quantum theory, partly books which were in general use at the time the ideas were being built up.   Often one gains a better insight into the development of the subject from these older books, written in a period of partial knowledge, than from modern textbooks. In addition to the books mentioned in the present section and others mentioned throughout the text, it is of course very important for the reader to become familiar with the original papers.   We have given references to a few of the most important ones in this chapter and the preceding one; further references are given in later chapters, and a quite inclusive bibliography will be given at the end of Vol. II.   We now list the suggested reference books:

Aston, F. W.: "Mass-spectra and Isotopes," Longmans, Green & Co., Inc., New York, 1933.
Bohm, D.: "Quantum Theory," Prentice-Hall, Inc., Englewood Cliffs, N.J., 1952.
Bohr, N.: "The Theory of Spectra and Atomic Constitution," Cambridge University Press, New York, 1922.
Born, M.: "Atomic Physics," Hafner Publishing Company, New York (many editions).
Condon, E. U., and P. M. Morse: "Quantum Mechanics," McGraw-Hill Book Company, Inc., New York, 1929.
Dampier, W. C.: "History of Science," Cambridge University Press, London; 3d ed., The Macmillan Company, New York, 1942.
Darrow, K. K.: "Introduction to Contemporary Physics," D. Van Nostrand Company, Inc., Princeton, N.J., 1939.
Einstein, A., and L. Infeld: "The Evolution of Physics," Simon and Schuster, Inc., New York, 1938.
Foote, P. D., and F. L. Mohler: "The Origin of Spectra," Reinhold Publishing Corporation, New York, 1922.
Frenkel, J.: "Wave Mechanics, Elementary Theory," Dover Publications, New York, 1950.
Gurney, R. W.: "Elementary Quantum Mechanics," Cambridge University Press, New York, 1934.
Heisenberg, W.: "The Physical Principles of the Quantum Theory," University of Chicago Press, Chicago, 1930.
Heitler, W.: "Elementary Wave Mechanics," Clarendon Press, Oxford, 1945.
Jeans, J. H.: "Report on Radiation and the Quantum Theory," 2d ed., Physical Society of London, 1924.
Kemble, E. C.: "Fundamental Principles of Quantum Mechanics," McGraw-Hill Book Company, Inc., New York, 1937.
Millikan, R. A.: "Electrons (+ and −), Protons, Photons, Neutrons, Mesotrons, and Cosmic Rays," University of Chicago Press, Chicago, 1947.
Mott, N. F., and I. N. Snedden: "Wave Mechanics and Its Applications," Clarendon Press, Oxford, 1948.
————: "Elements of Wave Mechanics," Cambridge University Press, New York, 1952.
Oldenberg, O.: "Introduction to Atomic Physics," 2d ed., McGraw-Hill Book Company, Inc., New York, 1954.
Pauling, L., and E. Bright Wilson, Jr.: "Introduction to Quantum Mechanics," McGraw-Hill Book Company, Inc., New York, 1935.

Planck, M.: "The Theory of Heat Radiation," trans. by M. Masius, P. Blakiston's Son & Company, Philadelphia, 1914.

———: "Scientific Autobiography," Philosophical Library, Inc., New York, 1949.

Richtmyer, F. K., E. H. Kennard, and T. Lauritsen: "Introduction to Modern Physics," 5th ed., McGraw-Hill Book Company, Inc., New York, 1955.

Rojansky, V.: "Introductory Quantum Mechanics," Prentice-Hall, Inc., Englewood Cliffs, N.J., 1938.

Ruark, A. E., and H. C. Urey: "Atoms, Molecules, and Quanta," McGraw-Hill Book Company, Inc., New York, 1930.

Rutherford, E., J. Chadwick, and C. D. Ellis: "Radiations from Radioactive Substances," Cambridge University Press, London; The Macmillan Company, New York, 1930.

Schiff, L. I.: "Quantum Mechanics," 2d ed., McGraw-Hill Book Company, Inc., New York, 1955.

Schrödinger, E.: "Collected Papers on Wave Mechanics," Blackie & Son, Ltd., Glasgow, 1929.

Slater, J. C.: "Modern Physics," McGraw-Hill Book Company, Inc., New York, 1955.

Sommerfeld, A.: "Atomic Structure and Spectral Lines," E. P. Dutton & Co., Inc., New York, 1934.

PROBLEMS

1. An electron moves with energies of 1 ev; 100 ev; 10,000 ev. Find the de Broglie wavelength in each case, and consider whether the wavelengths would be appropriate for use in electron-diffraction experiments with crystals.

2. A hydrogen atom moves with the energy $\frac{3}{2}kT$ associated with $T = 300°K$. Find the de Broglie wavelength, and consider whether atoms of such energies would be expected to be diffracted by crystals.

3. A beam of particles of mass m, traveling with velocity v ($v \ll c$), falls on a slit of width d. After traveling a distance D ($D \gg d$), the diffraction pattern is observed. For what value of d will this diffraction pattern have minimum width? (Use the uncertainty principle rather than working out the details of the diffraction pattern.)

4. A microscope cannot resolve objects much smaller than a wavelength. What energy of electrons (in electron volts) would be required to give a theoretical resolving power of 1 angstrom in an electron microscope? (*Note:* Real electron microscopes so far are still rather far from attaining theoretical resolving power.)

5. Show that the difference of radii of successive Bohr circular orbits for hydrogen is of the same order of magnitude as the de Broglie wavelength in one of the orbits. Since the uncertainty principle does not allow under any circumstances that a beam of particles can be of cross section much less than a wavelength, this means that according to the uncertainty principle the electrons cannot be localized sharply enough to tell which of two adjacent orbits they are occupying.

6. An electron moves in a circular path round the lines of force of a magnetic field. Apply the quantum condition to the rotation. Find the radius of the orbit corresponding to a quantum number of unity in a magnetic field of 10^5 gauss, and find the kinetic energy (in electron volts) of the electron in this orbit.

7. An electron beam passes through a small circular aperture adjusted so as to give the beam a minimum diameter after traveling a distance D. There is a magnetic field B along the direction of the beam, so that the electrons which acquire any component of velocity in the plane normal to B, on account of the uncertainty principle, will have a circular motion in the plane normal to B superposed on their motion along the direction of the field. Show that this circular motion will approximate that in the ground state of the rotator, as discussed in Prob. 6, at the distance D from the aperture.

8. A projectile shot horizontally with velocity v in the earth's gravitational field moves in a parabola, but at the top of the path this parabola can be approximated by a circle. Show that the radius of the circle is given by $r = v^2/g$. If the trajectory of the particle is approximately a circle, the wave fronts of the de Broglie waves are the radii of the circle. Since these radii get farther apart as we rise above the surface of the earth, the de Broglie wavelength must increase with height. Show that the increase of wavelength is just consistent with the decrease of momentum with height as given by classical mechanics. This is a simple case where we can find the shape of the trajectory of a particle as predicted from the de Broglie waves by elementary means.

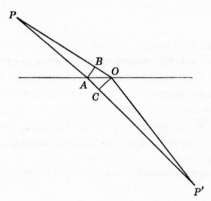

Fig. 2-3. Figure to illustrate Prob. 9.

9. Assume that in Fig. 2-3 POP' is the path of the optically correct ray passing from one medium into another of different refractive index. Prove Fermat's principle for this case, showing that the time for the ray to pass along a slightly different path, as PAP', differs from that along POP' by a small quantity of higher order than the distance AO. The figure is drawn so that AB, CO are arcs of circles with centers at P and P', respectively, and it is to be noted that, for small AO, the figures AOB, AOC are almost exactly right triangles.

3

Schrödinger's Equation and Its Solutions in One-dimensional Problems

3-1. Hamiltonian Mechanics and Wave Mechanics. In studying the structure of matter, we are considering the mechanics of an assembly of particles, electrons and nuclei, acted on by forces of an electromagnetic nature. By far the largest of these forces are the electrostatic, or Coulomb, attractions and repulsions between the particles, which can be derived from a potential energy which is a function of the positions of the particles, though in the presence of magnetic fields there are other forces depending on the velocities. Let us consider for the present the simple case of particles under the influence of a potential energy function like that arising from the Coulomb forces.

If these particles moved according to classical mechanics, their motions would be given by Newton's laws of motion. If the coordinates of the particles were $x_1 y_1 z_1$ for the first particle, $x_2 y_2 z_2$ for the second, and so on, down to the Nth, with coordinates $x_N y_N z_N$, then we know that the force acting on any one of these coordinates, such as x_j, is given by the negative partial derivative $-\partial V/\partial x_j$ of the potential energy with respect to the appropriate coordinate. If the mass of the jth particle is m_j, then Newton's second law states that the force component equals the mass times acceleration, or

$$m_j \frac{d^2 x_j}{dt^2} = - \frac{\partial V}{\partial x_j} \tag{3-1}$$

For purposes of advanced study, these equations of motion are often put in what is called the Hamiltonian form. This involves in the first place defining a momentum associated with, or, as it is often expressed, conjugate to, each coordinate. Thus, in the present case, the momentum component p_{x_j} conjugate to x_j would be defined in an obvious way as

$$p_{x_j} = m_j \frac{dx_j}{dt} \tag{3-2}$$

51

Ordinarily, in setting up the coordinates and momenta of the system, one does not distinguish between x, y, and z coordinates but merely denotes all the coordinates by a set q_1, q_2, . . . , q_n, where in the present case $q_1 = x_1$, $q_2 = y_1$, $q_3 = z_1$, $q_4 = x_2$, . . . , $q_{3N} = z_N$, and denotes the momentum component conjugate to q_j as p_j; the q_j's and p_j's are referred to as generalized coordinates and momenta. The simple definition of momentum component given in Eq. (3-2) is not general, though it applies in our special case; the general definition is given in Appendix 4, where we discuss the Hamiltonian method more in detail and give examples of cases where Eq. (3-2) does not apply. Two such examples come from particles moving in a magnetic field and particles moving according to the principle of relativity, with velocities so great that classical mechanics does not apply.

The next step in Hamiltonian mechanics is to define what is called the Hamiltonian function. This in ordinary cases is the energy, expressed in terms of the coordinates and momenta; here again in Appendix 4 we consider the general definition of the Hamiltonian function. When we are dealing with our present simple problem and are using rectangular coordinates, the kinetic energy is a sum of terms like $\frac{1}{2}m_j(dx_j/dt)^2$, which can be rewritten as $(p_{x_j})^2/2m_j$, and the potential energy is V, which is a function of the coordinates, so that in this case we have

$$H = \sum (j) \frac{p_j^2}{2m_j} + V(q_1, \ . \ . \ . \ , q_n) \tag{3-3}$$

Then we set up equations of motion called Hamilton's equations, which are

$$\frac{dq_j}{dt} = \frac{\partial H}{\partial p_j} \qquad \frac{dp_j}{dt} = -\frac{\partial H}{\partial q_j} \tag{3-4}$$

In our simple case, $\partial H/\partial p_j = p_j/m_j$, so that the first of Hamilton's equations is identical with Eq. (3-2). It is the same equation which we have met earlier in Eq. (2-2), in discussing group velocity in wave mechanics. The second of Hamilton's equations is simplified by use of the fact that $\partial H/\partial q_j = \partial V/\partial q_j$, which shows that it is equivalent to Newton's law, Eq. (3-1), when we take account of Eq. (3-2). Thus we see that Hamilton's equations are merely a way of rewriting Newton's equations. The importance of Hamilton's equations in classical mechanics arises because they form a convenient way of setting up the equations of motion in generalized coordinates, such as, for instance, polar or other types of coordinate systems. The importance for our present problem is, however, quite different: they furnish a basis for the general formulation of Schrödinger's equation and wave mechanics.

Newton's equations, or Hamilton's equations, allow us to integrate the motion of a system, in classical mechanics. That is, if we know the values of all q_j's and p_j's at an initial time, say $t = 0$, we can find the values of these same quantities at any later time. This is particularly clear from Hamilton's equations, Eq. (3-4): if we know the q's and p's at one instant, and hence the Hamiltonian function, we can find the derivatives $\partial H/\partial p_j$, $\partial H/\partial q_j$, and hence the time rate of change of the q's and p's. This allows us to find the values of the q's and p's at a later time $t + \Delta t$, when we can again find H, and so on. Often the results of this integration are exhibited, in classical mechanics, by setting up a phase space, a many-dimensional space in which the q_j's and p_j's are plotted as variables. A single point in this many-dimensional phase space gives all the q's and p's of the system; it is called a representative point. If we know the position of the representative point at $t = 0$, Hamilton's equations allow us to predict its subsequent motion. In Fig. 1-2 we have seen a very simple example of a phase space, for a one-dimensional problem, with a two-dimensional phase space. The line of constant energy in that diagram is the path of the representative point.

In contrast to Newtonian mechanics, wave mechanics does not allow us to find the coordinates of the particles as a function of time. Instead, as we have seen in the preceding chapter, it gives us only statistical information about the motion of the particles. The type of information which we can give is the following: If the probability of finding the coordinates in the ranges $dx_1\, dy_1\, dz_1 \cdots dz_N$ at time t_0 is $P_0(x_1 y_1 \cdots z_N)\, dx_1\, dy_1 \cdots dz_N$, then we can predict that the probability of finding them in corresponding ranges at time t is $P(x_1 y_1 \cdots z_N,t)\, dx_1\, dy_1 \cdots dz_N$, where P reduces to P_0 at time t_0. The quantity P is called the probability density.

To show the relation of wave mechanics to classical mechanics, we proceed as in the preceding chapter and set up a probability density P of a type called a wave packet, as concentrated in space as possible, subject to the uncertainty principle; we try to arrange it to give as small fluctuation of the momentum as possible consistent with its extension in space (which we can test, for instance, by computing the mean-square deviation of the momentum from its mean value). In the classical limit, this probability density, as we have seen, can indicate that both coordinates and momenta are so well determined that for practical purposes they are exactly known. We then investigate the subsequent motion of the systems described by this wave packet, finding the subsequent values of the average coordinates and momenta of the systems making up the wave packet. We can prove that this average motion exactly follows classical mechanics. Thus, in any case in which the spread of coordinates and momenta demanded by the uncertainty principle is of negligible importance, classical mechanics will apply correctly. In Appendix 3 we discuss wave packets, their relation to the principle of uncertainty, and their average motion and relation to classical mechanics, in detail.

It is necessary to clarify the concept of probability which we have just introduced. We cannot speak of a probability unless we have a large number of individuals to which statistical methods can be applied. The individuals concerned here are a great many repetitions of the same experiment. Such a collection of repetitions of the same experiment is what is called an ensemble in statistical mechanics. By the probability of finding coordinates in certain ranges we mean the fraction of all repetitions in which the coordinates in question are found in this range. In dealing with such an ensemble, we always in conception pass to the limit in which we have an infinite number of individuals in the ensemble. It is necessary to understand this statistical ensemble thoroughly and to understand that the average values over the ensemble, which we shall later introduce, definitely do not refer either to averages over time or averages over large numbers of particles. We can set up an ensemble and perform an average over it, at a specific time, and dealing with a system containing only one particle. Even with such a system, successive repetitions of the same experiment will lead to different results. As an example, we may be dealing with the experiment of diffraction through a slit, described in Fig. 2-1. Each time a particle comes through the slit and hits the screen, we can detect precisely the point of the screen where it hits. We could repeat the experiment many times, each time allowing only one particle to come through. Every time the particle would hit a different point of the screen. If we continued this long enough, we could set up a smooth function of position, giving the fraction of trials in which the particle hit in a given range of the screen. This would be the probability function P of which we are speaking.

3-2. Schrödinger's Equation, and the Existence of Stationary States.
In wave mechanics, the probability density P is expressed in terms of the wave function ψ, also a function of the coordinates $x_1 y_1 \cdots z_N$ and the time t. This is the quantity, like the ψ of Eq. (2-6), which satisfies Schrödinger's equation. This wave function in general is a complex number, and its complex conjugate is written as ψ^*. Then the fundamental postulate of wave mechanics is that $P = \psi^*\psi$, or that the probability that the system be found in the region $dx_1 \, dy_1 \cdots dz_N$ at time t is given by the quantity

$$\text{Probability} = \psi^*(x_1 \cdots z_N,t)\psi(x_1 \cdots z_N,t) \, dx_1 \cdots dz_N = \psi^*\psi \, dv$$

$$(3\text{-}5)$$

where dv is the generalized element of volume in the $3N$-dimensional space with coordinates $x_1 \cdots z_N$. The quantity $\psi^*\psi$ is the square of the absolute value of ψ; this dependence of the probability on the square of the amplitude of the wave function is analogous to the situation in electromagnetic theory, where the Poynting vector and energy density, which determine the probability of finding photons in a given region of space, are proportional to the square of the electric- or magnetic-field amplitudes.

Since the probability that the system must be somewhere is unity, we must have the integral of Eq. (3-5) over all values of the coordinates equal to unity, that is,

$$\int \cdots \int \psi^* \psi \, dx_1 \cdots dz_N = 1 \tag{3-6}$$

where the integration is to be over all possible values of all the coordinates $x_1 \cdots z_N$. This condition given in Eq. (3-6) is called the normalization condition. Our probability postulate of Eq. (3-5) can give us information about individual particles. Thus, for instance, if we wish to know the probability that x_1 will be found in the range dx_1, irrespective of what the other coordinates $y_1 z_1 x_2 \cdots z_N$ may be, we may integrate Eq. (3-6) over all values of these other coordinates, leading to

Probability that x_1 be in dx_1 is

$$\left(\int \cdots \int \psi^* \psi \, dy_1 \, dz_1 \cdots dz_N \right) dx_1 \tag{3-7}$$

where the integration is to be over all values of the variables $y_1 \cdots z_N$.

From what we have already seen about the wave function ψ and its relation to the probability density, we can see that the analogy between wave mechanics and optics is not as close as we have been indicating up to this point. We have just stated that the electric and magnetic fields lead to Poynting's vector and the energy density, which determine the probability of finding a photon at a given point of space. But the electromagnetic field is defined in an ordinary three-dimensional space, and a single field gives information about an indefinitely large number of photons. Its intensity is an indication of how many photons are in the field. On the other hand, our wave function is in a many-dimensional space, and separate dimensions give information about the various particles. It is normalized, which the electromagnetic field is not; it means nothing to speak of one wave function as being more intense than another, so to speak.

It is not possible in an elementary way to set up a single wave function, in three-dimensional space, to give probability information about a large number of particles. It can be shown that such a treatment is possible only for noninteracting particles; this is the reason why it is possible for photons, which do not interact with each other to an appreciable extent, but not for electrons and charged particles, which act on each other with Coulomb interactions. From these remarks we see that the analogy between optics and mechanics, which was so useful in the development of wave mechanics, is not anything to push too far. As a matter of fact, when we come to discuss quantum electrodynamics, in Chap. 6, we shall set up a many-dimensional wave function, quite analogous to our ψ, and our treatment will be very different from a simple one which would merely use the electromagnetic field to determine the probability of finding photons in given regions of space.

We have now defined the wave function ψ; we must next state how it is to be found. It is determined, according to the postulates of wave mechanics, by the requirement that it satisfy Schrödinger's equation. This equation, in the general case, is set up in the following way: We start with the Hamiltonian function $H(q_j,p_j)$ appropriate to the problem according to classical mechanics, where we have written q_j, p_j to symbolize the whole set of coordinates and momenta. Then we make an operator out of it, by replacing each p, wherever it occurs, by

$$p_j \to \frac{h}{2\pi i} \frac{\partial}{\partial q_j} = -i\hbar \frac{\partial}{\partial q_j} \qquad (3\text{-}8)$$

where h is Planck's constant, $\hbar = h/2\pi$, and $i = \sqrt{-1}$. Thus in case H is given by Eq. (3-3), the Hamiltonian operator is

$$(H)_{\text{op}} = \sum (j) \left(-\frac{\hbar^2}{2m_j} \frac{\partial^2}{\partial q_j^2} \right) + V(q_j) \qquad (3\text{-}9)$$

Then we set up the differential equation

$$(H)_{\text{op}}\psi = i\hbar \frac{\partial \psi}{\partial t} \qquad (3\text{-}10)$$

which in the case above becomes

$$\sum (j) \left(-\frac{\hbar^2}{2m_j} \frac{\partial^2 \psi}{\partial q_j{}^2} \right) + V(q_j)\psi = i\hbar \frac{\partial \psi}{\partial t} \qquad (3\text{-}11)$$

where again the q_j in $V(q_j)$ symbolizes the whole set of coordinates. This equation, Eq. (3-10) or (3-11), is Schrödinger's equation. It is to be solved subject to the condition that ψ be a continuous function which is not allowed to have such singularities that the normalization integral of Eq. (3-6) diverges.

Schrödinger's equation, Eq. (3-10), has solutions which can be written as products of a function of the coordinates, which we shall write $u(q_j)$, and a function of the time, which we shall write $T(t)$. To prove this, let us substitute this product into Eq. (3-10) and divide through by ψ or by uT. We find

$$\frac{1}{u} (H)_{\text{op}}u = \frac{1}{T} i\hbar \frac{dT}{dt} \qquad (3\text{-}12)$$

The left side of Eq. (3-12) is a function of the coordinates only, whereas the right side is a function of the time only. It is impossible for this equation to be satisfied for all values of the coordinates and time, unless each side of Eq. (3-12) is a constant. Let us call this constant E; we shall later show that it is the energy. Then we have two equations, which may be written

$$(H)_{op}u = Eu \qquad \frac{dT}{dt} = \frac{-iET}{\hbar} \qquad (3\text{-}13)$$

The second equation of Eq. (3-13) has as its solution $T = $ constant $e^{-iEt/\hbar}$. If we absorb the constant into the function u, we find that we have a solution of Schrödinger's equation in the form

$$\psi(q_j,t) = u(q_j)e^{-iEt/\hbar} \qquad (3\text{-}14)$$

where u satisfies the first equation of Eq. (3-13), $(H)_{op}u = Eu$, which is called Schrödinger's equation with the time eliminated. This latter equation, for a problem involving only one particle, is

$$-\frac{\hbar^2}{2m}\nabla^2 u + Vu = Eu \qquad (3\text{-}15)$$

which is identical with Eq. (2-12). In other words, our present very general formulation of Schrödinger's equation leads, in this simple case, to the equation which we arrived at rather intuitively in the preceding chapter, through de Broglie's postulate of waves accompanying particles.

If we have a solution of Schrödinger's equation in the form given in Eq. (3-14), we note that the probability density, given by

$$\psi^*\psi = u^*u \qquad (3\text{-}16)$$

depends on the coordinates only and is independent of time. For this reason such a solution represents a stationary state. General solutions of Schrödinger's equation, as we shall show later, can be written as linear combinations of solutions of the type of Eq. (3-14), and they do not have this property of having a probability density independent of time. A wave packet, for instance, is given by such a linear combination of stationary states.

A very interesting feature of the solution which we have found in Eq. (3-14) is the way in which the time dependence of the wave function is given by a complex exponential function. This is a very different situation from that found in any other branch of mathematical physics. It is very common in all sorts of problems in vibrations to assume solutions varying exponentially with time, in the form $e^{\pm i\omega t}$. This is always done, however, as a device to simplify the solution. In the ordinary wave equation of mathematical physics with a second time derivative, as in

Eq. (2-6), we find that either the plus or the minus sign in the exponential leads to an acceptable solution; and when we want physical results, we take the real part of the resulting function, which is also a solution, and use this real function. Our present situation, with the first time derivative, as in Eq. (3-10) or (3-11), and with the factor i appearing explicitly in the wave equation, is fundamentally different. Only the solution varying as the complex exponential of Eq. (3-14) forms an acceptable solution of Eq. (3-11). We are not allowed to take its real part; this would not be a solution of Schrödinger's equation. Our wave function is inherently a complex quantity; and we see that it was the complex nature of the time dependence which led to the probability density independent of time, in Eq. (3-16), and which gives stationary states, in agreement with Bohr's original concepts and with experiment. Since the probability density must be real, we see why a postulate like that of Eq. (3-5) is required to produce a real probability density from a complex wave function; for we remember that the product of any complex number and its complex conjugate is real.

3-3. Motion of a Particle in a Region of Constant Potential. Schrödinger's equation, with V given as an arbitrary function of the coordinates, cannot be solved exactly in general, and yet we must become familiar with the general nature of the solution in order to proceed intelligently with our discussion. Fortunately there is one broad class of problems which can be solved exactly and which will allow us to study enough types of potentials so that we can understand the general case. This is the case of a one-dimensional motion in which the potential has one constant value in one range of coordinates, another in another, and so on, with discontinuities between. Here, inside each region of constant potential, the solution is sinusoidal or exponential, and the conditions at the point of discontinuity prove to be quite simple: the solutions must join from one region to the next with continuous values of the function and slope. These are simple enough conditions so that we can set up exact solutions in this way, without analytical difficulties. Accordingly we shall proceed with this method, and with the discussion of a wide range of problems by means of it.

First we consider the solution of Schrödinger's equation in a one-dimensional problem with a constant potential. If $V = 0$, Schrödinger's equation with the time eliminated takes the form

$$ -\frac{\hbar^2}{2m}\frac{d^2u}{dx^2} = Eu \tag{3-17} $$

which has as a general solution

$$ u = A \exp\left(i\sqrt{2mE}\,x/\hbar\right) + B \exp\left(-i\sqrt{2mE}\,x/\hbar\right) \tag{3-18} $$

where A, B are arbitrary constants.   If we combine these functions with the time-dependent factor, as in Eq. (3-14), we have

$$\psi = A \exp\left[i(\sqrt{2mE}\,x - Et)/\hbar\right] + B \exp\left[i(-\sqrt{2mE}\,x - Et)/\hbar\right] \quad (3\text{-}19)$$

The first term represents a wave traveling along the x direction and the second a wave traveling along $-x$.   Such waves can be expressed in the form

$$\psi = A \exp\left[i(2\pi x/\lambda - 2\pi\nu t)\right] + B \exp\left[i(-2\pi x/\lambda - 2\pi\nu t)\right] \quad (3\text{-}20)$$

where λ is the wavelength, ν the frequency.   In this case, we see that λ and ν are determined in accordance with the assumptions of Planck and de Broglie.   That is, we have $\lambda = h/p$, where $p = \sqrt{2mE}$, and $\nu = E/h$.

We must assume that the square of the amplitude A measures in some way the intensity of the wave traveling along x, while the square of the amplitude B measures the intensity of the wave traveling along $-x$.   This is a special case in which the wave function cannot be normalized, for if we tried to extend an integral, such as that of Eq. (3-6), over all space, we should get an infinite result if A and B were finite.   In such problems as this, we must adopt alternative methods of normalization.   We can assume that the solution of Eq. (3-19) refers to a situation in which we have particles traveling both to the right and to the left along the x axis, with the energy E, momentum $\pm \sqrt{2mE}$, and that the probability of finding a particle traveling to the right is proportional to A^*A and that of finding a particle traveling to the left is proportional to B^*B.   By choosing $B = A$, we can set up a special case of Eq. (3-19) of the form

$$\psi = 2A \cos\left(\sqrt{2mE}\,x/\hbar\right) \exp\left(-iEt/\hbar\right) \quad (3\text{-}21)$$

and, by setting $B = -A$, we have

$$\psi = 2iA \sin\left(\sqrt{2mE}\,x/\hbar\right) \exp\left(-iEt/\hbar\right) \quad (3\text{-}22)$$

which are standing waves, rather than traveling waves.   These correspond to streams of particles of equal amplitudes traveling both to the right and to the left.

The possibility of making these linear combinations of traveling waves arises because we have two independent solutions of Schrödinger's equation for the energy E, with different coefficients A and B in Eq. (3-19). A case, such as this, in which we have more than one solution corresponding to the same energy, is called a case of degeneracy.   In every such case, it is immediately obvious from the linear nature of Schrödinger's equation that an arbitrary linear combination of the degenerate solutions is an equally good solution corresponding to the same energy.   As independent solutions of the time-independent equation (3-17), in the present case, we could have taken $\exp{(i \sqrt{2mE} \, x/\hbar)}$ and $\exp{(-i \sqrt{2mE} \, x/\hbar)}$; we could equally well have taken $\cos{(\sqrt{2mE} \, x/\hbar)}$ and $\sin{(\sqrt{2mE} \, x/\hbar)}$. An arbitrary linear combination of the functions of either set will represent the general solution of Schrödinger's equation for the energy E.

Let us consider $\psi^*\psi$ or u^*u. It is more convenient to do this if the constants A and B, which can be complex, are expressed in terms of their amplitudes and phases, in the form

$$A = A_0 e^{i\alpha_0} \qquad B = B_0 e^{i\beta_0} \qquad (3\text{-}23)$$

where A_0, B_0, α_0, β_0 are real. Then we find

$$\psi^*\psi = u^*u = A_0^2 + B_0^2 + 2A_0 B_0 \cos{[(2\sqrt{2mE}\, x/\hbar) + \alpha_0 - \beta_0]} \qquad (3\text{-}24)$$

This represents the interference between the waves traveling in the two opposite directions. Superposed on the constant value $A_0^2 + B_0^2$, we have a sinusoidal oscillation of probability density, oscillating with half the wavelength of the wave function ψ, and resulting in a periodic oscillation of $\psi^*\psi$ between the limits $(A_0 \pm B_0)^2$. This is the sort of behavior found in other examples of interference of waves traveling in opposite directions. It is found, for instance, in the study of standing-wave ratios in wave guides or other microwave transmission lines. It has a physical interpretation: it leads to a sinusoidal oscillation of the probability of finding an electron at a given point of space, whenever we have two streams of particles traveling in opposite directions, or whenever we have a standing wave. Such oscillations of probability are of very great physical significance in many aspects of the theory of matter.

The solutions we have been considering are those for which E is positive. If E is negative, we can more conveniently rewrite Eq. (3-18) in the form

$$u = A \exp{(\sqrt{-2mE}\, x/\hbar)} + B \exp{(-\sqrt{-2mE}\, x/\hbar)} \qquad (3\text{-}25)$$

where now $\sqrt{-2mE}$ is real, so that our solution, instead of representing traveling waves, represents functions which are exponentially damped in going along x. The first function of Eq. (3-25) becomes infinite as x becomes infinite, and the second becomes infinite as x becomes negatively infinite. Hence neither function can be used to represent a physical situation: in either case, the probability of finding the particle at infinite distance would be infinitely greater than that of finding it at a finite value of x. The normalization gave us difficulty in the earlier case of traveling waves; but here it leads to a much greater difficulty. We conclude, then, that, if we are dealing with free particles in infinite space, they cannot move with negative kinetic energy. This is in agreement with classical mechanics.

The situation is quite different, however, provided we are dealing only with a finite region of space, such as we shall meet when we begin joining solutions for finite regions in which the potential is constant. For instance, if we are interested in a solution holding only for positive values of x, there is no reason why the solution $\exp\left(-\sqrt{-2mE}\ x/\hbar\right)$ should not be used. On the other hand, the other solution, $\exp\left(\sqrt{-2mE}\ x/\hbar\right)$, would become infinite when x became infinite and would have to be ruled out. Hence it comes about that in wave mechanics we can have a situation which is not met in classical mechanics: particles can penetrate into regions where their kinetic energy is negative, provided these regions fill only part of space. In these regions, the wave function is of an exponentially decreasing nature, instead of varying sinusoidally. We shall find that such exponentially decreasing tails for our wave functions in regions of space where the classical particle could not penetrate are a very characteristic feature of solutions of problems in wave mechanics.

We have taken the case where the potential energy was zero. A glance at Schrödinger's equation will show that, if the potential energy is everywhere constant, equal to V_0, the only difference in the situation is that we must replace E by $E - V_0$ wherever it appears in Eqs. (3-17) to (3-25). The quantity $E - V_0$ is the kinetic energy, and our remarks of the preceding paragraph, as we indicated there, depend on whether the kinetic energy is positive or negative, not on the sign of the total energy, which is immaterial; we can always add an arbitrary constant to the potential energy and an equal constant to the total energy without making any change whatever in Schrödinger's equation or in the wave function.

3-4. Joining Conditions at a Discontinuity of Potential. We now approach the more general problem where the potential is one constant in one region, another constant in another region, with a discontinuity at the boundary between the two regions. In each region, we must have a solution of the type discussed in the preceding section, but these solutions must join somehow at the boundary. Let us inquire what are the boundary conditions.

In the first place, by our fundamental postulate we wish the wave function u to join continuously across the discontinuity of potential. The second condition, which is not quite so obvious, is that the first derivative of the wave function must be continuous. Let us see why this must be the case. We can see this by approaching the discontinuous potential by a limiting process, first letting the potential change very rapidly but at a finite rate from one value to the other in a small but finite distance along x, then letting this distance decrease to zero so that the jump of potential becomes discontinuous. When the change is in a distance Δx, let us assume that we can set up the exact solution of

Schrödinger's equation by some means. We then know that, within the range Δx, we have

$$\frac{d^2u}{dx^2} = \frac{2m}{\hbar^2} (V - E)u$$

a finite quantity, which does not go to infinity as Δx is reduced to zero. Let us integrate this expression over the range Δx; we have then

$$\left.\frac{du}{dx}\right|_{x+\Delta x} - \left.\frac{du}{dx}\right|_{x} = \frac{2m}{\hbar^2} \int_{x}^{x+\Delta x} (V - E)u \, dx \qquad (3\text{-}26)$$

As Δx goes to zero, the integrand on the right stays finite and the range of integration goes to zero; thus the right side of Eq. (3-26) goes to zero. But we see that this is simply the change in first derivative of the function as we go across the discontinuity of potential; hence in the limit there is no change in first derivative, or the first derivative is continuous.

If we then know the solution of Schrödinger's equation on one side of a discontinuity of potential, we use its value and the value of its first derivative to determine the values of these quantities for the solution on the other side of the discontinuity. Since two arbitrary constants are enough to determine a solution of a second-order differential equation uniquely, we see how to join solutions across such a discontinuity. It is frequently convenient to state the joining conditions in a somewhat different form: we demand the continuity of the function and of the ratio of first derivative to the function itself. The latter ratio is the logarithmic derivative,

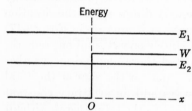

Fig. 3-1. Potential for case of a single discontinuity.

$$\frac{1}{u}\frac{du}{dx} = \frac{d \ln u}{dx} \qquad (3\text{-}27)$$

Let us now demonstrate how the process works by taking the case where the potential has only one discontinuity, at $x = 0$.

Let us assume, then, that the potential energy has one value, which we may take to be zero, for negative x and another value, which we take to be W (we assume $W > 0$), for positive x. Thus we have the situation shown in Fig. 3-1. We have two cases to consider: first, where E is greater than W, so that the solution is sinusoidal both for positive and negative x; second, where E is less than W, but greater than zero, so that the solution is exponential for positive x, sinusoidal for negative x. The third possible case, where E is negative, does not result in any solutions which are admissible; all solutions in this case go infinite for positive or negative values of x.

For the first case, we may take the solution for negative x to be

$$u = A \exp (i \sqrt{2mE}\, x/\hbar) + B \exp (-i \sqrt{2mE}\, x/\hbar)$$

and for positive x to be

$$u = C \exp [i \sqrt{2m(E - W)}\, x/\hbar] + D \exp [-i \sqrt{2m(E - W)}\, x/\hbar]$$

If we compute $d \ln u/dx$ and equate the values for the two functions, at $x = 0$, we find

$$\sqrt{E}\, \frac{1 - B/A}{1 + B/A} = \sqrt{E - W}\, \frac{1 - D/C}{1 + D/C} \qquad (3\text{-}28)$$

We cannot determine the solution further than this in the general case.

However, if we consider the physical meaning of this problem, we see that a less general solution is more interesting. The optical analogy to this problem is that where a wave falls from a medium with one index of refraction onto a medium with another index. We know in the optical case that in general part of the incident wave will be reflected, part refracted. The same thing happens in the present problem. If the incident wave approaches from the left, then we may expect an incident and a reflected wave in the region to the left and a transmitted wave in the region to the right. In other words, we seek in this case a solution which has $D = 0$, indicating no wave traveling to the left, for positive x. For such a special solution, Eq. (3-28) can be solved directly for the ratio B/A, and we find

$$\frac{B}{A} = \frac{\sqrt{E} - \sqrt{E - W}}{\sqrt{E} + \sqrt{E - W}} \qquad (3\text{-}29)$$

The ratio B/A is a quantity whose square gives the ratio of reflected to incident intensity. Thus we see that the reflected wave becomes more intense the greater W is in proportion to E. This is similar to the case of optical reflection, where the reflection coefficient at a boundary between air and a refracting medium with an index of refraction n has the value $(1 - n)/(1 + n)$, becoming greater the more n departs from unity. We can set up a similar solution in which an incident wave approaches from the right, so that we have only a transmitted wave for negative x. In that case we must have $A = 0$, and we find a reflection coefficient for the wave in the right-hand region equal numerically to the value found in the earlier case; there is an equal probability of reflection, no matter which side the particle is coming from. In either case we can easily find the amplitude of the transmitted wave, using the condition of continuity of the wave function, as well as the continuity of the logarithmic derivative.

Next let us consider the second case, for which $E - W$ is negative. In this case the solution for negative x takes the same form as before, but for positive x we must have

$$u = D \exp \left[- \sqrt{2m(W - E)} \, x/\hbar \right]$$

since the other solution, with an increasing exponential, would become infinite for large x. When we equate logarithmic derivatives of the two solutions at $x = 0$, we find

$$\frac{B}{A} = \frac{\sqrt{E} - i \sqrt{W - E}}{\sqrt{E} + i \sqrt{W - E}} \qquad (3\text{-}30)$$

This value is the ratio of a complex number to its complex conjugate (that is, the value obtained by changing the sign of i wherever it appears), and such a ratio is always a complex number whose magnitude is unity, though it has a phase different from zero. This is analogous to the case of total reflection in optics, where the reflected amplitude is equal in magnitude to the incident amplitude but where there is a change of phase. The exponential decrease of wave function in the region of positive x, where the classical kinetic energy would be negative, is an example of the penetration of particles into regions of negative kinetic energy in wave mechanics, of which we have spoken earlier. Here again there is an analogy to the optical case of total reflection: in that case, just as here, there is an exponentially decreasing disturbance in the region where no sinusoidal propagation is possible. Still another familiar case of similar phenomena is found in the study of wave guides. There are certain ranges of frequency in which a wave guide cannot propagate a sinusoidal disturbance in a given mode; it is said to be beyond cutoff, and only an exponentially decreasing disturbance can exist in it. If there is a junction between two wave guides, one of which can propagate a sinusoidal wave for the frequency in equation, while the other is beyond cutoff, we again meet a situation of total reflection, with change of phase but not of amplitude and an exponentially decreasing wave in the guide which is beyond cutoff.

It is interesting to inquire what happens to the joining conditions in the case where the potential for positive x becomes infinitely large, or the case of an infinitely high potential barrier. Here the rate of decay of the exponentially decreasing wave in the right-hand medium becomes infinitely fast, or the wave is damped to zero for infinitesimal values of x. This means that the wave function itself is zero at the boundary. We can see this also from Eq. (3-30) by setting $W = \infty$, in which case $B/A = -1$. From Eq. (3-22) we know that this means that the wave function in the left-hand medium varies as $\sin (\sqrt{2mE} \, x/\hbar)$, going to zero when $x = 0$. This boundary condition, that the wave function goes to zero at an infinitely high barrier, is often very useful.   This is a case in which the first derivative of the wave function is discontinuous, a result of the infinitely high potential barrier.

3-5. Wave Functions in a Potential Well, and Other Related Problems. For the problems which we have considered so far, solutions were possible for any positive energy.   It is easy to set up cases, however, for which we have only discrete allowed energy values.   The simplest such case is the potential well, the case in which $V = 0$ for a finite range of x, but where V is infinitely large outside this range.   Thus, let $V = 0$ from $x = 0$ to $x = X$, but let V be infinite outside this range.   Then, as we have just seen, u must go to zero at the potential barriers.   But now there are two such barriers, at $x = 0$ and $x = X$, and to have a function which goes to zero at both barriers, we must have

$$u = A \sin (\sqrt{2mE}\, x/\hbar) \qquad (3\text{-}31)$$

where
$$\sin (\sqrt{2mE}\, X/\hbar) = 0$$

The second condition of Eq. (3-31) requires that $\sqrt{2mE}\, X/\hbar = n\pi$, where n is an integer.   Hence we find that

$$u_n = A \sin \frac{n\pi x}{X} \qquad E_n = \frac{n^2\pi^2\hbar^2}{2mX^2} = \frac{n^2h^2}{8mX^2} \qquad (3\text{-}32)$$

Here n plays the part of a quantum number; we have solutions only for $n = 1, 2, \ldots$.   We have used n as a subscript on the function u_n and on E_n to indicate which value we are dealing with.

This is the first example which we have seen where we have only a discrete set of allowed wave functions and energy values.   In such a case, the u_n's are called eigenfunctions, and the E_n's are called eigenvalues (or characteristic functions and characteristic numbers, respectively).   As a rule, we have situations with discrete eigenvalues only if the potential is such that the particle cannot go to infinity on account of the existence of potential barriers.   We call the discrete set of E_n's a discrete spectrum of eigenvalues, by analogy with an optical spectrum.   In the type of case which we have met earlier, in which any energy is allowed, we say that we have a continuous spectrum of eigenvalues.   We shall shortly see that there can be cases where the two situations are combined, and we have both a discrete and a continuous spectrum.

Let us look into the relation between our allowed energy values and the Sommerfeld quantum condition.   In Eq. (2-1), where we examined the relation between de Broglie's hypothesis and the quantum condition, we saw that the quantum condition was equivalent to the statement that the total number of waves, in a complete circuit round the orbit, from one turning point to the other and back again, should be an integer. That is, in our case, there should be a whole number of half wavelengths between $x = 0$ and $x = X$. But this is just what we have achieved with our solution of Eq. (3-32). This corresponds to a wavelength of $2X/n$, so that there are n half wavelengths in the distance X, and it is Sommerfeld's quantum condition which has fixed the allowed energy levels of Eq. (3-32).

The eigenfunctions of Eq. (3-32) satisfy one condition which will prove to be general, and very important. This is the property called orthogonality. Stated mathematically, it is the property that

$$\int u_n^* u_m \, dx = 0 \qquad \text{if } n \neq m \tag{3-33}$$

where n and m are two different quantum numbers. Here the integration is to be extended over all space, but since the wave functions are zero except in the range from 0 to X, we can state the condition in this case,

$$\int_0^X \sin \frac{n\pi x}{X} \sin \frac{m\pi x}{X} \, dx = 0 \qquad \text{if } n \neq m \tag{3-34}$$

That this theorem holds can be proved at once from elementary properties of the sine functions. We shall later show that the property of orthogonality holds generally for solutions of Schrödinger's equation.

It is convenient to normalize the u_n's, just as we have normalized the whole wave function in Eq. (3-6). That is, it is convenient to choose the arbitrary constant A, in Eq. (3-32), so that

$$\int u_n^* u_n \, dx = 1 = \int_0^X A^2 \sin^2 \frac{n\pi x}{X} \, dx \tag{3-35}$$

The integral $\int_0^X \sin^2 (n\pi x/X) \, dx$ equals $X/2$. Hence, if we choose $A = (X/2)^{-\frac{1}{2}}$, our functions will be normalized; for the normalized functions, we have

$$u_n = \sqrt{\frac{2}{X}} \sin \frac{n\pi x}{X} \tag{3-36}$$

For functions satisfying both the orthogonality and normalization conditions, it is convenient to state the conditions in the form

$$\int u_n^* u_m \, dx = \delta_{nm}$$

where

$$\delta_{nm} = \begin{cases} 1 & \text{if } n = m \\ 0 & \text{if } n \neq m \end{cases} \tag{3-37}$$

The symbol δ_{nm} is called the Kronecker, or Weierstrass, delta symbol. A set of functions like the u_n's, which are normalized and orthogonal, is called a set of orthonormal functions. The normalization is, of course, required so that if we set up a solution of Schrödinger's equation of the form of Eq. (3-14), representing a single stationary state, this wave function will be normalized.

Now let us look for somewhat more general examples of the solution of Schrödinger's equation for a potential of the type we are considering, consisting of different constant values in different regions of space. As a next example, let us take a potential well bounded by barriers which are not infinitely high, but only of height W. It is more convenient in this case to place the center of the well at the origin, so that we can take advantage of the symmetry about the center of the well. We have, then, the case in which $V = 0$ for x between $-X/2$ and $X/2$, while $V = W$, a positive quantity, outside that range. We consider first the case where the energy E is less than W, but greater than zero; this leads to discrete or quantized energy levels.

In this case, for x less than $-X/2$, the solution is

$$u = A \exp\left[\sqrt{2m(W - E)}\, x/\hbar\right] \tag{3-38}$$

in order to have a solution which behaves properly for x negatively infinite. For x between $-X/2$ and $X/2$, it is more convenient to take a solution in the form

$$u = B \cos\left(\sqrt{2mE}\, x/\hbar - \alpha\right) \tag{3-39}$$

expressing the arbitrary constants in the form of an amplitude B and a phase constant α. For x greater than $X/2$, we have

$$u = C \exp\left[-\sqrt{2m(W - E)}\, x/\hbar\right] \tag{3-40}$$

For the joining conditions at $x = -X/2$, we equate the logarithmic derivatives of both solutions and have

$$\sqrt{W - E} = -\sqrt{E} \tan\left(-\sqrt{2mE}\, X/2\hbar - \alpha\right) \tag{3-41}$$

For the joining conditions at $x = X/2$, we have

$$-\sqrt{W - E} = -\sqrt{E} \tan\left(\sqrt{2mE}\, X/2\hbar - \alpha\right) \tag{3-42}$$

By combining Eqs. (3-41) and (3-42), we have

$$\tan\left(\sqrt{2mE}\, X/2\hbar + \alpha\right) = \tan\left(\sqrt{2mE}\, X/2\hbar - \alpha\right) \tag{3-43}$$

which shows that adding 2α to the argument of the tangent leaves it unchanged. Since the tangent is periodic with period of π, this means that 2α must be an integral multiple of π, or α is zero, $\pi/2$, π, $3\pi/2$, ... In other words, in Eq. (3-39), we must have either the cosine or the sine for the solution in the range between $-X/2$ and $X/2$. These possibilities are covered by the two choices $\alpha = 0$ and $\alpha = \pi/2$; the other values repeat the same solutions for u. For $\alpha = 0$, we see that u is an even function of x, and for $\alpha = \pi/2$, u is an odd function of x. Let us now consider these two cases together.

For $\alpha = 0$, the condition (3-41), which is equivalent to (3-42), is

$$\sqrt{W - E} = \sqrt{E} \tan (\sqrt{2mE}\, X/2\hbar) \qquad (3\text{-}44)$$

and for $\alpha = \pi/2$, it is

$$\sqrt{W - E} = -\sqrt{E} \cot (\sqrt{2mE}\, X/2\hbar) \qquad (3\text{-}45)$$

To solve Eqs. (3-44) and (3-45), we must proceed graphically. Let us plot the functions given on the left and on the right sides of the equation as functions of $\sqrt{E}$ and see where the curves intersect. This is done in Fig. 3-2. The left side, $\sqrt{W - E}$ as a function of $\sqrt{E}$, gives a circle of radius $\sqrt{W}$, and the right side gives a curve with an infinite number of branches, crossing the axis for the points

$$\sqrt{2mE}\, \frac{X}{2\hbar} = n\, \frac{\pi}{2}$$

where
$$n = 0, 1, 2, \ldots \qquad (3\text{-}46)$$
$$E = \frac{n^2 h^2}{8mX^2}$$

The intersections, giving eigenvalues, are shown in Fig. 3-2. We see

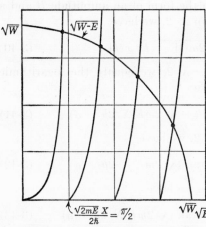

FIG. 3-2. Graph for determining eigenvalues of the problem of the potential well with finite potential barriers.

that we have a finite number of such intersections, the number being one greater than the maximum integer for which E, as given in Eq. (3-46), is less than W. When we compare Eqs. (3-46) and (3-32), we see that there is a simple rule describing the number of discrete eigenvalues: it is in every case one unit greater than the number of eigenvalues of the problem of the potential well with infinitely high barriers, lying at energies less than W. In any case of this problem, no matter how low W must be, we have at least one discrete eigenvalue.

The wave functions can be found easily by piecing together the sine or cosine functions inside the well and the exponential tails outside the well. For a particular case, they are shown in Fig. 3-3. Each function has one more node than the preceding one (a node is a point where the function is zero), as we go up in energy, and they alternate between symmetric and antisymmetric, or even and odd, functions of x. Now that we have established by direct calculation that all eigenfunctions of this problem are either even or odd, it is intuitively rather obvious why this must be the case: for an even or odd function, once we have fitted the boundary conditions at one boundary, as at $x = -X/2$, we shall automatically have the same boundary condition at the other boundary, $x = X/2$, since the curve for positive x is a mirror image of that for negative x. Such a property of having only even or odd eigenfunctions

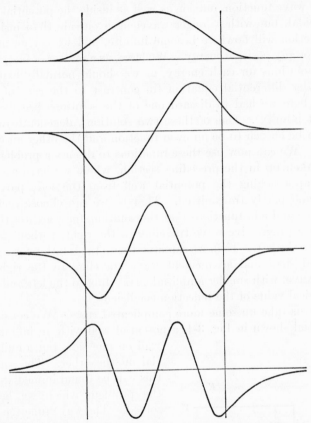

FIG. 3-3. Wave functions for the discrete levels of a potential well with barriers of finite height; computed for case shown in Fig. 3-2.

is characteristic of any problem for which the potential is an even function of x. To prove this, we start with Schrödinger's equation $-(\hbar^2/2m)[d^2u(x)/dx^2] + V(x)u(x) = Eu(x)$ and change x to $-x$. Since we have the case where $V(-x) = V(x)$, we see that $u(-x)$ satisfies the same differential equation as $u(x)$, as well as satisfying the same boundary conditions at $x = \pm\infty$. We shall then have a solution if $u(-x)$ is any constant times $u(x)$. The only constants resulting in a function which is continuous with continuous first derivative at $x = 0$ are ± 1, leading to the even and odd eigenfunctions, respectively. In the first case, we must have $du/dx = 0$ when $x = 0$, while in the second case $u = 0$ when $x = 0$.

We have now considered the case of energy less than W and have found that our problem has a finite number of discrete energy levels. Next let us consider an energy greater than W, such as E_1 in Fig. 3-1. Then the wave function, outside as well as inside the potential well, will be sinusoidal, but with a longer wavelength outside than inside. The wave function will nowhere become infinite, and we get an acceptable solution for any positive energy. We have, as a matter of fact, two independent solutions for each energy, as we should normally expect for a second-order differential equation (in contrast to the case of negative energy, where we had to discard one of the solutions because it went infinite at infinity). One of these two solutions, degenerate with each other, can be chosen to be an even function and the other an odd function of x. We can now use these functions to discuss a problem similar to that taken up in the preceding section, where we have a stream of particles approaching the potential well from the left, partly being reflected and partly transmitted. That is, we can choose such phases for the even and odd functions that the solution, for x greater than $X/2$, represents a progressive wave traveling to the right, without any wave traveling to the left. Then we can investigate the solution for x less than $-X/2$ and shall find an incident wave traveling to the right and a reflected wave, with smaller amplitude, traveling to the left and can find the numerical value of the reflection coefficient.

Now let us take up some more complicated cases. We consider next the potential shown in Fig. 3-4, a potential well with an infinitely high

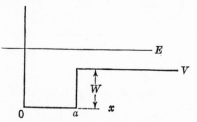

wall on one side, but a finite potential on the other. The solution of this can be found immediately from the problem which we have just solved. The wave function must go to zero at the infinitely high wall. Thus we can convert the earlier case into this one by using the solutions of the earlier case, but using only those solutions which are odd functions of

FIG. 3-4. Potential well, infinitely high wall on left, finite potential on right.

x, discarding the solutions which are even functions of x. Since the lowest eigenfunction of the preceding case corresponded to an even function of x, we see that this solution is excluded in the present case, and we must have a potential well of a finite size, large enough to have had at least two discrete stationary states in the earlier case, before we have a single discrete state in the present case. For a potential well of the present sort, with a potential of height W outside, and with the well extending from $x = 0$ to $x = X/2$, we shall have essentially half as many discrete states as for the earlier case.

As for the continuous energy levels, for positive energy, we no longer have degeneracy; for a given energy we have only one function, going to zero when $x = 0$. This corresponds to a standing wave, that is, to a stream of particles approaching from the right, being completely reflected at the infinitely high potential barrier, and traveling away again to the right. This example of Fig. 3-4 resembles two very important cases which we shall meet later: the energy levels of an electron in an atom, in which the radial part of the motion has a potential curve of this sort, and in which we have both a discrete and a continuous spectrum; and the vibration of a diatomic molecule, where the curve of potential energy as a function of distance of separation has this form, and where stable vibrations are possible for energies less than a certain critical value, while for higher energies the two particles fly apart and dissociate. It is only for the stable vibrations that the energy is quantized. In both these cases the potential curve

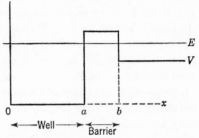

Fig. 3-5. Potential well, infinitely high wall on left, finite potential on right, with barrier between.

is rounded off, instead of being made of segments of straight lines as Fig. 3-4 is, but this does not affect the general nature of the wave functions and energy levels.

A still more complicated case, still capable of analytic solution by piecing sine curves together and demanding that the function and its first derivative be continuous, is shown in Fig. 3-5, with a high barrier between the potential well and the region of free motion. In such a case, the interesting problem comes for energies such as that shown, in which classically the motion could not extend over the barrier from one region to the other. In constructing the solution of Schrödinger's equation, we start at the left boundary, $x = 0$, with a sine function. When we reach the barrier, between $x = a$ and $x = b$, we must use both a decreasing and an increasing exponential to satisfy the boundary conditions at $x = a$. This combination of functions must then be joined, at $x = b$, to a sinusoidal function of the appropriate wavelength, with amplitude and phase chosen to satisfy the boundary conditions. Such a solution can be set up in every case, and it will correspond to the case of a particle coming from the right, being reflected by the barrier, and returning to the right and also to that of a particle confined to the well, being reflected back and forth there.   There will be certain energies for which a particle in the potential well would have stationary states, if the barrier were infinitely high, and others for which it would not.   It proves to be true that in the first case the amplitude of the wave function within the well is much greater than outside the barrier, while in the second case it is much less. In any case, the amplitude is not zero within the barrier itself, so that there is some chance of finding the particle within the barrier.

This problem becomes much more interesting if, instead of dealing only with stationary states, we build up wave packets.   When one examines Schrödinger's equation involving the time, which we have not yet done in detail, one finds that the following procedure is allowed: to take each wave function corresponding to a given energy E, multiply it by a sinusoidal function of the time, with frequency ν given by de Broglie's relation $E = h\nu$, and add any number of such solutions, with appropriate phases and amplitudes.   This process of addition is analogous to that which is carried out with vibrating strings, in which the general solution of the motion of a vibrating string is a superposition of all its possible overtone vibrations, each with its own frequency, and with arbitrary phases and amplitudes.   Such a superposition is always necessary to produce a wave packet, or in fact any disturbance except one which is only a sinusoidal function of the time.   We can now build up wave packets corresponding to certain initial conditions; examine the behavior of these packets as time goes on; and as the different wave functions associated with different stationary states get out of step with each other on account of their different frequencies, deduce the way in which systems change with time.

In the present case, one possible circumstance which we might want to describe is that in which, at the initial time $t = 0$, the particle is known to be located within the potential well, with an energy which would correspond to a stationary state if the walls of the well were infinitely high. We can set up such a wave packet by suitable superposition of wave functions of different energies.   It will have large amplitude within the well, no amplitude outside it.   But each of the wave functions of which it is composed has some amplitude outside the well, as well as within the barrier; the packet has no amplitude outside the well only because we arrange to have complete destructive interference of those parts of the wave functions to the right of the barrier.   This interference becomes inoperative after a sufficiently long time, because the waves have different frequencies, and their phase relationships are eventually lost.   The result is that, after a certain lapse of time, intensity begins to appear to the right of the barrier, and correspondingly the intensity within the well decreases.   We interpret this as saying that particles can penetrate the barrier, even though classical mechanics says that it would be impenetrable.   Calculation shows that the rate of penetration gets rapidly slower as the barrier becomes either wider or higher.   This process of penetrating barriers is called the tunnel effect and is an important non-classical effect of quantum mechanics.   It is encountered, among other places, in the theory of radioactive decay, where the potential energy of a nuclear particle is in some cases similar to the one we have just been

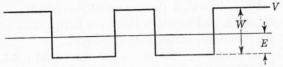

FIG. 3-6. Two equal potential wells, with barrier between.

considering.   It is worth noting that the penetration of barriers works in the other direction, too: we can build up a wave packet corresponding to a particle approaching the barrier from the right, with no intensity within the well, and after a lapse of time intensity will be found within the well, corresponding to penetration of the barrier by the incoming particle. Furthermore, we find that, if the energy corresponds to the approximately quantized energies within the well, the probability of penetrating is much greater than it is in other cases.

A final case, again involving penetration of barriers, is the case of a particle in two identical potential wells, separated by a barrier, as shown in Fig. 3-6.   Here, since the particle is confined to a limited region of space, there will be real stationary states, and they will be close to the stationary states of a particle in a single potential well.   An interesting fact now appears.   Corresponding to each stationary state of a single well, there will be two for the problem of two wells, separated from each other by an energy difference which is smaller, the higher or wider the barrier between them, so that their energy levels finally coincide in the limit as the barrier gets infinitely high.   The wave functions corresponding to these two energy levels are particularly interesting.   They look as in Fig. 3-7;

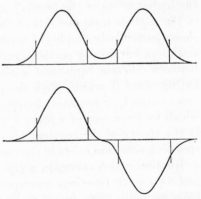

FIG. 3-7. Symmetric and antisymmetric wave functions for problem of two equal potential wells.   Classical turning points shown by vertical lines.

one is symmetrical, the other antisymmetrical, in the mid-point of the barrier.   The antisymmetrical wave function corresponds to the higher energy (for it proves to be a general rule that, the more nodes or zeros a wave function has, the higher is its energy). This splitting of each energy level into two, with symmetrical and antisymmetrical wave functions, when the number of potential minima is doubled, is a general characteristic of all such problems of two potential minima, not confined to the particular potential function which we have in this case. It is found, for instance, in the problem of the diatomic molecule composed of two identical atoms, in which the potential energy of an electron has minima at each atom, and in which there are both symmetric and anti-symmetric wave functions, with different energies.

Here, as in the preceding case of a single potential barrier, we have interesting results if we set up wave packets. Let us superpose the symmetric and antisymmetric wave functions at a certain instant of time, with equal amplitudes. Then the amplitude of the resultant wave function will be large in one of the potential wells, where the two functions have the same sign, and will be small in the other well, where they are opposite to each other. After a lapse of time, however, the two waves will have got opposite in phase, and the wave functions will reinforce on the other side of the barrier, so that we shall say that the particle has penetrated the barrier. After another lapse of time it will have gone back to the original side and, in general, will oscillate between one side and the other. The frequency of this oscillation is the difference between the frequencies of the two waves, just as in the phenomenon of beats in acoustics. Thus, the closer the energies of the two states (that is, as we have seen, the higher or wider the barrier), the less frequent will be the oscillation of the particle from one side of the barrier to the other. This example shows particularly simply the mathematical mechanisms behind the penetration of barriers by particles and the process of oscillation of a particle between different equivalent minima. This process is often called resonating, since it occurs when the particle in either well would have the same natural, or resonant, frequency, and it furnishes the first example which we have seen of a process which proves to be of great importance in the theory of the covalent bond and in many other cases. A corresponding situation exists in the case of many identical potential minima, a situation which occurs in a crystalline solid; there, instead of having just two wave functions corresponding to almost identical energies, we have as many wave functions as there are identical potential minima. In all these cases, we must emphasize that it is only when we set up wave packets, composed of the superposition of many stationary states, that we get these phenomena of oscillation; if we consider a single stationary state, the charge density is always independent of time.

3-6. The WKB Solution and the Quantum Condition. The problem we have been taking up in the preceding sections, a one-dimensional problem in which the potential has one constant value in one range of x, another in another, and so on, is one of the few soluble cases of Schrödinger's equation. There are a few others—the linear oscillator, the hydrogen atom, and some others—which we shall consider later. But beyond these simple cases, there are hardly any important soluble cases. There is, however, an approximate solution called the WKB method (abbreviation for the names of Wentzel,[1] Kramers,[2] and Brillouin,[3] who separately suggested it, as in fact several other persons also did), which gives a good deal of insight into the nature of solutions of Schrödinger's equation, and which is sometimes useful for calculation. This method is very closely related to the quantum condition. Like the case we have been taking up, it is readily applied only to the one-dimensional case.

The idea behind the WKB method, which is a method applicable to any problem of wave propagation in a medium where the wavelength depends on position, is that, if the wavelength varies only slowly with position, the wave function u in a restricted range of coordinates will be very similar to what would be found if the wavelength were constant and equal to the average value through the range considered. We already know that such a solution is a sinusoidal oscillation, similar to $\sin (2\pi x/\lambda)$, where λ is the local value of the wavelength. Such a solution really has three parameters determining its character: the wavelength, the amplitude, and the phase. The WKB method assumes that the wave function can be written approximately in the form of a sinusoidal function with the amplitude, as well as the wavelength, varying appropriately with position. It operates by substituting such a function in Schrödinger's equation and finding the differential equations obeyed by the amplitude and wavelength. Such differential equations are set up in Appendix 5. It then proves to be possible to state very simple rules telling how these quantities must vary with x, provided the relative change of wavelength is small in a distance of one wavelength.

The result of the WKB method is that u, the solution of Eq. (2-12) or (3-15), can be written approximately in the form

$$u = \frac{A}{\sqrt{p}} \sin \left(\frac{1}{\hbar} \int p \, dx + \alpha \right) \qquad (3\text{-}47)$$

where p is to be determined from the equation $p = \sqrt{2m(E - V)}$ as a function of x, V being a function of x, and where A, α are arbitrary constants. This type of solution holds in the regions where $E - V$ is positive, or where the classical kinetic energy is positive. Let us now examine

[1] G. Wentzel, Z. Physik, **38**:518 (1926).

[2] H. A. Kramers, Z. Physik, **39**:828 (1926).

[3] L. Brillouin, J. phys. radium, **7**:353 (1926).

the interpretation of this solution and see why it is reasonable. First, the quantity $(1/\hbar) \int p \, dx + \alpha$ increases in a distance dx by the amount $(2\pi/\lambda) \, dx$, the correct increment for a sine function of wavelength λ; thus Eq. (3-47) is correctly associated with the wavelength varying with position which we have already assumed. As for the amplitude, proportional to $1/\sqrt{p}$, the interpretation is simple. It will lead to a probability density, which is proportional to the square of u, varying inversely as the velocity of the classical particle. This is what we should expect. For a stationary state, though not in general, the statistical average contemplated in Schrödinger's theory is equivalent to a time average. If we had a classical particle traveling along the x axis, the length of time it would be found in a distance dx would be simply dx/v, where v was its velocity. We should expect statistically, then, that the probability of finding the particle in a range dx, or the probability density, should be inversely proportional to the velocity, as we have found.

In a region where $E - V$ is negative, or where the classical kinetic energy is negative, the approximate solution equivalent to that of Eq. (3-47) is

$$u = [2m(V - E)]^{-\frac{1}{4}}\{B \exp [(1/\hbar) \int \sqrt{2m(V - E)} \, dx] \\ + C \exp [(-1/\hbar) \int \sqrt{2m(V - E)} \, dx]\} \quad (3-48)$$

That is, we have exponentially increasing and decreasing functions, just as in the case of a constant potential, and we must set either B or C equal to zero, so as not to have an exponential which becomes infinite. As with the case of constant potentials, which we have been taking up in preceding sections, the sinusoidal functions like (3-47) must be joined to the exponential functions, like (3-48), at the point where $E - V$ goes to zero. This joining process, however, is not simple, as it was in the earlier case. We note that on account of the fourth root of $E - V$, or of $V - E$, in the denominator, the functions of Eq. (3-47) or (3-48) become infinite where $V = E$. In other words, these approximations, though they are good when we are some distance away from the point where $V = E$, diverge as we approach that point, so that we cannot apply any such simple joining condition as that the functions and their slopes must be continuous at the point where $V = E$.

The joining conditions have been examined in detail by Wentzel, Kramers, and Brillouin in the papers cited above. We shall not go into the proper method of joining but can point out a very simple method of looking at the problem. In the neighborhood of the point where $V = E$, we can see, by looking at Schrödinger's equation, that $d^2u/dx^2 = 0$, or we have the equation of a straight line; in fact, this is just the condition which demands that u have a point of inflection where $V = E$. Hence we may use Eq. (3-47) some distance away from the point where $V = E$

in the region where the kinetic energy is positive, and (3-48) some distance away in the region where the kinetic energy is negative, and interpolate with a straight line.   This is a rather indefinite procedure, but as we have stated, the exact theory prescribes the joining conditions exactly, telling us the relation between the constants A and α holding in the region of positive kinetic energy and the constants B and C in the region of negative kinetic energy.

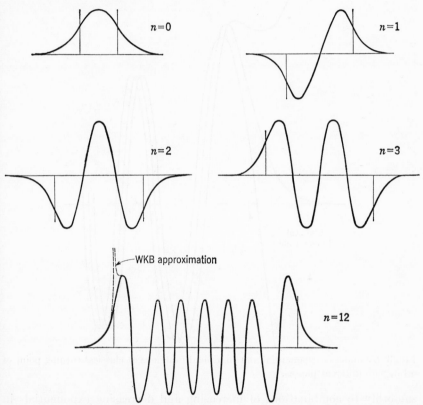

FIG. 3-8. Wave functions for the linear oscillator.   Vertical lines show classical turning points.   WKB approximation shown, for case $n = 12$.

The accuracy of the WKB approximation is indicated in Fig. 3-8, which shows several of the eigenfunctions for the linear oscillator, determined by the exact method which we shall discuss in the next section. For the case $n = 12$, we have shown the behavior of the WKB approximation, in the neighborhood of the classical turning point, the point where $E = V$.   Here we see how both exponential and sinusoidal approximations go infinite just at this point.   However, when we go slightly away from the turning point, the WKB approximation becomes so good that it is indistinguishable from the true wave function, on a graph of the scale we are using.

It is interesting to consider how a solution of fixed energy and phase (in the sinusoidal region) behaves as we pass into the region where the kinetic energy is negative. In Fig. 3-9, we show a series of solutions of Schrödinger's equation, for a fixed energy and different phases α, joined

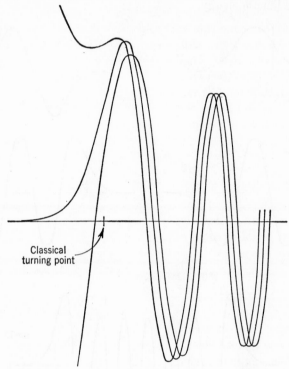

FIG. 3-9. Joining of exponential and sinusoidal functions at classical turning point of orbit, with different phases.

smoothly to combinations of increasing and decreasing exponentials in the region of negative kinetic energy. These represent exact solutions, which do not show the misbehavior of WKB approximations near the classical turning point. We observe that, for one particular phase, we have only the exponentially decreasing function but that, as the phase is varied slightly from this value, we have an exponentially increasing function as well. Only the solution with the decreasing exponential is, of course, admissible. This then determines a definite phase in the sinusoidal region. We observe that the sine curve occurring to the right of the classical turning point is not headed precisely to zero at this turning point, since it joins onto the decreasing exponential. As a matter of fact, the more exact theory of the WKB approximation which we have mentioned earlier shows that, to a good approximation, it is as if one used up one-eighth of a wavelength to the left of the classical turning point.

If we now consider a problem in which the classical motion would have two turning points, as with the linear oscillator, there will be a boundary condition of the type we have considered at each turning point: the phase of the oscillation, in the region where the classical motion would occur, will be set by the condition that the wave function must go to zero at infinity in each direction.   In general, these two conditions will be inconsistent with each other.   They will be consistent only if a single oscillatory solution satisfies the two conditions simultaneously, having an eighth of a wavelength extending outside of the classical regions of motion on each end.   If x_1 and x_2 are the two turning points, the number of wavelengths between these two points is

$$\int_{x_1}^{x_2} \frac{p}{h} \, dx$$

and the number of half wavelengths is twice as great.   Our condition is then that the number of half wavelengths between x_1 and x_2, plus a quarter wavelength to account for the two ends (or half of a half wavelength), must be an integer.   That is,

$$2 \int_{x_1}^{x_2} \frac{p}{h} \, dx + \tfrac{1}{2} = \text{integer}$$

$$2 \int_{x_1}^{x_2} p \, dx = (n + \tfrac{1}{2})h \qquad n = 0, 1, 2, \ldots \tag{3-49}$$

This is like the quantum condition of Eq. (1-16), only using half integers instead of integers; for twice the integral of $p \, dx$ from x_1 to x_2 is the integral round the complete cycle, as in Eq. (1-16).

It is an interesting fact that the quantum condition of Eq. (3-49), though it is derived from the WKB approximation, which is only approximately correct, nevertheless gives exactly the correct values for energy levels for several important problems, in particular for the linear oscillator and the hydrogen atom.   The wave functions determined by the WKB method, however, are only approximate, as is clear from the fact that the analytical formula breaks down at the turning point of the classical orbit.   Nevertheless it is still capable of giving rather good approximations in actual cases, and it is often very useful.

3-7. The Linear Oscillator.   We have discussed some exact solutions of Schrödinger's equation, namely, those cases in which the potential is made up of several constant values in different regions of x, and a useful approximation, the WKB method.   Now we shall take up one of the most famous of the exactly soluble cases, the linear oscillator.   Here we have a turning point at each end of the path, and the arguments of the preceding section hold for it, so that the quantum condition is as in Eq. (3-49). The phase integral has been computed in the discussion of Eq. (1-29) and is E/ν. Hence we see, from Eq. (3-49), that the energy levels according to the WKB method are given by

$$E = (n + \tfrac{1}{2})h\nu \qquad (3\text{-}50)$$

As we have stated in the preceding paragraph, this is a case where the WKB method gives exactly the correct energy levels. Let us proceed with the exact analytical solution and verify this fact.

The potential energy of a particle moving with simple harmonic motion with natural frequency ν, in classical mechanics, is $V = 2\pi^2 m\nu^2 x^2$. Schrödinger's equation is then

$$\frac{d^2u}{dx^2} + \frac{8\pi^2 m}{h^2}(E - 2\pi^2 m\nu^2 x^2)u = 0 \qquad (3\text{-}51)$$

In getting solutions of such differential equations, it is generally helpful to find how the solutions behave in the limits where x is large. Here the WKB method can be used. From Eq. (3-48), the solution for large x will involve the exponential

$$\exp\{(-1/\hbar)\int[2m(2\pi^2 m\nu^2 x^2 - E)]^{\frac{1}{2}}\,dx\} \qquad (3\text{-}52)$$

If x is large enough, we can disregard the energy E in comparison with the potential energy, which increases proportionally to x^2. If we do this, the integration in Eq. (3-52) can be carried out and we find that the function will involve the exponential

$$\exp(-2\pi^2 m\nu x^2/h) \qquad (3\text{-}53)$$

For large negative values of x, the decreasing solution is the same as is given in Eq. (3-53). This suggests in the first place that it would be convenient to make a change of variables, to remove the various dimensional constants. If we let $y = 2\pi x\sqrt{m\nu/h}$, the exponential above becomes $\exp(-y^2/2)$ and the differential equation, Eq. (3-51), is transformed into

$$\frac{d^2u}{dy^2} + \left(\frac{2E}{h\nu} - y^2\right)u = 0 \qquad (3\text{-}54)$$

Since we know that the function u must act like $\exp(-y^2/2)$ for numerically large values of y, it is reasonable to write u in the form $u = v\exp(-y^2/2)$. When we do this, we find that

$$\frac{d^2v}{dy^2} - 2y\frac{dv}{dy} + \left(\frac{2E}{h\nu} - 1\right)v = 0 \qquad (3\text{-}55)$$

This equation has one very simple solution: if $2E/h\nu = 1$, or $E = \frac{1}{2}h\nu$, corresponding to $n = 0$ in Eq. (3-50), we can set v equal to a constant and Eq. (3-55) is satisfied. This is, then, the solution for the ground state of the linear oscillator. For the higher levels, however, we must look for solutions of Eq. (3-55) corresponding to different values of the energy E.

We can get the general solution of Eq. (3-55) by expanding v as a power series in y and determining the coefficients of this expansion, a standard method of attack on such differential equations. If we assume

$$v = A_0 + A_1 y + A_2 y^2 + \cdots$$

we can differentiate the series to obtain the derivatives needed in Eq. (3-55), substitute in that equation, and combine terms in the same power of y. The resulting equation can be written in the form

$$\sum_{n=0}^{\infty} \left[(n+2)(n+1)A_{n+2} + \left(\frac{2E}{h\nu} - 1 - 2n \right) A_n \right] y^n = 0 \quad (3\text{-}56)$$

This is a power series in y which must be equal to zero for every value of y if Eq. (3-55) is to be satisfied. But no power series can equal zero for all values of the argument unless all its coefficients are zero. Hence each of the expressions in brackets in Eq. (3-56) must be separately zero. This gives us an equation for A_{n+2} in terms of A_n. If we assume values for A_0 and A_1 [the two arbitrary constants which we must have in the general solution of a second-order differential equation like Eq. (3-55)], we can then determine all the other A's from these and we have the complete solution of Eq. (3-55) in power-series form.

The resulting function is not of elementary form; if it had been, we should have been able to solve Eq. (3-55) directly, without resorting to power-series expansion. However, we can investigate its behavior for very large values of y, and this is important to our problem, because this is the region of negative kinetic energy, where we hope the function u will behave like $\exp(-y^2/2)$. On the other hand, if the energy E is not an eigenvalue of the problem, we must expect that u will increase for large y like $\exp(y^2/2)$, the increasing exponential solution rather than the decreasing function; it is only for the eigenvalues that we expect to have a function which goes exponentially to zero at infinity. Since $u = v \exp(-y^2/2)$, it must then be that in general v will act, for large y, like $\exp(y^2)$; somehow, for the eigenvalues, we must avoid this type of behavior.

We can now show quite generally that, if the series for v is really an infinite series, its behavior for large y will be like the function $\exp(y^2)$.

If we express the function $\exp(y^2)$ in power series, we may write it

$$\exp(y^2) = \sum (n = 0, 2, 4, \ldots) \frac{1}{(n/2)!} y^n \qquad (3\text{-}57)$$

where we have expressed it as a series over even integers n. If we let the coefficient $1/(n/2)!$ of the term in y^n be B_n, we see that

$$B_{n+2} = \frac{B_n}{(n+2)/2} \qquad \text{or} \qquad (n+2)B_{n+2} - 2B_n = 0 \qquad (3\text{-}58)$$

But this recursion formula for the B_n's is just the same that we should get for the A_n's from Eq. (3-56) if we had such a large value of n that $2E/h\nu$ could be neglected in comparison with n; for then we could approximately write the condition of Eq. (3-56) in the form

$$(n+2)(n+1)A_{n+2} - 2(n+1)A_n = 0$$

which is equivalent to Eq. (3-58). As far as the terms of high powers of y are concerned, then, the function v is equivalent to $\exp(y^2)$. But, at very large y values, it is these terms in very high powers of y that are important. Hence, in the limit of large y, we see that our function v does in fact approach $\exp(y^2)$, if it is expressed in power series, and the function u approaches $\exp(y^2/2)$.

We must now ask how this situation can be avoided, so that u will in fact behave like $\exp(-y^2/2)$ at infinity, rather than like $\exp(y^2/2)$. There is only one possible answer: the power series for v must not have any terms corresponding to large n values. This can be accomplished only if the series breaks off somewhere and is only a polynomial instead of an infinite series. We have already seen one example of this in the solution for the ground state, for which v is a constant. If it were a polynomial whose highest term was in y^n, with n a definite integer, the behavior of u for very large values of y would be like the function $y^n \exp(-y^2/2)$, and the exponential makes the function decrease so strongly for large y's that even this function goes to zero as y approaches infinity, in spite of the factor y^n. But we can now see easily from Eq. (3-56) how to make the series for v break off after the nth term. If we set $2E/h\nu - 1 - 2n = 0$, or

$$E = (n + \tfrac{1}{2})h\nu \qquad (3\text{-}59)$$

then we see from Eq. (3-56) that $A_{n+2} = 0$, and from that $A_{n+4} = 0$, $A_{n+6} = 0$, and so on. In other words, if n is even, all the even terms beyond that in y^n will be zero, or if n is odd, all the odd terms beyond that in y^n will be zero. Let us then choose $A_1 = 0$ if n is even, or $A_0 = 0$ if n is odd, so that v will have only even or only odd terms, respectively, and we shall find a polynomial for v, so that the function u

will go exponentially to zero as y becomes infinite. These are the wave functions of the problem; from Eq. (3-56) we can get the recursion formula to set up the coefficients of the polynomial in terms of A_0 or A_1; and the energy levels, as given by Eq. (3-59), are those already found from the quantum condition as given by the WKB method. In Appendix 6 we give further properties of the wave functions, including the method of normalizing them.

In Fig. 3-8 we have already shown a number of the wave functions for this problem. We see the way in which the wave function for a given value of n has essentially $n + 1$ half wavelengths in the whole range of the variable, or has n nodes. Furthermore, for the case of large n value which we have included, we see how the amplitude of the oscillation and the wavelength both increase as we approach the turning point of the classical motion, in agreement with the requirements of the WKB approximation. We also note the resemblance between these wave functions for the linear oscillator and those given in Fig. 3-3 for the potential well with finite barriers.

3-8. The Numerical Solution of Schrödinger's Equation. We have seen in this chapter a number of examples of exact or approximate solutions of Schrödinger's equation for problems in one dimension. In many important cases, an exact solution is impossible by analytical means, and the WKB approximation is not good enough to satisfy us. In such cases, we can always resort to numerical integration of the differential equation. This is a well-known procedure, which can always be used with differential equations of this type. Briefly, the method is as follows: To a first approximation, a first derivative of a function can be replaced by a first difference and a second derivative by a second difference. These differences have the following significance: If we have a table of values of a function $f(x)$, at equally spaced values of x, say separated by an amount h, we can denote these values as $f_1, f_2, f_3, \ldots .$ Then a first difference is $f_n - f_{n-1}$, and the first derivative is approximately equal to $(f_n - f_{n-1})/h$. The second difference is $(f_{n+1} - f_n) - (f_n - f_{n-1})$, or $f_{n+1} - 2f_n + f_{n-1}$, and the second derivative is approximately equal to $(f_{n+1} - 2f_n + f_{n-1})/h^2$. Now if we have a differential equation of the form of

$$\frac{d^2f}{dx^2} = F(x) \tag{3-60}$$

which Schrödinger's equation is, we can approximately replace this by

$$(f_{n+1} - 2f_n + f_{n-1})/h^2 = F_n \tag{3-61}$$

where F_n is the value of $F(x)$ computed for x_n. We may rewrite this in the form

$$f_{n+1} = 2f_n - f_{n-1} + h^2 F_n \tag{3-62}$$

If, then, we have a table of values of the function f, extending up to the entry f_n, Eq. (3-62) allows us to compute f_{n+1}. We can then use the same procedure to find f_{n+2} by the equation

$$f_{n+2} = 2f_{n+1} - f_n + h^2 F_{n+1} \qquad (3\text{-}63)$$

and this process can be extended to make up a complete table of values of the function. This scheme can be made into a very workable procedure for integrating Schrödinger's equation in a practical way. Hence we may assume that any one-dimensional Schrödinger equation can be solved, in the sense of deriving its solution in the form of a table of values. Unfortunately this scheme is very difficult to extend to problems with more than one independent variable.

PROBLEMS

1. Bessel's equation is

$$\frac{d^2 y}{dx^2} + \frac{1}{x}\frac{dy}{dx} + \left(1 - \frac{m^2}{x^2}\right) y = 0$$

Show that by making the change of variables $u = y\sqrt{x}$ the differential equation for u has the form of Schrödinger's equation. Use the WKB method to get an approximate solution for $J_m(x)$, the solution of Bessel's equation above, which remains finite at $x = 0$.

2. Using the approximation of Prob. 1, compute approximate values of the functions J_0 and J_1 for a number of values of x, and show by a table of values how well these agree with the correct functions. Choose the arbitrary amplitude and phase factors to make the functions agree with the values of J_0 and J_1 which you can find in tables of Bessel's functions, for example, making the zeros agree by adjusting the phase and the maxima by adjusting the amplitude, taking such values as to get the best agreement possible for large x's.

3. Note that in Bessel's equation, when $m > 0$, there is a region near the origin where the WKB approximate solution is exponential rather than sinusoidal. Discuss the solution qualitatively for $x < m$, where m is fairly large, showing how this solution joins onto the sinusoidal one found in Prob. 1.

4. Compute and plot wave functions of the linear oscillator corresponding to $n = 0, 1, 2, 3, 4$. From the graphs find the region in which the solution is oscillatory (that is, the region between the points of inflection). Draw the potential curve and the values of E corresponding to these five stationary states, and show that the motion is oscillatory in the region where the kinetic energy is positive.

5. Set up the approximate solution for the linear-oscillator problem by the WKB method, getting expressions for the functions in both the sinusoidal and exponential ranges. Investigate to see how well these functions join on at the point of inflection.

6. Compute and plot the approximation of Prob. 5 corresponding to $n = 4$, and compare with the exact solution.

7. The potential energy in a Schrödinger problem is as shown in Fig. 3-10. Set up the exact solution of Schrödinger's equation, for $E < W$, finding the equation determining the stationary states. For $E \ll W$, show that you can get approximate analytic solutions for the energies of the symmetric and antisymmetric wave functions.

Show how the separation between the energies of symmetric and antisymmetric states decreases to zero as the barrier gets larger, either W or the width becoming infinite.

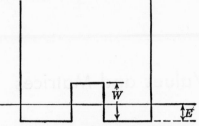

Fig. 3-10. Figure to illustrate Prob. 7.

8. In the case $E \ll W$ in Prob. 7, set up a solution which at $t = 0$ corresponds as closely as possible to the particle being in the left-hand potential well, with no probability that it is in the right-hand well.   Investigate the beat phenomenon, finding after how long a time the particle will be found in the right-hand well.   How does this time depend on the height and breadth of the barrier?

9. The potential energy of a particle is everywhere zero, except in a potential barrier between $x = 0$ and $x = d$, where it equals W, greater than zero.   Set up a solution of Schrödinger's equation representing a wave of particles of energy E approaching the barrier and being partially reflected backward.   To simplify the problem, assume that d is very small compared with the wavelength and that W is very small compared with the energy of the particle.   Find the amplitude of the reflected wave.

10. A particle moves in a potential as shown in Fig. 3-11, with an energy E so much less than W that $\sqrt{2m(W - E)}\,(x_2 - x_1)/\hbar$ is large compared with unity.   Show that the amplitude of the wave function in the region $0 < x < x_1$ is small compared with that in the region $x_2 < x$, except in the special case where the energy is almost exactly equal to one of the energy levels of a particle confined by infinitely high barriers at $x = 0$ and $x = x_1$.

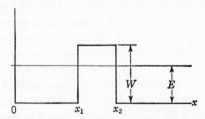

Fig. 3-11. Figure to illustrate Prob. 10.

11. Solve Schrödinger's equation for the linear oscillator, Eq. (3-54), by numerical integration for the state $n = 0$, $E = \frac{1}{2}h\nu$.   You will find that intervals of 0.1 for y will give fairly good results.   Since we know that the eigenfunction for the state is symmetric, take $u(0) = $ constant, say 1.   Find $u(0.1)$ from the power-series expansion of the solution, $\exp(-y^2/2)$, an expansion which could be found directly from the differential equation without having an analytic solution.   Carry on from there by Eq. (3-62).   Carry the calculation out to a large enough value of y to show that the calculated function is behaving approximately right at large y.   Compare the computed values with the correct solution $u = \exp(-y^2/2)$.   The errors come from the use of an interval as large as 0.1; an interval ten times smaller would give much more accurate results.

4

Average Values and Matrices

4-1. Introduction. In the preceding chapter we have seen how Schrödinger's equation is to be set up and how it results in solutions which, in the case of motion which would be periodic according to classical mechanics, have acceptable properties only for certain discrete values of the energy, which we interpret as the energy levels of the problem. We are now ready to look at Schrödinger's equation and its solutions in a rather broader manner. We recall that in Chap. 2 we have seen that the de Broglie wave had a statistical connection with the motion of particles. Its intensity measured the probability of finding the particle at a given point. We saw that we could set up waves which were in the form of wave packets, whose motion approximated the motion of classical particles. These packets, however, could not be too sharply localized in space; we were limited by the uncertainty principle. The stationary states and discrete energy levels were a result of standing de Broglie waves; but these form only a part of the whole problem of interpreting wave mechanics. In the present chapter we consider the general question of the statistical relations between the wave function and the motion of particles and related questions of average values of physical quantities. We look more closely into the nature of wave packets and their behavior and the whole problem of the physical interpretation of the wave function. In connection with this, we encounter an interesting mathematical aspect of the problem, the relation of certain quantities to the matrices met in the study of algebra. The first step in our discussion will be to set up the general solution of Schrödinger's equation involving the time, and the relation of the orthogonality of the eigenfunctions to this solution.

4-2. The Orthogonality of Eigenfunctions, and the General Solution of Schrödinger's Equation. In the preceding chapter we have seen that Schrödinger's equation not involving the time has acceptable solutions only for certain energy values which we called eigenvalues, the corresponding functions being called eigenfunctions. We saw an example of this in Eq. (3-32), and again in the discussion of the linear oscillator.

The general situation is that this equation has solutions u_n only for certain values E_n, which satisfy the equation

$$(H)_{op}u_n = E_n u_n \tag{4-1}$$

There is a very important property which the set of eigenfunctions u_n for all eigenvalues E_n possesses: they form what is called a complete set of functions, which means that any arbitrary function can be expanded as a linear combination of these functions. The simplest example of this is the Fourier series. If we have a particle in a potential well extending from $x = 0$ to $x = X$, we have seen in Eq. (3-36) that the normalized eigenfunctions are given by $u_n = (2/X)^{1/2} \sin (n\pi x/X)$. An expansion

$$\sum (n) C_n u_n(x) = \left(\frac{2}{X}\right)^{1/2} \sum (n) C_n \sin \frac{n\pi x}{X} \tag{4-2}$$

is then a sine Fourier series, and we know from the theory of Fourier series that any arbitrary function, subject to certain conditions of continuity, can be expanded in the range from $x = 0$ to $x = X$ in such a series. Similarly in general we can prove that an arbitrary function can be expanded in the u_n's appropriate to any Schrödinger problem. That is, any arbitrary function, again subject to certain conditions of continuity, can be expanded as a series $\Sigma(n)C_n u_n$, where the u_n's are the solutions of Eq. (4-1).

The determination of the coefficients C_n in such an expansion is made very simple by the orthogonality of the eigenfunctions, which we have stated for the sine functions in Eq. (3-34), and which we shall shortly prove in general. Let us suppose our eigenfunctions are normalized as well as orthogonal, so that they satisfy the equation

$$\int u_n^* u_m \, dv = \delta_{nm} \tag{4-3}$$

where we are now dealing with a problem with many dimensions, and where the integration over dv symbolizes the integration over all coordinates. If we have an arbitrary function ψ_0 expanded in the form

$$\psi_0 = \Sigma(m)C_m u_m \tag{4-4}$$

we may then multiply both sides of Eq. (4-4) by u_n^*, and integrate over all coordinates. We have

$$\int u_n^* \psi_0 \, dv = \Sigma(m)C_m \int u_n^* u_m \, dv = \Sigma(m)C_m \delta_{nm} = C_n \tag{4-5}$$

furnishing a very simple means of finding C_n. This is analogous to the method of determining the coefficients of a Fourier expansion. The reader will realize that there are two parts to the discussion of the Fourier representation of a given function. First, one must find the coefficients; this is very simple and is analogous to Eq. (4-5). Next, one must prove that the series so determined, analogous to Eq. (4-4), really converges to represent the function. This is a difficult process, either for Fourier series or for the general case, and we shall not give such a proof.

We shall shortly give the general proof of the orthogonality of solutions of Eq. (4-1). Before doing so, however, let us show how this allows us to give a simple general solution of Schrödinger's equation involving the time, Eq. (3-10), or

$$(H)_{\text{op}}\psi = i\hbar\,\frac{\partial\psi}{\partial t} \tag{4-6}$$

We know that a particular solution of this equation, following Eq. (3-14), is

$$\psi = u_n \exp\left(-iE_n t/\hbar\right) \tag{4-7}$$

We observe, from the linear nature of Eq. (4-6), that a linear combination of solutions, with arbitrary coefficients, is also a solution. Thus we can set up a more general solution of Eq. (4-6) in the form

$$\psi = \Sigma(n)C_n u_n \exp\left(-iE_n t/\hbar\right) \tag{4-8}$$

We can now show that this is in fact the general solution of Eq. (4-6); any solution can be written in this form.

Schrödinger's equation is a first-order differential equation as far as the time is concerned, so that if we know the value of ψ as a function of coordinates at a given initial time, say $t = 0$, the equation allows us to predict the subsequent behavior of ψ. In other words, the most general solution of Eq. (4-6) will be found by giving a perfectly general value ψ_0 for the wave function, as a function of coordinates, at $t = 0$. But the solution of Eq. (4-8) reduces to $\psi = \Sigma(n)C_n u_n$ when $t = 0$. In Eqs. (4-4) and (4-5) we have learned how to find coefficients C_n so as to make this expansion reduce to an arbitrary function ψ_0. If we substitute these coefficients, from Eq. (4-5), in Eq. (4-8), we shall have a function which satisfies Schrödinger's equation and which reduces to ψ_0 when $t = 0$. It is, then, the general solution of Schrödinger's equation. We observe, as we have mentioned earlier, that it takes the form of a superposition of solutions referring to the various stationary states, just as the general solution of the problem of a vibrating string is a superposition of the solutions describing the various harmonics, or overtone vibrations. We have also mentioned earlier that the solution for a wave packet or other time-dependent problem must be set up in the form of Eq. (4-8) and cannot be expressed in terms of a single stationary state. We remind the reader that the case of wave packets is taken up in Appendix 3.

Now let us come to the proof of orthogonality, which is fundamental in these results. We write an equation like Eq. (4-1) for u_m and multiply this equation by u_n^* [where in writing the product we are careful to write u_n^* to the left of $(H)_{op}u_m$, since we adopt the convention that the operator $(H)_{op}$ operates on everything to the right of it]. We integrate the result over all values of the coordinates, obtaining

$$\int u_n^*(H)_{op}u_m \, dv = E_m \int u_n^* u_m \, dv \qquad (4\text{-}9)$$

Next we take the complex conjugate of Eq. (4-1), multiply by u_m, and integrate, obtaining

$$\int u_m(H^*)_{op}u_n^* \, dv = E_n \int u_m u_n^* \, dv \qquad (4\text{-}10)$$

Next we prove that $(H)_{op}$ has a property which is described by saying that it is a Hermitian operator, namely, that

$$\int u_n^*(H)_{op}u_m \, dv = \int u_m(H^*)_{op}u_n^* \, dv \qquad (4\text{-}11)$$

On account of this proof, which we shall give in the next paragraph, we can subtract Eq. (4-10) from Eq. (4-9), obtaining

$$0 = (E_m - E_n)\int u_n^* u_m \, dv \qquad (4\text{-}12)$$

which states that either $E_m = E_n$ or $\int u_n^* u_m \, dv = 0$. From this conclusion we shall show shortly that the orthogonality can be proved.

We must prove Eq. (4-11). In the first place, the two integrals $\int u_n^* V u_m \, dv$ and $\int u_m V^* u_n^* \, dv$, where V is the potential energy, are obviously equal, since V is merely a multiplicative operator and is real. As for the integrals involving the partial derivatives, we can use an integration by parts, which is equivalent to a $3N$-dimensional Green's theorem (we are still assuming that the coordinates of the problem are $x_1 \cdots z_N$). Let us take the term $(-\hbar^2/2m_j)\int u_n^*(\partial^2 u_m/\partial x_j^2) \, dv$ from Eq. (4-9), and let us integrate first over x_j, then over all the remaining $3N - 1$ coordinates, symbolizing the latter by integrating over a volume element dv'. We take the integral $\int u_n^*(\partial^2 u_m/\partial x_j^2) \, dx_j$ and integrate by parts with respect to x_j, obtaining

$$\int u_n^* \frac{\partial^2 u_m}{\partial x_j^2} \, dx_j = u_n^* \frac{\partial u_m}{\partial x_j}\Big|_{x_j'}^{x_j''} - \int \frac{\partial u_n^*}{\partial x_j}\frac{\partial u_m}{\partial x_j} \, dx_j \qquad (4\text{-}13)$$

where the integrated terms are to be computed at the limits x_j'', x_j' of the integration. In the ordinary case the integral is over all space, and we are dealing with eigenfunctions which fall off exponentially as we go to infinity, so that the integrated terms in Eq. (4-13) will vanish; we consider in a later paragraph the cases where this is not true. We see, then, that, if the integrated terms vanish, the terms of Eq. (4-9) involving the partial derivatives can be expressed in the form

$$\hbar^2 \sum (j) \frac{1}{2m_j} \int \frac{\partial u_n^*}{\partial x_j}\frac{\partial u_m}{\partial x_j} \, dv \qquad (4\text{-}14)$$

where the summation includes terms in x_j, y_j, z_j. But examination of Eq. (4-10) shows that, if we had performed a similar integration by parts on it, we could have reduced the terms involving the partial derivatives to a form identical with that of Eq. (4-14). Thus we complete the proof of Eq. (4-11), provided the integrated terms vanish.

Let us now show how Eq. (4-12) leads to orthogonality. First, if $E_m \neq E_n$, we have $\int u_n^* u_m \, dv = 0$, or the orthogonality which we wished to prove. In the other case, where $E_m = E_n$, we get no information from Eq. (4-12) about the possible orthogonality of u_n and u_m. We can have $E_m = E_n$ in either of two cases. First, we may have $n = m$, in which case it is obvious that the integral $\int u_n^* u_m \, dv$ will not be zero, since by Eq. (4-3) it will be unity. Second, we may have the case of degeneracy, where two or more different eigenfunctions have the same eigenvalue.

We can have a case of p-fold degeneracy, where there are p eigenfunctions, say u_{j+1}, u_{j+2}, . . . , u_{j+p}, which all belong to the same eigenvalue E, and which are linearly independent in the sense that no one of them can be expressed as a linear combination of the others. We can at once prove that any linear combination of these functions will satisfy Eq. (4-1), as we see by direct substitution of such a linear combination in the equation. Then we can always set up p linear combinations of the p functions u_{j+1}, u_{j+2}, . . . , u_{j+p}, which are orthogonal to each other. For example, we can use the function u_{j+1}, the function $c_1 u_{j+1} + c_2 u_{j+2}$, where the ratio c_2/c_1 is determined to make the combination orthogonal to u_{j+1} and c_1 is determined to normalize the function, and so on, each linear combination involving one more of the functions u_{j+1}, u_{j+2}, . . . , u_{j+p} and being orthogonalized to the preceding linear combinations. This particular way of setting up p orthogonal linear combinations is known as the Schmidt method; it is only one out of an infinite number of ways of setting up such a set of orthogonal functions. Thus we see that, though Eq. (4-12) does not require that eigenfunctions associated with degenerate eigenvalues be orthogonal to each other, nevertheless we can always use the arbitrariness which exists in the specification of the eigenfunctions associated with degenerate eigenvalues to choose eigenvalues which are orthogonal to each other. Hence we may interpret Eq. (4-3) in the sense that two eigenfunctions associated with different eigenvalues must be orthogonal to each other, while two different eigenfunctions associated with the same degenerate eigenvalue can always be chosen to be orthogonal to each other.

We have passed over the case in which the integrated terms in Eq. (4-13) do not vanish, even though we extend our integration over an indefinitely large volume of space. For discrete eigenvalues, for which the eigenfunctions fall off exponentially as we go out of the region where the motion can occur classically, we never meet such a situation; we can meet it only if the wave functions extend to infinity with finite amplitude. This is also the case in which we have trouble carrying through normalization.   Special means must be used to handle such a situation, involving a continuous spectrum of eigenvalues.   The simplest method of taking care of it, which will be satisfactory for our purposes, is to modify the system by imagining that it is enclosed in an extremely large box, large compared with any of the physical systems we are interested in, bounded by infinitely high barriers.   Then the wave function must go to zero on the surface of the barrier.   This will have the effect of converting the continuous spectrum into a discrete spectrum, but with extremely closely spaced energy levels.   So long as the volume enclosed in the barrier is finite, though very large, we can normalize the eigenfunctions.   Furthermore, the integrations in Eq. (4-13) will now be carried to the barrier, where the wave function goes to zero, so that the integrated terms vanish, and the proof of orthogonality goes through without trouble.   Whenever we have a problem with a continuous spectrum, we shall assume that we are adopting this device to convert it into a discrete spectrum and to remove the difficulties connected with orthogonality and normalization. We can then make the volume enclosed by the barrier indefinitely large without running into trouble.

Let us now return to our general case and the significance of the orthogonality and normalization of the eigenfunctions, as stated in Eq. (4-3). There is a close relation between these orthogonality and normalization conditions for two functions and corresponding relations for two vectors. If we have two vectors, $\mathbf{U}_n$ and $\mathbf{U}_m$, each of unit magnitude (or normalized) and at right angles to each other (or orthogonal), the scalar product $\mathbf{U}_n \cdot \mathbf{U}_m$ will be unity if $n = m$ and zero if $n \neq m$, or will be δ_{nm}, so that the scalar product $\mathbf{U}_n \cdot \mathbf{U}_m$ and the integral $\int u_n^* u_m \, dv$ can be treated as being analogous.   This analogy will guide us in all our treatment of orthogonal functions, and it is the reason why they are called orthogonal.

To see more clearly why the analogy should hold, let us assume that u_n and u_m, instead of being functions of a set of continuous variables $x_1 \cdots z_N$, are defined only at discrete values of the variables, say at points $1, 2, \ldots, g$, in the $3N$-dimensional space.   The closest thing to the integral which we can define will then be something like the summation $\Sigma(k) u_n^*(k) u_m(k)$, where k denotes one of the g discrete points; more generally, we should have $\Sigma(k) w(k) u_n^*(k) u_m(k)$, where $w(k)$ is a weighting function, representing the volume of the $3N$-dimensional space associated with the kth point.   However, this is a generalization of the scalar product, which can be written $\Sigma(k) U_{nk} U_{mk}$, where now k is to go over three indices, indicating the x, y, and z components of the vectors $\mathbf{U}_n$ and $\mathbf{U}_m$ in a three-dimensional space.   If we go to a g-dimensional space, we get something which approaches the integral, as g becomes infinite. Such an infinite-dimensional space, in which a single point, or single vector, represents a whole function, is sometimes called a function space, and the orthogonality of our functions u_n is analogous to the orthogonality of vectors in such a space. One feature of our wave-mechanical theory does not have a simple geometrical analogue: the fact that we are dealing with complex quantities u_n and that in forming the sum, or integral, we must use the complex conjugate of u_n. We can still use the geometrical analogy, however, in spite of this complication.

Let us use the idea of the function space to discuss the orthogonality of solutions of Schrödinger's equation in a degenerate case. Suppose we have the p-fold degenerate solutions $u_{j+1}, \ldots, u_{j+p}$ of Schrödinger's equation, which we have just been considering. We know that any arbitrary linear combination $c_1 u_{j+1} + c_2 u_{j+2} + \cdots + c_p u_{j+p}$ is a solution of Schrödinger's equation, for the degenerate eigenvalue. But now consider the p-dimensional subspace of the function space, determined by all linear combinations of this type. For instance, if $p = 3$, to have a specific case in mind, all linear combinations $c_1 u_{j+1} + c_2 u_{j+2} + c_3 u_{j+3}$ will fill a three-dimensional space. We may then choose any three vectors of unit magnitude and at right angles to each other, in this space, just as if we were choosing the unit vectors of an ordinary coordinate system, and these three vectors, or functions, will have the property of satisfying Schrödinger's equation and at the same time of being orthogonal and normalized. The choice can obviously be made in an infinite number of ways, just as we can set up an infinite number of sets of rectangular coordinates in space.

4-3. The Average Values of Various Quantities. An essential part of wave mechanics, in addition to Schrödinger's equation determining the wave function and hence the probability density, is the rule for finding the average value of any physical quantity, averaged over the wave function. Suppose we have a function F of the coordinates and momenta of the system, so that we can write it $F(q_j, p_j)$, where q_j, p_j are typical coordinates and momenta, as before. Then we can make an operator from it, by using the same method used in making an operator from the Hamiltonian function, in Eq. (3-8). That is, we replace each p_j, wherever it occurs, by a differential operator $-i\hbar \partial/\partial q_j$. Then the postulate of wave mechanics is that the average value of the quantity F, which we shall denote by $(F)_{av}$, is given by

$$(F)_{av} = \int \psi^*(F)_{op} \psi \, dv \qquad (4\text{-}15)$$

where $(F)_{op}$ is assumed to operate on the function ψ which follows it, and where the integration with respect to dv is to be carried over all values of all coordinates of the system.

The rule of Eq. (4-15) is self-evident if F is a function of the coordinates only. For then $(F)_{op}$ is not a differential operator, but only an ordinary function of the coordinates. Then the mean of Eq. (4-15) becomes an ordinary weighted mean, in which we multiply the function $F(q_j)$ by the probability $\psi^*\psi(q_j,t)\, dv$ that the coordinates q_j are to be found in the volume element dv, and sum over all volume elements. The really interesting applications of Eq. (4-15) come rather when F involves the momentum components; for then we see how to extract information about the momenta from a probability distribution in coordinate space alone.

As a first illustration of an operator involving the momenta, let us take the Hamiltonian operator $(H)_{op}$. We know that if we are using a wave function of the type of Eq. (4-7), describing a stationary state, then $(H)_{op}\psi = E_n\psi$. Then from Eq. (4-15), combined with the normalization condition of Eq. (4-3), we have

$$(H)_{av} = E_n \qquad (4\text{-}16)$$

That is, the parameter E_n which we have found, in our stationary-state solution of Schrödinger's equation, represents the average energy of the systems in this stationary state. We can go further than this, however, and prove that all systems in the stationary state have the same energy. To do this, let us compute the mean-square deviation of the energy from its mean value. We have

$$\begin{aligned}
[(H - E_n)^2]_{av} &= (H^2)_{av} - 2E_n(H)_{av} + E_n^2 \\
&= (H^2)_{av} - E_n^2 \qquad (4\text{-}17)
\end{aligned}$$

where we use Eq. (4-16). But $(H^2)_{op}\psi = (H)_{op}(H)_{op}\psi = (H)_{op}E_n\psi = E_n^2\psi$, so that $(H^2)_{av} = E_n^2$, and the mean-square deviation given in Eq. (4-17) is zero. But the mean-square deviation, being the mean of a quantity which is necessarily positive, cannot be zero unless the quantity, the deviation, is everywhere zero. In other words, for systems in a stationary state, there is no deviation from the average energy, or all systems have the same energy. Thus we have the justification for our assumption, in the preceding chapter, that the parameter E_n appearing in Schrödinger's equation represented the energy.

We can get a better understanding of our method of finding the average of a function involving the momenta if we consider the case of a particle in free space. If we have a single particle, with no potential energy, Schrödinger's equation becomes

$$-\frac{\hbar^2}{2m}\nabla^2\psi = i\hbar\frac{\partial\psi}{\partial t} = E\psi \qquad (4\text{-}18)$$

where $\nabla^2 = \partial^2/\partial x^2 + \partial^2/\partial y^2 + \partial^2/\partial z^2$, and where the latter form of the equation refers to a stationary-state solution. We can find a solution of this equation of the form

$$\psi = \exp\left[i(k_x x + k_y y + k_z z)\right] \exp\left(-iEt/\hbar\right)$$
$$= \exp\left[i(\mathbf{k} \cdot \mathbf{r} - Et/\hbar)\right] \qquad (4\text{-}19)$$

where k_x, k_y, k_z, or the vector $\mathbf{k}$, represent constant quantities and $\mathbf{r}$ is the vector whose components are x, y, z. This is a three-dimensional generalization of the solution of Eq. (3-19). In order that Eq. (4-19) be a solution of Schrödinger's equation, we must have

$$\frac{k^2\hbar^2}{2m} = E \qquad (4\text{-}20)$$

The function of Eq. (4-19) represents a plane wave, whose wave normal is along the direction of the vector $\mathbf{k}$, and which has a wavelength λ given by the relation

$$|k| = \frac{2\pi}{\lambda} \qquad (4\text{-}21)$$

Now let us apply our method to find the average value of the momentum, for such a case. The operator associated with p_x, the x component of momentum, is $-i\hbar\,\partial/\partial x$. Hence we have

$$(p_x)_{\text{op}}\psi = -i\hbar\frac{\partial\psi}{\partial x} = k_x\hbar\psi \qquad (4\text{-}22)$$

From Eq. (4-22) we can deduce that the average value of p_x is $k_x\hbar$, and by using an argument like that involved in Eq. (4-17), we find that all systems described by the wave function of Eq. (4-19) have the same momentum, whose magnitude is $|p| = h/\lambda$, given by de Broglie's relation. We see, then, that our operator method of finding averages of functions of the momentum extracts information about the momentum from the complex phase of the wave function, while the information about the coordinates comes from the amplitude, or the magnitude of the complex number representing the wave function. Thus the amplitude of the function of Eq. (4-19) is unity: $\psi^*\psi = 1$, showing that the particle is equally likely to be found at any point of space. On the other hand, in this case, the momentum is definitely determined. This is an extreme case of the principle of uncertainty, in which the uncertainty in the momentum has gone to zero, that in the coordinates has become infinite. We note that here, as in Sec. 3-3, it is impossible to normalize a wave function like that of Eq. (4-19) over all space. The function we have used is normalized over unit volume, which is sometimes convenient.

From the result of Eq. (4-22), that the momentum of the particles represented by the wave function of Eq. (4-19) is definitely determined and equal to $k\hbar$, we see that Eq. (4-20) has a very simple meaning: it merely states that $p^2/2m = E$, as in the classical case, the left-hand side being the kinetic energy. We further observe that we can have cases in which the energy E is not the only quantity which is definitely determined in a stationary state, and remains independent of time, for all systems in the stationary state: here each component of momentum has the same property. We realize that the constancy of such a quantity is equivalent to a conservation theorem. In all cases which can be handled by the Hamiltonian method, energy is conserved, so that the existence of stationary states, in which the energy remains constant for all systems, is equivalent to the conservation of energy. In the present case, where there is no external force, the three components of momentum will be conserved in addition, and this is the reason why we have found definite values for p_x, p_y, and p_z. More generally, we can see that if we have any operator F, such that

$$(F)_{op}u = \text{constant } u \qquad (4\text{-}23)$$

as we have for the energy in Schrödinger's equation or for the components of momentum in Eq. (4-22), we can prove that the corresponding quantity is conserved, or is constant for all systems in a stationary state. Such an operator $(F)_{op}$ represents what Dirac calls an observable: a quantity whose value can be directly observed, for systems in a given stationary state. For a quantity which does not satisfy such a relation, we can give only statistical information.

4-4. Matrix Components. We have found in Eq. (4-8) a general solution of Schrödinger's equation,

$$\psi = \Sigma(n)C_n u_n \exp\left(-iE_n t/\hbar\right)$$

It is now very interesting to substitute this solution into the expression $\psi^*\psi$ for the probability density and into the expression of Eq. (4-15) for the average value of an operator. First, the probability density is

$$\psi^*\psi = \Sigma(n,m)C_n^* C_m u_n^* u_m \exp\left[i(E_n - E_m)t/\hbar\right] \qquad (4\text{-}24)$$

We note that this expression contains terms of two kinds: those for which $n = m$, and those for which $n \neq m$. The terms of the first type refer each to a single stationary state and are independent of time. We can interpret a wave function of the form of that given by Eq. (4-8) by the statement that there is a certain probability of finding the system in each of its stationary states, and this probability is given by $C_n^* C_n$, called the occupation number of the nth stationary state. We shall justify this interpretation shortly, when we come to find the average values of various quantities over the wave function. These probabilities satisfy one obvious requirement, namely,

$$\Sigma(n)C_n^*C_n = 1 \qquad (4\text{-}25)$$

as we find by integrating Eq. (4-24) over all values of the coordinates $x_1 \cdots z_N$ and using the fact that the probability density is normalized, Eq. (3-6). We furthermore verify in this way the fact that it is possible to normalize the probability density independent of time, even with the most general solution of Schrödinger's equation, an obvious requirement if we are to be able to interpret $\psi^*\psi$ as a probability density.

The second type of term in Eq. (4-24) comes for $n \neq m$ and is oscillating sinusoidally with time, with the angular frequency $(E_n - E_m)/\hbar$. This is the frequency given by Bohr's frequency condition,

$$E_n - E_m = h\nu \qquad (4\text{-}26)$$

as the frequency of radiation emitted or absorbed when we have a transition between stationary states whose energies are E_n and E_m; it is in this way that Bohr's condition enters into wave mechanics. We shall find later, when we study the radiation field, that the oscillations of probability density given by these terms give rise to oscillations of charge, and to emission and absorption of electromagnetic radiation, with frequencies given by Bohr's condition. We note that such terms occur in the probability density in pairs: if n equals a particular number, say 1, and m equals another number, say 2, then we naturally group with this term the other one in which n equals 2, m equals 1. That is, in Eq. (4-24) we may sum over each pair of different indices n, m only once but take the two terms explicitly, in the form

$$C_n^*C_m u_n^* u_m \exp\left[i(E_n - E_m)t/\hbar\right] + \text{conjugate} \qquad (4\text{-}27)$$

since the term with n and m interchanged is the conjugate of the one written explicitly in Eq. (4-27). Thus we see that these oscillating terms in the probability density are real, as they must be to represent real probabilities.

From Eq. (4-24), we can understand the rather arbitrary way in which the complex quantities are manipulated in setting up the theory of wave mechanics. It is only because we took ψ to be a complex quantity, and multiplied by its conjugate in Eq. (4-24), that all the sinusoidal oscillations came out with frequencies given by Bohr's condition. If instead we had first taken the real part of ψ, then squared, we should have found terms, not only in the differences, but also in the sums, of the energies, which is contrary to assumptions of quantum theory.

Now let us find the average value of an operator $(F)_{op}$, averaged over the wave function of Eq. (4-8). When we use Eq. (4-15), this is

$$(F)_{av} = \Sigma(n,m)C_n^*C_m F_{nm} \exp\left[i(E_n - E_m)t/\hbar\right] \qquad (4\text{-}28)$$

where $\qquad F_{nm} = \int u_n^*(F)_{op} u_m \, dv \qquad\qquad\qquad\qquad (4\text{-}29)$

The quantities F_{nm} are called the matrix components, or matrix elements, of the operator $(F)_{op}$.[1] They are ordinarily written in a square array, with the rows denoting the first index n, the columns the second index m, as follows:

$$
\begin{array}{lllll}
F_{11} & F_{12} & F_{13} & \cdot & \cdot & \cdot \\
F_{21} & F_{22} & F_{23} & \cdot & \cdot & \cdot \\
F_{31} & F_{32} & F_{33} & \cdot & \cdot & \cdot \\
\cdot & \cdot & \cdot & \cdot & \cdot & \cdot & \cdot & \cdot & \cdot & \cdot & \cdot
\end{array}
\qquad (4\text{-}30)
$$

In such an array, we call the matrix components F_{nn}, which appear along the diagonal in the expression (4-30), the diagonal matrix components, and the components F_{nm}, for which $n \neq m$, are called nondiagonal matrix components. All the operators which we shall meet in such a connection as this are what are called Hermitian operators; that is, they have

$$F_{mn}^* = F_{nm} \qquad\qquad\qquad\qquad (4\text{-}31)$$

This is required in order that $(F)_{av}$ of Eq. (4-28) should be real. In Appendix 7 we prove that the ordinary operators with which we are concerned are Hermitian. We have already given such a proof for the Hamiltonian operator in Sec. 4-2; we see that Eq. (4-11), which was used there as a definition of a Hermitian operator, is equivalent to Eq. (4-31).

Some operators have diagonal matrices; that is, the only nonvanishing matrix components are the diagonal components. In such a case, we see from Eq. (4-28) that the average value of such an operator is independent of time. We can see that any operator satisfying Eq. (4-23), namely, that $(F)_{op}u_m = $ constant $\times u_m$, must have this property; we need only multiply by u_n^*, and integrate over the coordinates and use the ortho-normal properties of the u's, to prove it. Our present proof from the expression of Eq. (4-28) that the average value of such an operator is independent of time is equivalent to the proof of the same result which we gave in our discussion of Eq. (4-23). The simplest example of an operator of this type is a numerical constant; in this case, all diagonal matrix components are equal, and equal to the constant. For a less

---

[1] Many writers use the symbol $\langle u_n|F|u_m \rangle$, introduced by Dirac, for the matrix component F_{nm}. The latter notation, which we use, was introduced by Heisenberg, who developed the use of matrix methods before wave mechanics was invented, in a paper whose reference is *Z. Physik*, **33**:879 (1925).

trivial example, we have the Hamiltonian, whose diagonal matrix components are the energy values E_m.

The average value of an operator having a diagonal matrix, or satisfying Eq. (4-23), is

$$(F)_{av} = \Sigma(n)C_n^*C_nF_{nn} \tag{4-32}$$

We have seen, from our discussion of Eq. (4-23), that in the nth stationary state all systems will have an equal value of the quantity F, its value being F_{nn}. Thus Eq. (4-32) represents a weighted mean of these values, and this weighting process indicates that we were correct in interpreting $C_n^*C_n$ as the probability of finding the system in the nth stationary state.

It is to be noted that a matrix depends on two things: first, the operator, and second, the set of orthogonal functions with respect to which it is computed. Thus a given operator, such as energy or angular momentum or x coordinate, can have its matrix computed with respect to any set of orthonormal functions. When we have stated that the Hamiltonian function, or energy, has a diagonal matrix, we are assuming that its matrix components are being computed with respect to the set of functions which are solutions of Schrödinger's equation. The problem of solving Schrödinger's equation with a given energy operator may, in fact, be considered as that of finding the particular set of orthogonal functions which makes the matrix derived from that operator diagonal. In a similar way, we can find a set of orthogonal functions which would make any other desired operator have a diagonal matrix. Sometimes we can find a set of functions with respect to which two operators, as the energy and a component of linear or angular momentum, simultaneously have diagonal matrices, or are constant; for the average value of any operator which has a diagonal matrix is necessarily independent of time. We shall inquire later regarding the necessary condition for this to be possible.

4-5. Some Theorems Regarding Matrices. We can compute the matrix components of an arbitrary operator by the rule of Eq. (4-29); but sometimes it is a help to be able to find the matrix of a complicated function from the matrix components of simpler functions, by processes analogous to ordinary algebra. To solve such problems, we set up a set of rules, called matrix algebra, which we shall now consider. As a preliminary step, we must note that there is one difficulty which has not previously been pointed out in connection with our rule (4-29). It turns out that, if there are any terms of F involving products of coordinates and momenta, the answer will depend on the order in which they occur. The best example is the case of the product $p_x x$, where x is one of the coordinates, p_x the momentum conjugate to it. We have

$$(p_x x)_{av} = \int \psi^* \left[-i\hbar \frac{\partial}{\partial x} (x\psi) \right] dv$$

$$= \int \psi^* \left(-i\hbar\psi - i\hbar x \frac{\partial \psi}{\partial x} \right) dv$$

$$= -i\hbar + \int \psi^* \left(-i\hbar x \frac{\partial}{\partial x} \right) \psi \, dv$$

$$= -i\hbar + (xp_x)_{av}$$

$$(p_x x - x p_x)_{av} = -i\hbar \tag{4-33}$$

This is the so-called commutation rule; it states that interchange, or commutation, of the order of a coordinate and momentum operator changes the value, since the difference is not zero. In most actual cases that we meet, we shall not be troubled by this difficulty of noncommutability of coordinates and momenta, but it is something against which we must be on our guard.

Let us now approach our problem of building up the matrix of a complicated function from the matrices of simpler functions. We can do this if we know how to find the matrix of the sum of two functions F and G from the matrices of F and G separately and how to find the matrix of the product. As far as the sum is concerned, the result is trivial; we can prove at once that the matrix components of the sum of two operators are the sum of the matrix components of the separate operators. But the result for the product is not trivial. We shall now derive the formula for finding the matrix components of the operator $(FG)_{op}$ if the matrix components of $(F)_{op}$ and $(G)_{op}$ are known separately.

As a first step in our proof, let us take the function $(G)_{op}u_m$ and expand it in a series of the orthonormal functions u_n; we know that any function can be expanded in such a series. If we assume that

$$(G)_{op}u_m = \Sigma(k)C_k u_k \tag{4-34}$$

multiply by the conjugate of one of the functions, and integrate, as in our derivation of Eq. (4-5), we have

$$C_k = \int u_k^*(G)_{op}u_m \, dv = G_{km} \tag{4-35}$$

which leads to

$$(G)_{op}u_m = \Sigma(k)G_{km}u_k \tag{4-36}$$

We note that Eq. (4-23) is the special case of Eq. (4-36), when $(G)_{op}$ has a diagonal matrix. Next we write $(F)_{op}(G)_{op}u_m$, expressing $(G)_{op}u_m$ in the form of Eq. (4-36), multiply by u_n^*, and integrate. We have

$$(FG)_{nm} = \int u_n^*(FG)_{op}u_m \, dv$$

$$= \Sigma(k)\int u_n^*(F)_{op}G_{km}u_k \, dv$$

$$= \Sigma(k)F_{nk}G_{km} \tag{4-37}$$

The multiplication rule of Eq. (4-37) is the same one which holds for matrices in algebra, justifying us in treating our quantities F_{nm} as algebraic matrices. In applying this multiplication rule, we must remember that we have shown in Eq. (4-33) that operators do not always commute; consequently their matrix components do not commute either. For example, if we take matrix components of an equation like Eq. (4-33), we have the matrix equation

$$(p_x x - x p_x)_{nm} = -i\hbar \, \delta_{nm} \qquad (4\text{-}38)$$

showing that $(p_x x)_{nm}$ is not equal to $(x p_x)_{nm}$.

A study of the commutation properties of operators and their matrices gives us much useful information. In particular, we shall now prove that any quantity whose operator commutes with the energy, or Hamiltonian, represents a quantity which is independent of time. We shall find in important cases that there are other dynamical quantities besides the energy which remain constant, as, for example, the momentum of a particle on which no forces act or the angular momentum of a system on which no torques act. Thus, let

$$(FH - HF)_{nm} = 0 \qquad (4\text{-}39)$$

which will be the case for all values of n and m if the operator $(F)_{op}$ commutes with the Hamiltonian. We use Eq. (4-37) and write out this equation in terms of the matrix components of $(F)_{op}$ and $(H)_{op}$, taking advantage of the fact that H has a diagonal matrix. Then we find

$$F_{nm}(H_{mm} - H_{nn}) = 0$$
or
$$F_{nm}(E_m - E_n) = 0 \qquad (4\text{-}40)$$

This tells us that the nondiagonal matrix components F_{nm} are necessarily zero, except between two states which are degenerate with each other, so that they have the same energy. But now consider Eq. (4-28) for the average value of any quantity. We see that all the nonvanishing terms of $(F)_{av}$, when $(F)_{op}$ commutes with the energy, either are diagonal, therefore independent of time, or have $E_n = E_m$, which means that the time-dependent term, $\exp\left[i(E_n - E_m)t/\hbar\right]$, is really a constant independent of time. Hence we have our proof that, if the operator F commutes with the energy, it represents a quantity whose average value does not depend on time.

The result we have just stated suggests that the commutator $(FH - HF)_{nm}$, which vanishes if F represents a constant quantity, might be connected with the expression for the time rate of change of F. This is the case. To prove it, let us start with Eq. (4-28) for the average value of an operator $(F)_{op}$ and differentiate with respect to time. We then have

$$\left(\frac{\partial F}{\partial t}\right)_{av} = \sum (n,m) C_n^* C_m F_{nm}[i(E_n - E_m)/\hbar] \exp\left[i(E_n - E_m)t/\hbar\right] \qquad (4\text{-}41)$$

But this must equal

$$\sum_{n,m} (n,m) C_n^* C_m \left(\frac{\partial F}{\partial t}\right)_{nm} \exp\left[i(E_n - E_m)t/\hbar\right] \qquad (4\text{-}42)$$

By comparing terms, we see that

$$\left(\frac{\partial F}{\partial t}\right)_{nm} = [i(E_n - E_m)/\hbar]F_{nm} \qquad (4\text{-}43)$$

But this can be written in the form

$$i\hbar \left(\frac{\partial F}{\partial t}\right)_{nm} = (FH - HF)_{nm} \qquad (4\text{-}44)$$

when we use the multiplication rule of Eq. (4-37) and take advantage of the fact that H has a diagonal matrix. We have shown that Eq. (4-44) holds for each matrix component; but one can prove that if two operators have all their matrix components equal to each other, with respect to a complete set of functions, the operators must be identical. Hence we have the operator equation

$$i\hbar \left(\frac{\partial F}{\partial t}\right)_{op} = (FH - HF)_{op} \qquad (4\text{-}45)$$

This supplies our desired relation between the commutator of an operator F with H and the time derivative of F. It shows that, if we have an operator representing a quantity independent of time, it must commute with the Hamiltonian, the inverse of our earlier theorem that, if an operator commutes with the Hamiltonian, it must represent a quantity independent of time.

It is a rather remarkable fact that the method of operating with matrices was discovered before wave mechanics. The multiplication rule and method of differentiating with respect to time, as well as the commutation rule, were postulated by Heisenberg and developed by Born, Heisenberg, Jordan, Pauli, and Dirac,[1] in 1925, a year before Schrödinger's equation was suggested. They were used for a number of complicated calculations, without use of wave functions, for example for finding the energy levels of the linear oscillator, its matrix components of x, and even the energy levels of the hydrogen atom. For most of these problems the method of matrices is more complicated than that of wave functions, but this is by no means always the case. For getting a general

[1] Heisenberg, loc. cit.; M. Born and P. Jordan, Z. Physik, 34:858 (1925); M. Born, W. Heisenberg, and P. Jordan, Z. Physik, 35:557 (1926); W. Pauli Jr., Z. Physik, 36:336 (1926); W. Heisenberg and P. Jordan, Z. Physik, 37:263 (1926); P. A. M. Dirac, Proc. Roy. Soc. (London), A109:642 (1925); A110:561 (1926); A111:281 (1926).

understanding of the structure of quantum mechanics, on an advanced level, the matrix methods are more appropriate than the use of Schrödinger's equation, and these methods are used in two of the very important advanced texts on quantum mechanics, those of Dirac[1] and of von Neumann.[2]   In the next section, we shall give some of the properties of the matrix components of the linear oscillator, as an illustration of matrix methods.

4-6. Matrix Components for the Linear Oscillator.   In Appendix 6, where we treat the properties of the wave functions of the linear oscillator more in detail, we show that the matrix components of the coordinate x are given by

$$x_{n,n+1} = x_{n+1,n} = \sqrt{\frac{(n+1)h}{8\pi^2 m\nu}}$$

$$x_{nm} = 0 \qquad \text{unless } m = n \pm 1$$

(4-46)

where n is any integer equal to or greater than zero.   We can draw two conclusions from this.   In the first place, the diagonal matrix components of x are zero.   That is, the average value of x in a stationary state is zero, which is natural by comparison with the classical case, since we expect the particle to be oscillating in such a way that it has positive values of x as often as negative values.   In the second place, the only nondiagonal matrix components come when n changes by just one unit. We shall show in Chap. 6 that this means that a linear oscillator can jump, under the action of radiation, only by one unit of quantum number.   On account of the very simple form which the matrix components for x have, this furnishes us with a convenient example to use in illustrating some of the properties of matrices which we have just been discussing.

We should expect from Eq. (4-43) that the matrix components of the velocity would be given by

$$\dot{x}_{n,n+1} = -\dot{x}_{n+1,n} = -2\pi i \nu x_{n,n+1}$$

(4-47)

where $\dot{x}$ indicates the time rate of change of x, and where we have used the fact that $E_{n+1} - E_n = h\nu$.   It seems plausible that the matrix components of the momentum p should be m times those of the velocity $\dot{x}$; we shall later prove in Eqs. (4-52) to (4-56) that this must be the case. If we assume this, and insert the value of $x_{n,n+1}$ in Eq. (4-47), we find

$$p_{n,n+1} = -p_{n+1,n} = -i\sqrt{\frac{(n+1)mh\nu}{2}}$$

(4-48)

[1] P. A. M. Dirac, "Quantum Mechanics," Oxford University Press, New York, 1st ed., 1930, 4th ed., 1958.

[2] J. von Neumann, "Mathematical Foundations of Quantum Mechanics," Princeton University Press, Princeton, N.J., 1955.

We can now check the commutation rule, Eq. (4-38). We find by substitution that the nondiagonal matrix components of $(px - xp)_{op}$ are zero, and for the diagonal components, which by the rule for matrix products are

$$(px - xp)_{n,n} = p_{n,n+1}x_{n+1,n} + p_{n,n-1}x_{n-1,n}$$
$$- x_{n,n+1}p_{n+1,n} - x_{n,n-1}p_{n-1,n} \quad (4\text{-}49)$$

we find $-i\hbar$, as we should, when we substitute the matrix components from Eqs. (4-46) and (4-48).

Now that we have the matrix components of x and p, we can find the matrix components of kinetic and potential energy and check the fact that the total energy has a diagonal matrix. We find that the only non-vanishing matrix components of the kinetic energy are

$$\left(\frac{p^2}{2m}\right)_{n,n} = \frac{1}{2m}(p_{n,n+1}p_{n+1,n} + p_{n,n-1}p_{n-1,n})$$
$$= \left(n + \frac{1}{2}\right)\frac{h\nu}{2} \quad (4\text{-}50)$$

and
$$\left(\frac{p^2}{2m}\right)_{n,n+2} = \left(\frac{p^2}{2m}\right)_{n+2,n} = \frac{1}{2m}p_{n,n+1}p_{n+1,n+2}$$
$$= -\frac{h\nu}{4}\sqrt{(n+1)(n+2)} \quad (4\text{-}51)$$

For the potential energy, the diagonal matrix component is the same as for the kinetic energy, and the nondiagonal component is the negative of that for the kinetic energy. Hence the total energy has a diagonal matrix, and the matrix components agree with those given in Eq. (3-59). As for the potential and kinetic energies separately, their diagonal components or time averages are equal, as in classical mechanics, where the mean kinetic and potential energies of a linear oscillator are equal. Their nondiagonal matrix components, corresponding to a jump of two units in quantum number, suggest the classical case, in which the kinetic or potential energies of a linear oscillator have terms like $\cos^2 \omega t$ or $\sin^2 \omega t$, where ω is the angular frequency, so that they can be expanded in terms of cosine functions of angular frequency 2ω.

We see, in other words, that in this case it is easy to check our general matrix relations by direct calculation. It is an interesting fact that for this problem the process can be reversed: from the commutation rule for p and x, and the constancy of the energy, we can work backward to deduce the matrix components of x and p uniquely. This was done during the year 1925, when as we mentioned earlier the matrix methods were available, but not wave mechanics. In this particular case, this is a somewhat simpler way to deduce the matrix components than by direct use of the wave function.

4-7. Average Values and the Motion of Wave Packets. In earlier chapters we have made statements about the way in which packets move according to wave mechanics; now we can investigate their motion by simple and straightforward methods. We shall investigate the motion of the center of gravity of a wave packet, the point whose coordinates are $(x)_{av}$, $(y)_{av}$, and $(z)_{av}$, and shall show that in fact it moves precisely according to Newton's equations of motion. This is then, in a sense, the fundamental theorem of classical mechanics, or a proof of Newton's laws from wave mechanics. Fortunately we can give a perfectly general proof, first given by Ehrenfest[1] in 1927, without having to assume any particular form for the wave packet; as long as the wave function is concentrated enough so that we can identify any value of x found within the wave packet with the average value of x, we can say that any system described by the wave packet obeys Newtonian mechanics.

The first step in our proof is to show that the time rate of change of the average value of one of the coordinates equals the corresponding average value of the momentum, divided by the mass. If we have a system of N particles, and if x_i represents a typical coordinate, we wish to show that

$$\frac{d}{dt}(x_i)_{av} = \frac{1}{m_i}(p_i)_{av} \tag{4-52}$$

This is the theorem which we have already presupposed in going from Eq. (4-47) to (4-48). We start our proof by setting up $(x_i)_{av} = \int \psi^* x_i \psi \, dv$ and differentiating with respect to the time. We differentiate under the integral sign and note that x_i is not differentiated, since it is an independent variable. Thus we have

$$\frac{d}{dt}(x_i)_{av} = \int \frac{\partial \psi^*}{\partial t} x_i \psi \, dv + \int \psi^* x_i \frac{\partial \psi}{\partial t} \, dv \tag{4-53}$$

We then substitute for $\partial\psi/\partial t$ from Eq. (3-11) and for $\partial\psi^*/\partial t$ from the conjugate of that equation. We find immediately that the terms in the potential energy cancel, and by a simple integration by parts, like that used in Eq. (4-13), we show that all terms involving differentiations with respect to any variable except x_i cancel. The only other term then involves

$$-\frac{\hbar^2}{2m_i}\frac{i}{\hbar}\int\left(\frac{\partial^2\psi^*}{\partial x_i^2}x_i\psi - \psi^* x_i\frac{\partial^2\psi}{\partial x_i^2}\right)dx_i \tag{4-54}$$

where we first integrate with respect to dx_i, later integrating with respect to the other variables. We integrate by parts, discarding the integrated

[1] P. Ehrenfest, *Z. Physik*, **45**:455 (1927).

terms as in Eq. (4-13), and the expression above reduces to

$$\frac{i\hbar}{2m_i} \int \left(\frac{\partial \psi^*}{\partial x_i} \psi - \psi^* \frac{\partial \psi}{\partial x_i} \right) dx_i \tag{4-55}$$

Another integration by parts of the first term shows that it is identical with the second, so that we finally have

$$-\frac{i\hbar}{m_i} \int \psi^* \frac{\partial \psi}{\partial x_i} dx_i \tag{4-56}$$

When we integrate over the remaining variables, we have the proof of Eq. (4-52). This result gives us a justification of the rule for calculating the average value of the momentum.

The remaining part of the proof of Newton's laws comes by differentiating Eq. (4-52) again, with respect to time, to get the acceleration of the center of mass, or the time rate of change of the momentum. We should like, in fact, to prove that the time rate of change of the average momentum equals the average over the wave packet of the force. Now the x_i component of force is $-\partial V/\partial x_i$. Thus we wish to prove that

$$\frac{d(p_i)_{\mathrm{av}}}{dt} = -\left(\frac{\partial V}{\partial x_i} \right)_{\mathrm{av}} \tag{4-57}$$

To do this, we multiply Eq. (4-52) by m_i and differentiate with respect to time. We have

$$\frac{d(p_i)_{\mathrm{av}}}{dt} = -i\hbar \int \left(\psi^* \frac{\partial}{\partial t} \frac{\partial \psi}{\partial x_i} + \frac{\partial \psi^*}{\partial t} \frac{\partial \psi}{\partial x_i} \right) dv \tag{4-58}$$

We interchange the order of differentiation in the first term and substitute for $\partial \psi/\partial t$ and $\partial \psi^*/\partial t$ from Eq. (3-11) and its conjugate. The terms arising from the kinetic energy all vanish when we integrate by parts, and we find that the only nonvanishing terms are

$$\frac{d(p_i)_{\mathrm{av}}}{dt} = -\int \psi^* \frac{\partial V}{\partial x_i} \psi \, dv \tag{4-59}$$

which is the result which we wished to prove. We thus have a general proof that the center of gravity of a wave packet, or in fact of any wave function (for we have not made any assumptions regarding the nature of ψ), satisfies Newton's equations of motion if we interpret the force as the average force averaged over the wave function. In Appendix 3 we give a corresponding proof for any arbitrary Hermitian Hamiltonian.

4-8. The Equation of Continuity for the Probability Density. We have seen that the quantity $\psi^*\psi$ plays the part of a probability density, in the sense that $\psi^*\psi \, dv$ gives the probability of finding the system in the volume element dv. Let us inquire whether we cannot set up a function representing the density of particles, and also a vector quantity representing the flux of the particles, such that the component of flux normal to any given surface gives the amount of material crossing unit area of the surface per second. If the density is ρ, the flux density $\mathbf{f}$, then we always have the so-called equation of continuity,

$$\frac{\partial \rho}{\partial t} + \nabla \cdot \mathbf{f} = 0 \qquad (4\text{-}60)$$

This has the following significance: $\partial \rho / \partial t$ represents the increase in the amount of material per unit volume in unit time. By the divergence theorem, the integral $\nabla \cdot \mathbf{f}$ over unit volume can be converted into the surface integral of the outward flux of $\mathbf{f}$ over the surface of the unit volume. Thus Eq. (4-60) states that the amount of increase of material in unit time is the negative of the outward flux, or is the inward flux of material. In other words, the material is conserved: the amount within the unit volume increases in unit time by just the amount which has flowed in over the surface of the volume, and no material is created inside.

Now let us find the expressions for ρ and $\mathbf{f}$ in wave mechanics. We assume that our system consists of many identical particles, such as electrons, so that we can find the density merely by finding the number of particles per unit volume. In Eq. (3-7) we have found that the probability of finding the coordinates x_1 of the first particle in a range dx_1 is $(\int \cdots \int \psi^* \psi \, dy_1 \, dz_1 \cdots dz_N) \, dx_1$, where the integration is to be over all values of the variables $y_1 \cdots z_N$. In a similar way, the probability that the first particle be in a volume element $dx_1 \, dy_1 \, dz_1$ is $\rho_1 \, dx_1 \, dy_1 \, dz_1$, where

$$\rho_1(x_1 y_1 z_1) = \int \cdots \int \psi^* \psi \, dx_2 \, dy_2 \cdots dz_N \qquad (4\text{-}61)$$

where the integration is extended over all values of the variables $x_2 y_2 z_2 \cdots z_N$. We may regard the quantity $\rho_1(x,y,z)$ as a density function for the first particle, giving the probability of finding this particle per unit volume at the position $x_1 y_1 z_1$. For the total density at an arbitrary point xyz of space, we may simply add the densities of the various particles at this point:

$$\rho(x,y,z) = \Sigma(i)\rho_i(x,y,z) \qquad (4\text{-}62)$$

Here $\rho_i(x,y,z)$ is defined in a manner analogous to that of Eq. (4-61); that is, we integrate $\psi^* \psi$ over all values of all coordinates except those of the ith particle and set the coordinates of that particle equal to x, y, z.

We must now expect that our density function ρ_i will have a flux density associated with it, such that the two together will satisfy the continuity equation, Eq. (4-60), so that, when we add the densities of all particles, as in Eq. (4-62), and the fluxes of all particles, the total density and flux will also satisfy the continuity equation. To guide us in setting up this flux density, we point out that a flux **f** is often written in an alternative way as $\rho\mathbf{v}$, where ρ is the density, **v** the velocity, of the material, for the amount of material crossing unit area per second is always the density, times the component of velocity perpendicular to the surface. Thus there should be a relation between the flux density of a particle and its average velocity: if we integrate $\rho\mathbf{v}$ over space, or find $\int\rho\mathbf{v}\,dv$, we should be finding a weighted mean of the velocity, or the average velocity. Since we know how to find the average velocity of an individual particle, from Eq. (4-52), we at least know the integral of our desired flux density over all space. If we call $\mathbf{f}_i$ the flux density of the ith particle, we must have

$$\iiint \mathbf{f}_i\,dv = -\frac{i\hbar}{m_i}\int\cdots\int \psi^*\nabla_i\psi\,dv \qquad (4\text{-}63)$$

where we have used Eq. (4-56), and where the flux $\mathbf{f}_i$ is a function in three-dimensional space, whereas the integration on the right side of Eq. (4-63) is over a $3N$-dimensional space. The operator ∇_i refers to differentiation with respect to the coordinates of the ith particle.

We might plausibly assume, then, that our flux $\mathbf{f}_i$ should be given by

$$-\frac{i\hbar}{m_i}\int\cdots\int \psi^*\nabla_i\psi\,dv' \qquad (4\text{-}64)$$

where dv' indicates integration over all coordinates except those of the ith particle. However, this is an impossible assumption, for it gives a complex quantity, and it does not satisfy the continuity equation. In its place, Schrödinger assumed that we must take the real part of the expression of Eq. (4-64), or half the sum of this quantity and its conjugate,

$$\mathbf{f}_i = -\frac{i\hbar}{2m_i}\int\cdots\int (\psi^*\nabla_i\psi - \psi\nabla_i\psi^*)\,dv' \qquad (4\text{-}65)$$

where again the integration is to extend over all coordinates except those of the ith particle. This expression follows from Eq. (4-55) rather than (4-56); by integration by parts, as in passing from Eq. (4-55) to (4-56), we can show that the integral of Eq. (4-65) over all values of the coordinates of the ith particle is identical with the integral of Eq. (4-64).

One can now substitute the density ρ_i and flux $\mathbf{f}_i$ of the ith particle in the continuity equation, Eq. (4-60), and prove that that equation is satisfied. In finding $\nabla_i\cdot\mathbf{f}_i$, we find Laplacians under the integral sign, which are evaluated from Schrödinger's equation, and it is a straightforward process to demonstrate the equation of continuity. This then is a justification of our assumptions about the densities of particles and of flux.   The flux f_i, as given in Eq. (4-65), has an important place in quantum mechanics, as we see by analogy with electromagnetic theory. In that theory, we remember that there are quantities analogous to the density and flux: they are the energy density in the electromagnetic field and Poynting's vector, measuring the flux of energy across a surface. When we set up the connection between classical electromagnetics and the quantum theory, we assume that the energy density measures the probability that a photon will be found in a given volume and that Poynting's vector measures the probability that a photon will cross a given surface.   In a similar way here ρ_i measures the probability of finding a particular particle in a given volume, and f_i measures the probability that it will cross a given surface.   In other words, it has an analogy to Poynting's vector, and is used in the same sort of way that Poynting's vector is, in computing the flow of particles.   We find it particularly useful, for instance, in studying electrical conduction, where we wish to get the flow of electrons constituting a current.

PROBLEMS

1. Prove that a coordinate commutes with another coordinate, a momentum commutes with another momentum, and a coordinate commutes with a momentum conjugate to another coordinate.

2. Write down the operators for the three components of angular momentum in rectangular coordinates.

3. Find what $p^2x - xp^2$ is equal to, using the commutation rule for $px - xp$.

4. Solve Schrödinger's equation for a rotator, whose kinetic energy is $\frac{1}{2}I\dot{\theta}^2$, in the absence of an external force.   Find wave functions, showing that the angular momentum is an integral multiple of $\hbar$.   Compute the matrix of $R\cos\theta$, one component of the displacement of a point attached to the rotator at a distance R from the axis.   Show that all matrix components are zero except those in which the angular momentum changes by $\pm$ 1 unit.

5. Show that $\exp[(i/\hbar)p\alpha]u(x)$, where p is the x component of momentum, α is a constant, is equal to $u(x + \alpha)$.   Use Taylor's expansion of the exponential operator.

6. Write down Schrödinger's equation in spherical polar coordinates, by using the Laplacian in these coordinates, assuming a potential $V(r)$.   Discuss the method of deriving the equation from the Hamiltonian by replacing the momenta by differentiations, showing that the former method is consistent with the latter, but that the latter method does not lead to unique results.

7. A particle moves in a region of constant potential, bounded by infinitely high potential barriers at $x = 0$ and $x = L$.   From the normalized wave functions find the matrix components of the momentum operator.   Find also the matrix components of the coordinate.   From this find the matrix components of the velocity by differentiating with respect to time.   Prove by direct comparison that the matrix of the velocity is $1/m$ times that of the momentum, where m is the mass of the particle.

8. A wave packet can be represented at time $t = 0$ by a function $\exp(ikx)$ $\exp[-a(x - x_0)^2]$, or a sinusoidal wave with propagation constant k, modulated by a Gauss error curve which has its amplitude fall off as we go away from $x = x_0$.   Assume that the wave packet is set up at $t = 0$, for the Schrödinger problem of motion of a free particle in a region between $x = 0$ and $x = L$, bounded at each limit by an infinitely high repulsive barrier. Find the coefficients C_i for the expansion of this wave packet in terms of the wave functions of the problem.

9. In the preceding problem it might be supposed that the wave packet would move, as time went on, with the group velocity (or velocity of the particle) along the x axis. Set up an expression for such a moving wave packet, and investigate how nearly this represents the appropriate solution of Schrödinger's equation.

5

The Variation and Perturbation Methods

5-1. The Variation Principle. In the preceding chapters, we have stated Schrödinger's equation, have given its general physical interpretation, and have indicated some simple cases in which the equation can be solved exactly. Unfortunately, there are many more cases, including most of the important ones which we shall meet, in which exact solutions are impossible and we are forced to use approximate methods to attack our fundamental problem of solving Schrödinger's equation. It has been found that one of the most useful ways of getting approximate solutions is to set up functions containing a number of parameters, which by suitable variation of the parameters may approximate the true solution quite accurately. The question is: How do we choose these parameters so that our function will form the best approximation of the given form to a solution of Schrödinger's equation? An answer to this question is provided by the variation principle of wave mechanics.

This principle is stated as follows: Let us take a function u, which is variable at will, subject only to the condition that it be always normalized. Let us compute the average value of the Hamiltonian operator for this function:

$$(H)_{\mathrm{av}} = \int u^*(H)_{\mathrm{op}} u \, dv \qquad (5\text{-}1)$$

Let us vary the function u at will and find the way in which $(H)_{\mathrm{av}}$ varies. Then we can prove that for certain values of the function u the integral $(H)_{\mathrm{av}}$ will be stationary; that is, a small change in u will not make any first-order change in $(H)_{\mathrm{av}}$, but only a second-order change, of the order of magnitude of the square of the change in u. We can prove furthermore that these functions are the eigenfunctions of Schrödinger's equation. In other words, Schrödinger's equation can be replaced by a variation principle. We shall shortly prove this theorem.

If for the moment we grant the correctness of the variation principle, we can draw various conclusions from it. If an integral like $(H)_{\mathrm{av}}$ is stationary, this can mean any one of three things. The integral may be an absolute minimum, such that all possible changes in the function u will increase its value by small quantities of the second order; it can be such that some changes in u increase its value, some decrease it; or it can be an absolute maximum, such that all possible changes in u decrease its value. Now of all the eigenfunctions u_n of the variation problem, or functions which render the integral $(H)_{av}$ stationary, one will have the lowest eigenvalue, or value of $(H)_{av}$. It is obvious that this must be an absolute minimum, since otherwise some changes in u_n would decrease the integral, which is contrary to hypothesis. In other words, the average energy $(H)_{av}$ for the true ground-state eigenfunction is lower than for any other function whatever.

It is this aspect of the variation principle which proves most useful in practice. As stated earlier, we ordinarily take a function u which contains certain parameters which we can vary at will, thus varying the function. It is impracticable to have a completely flexible function, but we try to use a function which, by proper choice of the parameters, comes as close as possible to what we imagine to be the true eigenfunction of the problem. Then we compute the integral $(H)_{av}$ and vary the parameters to minimize this integral. The lowest value which we can find for this integral will lead to values of the parameters which give what may be considered the best approximation to the true ground-state eigenfunction which we can set up using the function we have assumed. And the energy integral $(H)_{av}$ will represent the best approximation to the ground-state energy which we can set up but will necessarily lie higher than the true value. If we know the true value, for instance by experiment, we can form some estimate as to the accuracy of our approximation by finding how much our average $(H)_{av}$ lies above the true ground-state energy.

Now let us fill in our argument by proving the variation principle. Let us start with a function u and go from that to a varied function $u + \delta u$, where both u and δu are functions of the variables x_i, and where δu is considered to be small of the first order. We can find the change in $(H)_{av}$ made by this change in u by using Eq. (5-1). We must remember that an arbitrary change in u will in general destroy its normalization and that Eq. (5-1) is not correct for an unnormalized function. More generally, if u is unnormalized, then the corresponding normalized function is $u/(\int u^*u\, dv)^{1/2}$. Then, if we use this function, we find that

$$(H)_{av} = \frac{\int u^*(H)_{op}u\, dv}{\int u^*u\, dv} \qquad (5\text{-}2)$$

We now replace u by $u + \delta u$, let the corresponding value of average energy be $(H)_{av} + \delta(H)_{av}$, and solve for $\delta(H)_{av}$, discarding terms of the second or higher order in the small quantities. We find

$$\delta(H)_{av} = \frac{\int (u^* + \delta u^*)(H)_{op}(u + \delta u)\, dv}{\int (u^* + \delta u^*)(u + \delta u)\, dv} - (H)_{av}$$
$$= \int \delta u^*\, (H)_{op} u\, dv + \int u^*(H)_{op}\, \delta u\, dv$$
$$- (H)_{av}(\int \delta u^* u\, dv + \int u^*\, \delta u\, dv) + \text{higher terms}\qquad(5\text{-}3)$$

in which we have assumed that the unvaried function u was normalized. We wish to set $\delta(H)_{av}$ equal to zero, for our variation principle. In doing this, we make use of the fact that $(H)_{op}$ is Hermitian, which implies, as we show in Appendix 7, that $\int u^*(H)_{op}\, \delta u\, dv$ equals $\int \delta u\, (H)_{op}^* u^*\, dv$, or is the complex conjugate of $\int \delta u^*\, (H)_{op} u\, dv$. Then we can write our variation principle in the form

$$\int \delta u^*\, [(H)_{op} - (H)_{av}]u\, dv + \text{complex conjugate} = 0\qquad(5\text{-}4)$$

In Eq. (5-4) we have the statement that a certain quantity $\int \delta u^*\, [(H)_{op} - (H)_{av}]u\, dv$ plus its conjugate is zero. We satisfy this by letting the quantity itself equal zero, which automatically means that its conjugate also equals zero. We then have the integral of a perfectly arbitrary variation function δu^*, multiplied by another function $[(H)_{op} - (H)_{av}]u$, equal to zero. This cannot be satisfied for all values of the coordinates unless the function $[(H)_{op} - (H)_{av}]u$ is everywhere zero. But this demands that

$$(H)_{op}u = (H)_{av}u\qquad(5\text{-}5)$$

which is Schrödinger's equation, when we remember that the eigenvalue E of Schrödinger's equation is equal to $(H)_{av}$. Hence we have proved that the imposition of the variation principle leads to eigenfunctions u which are solutions of Schrödinger's equation, so that the variation principle is merely an alternative formulation of Schrödinger's equation.

There is another slightly different way of applying the variation principle to this problem, leading to the same answer, but proving more convenient in the use which we shall later make of the method. This is the method of undetermined multipliers, a method used when we wish to make the variation of a certain integral equal to zero, subject to the auxiliary condition that another integral (or integrals) should remain constant. In our present case, we wish to vary u so as to make $(H)_{av}$ stationary, subject to the condition that the normalization integral $\int u^* u\, dv$ should remain constant, equal to unity.

If we wish to accomplish this, the method of undetermined multipliers states that we are to set up a linear combination of all the integrals concerned, with undetermined multipliers, and set the variation of this linear combination equal to zero. That is, if integrals $I_0, I_1, \ldots, I_k$ are all to have simultaneously zero variation, we set

$$\delta(I_0 + \lambda_1 I_1 + \lambda_2 I_2 + \cdots + \lambda_k I_k) = 0 \qquad (5\text{-}6)$$

where the λ's are constants whose values are to be determined later. If this equation is satisfied, then we see that for any variations which make $\delta I_1 = 0$, $\delta I_2 = 0$, . . . , $\delta I_k = 0$, we shall necessarily have $\delta I_0 = 0$, which is what we require.

In our present case, we have

$$\delta[(H)_{\text{av}} + \lambda \int u^* u \, dv] = 0 \qquad (5\text{-}7)$$

As in Eqs. (5-3) and (5-4), we can write $\delta(H)_{\text{av}}$ as the sum of a quantity and its complex conjugate, and we can do the same for $\delta \int u^* u \, dv$. As before, we can set this quantity alone equal to zero, which amounts to varying u^* in the integrals and leaving u unchanged. That is, we can rewrite Eq. (5-7) in the form

$$\int \delta u^* [(H)_{\text{op}} + \lambda] u \, dv + \text{complex conjugate} = 0 \qquad (5\text{-}8)$$

Then, just as in the derivation of Eq. (5-5), we may conclude that the variation principle demands that

$$(H)_{\text{op}} u = -\lambda u \qquad (5\text{-}9)$$

which again is Schrödinger's equation. We furthermore see that the undetermined coefficient λ is necessarily equal to $-(H)_{\text{av}}$.

We have now proved the variation method and have shown that, if the function u is capable of completely flexible variation, the functions which satisfy the variation principle form solutions of Schrödinger's equation. This method has been used for the most accurate approximate solutions of Schrödinger's equation which we possess. As we shall show in the next section, it can be made the foundation of one of the most useful procedures for setting up approximate solutions of Schrödinger's equation: the process of approximating the solution as a linear combination of a number of functions, the coefficients being the parameters to be determined by variation methods.

5-2. The Expansion of the Wave Function in Orthogonal Functions. Any arbitrary function, and therefore in particular a solution of Schrödinger's equation, can be expanded as a series of any convenient complete set of orthonormal functions. We can then convert the problem of solving Schrödinger's equation into that of finding the coefficients of the expansion, an algebraic problem. Thus, let one of the true solutions of Schrödinger's equation, u, be expanded in series in a given complete orthonormal set of functions u_k^0. We can write

$$u = \Sigma(k) C_k u_k^0 \qquad (5\text{-}10)$$

We note that if we calculate the matrix components of the Hamiltonian with respect to these wave functions, which we may denote as

$$H^0_{nm} = \int u^0_n{}^*(H)_{op}u^0_m \, dv \qquad (5\text{-}11)$$

the matrix will not be diagonal, for the u^0's are not solutions of Schrödinger's equation. Our problem is now to find the expansion coefficients C_k.

Let us express one of the true solutions of Schrödinger's equation in the form of Eq. (5-10) and substitute this quantity into Schrödinger's equation, $(H)_{op}u = Eu$. We multiply on the left by one of the functions $u^0_n{}^*$ and integrate over the coordinate space. We take advantage of the orthonormal character of the u^0's, use the definition of Eq. (5-11), and find

$$\Sigma(k)C_k(H^0_{nk} - E\delta_{nk}) = 0 \qquad (5\text{-}12)$$

We have an infinite number of simultaneous equations of the type of Eq. (5-12), obtained by giving n all possible values. That is, the equations when written out have the form

$$\begin{aligned}
C_1(H^0_{11} - E) + C_2H^0_{12} + C_3H^0_{13} + \cdots &= 0 \\
C_1H^0_{21} + C_2(H^0_{22} - E) + C_3H^0_{23} + \cdots &= 0 \\
C_1H^0_{31} + C_2H^0_{32} + C_3(H^0_{33} - E) + \cdots &= 0 \\
\cdots\cdots\cdots\cdots\cdots\cdots\cdots\cdots\cdots\cdots
\end{aligned} \qquad (5\text{-}13)$$

If we could solve the algebraic equations, Eq. (5-12) or (5-13), for the C_k's and the eigenvalue E, we should have the solution of our problem. With an infinite set of unperturbed functions, this is not practicable. If the series of Eq. (5-10) converges moderately rapidly, however, we can choose a finite set of functions u^0_k, where k goes from 1 to an upper limit M, in terms of which we can get a moderately satisfactory description of our wave function. We then ask how to determine the coefficients C_k in this case. For this purpose it is natural to use the variation principle: we are expressing the functions in terms of the parameters C_k, and we vary these to make the average energy stationary. This will give the best approximation to a solution of Schrödinger's equation which we can get in the assumed form of a linear combination of our M functions.

If we approximate u in the form of Eq. (5-10), using now a finite summation from $k = 1$ to M, we can write the energy and normalization integrals for the function u in the following form:

$$(H)_{av} = \Sigma(n,k)C^*_n C_k H^0_{nk} \qquad (5\text{-}14)$$

$$\int u^*u \, dv = \overline{\Sigma}(n)C^*_n C_n \qquad (5\text{-}15)$$

We can then vary the functions by changing C_n into $C_n + dC_n$, and so on, and substitute in Eq. (5-7). We proceed as in the derivation of Eq. (5-8), again using the Hermitian character of the Hamiltonian, and find

$$\delta[(H)_{av} + \lambda\int u^*u \; dv] = 0$$
$$= \Sigma(n,k) \; dC_n^* \; C_k(H_{nk}^0 + \lambda\delta_{nk}) + \text{conjugate} \quad (5\text{-}16)$$

Since the quantities dC_n^* are perfectly arbitrary, the coefficient of each must be zero. That is, we have the equations

$$\Sigma(k)C_k(H_{nk}^0 + \lambda\delta_{nk}) = 0 \quad\quad\quad (5\text{-}17)$$

where now the summation over k runs from 1 to M, and where we have M separate equations, for each value of n from 1 to M. We see that Eqs. (5-17) are identical with Eq. (5-12) or (5-13), provided as before we set the coefficient λ equal to $-E$, and provided we now understand that the summations run only from 1 to M.

In other words, we have found that Eq. (5-12) or (5-13), which we formerly derived by taking the general expansion of the eigenfunction in a series of a complete set of orthonormal functions, is the same set of equations which we get by breaking off the expansion at M terms, choosing the coefficients of this finite expansion so as to satisfy the variation principle, and then passing to the limit as M becomes infinite. As we have stated, in practical cases we must limit ourselves to a finite value of M, and it is simpler to describe the solutions of Eq. (5-12) or (5-13) in this case of finite M, since then we can use our knowledge of the algebra of a finite number of simultaneous linear equations.

In Eq. (5-12) or (5-13), for the case of M functions, we have a set of M simultaneous algebraic linear equations for the M constants C_k, $k = 1, \ldots, M$. These are homogeneous linear equations: there are terms linear in the C's, but no constant terms independent of the C's. Such a set of equations in general has no solutions, other than $C_k = 0$. To see the reason for this, we can divide Eqs. (5-17) by one of the C's, say C_1. Then only the ratios C_k/C_1 appear in the equations. There are $M - 1$ of these ratios. We have M equations for $M - 1$ unknowns, and these in general are incompatible. It is shown in algebra that the equations will be compatible with each other only in case a special condition is satisfied, namely, that the determinant of coefficients vanish, as follows:

$$\det |H_{nk}^0 - E\delta_{nk}| = 0 \quad\quad\quad (5\text{-}18)$$

where the rows and columns of the determinant are given by using the various values of the indices n and k. To see why this should be the condition of compatibility, let us remind the reader of a few facts about the solution of simultaneous linear equations in algebra.

Suppose we have M simultaneous linear equations for M unknowns $C_1, \ldots, C_M$, of the form

$$a_{11}C_1 + a_{12}C_2 + \cdots + a_{1M}C_M = b_1$$
$$a_{21}C_1 + a_{22}C_2 + \cdots + a_{2M}C_M = b_2$$
$$\cdots\cdots\cdots\cdots\cdots\cdots\cdots\cdots\cdots$$
$$a_{M1}C_1 + a_{M2}C_2 + \cdots + a_{MM}C_M = b_M$$
$$(5\text{-}19)$$

These form the general case of simultaneous linear equations. In Eq. (5-13), the a's are obviously given by the equation $a_{nk} = H_{nk}^0 - E\delta_{nk}$. Our case of Eq. (5-13) is the special one where the b's are zero. Now the general solution of Eq. (5-19) for the C's is well known from algebra and can be written in terms of determinants. For C_1, for instance, we have

$$C_1 = \frac{\begin{vmatrix} b_1 & a_{12} & \cdots & a_{1M} \\ b_2 & a_{22} & \cdots & a_{2M} \\ \cdots\cdots\cdots\cdots\cdots\cdots \\ b_M & a_{M2} & \cdots & a_{MM} \end{vmatrix}}{\begin{vmatrix} a_{11} & a_{12} & \cdots & a_{1M} \\ a_{21} & a_{22} & \cdots & a_{2M} \\ \cdots\cdots\cdots\cdots\cdots\cdots \\ a_{M1} & a_{M2} & \cdots & a_{MM} \end{vmatrix}} \qquad (5\text{-}20)$$

The similar equation for any of the other C's is obtained by replacing the appropriate column of a's in the determinant in the numerator by the b's.

The general solution of Eq. (5-20) is not applicable in our case of the homogeneous equations. The reason is seen at once by considering the determinant in the numerator of Eq. (5-20) in case all the b's are zero, as they are if the equations are homogeneous. In this case the determinant is zero, for each one of the products out of which the determinant is constructed contains one of the b's as a factor. Thus we should conclude that all the C's were zero, except in one special case: that in which the determinant in the denominator was also zero. In that case the C's would be indeterminate, each equal to the ratio $0:0$, and they could well be different from zero. In other words, our homogeneous case has no nonvanishing solutions unless the determinant of coefficients is zero, the condition which we have stated for our case in Eq. (5-18).

The determinantal equation, Eq. (5-18), is often called the secular equation. The reason for this comes from a problem in celestial mechanics. It is common to solve the problems of the perturbations of the planetary orbits by other planets by a perturbation method, applied to classical mechanics of oscillating systems, which has a considerable analogy to our present methods. In place of E, the equation similar to Eq. (5-18) gives the perturbed frequencies of oscillation. Sometimes these perturbations lead to frequencies which, instead of being real, are pure imaginary; that is, the oscillations, instead of being given by an oscillatory term like $\exp(i\omega t)$, are given by a real exponential, $\exp(at)$, increasing exponentially with the time. Such an exponential increase, denoting an unstable situation, is called a secular perturbation, and the equation analogous to Eq. (5-18) tells us which perturbations are secular. It is from this use that the term "secular equation" arose. Equations similar to this are met in many branches of mathematical physics.

The secular equation, Eq. (5-18) in our case, is an algebraic equation of the Mth degree and as such has M roots. We can see this more clearly if we write out the equation. It is

$$
\begin{vmatrix}
H_{11}^0 - E & H_{12}^0 & \cdots & H_{1M}^0 \\
H_{21}^0 & H_{22}^0 - E & \cdots & H_{2M}^0 \\
\cdots\cdots\cdots\cdots\cdots\cdots\cdots\cdots\cdots \\
H_{M1}^0 & H_{M2}^0 & \cdots & H_{MM}^0 - E
\end{vmatrix} = 0 \qquad (5\text{-}21)
$$

We remember that the determinant is defined as follows: We take all possible products of M elements, choosing only one from each row, one from each column; there are $M!$ such products. We give each a coefficient ± 1, according as the number of transpositions of rows or columns required to bring this product into the principal diagonal is even or odd, and add the products with their appropriate coefficients. We see, then, that the term with the highest power of E is found by multiplying the terms on the principal diagonal and that we shall in fact have a term $(-E)^M$ as the leading term in the expansion of the determinant in descending powers of E. We thus prove our statement that Eq. (5-21) is an algebraic equation of the Mth degree.

The roots of the secular equation are called the eigenvalues of the algebraic problem, and we see that, if we use M basis functions, we find M eigenvalues. There is a theorem in algebra which states that the eigenvalues of an equation such as Eq. (5-21) are all real, provided the matrix components are Hermitian, as the Hamiltonian is. We may, if we choose, number the eigenvalues in order of increasing value, E_m, where m is the ordinal number of the eigenvalue. For each of the M eigenvalues, we can solve Eq. (5-13) for a set of coefficients C_{km}, which then form the expansion coefficients of the corresponding function u_m in series in the u_k^0's, according to Eq. (5-10). This expansion, of course, will not give an exact solution of Schrödinger's equation for a finite value of M, but by letting M approach infinity, we can approach the true expansion of a solution of Schrödinger's equation in a complete set of functions u_k^0, $k = 1, \ldots, \infty$.

The lowest eigenvalue of Eq. (5-18) will be the best approximation to the true eigenvalue of the ground state obtainable by using as approximate eigenfunction the linear combination of the M functions u_k^0, $k = 1$, $\ldots$, M, and as we have seen from our earlier discussion, it must necessarily lie higher than the true eigenvalue of the ground state. As we let

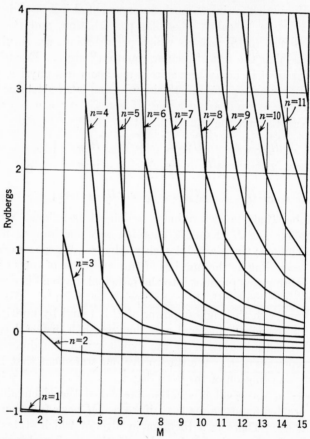

FIG. 5-1. Approximate eigenvalues of the $1s$ states of the hydrogen problem, computed from secular equations with M rows and columns, using a set of orthonormal functions constructed as follows: we take functions $\exp(-ar)$, $r\exp(-ar)$, $r^2\exp(-ar)$, . . . , $r^{M-1}\exp(-ar)$ and orthogonalize them by the Schmidt process. In the case illustrated, a was taken to be $2\frac{7}{32}$, in atomic units. The correct eigenvalues are $-1/n^2$ Rydbergs. It will be observed that, even with 15 orthogonal functions, only the states for $n = 1, 2, 3, 4$ have moderately accurate eigenvalues. The scale of the diagram does not allow showing the higher eigenvalues of the secular problems, for M greater than 4. (The author is indebted to Dr. F. J. Corbato for computing these eigenvalues on the Whirlwind digital computer at MIT.)

M become greater and greater, adding more and more functions u_k^0 to our series, this lowest eigenvalue of the determinantal equation, Eq. (5-18), will gradually become lower, eventually approaching the true ground-state eigenvalue as closely as we please. One can show from the theory of determinants that in a similar way the nth eigenvalue of the determinantal equation, Eq. (5-18), with finite M, will lie higher than the nth true eigenvalue of the problem but will also approach the true value as M becomes infinite.[1]

As an illustration of this behavior, we show in Fig. 5-1 a calculation, which was made purely for the sake of providing an example, in which the true eigenfunctions of the hydrogen atom were expanded in terms of a set of functions which were not particularly appropriate for the purpose. We see the way in which the ground state, $n = 1$, is well described by only about three terms of the series. We get a good value for the next state, $n = 2$, with $M = 4$, but it requires about 10 terms to give a good value for $n = 3$ and about 15 for $n = 4$. Even with 20 terms, which is as far as the calculation was carried, the $n = 5$ term was not very well represented.

It is clear from the example we have just given that, in using this determinantal method, we are faced with serious algebraic difficulties in solving the secular equation. Of course, if we have only two functions, it is a quadratic equation; this case is discussed in the next section. For three or four functions, there are formulas for solving the algebraic equation; in Appendix 8 we give the form which the solution of the cubic equation by formula takes for the secular problem. But if we must go further than this, present technique favors solving the problem by means of digital computers. They can, for instance, relatively easily handle a determinantal equation with 20 rows and columns (often referred to as a 20×20 secular equation), and some of them have been programmed for secular equations approaching 50×50, but this represents a great effort, not only in the solution of the secular equation, but in the computation of the matrix components H_{nk}^0. Thus our practical interest is in finite sets of basis functions, and we hope that we can find such finite sets in terms of which the true wave functions can be approximated with reasonable accuracy.

5-3. The Secular Problem with Two Eigenfunctions. For many purposes we are dealing with a fairly large value of M and with solution of the secular equation by means of computers. However, our understanding of the problem is much enhanced if we study the case of small M and cases in which we can get approximate solutions of the secular problem by simple methods. The first case which we shall take up is that of $M = 2$, where we can get the exact solution of the secular problem as the solution of a quadratic, and yet where many of the problems met in more complicated cases are encountered.

Here the equations for the C's, Eq. (5-13), reduce to

$$
\begin{aligned}
C_1(H_{11}^0 - E) + C_2 H_{12}^0 &= 0 \\
C_1 H_{21}^0 + C_2(H_{22}^0 - E) &= 0
\end{aligned}
\tag{5-22}
$$

[1] For proof, see E. A. Hylleraas and B. Undheim, *Z. Physik*, **65**:759 (1930).

where we have omitted the second subscript m on the C_{km}'s and the subscript m on E_m. We shall restore these subscripts as soon as we have solved the secular problem, using $m = 1$ for the state of lower energy, $m = 2$ for that of higher energy. For the sake of definiteness, we shall assume that $H_{11}^0 \leq H_{22}^0$.

We now notice that we can divide each equation by C_1, so that there is only one quantity, C_2/C_1, which is unknown, in addition to E. With two equations, we can solve for these two quantities; but obviously we cannot find C_1 and C_2 separately, but only their ratio. This is natural; Schrödinger's equation cannot determine the functions uniquely, but only to an arbitrary factor, which must be determined by normalization. The easiest way to solve the simultaneous equations, Eq. (5-22), is to set up the ratio C_2/C_1 from each and equate them. That is, we have

$$\frac{C_2}{C_1} = -\frac{H_{11}^0 - E}{H_{12}^0} = -\frac{H_{21}^0}{H_{22}^0 - E} \tag{5-23}$$

Using the last two, we have

$$(H_{11}^0 - E)(H_{22}^0 - E) - H_{12}^0 H_{21}^0 = 0 \tag{5-24}$$

This is a quadratic for E, and if we multiply it out and solve it by formula, we find

$$E = \frac{H_{11}^0 + H_{22}^0}{2} \pm \sqrt{\left(\frac{H_{22}^0 - H_{11}^0}{2}\right)^2 + H_{12}^0 H_{21}^0} \tag{5-25}$$

In Eq. (5-25) we have an expression for the two values of E, arising from the two signs of the square root. We have already stated that we shall denote the lower one, or that with the minus sign, as E_1 and the upper one, with the plus sign, as E_2, so that

$$E_1 = \frac{H_{11}^0 + H_{22}^0}{2} - \sqrt{\left(\frac{H_{22}^0 - H_{11}^0}{2}\right)^2 + H_{12}^0 H_{21}^0}$$

$$E_2 = \frac{H_{11}^0 + H_{22}^0}{2} + \sqrt{\left(\frac{H_{22}^0 - H_{11}^0}{2}\right)^2 + H_{12}^0 H_{21}^0} \tag{5-26}$$

Now that E_m has been determined, for $m = 1, 2$, we can substitute in Eq. (5-23) and find the ratio C_{2m}/C_{1m}, for $m = 1, 2$, and hence can find the eigenfunctions as well as the eigenvalues. We note that Eq. (5-24), for determining the energy, is identical with Eq. (5-18), for the expression on the left of Eq. (5-24) is just the determinant of coefficients. We also note that, since the Hamiltonian has a Hermitian matrix, $H_{21}^0 = H_{12}^{0*}$, so that the product $H_{12}^0 H_{21}^0$ is the product of a complex quantity and its conjugate, which equals the square of its absolute value, and is necessarily positive. Hence the square root in Eq. (5-26) is the square root of a positive quantity, verifying in this special case that the roots E_1 and

E_2 are real. We see, in other words, how our special case of $M = 2$ falls in with the general scheme outlined in the preceding section.

There are several interesting special cases of our problem in which we can get simple solutions. First, if the nondiagonal matrix component H_{12}^0 equals zero, then we expect that our original functions u_1^0 and u_2^0 themselves represent the two best approximations to solutions of Schrödinger's equations which we can set up as linear combinations of these two functions. In this case, Eq. (5-26) leads to $E_1 = H_{11}^0$, $E_2 = H_{22}^0$, and when we substitute these values in Eq. (5-23), we find $C_{21}/C_{11} = 0$, $C_{22}/C_{12} = \infty$. That is, $C_{21} = 0$, $C_{12} = 0$, as we can see more directly from Eq. (5-22). For normalization, we must then have C_{11}, C_{22} each equal to unity, in absolute magnitude; the phase is not determined by the normalization condition. We thus verify that our earlier statement was true, that u_1^0 and u_2^0 formed the best approximations of the type which we are considering.

A second interesting special case is that of degeneracy: the case where $H_{11}^0 = H_{22}^0$. Here we have

$$E_1 = H_{11}^0 - |H_{12}^0|$$
$$E_2 = H_{11}^0 + |H_{12}^0|$$
$$\frac{C_{21}}{C_{11}} = -\frac{|H_{12}^0|}{H_{12}^0} = -\frac{H_{21}^0}{|H_{12}^0|} \tag{5-27}$$
$$\frac{C_{22}}{C_{12}} = \frac{|H_{12}^0|}{H_{12}^0} = \frac{H_{21}^0}{|H_{12}^0|}$$

In other words, if the diagonal matrix components of the two states are identical with respect to the original wave functions, the eigenvalues will be spread apart when we make linear combinations of the two functions by $\pm$ the magnitude of the nondiagonal matrix component of energy between the states. And the resultant wave functions will be linear combinations of the two original wave functions in which the two coefficients have the same absolute magnitude, though different phases. The simplest case is that in which H_{12}^0 is real and positive, in which case

$$u_1 = (2)^{-\frac{1}{2}}(u_1^0 - u_2^0)$$
$$u_2 = (2)^{-\frac{1}{2}}(u_1^0 + u_2^0) \tag{5-28}$$

where the factor $(2)^{-\frac{1}{2}}$ is required for normalization. That is, the wave functions are proportional to the sum and difference of the original functions.

As a somewhat more general case, we take that in which H_{12}^0 is small compared with the difference $H_{22}^0 - H_{11}^0$ of the diagonal matrix components. This is the case usually known as that of a perturbation, for the following reason: There are many problems in which one term in the Hamiltonian can be considered as a perturbation. We assume that we can solve the unperturbed problem, which lacks the perturbing term in the Hamiltonian. We then choose for the functions u_m^0 the solutions of Schrödinger's equation for the unperturbed problem. We must find the matrix components of the true Hamiltonian of the problem with respect to these unperturbed wave functions. The unperturbed Hamiltonian has no nondiagonal matrix components with respect to these unperturbed wave functions, by hypothesis, so that the nondiagonal matrix components must arise only from the perturbative terms in the Hamiltonian, and therefore they will be small if the perturbation is small.

In such a case, provided the energy differences $H_{22}^0 - H_{11}^0$ arising from the unperturbed Hamiltonian are large—that is, provided the unperturbed problem is not degenerate—we can expand the solution in power series in H_{12}^0 or, more generally, in the nondiagonal matrix components of energy. We can do this explicitly in our case of $M = 2$ by expanding the square roots of Eq. (5-26) in binomial series. We find

$$E_1 = H_{11}^0 + \frac{|H_{12}^0|^2}{H_{11}^0 - H_{22}^0} - \frac{|H_{12}^0|^4}{(H_{11}^0 - H_{22}^0)^3} + \cdots$$

$$E_2 = H_{22}^0 + \frac{|H_{21}^0|^2}{H_{22}^0 - H_{11}^0} - \frac{|H_{21}^0|^4}{(H_{22}^0 - H_{11}^0)^3} + \cdots$$

$$(5\text{-}29)$$

The series converges only when $|H_{12}^0| < H_{22}^0 - H_{11}^0$, and for rapid convergence we should have $|H_{12}^0|$ quite small compared with $H_{22}^0 - H_{11}^0$. Thus the series method diverges long before we approach the situation of degeneracy. The first term in the expressions of Eq. (5-29) is referred to as coming from first-order perturbation theory, stating that to this order of approximation the energy equals the average value of the correct Hamiltonian averaged over the unperturbed wave function. The next term is called the second-order perturbation, the last one written in Eq. (5-29) the fourth-order perturbation. A great deal of use is made of the second-order term, but not much of the fourth order term.

From Eq. (5-29) we can see that the effect of the perturbation is to push the energies of the two states apart, in the sense that the second-order term in E_1 is necessarily negative, that in E_2 necessarily positive, so that E_1 is less than H_{11}^0, E_2 greater than H_{22}^0. This is consistent with the following variation principle: making a linear combination of the two functions u_1^0 and u_2^0 has resulted in a wave function u_1 whose eigenvalue E_1 is lower than the value H_{11}^0 arising from the function u_1^0 alone. We note further that the average value of E_1 and E_2 equals the average of H_{11}^0 and H_{22}^0, or, stated differently, the sum of the unperturbed energies H_{11}^0 and H_{22}^0 equals the sum of the perturbed energies $E_1 + E_2$. We can see this directly from the quadratic solutions of Eq. (5-26), and we shall shortly prove that this is a special case of a general sum rule holding for any value of M. In our particular case of $M = 2$, this means that E_2 is as much greater than H_{22}^0 as E_1 is less than H_{11}^0.

The wave functions u_1 and u_2, which we may call the perturbed wave functions, can be found by use of Eq. (5-23). Their values, correct to the same approximation as the second-order perturbation of the energy, are

$$u_1 = u_1^0 + \frac{H_{21}^0}{H_{11}^0 - H_{22}^0} u_2^0 - \cdots$$

$$u_2 = u_2^0 + \frac{H_{12}^0}{H_{22}^0 - H_{11}^0} u_1^0 - \cdots$$

$$(5\text{-}30)$$

The effect of the perturbation, then, is to modify each unperturbed wave function by adding to it a small amount of the unperturbed wave function associated with the other stationary state. The coefficient of this other function is proportional to the nondiagonal matrix component of energy between the two states and inversely proportional to the energy difference between them. Thus, the closer the two unperturbed energy levels, and the larger the nondiagonal matrix component between them, the greater will be the perturbation. A perturbation, then, in a sense mixes up the unperturbed wave functions. We shall find this same situation to hold in the general case, and it gives us a valuable physical insight into the effect of perturbations and the way in which a real stationary state can be, in a sense, a mixture of several unperturbed states.

5-4. The Perturbation Method in the General Case. We have been able to give a complete discussion of the problem for two unperturbed functions, $M = 2$. For the case of arbitrary M, we cannot go so far, but still we can carry through the problem of second-order perturbations, even in this general case, in the following way: Suppose we are interested in finding the approximate values of u_m and E_m, for a particular m. We write Eq. (5-12), for the function u_m, and discard all nondiagonal matrix components H_{nk}^0 for which n and k are both different from m; further examination shows that these matrix components enter only in the next higher approximation. Then the equations become

$$(H_{nn}^0 - E_m)C_{nm} + H_{nm}^0 C_{mm} = 0 \qquad n \neq m \qquad (5\text{-}31)$$

$$\Sigma(k)C_{km}(H_{mk}^0 - E_m\delta_{mk}) = 0 \qquad\qquad (5\text{-}32)$$

From Eq. (5-31), we have

$$C_{nm} = C_{mm} \frac{H_{nm}^0}{E_m - H_{nn}^0} \qquad n \neq m \qquad (5\text{-}33)$$

and when we substitute Eq. (5-33) in Eq. (5-32), we have

$$(H_{mm}^0 - E_m) + \sum (k \neq m) \frac{H_{mk}^0 H_{km}^0}{E_m - H_{kk}^0} = 0 \qquad (5\text{-}34)$$

or
$$E_m = H_{mm}^0 + \sum (k \neq m) \frac{|H_{mk}^0|^2}{E_m - H_{kk}^0} \qquad (5\text{-}35)$$

If we are working only to the order of second-order perturbations, we can replace E_m, in the second term of Eq. (5-35), by its approximate value H^0_{mm} and get the approximate result

$$E_m = H^0_{mm} + \sum (k \neq m) \frac{|H^0_{mk}|^2}{H^0_{mm} - H^0_{kk}} + \cdots \qquad (5\text{-}36)$$

In Eq. (5-36) we have the general form for the energy in second-order perturbations; we observe that Eq. (5-29), for $M = 2$, forms a special case of it.

We see from Eq. (5-36) that the effect of the nondiagonal matrix components of the energy is to push the energy levels apart. The first approximation to E_m, as before, is H^0_{mm}. Each of the states whose diagonal energy lies above H^0_{mm} contributes a negative term to Eq. (5-36), or tends to push the energy down, while each one whose diagonal energy lies below H^0_{mm} tends to push the energy up. Just as for the case $M = 2$, the lowest energy level will always be pushed down by the perturbation. We must be on our guard, however, against using the second-order formula of Eq. (5-36) in cases where it does not apply, that is, where the perturbation terms are large enough so that further terms in the series are appreciable. The series of Eq. (5-36) is an alternating series, as in the case of $M = 2$, Eq. (5-29), so that if we use only second-order perturbations, we shall generally get too low a value for the energy of the lowest state, in some cases lower than the true energy; the further terms in the series would raise this value to the correct point.

From Eq. (5-33), we can get the perturbed wave functions, correct to the same approximation as Eq. (5-36). The wave function can be written

$$u_m = u^0_m + \sum (k \neq m) \frac{H^0_{km}}{E_m - H^0_{kk}} u^0_k \qquad (5\text{-}37)$$

which can be approximated, corresponding to Eq. (5-36), as

$$u_m = u^0_m + \sum (k \neq m) \frac{H^0_{km}}{H^0_{mm} - H^0_{kk}} u^0_k + \cdots \qquad (5\text{-}38)$$

To the first order of approximation, u_m of Eq. (5-38) is normalized. Each perturbing term, as we see, makes a contribution to the perturbed wave function, which is proportional to the nondiagonal matrix component of energy between the two states, divided by the difference of diagonal energy between them.

We have mentioned earlier the sum rule: the fact that the sum of the diagonal matrix components of energy with respect to the unperturbed wave functions equals the sum of the eigenvalues of the perturbed problem, which means that the perturbations have pushed the energy levels apart but have not altered their center of gravity. We can easily give the rigorous proof of this result; that is, we can prove that

$$\Sigma(k)H_{kk}^0 = \Sigma(k)E_k \tag{5-39}$$

where the summation goes from 1 to M. To prove this, we write the determinant of Eq. (5-21) in descending powers of E. The terms of the highest, and next highest, order in E are all derived from the product of terms along the principal diagonal; we have

$$(-E)^M + (-E)^{M-1}\Sigma(k)H_{kk}^0 + \cdots = 0 \tag{5-40}$$

But we know that an algebraic equation of the Mth degree can be written in the form

$$C(E - E_1)(E - E_2) \cdots (E - E_M) = 0 \tag{5-41}$$

where C is a constant and E_1, E_2, . . . , E_M are the roots. Let us expand this equation, like Eq. (5-40), in descending powers of E. We have

$$CE^M - CE^{M-1}\Sigma(k)E_k + \cdots = 0 \tag{5-42}$$

To make the terms in E^M agree, we must have $C = (-1)^M$. Then Eqs. (5-42) and (5-40) must agree identically, which means that the terms in E^{M-1} must agree. This leads at once to Eq. (5-39). This result is sometimes called the diagonal sum rule.

We derived Eqs. (5-33) and (5-35) as steps in the process of deriving the second-order perturbation calculation; but we notice that these two equations gave exact solutions of the secular problem, for the case where the only nonvanishing nondiagonal matrix components of energy were those for which either n or k, in the term H_{nk}^0, was equal to m. This case is called that of a bordered determinant, and the exact solution can be very useful in some cases.

Thus, suppose we have solved the secular problem for a set of $M - 1$ unperturbed functions and have set up functions u_1^0, . . . , u_{M-1}^0, such that the matrix of the energy with respect to these $M - 1$ functions is diagonal. Let us now add the Mth function, u_M^0, to the list of functions in terms of which we are expanding the correct eigenfunction. The only nonvanishing nondiagonal matrix components of energy will be those for which n or k equals M. Thus, in the determinant of Eq. (5-21), the only nonvanishing matrix components will be along the principal diagonal and in the right-hand column and the bottom row, which is the reason for the name bordered determinant. We can now solve this $M \times M$ secular equation exactly for E_M by use of Eq. (5-35). Since E_M appears on both sides of the equation, we can best solve it by iteration: we use our best guess of E_M (which presumably would be H_{MM}^0) on the right side of the equation, compute a value of E_M from the equation, substitute this computed value on the right, compute again, and so on, continuing until the value of E_M which we substitute on the right equals the result given by the equation. This process is usually not very tedious to apply. In this way, we have found the Mth eigenvalue, and substitution in Eq. (5-33) immediately gives the coefficients for expansion of the Mth eigenfunction.

We can also proceed equally easily to find the other eigenvalues, and hence eigenfunctions, of this problem. In place of Eqs. (5-31) and (5-32), we have

$$(H^0_{nn} - E_m)C_{nm} + H^0_{nM}C_{Mm} = 0 \qquad n \neq M \qquad (5\text{-}43)$$

$$\Sigma(k)C_{km}(H^0_{Mk} - E_m\delta_{Mk}) = 0 \qquad (5\text{-}44)$$

From Eq. (5-43) we have

$$C_{nm} = C_{Mm}\frac{H^0_{nM}}{E_m - H^0_{nn}} \qquad n \neq M \qquad (5\text{-}45)$$

We substitute this in Eq. (5-44) and can write the resulting equation in the form holding when $m \neq M$,

$$E_m = H^0_{mm} + \cfrac{|H^0_{mM}|^2}{E_m - H^0_{MM} - \sum (k \neq m, M)\cfrac{|H^0_{kM}|^2}{E_m - H^0_{kk}}} \qquad (5\text{-}46)$$

The last term in the denominator on the right renders this an exact equation, rather than an approximation. We can solve this by a process of iteration, as we have just described for finding E_M, and when we have found E_m, we can at once find the expansion coefficients of the eigenfunctions u_m from Eq. (5-45).

By this procedure, it is not impractical to find the solution of a secular equation with M rows and columns when we have already diagonalized the energy for the secular equation with $M - 1$ rows and columns. We can then make this a basis of a procedure for solving any secular problem: we proceed by adding one function at a time, each time finding the suitable linear combinations of the unperturbed wave functions to diagonalize the energy. When we have solved for the eigenfunctions of this problem with M rows and columns, for instance, we can use this as a starting point for the problem with $M + 1$ rows and columns, and so on. Though this procedure is not that ordinarily programmed for the digital computers, it is one of the more convenient schemes to use if one must solve a secular equation with a fairly large M value accurately by means of a desk computer.

5-5. Properties of Unitary Transformations. The set of M eigenfunctions u_m, $m = 1, \ldots, M$, which we find from solving our secular problem with M rows and columns, can be proved to be orthogonal to each other, just as are the real eigenfunctions of Schrödinger's equation; the proof is given in Appendix 9. Then the linear transformation from the functions u^0_k to the functions u_m, defined by Eq. (5-10), has the characteristic that it transforms an original set of orthonormal functions u_k^0 to another set of functions u_m which are also orthonormal. Such a transformation is known as a unitary transformation, and we shall investigate some of the properties of such transformations.

In the first place, we are often interested in the inverse transformation to the one given above. Thus, if $u_n = \Sigma(k)C_{kn}u_k^0$, we may wish the coefficients in the transformation $u_n^0 = \Sigma(k)D_{kn}u_k$. We find at once that

$$u_n^0 = \Sigma(k,l)D_{kn}C_{lk}u_l^0 \qquad (5\text{-}47)$$

which demands that

$$\Sigma(k)C_{lk}D_{kn} = \delta_{ln} \qquad (5\text{-}48)$$

This relation, stating that the matrix product of the matrices of C and D is the unit matrix, is used as the definition of a reciprocal or inverse matrix: D is reciprocal or inverse to C and may be denoted as C^{-1}.

We can now easily find the relation between the C's and the C^{-1}'s for the case of the unitary transformation, from the property that the u's and the u^0's are orthonormal. For we can see immediately that

$$\int u_k^{0*}u_n \, dv = C_{kn} \qquad (5\text{-}49)$$

on account of the orthogonality of the u^0's, and similarly

$$\int u_k^* u_n^0 \, dv = (C^{-1})_{kn} \qquad (5\text{-}50)$$

on account of the orthogonality of the u's. But we can now take the conjugate of Eq. (5-49), interchange the subscripts, and find that

$$(C^{-1})_{kn} = C_{nk}^* \qquad (5\text{-}51)$$

The condition of Eq. (5-51) is often used as the definition of a unitary matrix.

We often wish to find the matrix components with respect to the functions u_n of an operator $(F)_{op}$ whose matrix components we know with respect to the basis functions u_k^0. If we use Eq. (5-10), we can prove at once that

$$\begin{aligned} F_{nm} &= \Sigma(k,l)C_{kn}^* F_{kl}^0 C_{lm} \\ &= \Sigma(k,l)(C^{-1})_{nk}F_{kl}^0 C_{lm} \end{aligned} \qquad (5\text{-}52)$$

where F_{nm} represents the matrix components with respect to the u_n's, F_{kl}^0 with respect to the u_k^0's. A transformation of the type of Eq. (5-52) is called a similarity transformation. As a first example, let us consider the consequences of the fact that both the u_n's and the u_k^0's are orthonormal. Thus, let us take as our operator the unit operator, whose matrix components with respect to both sets of functions will be delta functions. If we make this assumption in Eq. (5-52), we have

$$\begin{aligned} \delta_{nm} &= \Sigma(k,l)C_{kn}^* \, \delta_{kl}C_{lm} \\ &= \Sigma(k)C_{kn}^* C_{km} \end{aligned} \qquad (5\text{-}53)$$

But we can interchange the role of the functions u_n and u_k^0 if we also interchange the matrices C_{kn} and $(C^{-1})_{kn}$. That is, we have in addition to Eq. (5-53)

$$\delta_{nm} = \Sigma(k)(C^{-1})_{kn}^*(C^{-1})_{km}$$
$$= \Sigma(k)C_{mk}^*C_{nk} \qquad (5\text{-}54)$$

The two rules of Eqs. (5-53) and (5-54), which hold for any unitary transformations, are frequently useful.

As another example of Eq. (5-52), let us consider the Hamiltonian. From Eq. (5-12), we have $\Sigma(l)H_{kl}^0C_{lm} = E_mC_{km}$. If we substitute this in Eq. (5-52), we have

$$H_{nm} = \Sigma(k)C_{kn}^*E_mC_{km} = E_m\delta_{nm} \qquad (5\text{-}55)$$

where we have used Eq. (5-53). Thus we have verified that the matrix of the Hamiltonian is diagonal with respect to the functions u_n. In other words, our transformation of Eq. (5-10) is one which has made the Hamiltonian into a diagonal matrix, or, as we say, which has diagonalized the Hamiltonian. When we are using a finite set of basis functions, we regard the problem of solving Schrödinger's equation as that of finding the unitary transformation from the basis functions u_k^0 to new functions u_n which diagonalize the Hamiltonian.

In our discussions of the present and the preceding sections, we have not used any properties of the Hamiltonian except its Hermitian nature. We can consequently use similar methods to find a unitary transformation which will diagonalize any other Hermitian operator. The procedure for finding the coefficients of the transformation would be equivalent to the use of Eqs. (5-11) and (5-12), except that we should have another operator in place of H. A question which often arises is: Are there any other operators F which can be diagonalized simultaneously with the Hamiltonian? The answer is that any Hermitian operator which commutes with the Hamiltonian can be diagonalized simultaneously with it. Let us prove this fact.

Let F commute with H, and let us assume that H has a diagonal matrix. Then we can write the commutation relation in the form

$$(FH - HF)_{nm} = 0 = F_{nm}(H_{mm} - H_{nn}) \qquad (5\text{-}56)$$

identical with Eq. (4-40). This tells us that F can have nondiagonal matrix components only between states which are degenerate with each other. But any linear combination of a number of degenerate states is itself a solution of Schrödinger's equation, or still diagonalizes the Hamiltonian. We can always diagonalize a matrix like F_{nm} by making suitable linear combinations of the functions between which it has matrix components. On account of Eq. (5-56), we have just seen that this does not destroy the diagonalization of H, so that we see that we can always diagonalize an operator F which commutes with the Hamiltonian and simultaneously preserve the diagonalization of the Hamiltonian.

On the other hand, suppose we have two operators F and G, each of which commutes with H, but which do not commute with each other. Either F or G can be diagonalized simultaneously with H, but in general they cannot both be diagonalized at the same time, for ordinarily the linear transformation of the degenerate eigenfunctions which is suitable to diagonalize F will not at the same time diagonalize G. The operator which is not diagonalized, then, will obey Eq. (5-56), and since by hypothesis it has nondiagonal matrix components, this means that we must have degeneracy, or there must be eigenvalues H_{mm} and H_{nn} for the energy which are equal to each other and yet which correspond to different eigenfunctions and different values n and m. Hence we see that the existence of noncommuting operators which commute with the energy is intimately tied up with the subject of degeneracy. We shall find an interesting example of this situation in Chap. 11 when we consider the operators representing the angular momentum of a particle on which no torques act. We shall find that the three rectangular components of the angular momentum all commute with the Hamiltonian, so that any one of the components can be diagonalized simultaneously with the Hamiltonian. However, the three components of angular momentum do not commute with each other, so that in general we can diagonalize only one of these components. Closely related to this situation is the degeneracy which we meet with the central-field problem.

PROBLEMS

1. Show that, if we expand the correct wave functions in a series of functions which are not exactly orthogonal or normalized, the equations for the transformation coefficients, equivalent to Eq. (5-12), are

$$\Sigma(k)C_k(H_{nk}^0 - Ed_{nk}) = 0$$

where $d_{nk} = \int u_n^{0*} u_k^0 \, dv$, which now is not diagonal and is not equal to δ_{nk}.

2. Consider a degenerate system in which there are two unperturbed wave functions, each having equal diagonal energies $H_{11}^0 = H_{22}^0$, which are normalized but not orthogonal to each other, so that $d_{12} = \int u_1^{0*} u_2^0 \, dv \neq 0$. Show that the two energy levels arising from the perturbation problem are

$$\frac{H_{11}^0 + H_{12}^0}{1 + d_{12}} \qquad \frac{H_{11}^0 - H_{12}^0}{1 - d_{12}}$$

where it is assumed that H_{12} is real, so that $H_{12} = H_{21}$.

3. Show that the two correct wave functions in Prob. 2 are

$$\frac{u_1^0 + u_2^0}{\sqrt{2(1 + d_{12})}} \qquad \frac{u_1^0 - u_2^0}{\sqrt{2(1 - d_{12})}}$$

respectively. Prove them to be normalized and orthogonal.

4. Assume that you have solved the Schrödinger equation for the lowest eigenfunction of the problem of a potential well of width X, potential energy zero within the well and W outside, as was discussed in Sec. 3-5. Consider how these eigenfunctions can be used to help out in the approximate solution of the problem of two such potential wells, as shown in Fig. 3-6. As two unperturbed functions use the solutions appropriate to each of the wells separately. Make linear combinations of these two solutions to approximate the solution of the problem of two wells. First show that the correct linear combinations of the unperturbed functions are the symmetric and antisymmetric combinations, as mentioned in Sec. 3-5. Find the energies of these states by first-order perturbation theory.

5. Discuss the problem of a particle in three identical and equally spaced potential wells, an extension of the case of two potential wells taken up in Prob. 4, by using the same method of linear combinations of solutions of the separate potential wells. If you proceed directly, you will encounter a cubic secular equation. To avoid having to solve this, note that all solutions may be expected to be either symmetric or antisymmetric in the mid-point of the system of wells. Set up symmetric and antisymmetric combinations of the solutions of the separate wells, and use these as the unperturbed solutions. You will find that there are no matrix components of energy between a symmetric and an antisymmetric function, and this will simplify the problem enough so that you can solve the problem of degeneracy. Draw the form of the correct wave functions found from perturbation theory, discuss their qualitative nature, and find the energy levels.

6. Find whether a rotator's energy is affected, to the first or higher orders of approximation, by a constant external field in the plane of the rotator.

7. Prove by perturbation theory that the energy levels of a linear oscillator are not affected by a constant external field, except in absolute value, all being shifted up or down together. Why should this be expected physically?

8. A linear oscillator is perturbed by having a small perturbative potential ax^3, where x is the displacement from equilibrium. Find the matrix components of the perturbative energy. (*Hint:* you can do this easily by matrix algebra from the matrix components for x found in Sec. 4-6.) Will this perturbation make any first-order change in the energy levels?

9. In Sec. 3-7, it is shown that the wave function for the ground state of the linear oscillator is exp $(-y^2/2)$, where y is given in that section. Suppose you did not know this solution but felt that a function exp $(-cy^2)$, where c is to be determined, might well form an acceptable wave function. Use this function exp $(-cy^2)$, compute the average energy for it, vary c to minimize the energy, and show that the resulting solution is identical with the exact solution of Schrödinger's equation.

10. Carry out the same calculation as in Prob. 9, but for the lowest antisymmetric wave function of the linear oscillator, expressing it in the form y exp $(-cy^2)$, and varying c to minimize the energy.

6

The Interaction of Radiation and Matter

6-1. The Quantization of the Electromagnetic Field. In Sec. 1-3 we
have sketched the development of the quantum theory and have mentioned briefly the origins of Planck's law of black-body radiation. Then
in Sec. 1-5 we have taken up the postulates of Einstein regarding the
probabilities of emission and absorption of radiation, expressed in Eqs.
(1-9) and (1-10). In the present chapter, we wish to treat these problems in much greater detail. So far, our discussion of wave mechanics,
in the preceding three chapters, has dealt entirely with the existence and
properties of stationary states. We must now learn how transitions
between stationary states are to be handled. Since these problems are
tied up so closely with the nature of radiation, and particularly of temperature radiation, we shall start our discussion by giving one of the
important and early derivations of Planck's law: that given by Debye[1]
in 1910. This is a method of treatment, going back originally to Jeans
and his derivation of the Rayleigh-Jeans law, which is particularly suited
for introducing the subject of quantum electrodynamics.

Jeans and Debye started by considering the type of electromagnetic
field which could exist in a rectangular cavity bounded by perfectly
reflecting walls, such as is now used for a microwave cavity. Standing
electromagnetic waves can be set up in such a cavity, and in the absence
of any interaction with matter, each mode can oscillate with an arbitrary
phase and amplitude, with a frequency determined by the wavelength.
If there is any absorbing matter in the cavity, however, electromagnetic
waves will be absorbed by the matter, or emitted by it, until they reach
the intensity characteristic of thermal radiation at the temperature of
the matter. The equilibrium between the radiation and the matter was
studied extensively by Kirchhoff, Planck, and others in the latter days
of the nineteenth century. We shall consider it shortly. But to start
with, let us consider the nature of the electromagnetic field in the empty
cavity.

[1] P. Debye, *Ann. Physik*, **33**:1927 (1910).

Perfectly reflecting walls, for an electromagnetic cavity, are equivalent to perfect conductors. At such a surface, there can be no tangential component of the electric field. The reason is that we can prove from Maxwell's equations that the tangential component of the field is continuous at a surface of discontinuity, so that a tangential component of **E** outside the surface would lead to the existence of an equal tangential component inside the surface, and by Ohm's law the existence of a finite value of **E** inside the perfect conductor would lead to an infinite current density, which is impossible.

Let us assume that the cavity is bounded by walls at $x = 0$, $x = X$, $y = 0$, $y = Y$, $z = 0$, $z = Z$. We must then have $E_x = 0$ when $y = 0$, $y = Y$, $z = 0$, $z = Z$, with corresponding conditions on the other components. An oscillating solution for the electric field E satisfying these conditions is

$$E_x = E_x^0 \cos \frac{n_x \pi x}{X} \sin \frac{n_y \pi y}{Y} \sin \frac{n_z \pi z}{Z} \cos (\omega t - \alpha)$$

$$E_y = E_y^0 \sin \frac{n_x \pi x}{X} \cos \frac{n_y \pi y}{Y} \sin \frac{n_z \pi z}{Z} \cos (\omega t - \alpha) \qquad (6\text{-}1)$$

$$E_z = E_z^0 \sin \frac{n_x \pi x}{X} \sin \frac{n_y \pi y}{Y} \cos \frac{n_z \pi z}{Z} \cos (\omega t - \alpha)$$

where n_x, n_y, n_z are integers. In order that this may satisfy Maxwell's equations, we must have $\nabla \cdot \mathbf{E} = 0$, and **E** must satisfy the wave equation,

$$\nabla^2 \mathbf{E} - \frac{1}{c^2} \frac{\partial^2 \mathbf{E}}{\partial t^2} = 0 \qquad (6\text{-}2)$$

where c is the velocity of light.

The standing-wave solution of Eq. (6-1) is a superposition of eight traveling waves, which could be written in an exponential form,

$$\mathbf{E} = \mathbf{E}^0 \exp [i(\omega t - \alpha - \mathbf{k} \cdot \mathbf{r})] \qquad (6\text{-}3)$$

where **r** is the radius vector, of components x, y, and z, and **k** is a propagation vector, of magnitude $2\pi/\lambda$, where λ is the wavelength, whose x, y, z components are $\pm n_x \pi/X$, $\pm n_y \pi/Y$, $\pm n_z \pi/Z$, respectively. If we take the divergence of Eq. (6-1) and demand that it be zero, we have

$$-\left(\frac{n_x \pi E_x^0}{X} + \frac{n_y \pi E_y^0}{Y} + \frac{n_z \pi E_z^0}{Z} \right) \sin \frac{n_x \pi x}{X} \sin \frac{n_y \pi y}{Y} \sin \frac{n_z \pi z}{Z}$$
$$\times \cos (\omega t - \alpha) = 0 \quad (6\text{-}4)$$

For this equation to be satisfied, we must have the first parentheses equal to zero, which means that the vector of components E_x^0, E_y^0, E_z^0 must be at right angles to the particular vector **k** whose components are $n_x \pi/X$, $n_y \pi/Y$, $n_z \pi/Z$. For the wave equation to be satisfied, we find that we must have the magnitude of **k** equal to ω/c, thus giving the ordinary relation between wavelength and frequency.

The condition that the vector of components E_x^0, E_y^0, E_z^0 be at right angles to **k** can be satisfied in an infinite number of ways. It is the requirement that **E** be a transverse vector, at right angles to the direction of propagation of the wave. For a given vector **k**, we can, however, set up only two independent waves, with two different vectors E_x^0, E_y^0, E_z^0, which must be at right angles to each other, as well as at right angles to **k**. The possibility of these two different vectors corresponds to the two directions of polarization of a transverse wave. Each of these two waves can have an independent amplitude, and phase α, for its oscillation.

If we were dealing with classical mechanics, this is as far as we could go with the free oscillations of the cavity. In quantum theory, however, we must assume that the energy in the electromagnetic field is quantized: it exists as photons, of energy $h\nu$ or $\hbar\omega$. Let us ask how this is to be fitted in with our treatment. A single one of the waves we have been discussing, or a single mode of oscillation, has many analogies to a linear oscillator. It represents an oscillation of frequency ν. It seems very plausible, then, that its energy should be quantized, just as is the energy of an ordinary mechanical oscillator. That is, in the older Bohr theory, we should assume that the energy of such a mode of oscillation was $nh\nu$, where n was a quantum number, or in wave mechanics we should assume that it was $(n + \frac{1}{2})h\nu$. A change of this quantum number by one unit would correspond to a change in the energy of the radiation field of $h\nu$. It is this change of energy which we interpret as the addition of a photon to the radiation field or the removal of a photon. If we use wave mechanics, in which the energy in the mode is $(n + \frac{1}{2})h\nu$, we consider that the energy $\frac{1}{2}h\nu$, ordinarily called the zero-point energy, is simply an additive term in the energy, and no matter which type of theory we use, we consider that the quantum number n, relating to one of the oscillators, measures the number of photons of energy $h\nu$ in that oscillator.

We now see what is necessary according to this picture to carry out a derivation of Planck's law. First, we must find the average energy in one of the modes of oscillation at temperature T. Second, we must find how many of these modes have frequency between ν and $\nu + d\nu$. By combining these two pieces of information, we can find the energy in the range of frequencies between ν and $\nu + d\nu$. In the next two sections we proceed to carry through these calculations.

6-2. Quantum Statistics and the Average Energy of an Oscillator. It is a fundamental principle of statistical mechanics that, if a body is able to interchange energy with an object at a given temperature and is in a steady state, it must have the same temperature as that object. Our radiation field in the cavity, then, if it can interchange energy with some piece of matter in the cavity, will come to the same temperature as that piece of matter. Furthermore, quantum statistics shows that, at a given temperature, a system does not necessarily have a definite energy. Rather, there is a chance of finding it in many different energy levels. But the important practical result of statistical mechanics is the statement regarding the probability of finding the system in a given energy level. This is the statement that the probability of finding an isolated system in an energy level of energy E_i, at absolute temperature T, in thermal equilibrium, is given by the Boltzmann factor,

$$\text{Probability} = \frac{\exp\left(-E_i/kT\right)}{\Sigma(j)\,\exp\left(-E_j/kT\right)} \tag{6-5}$$

where k is Boltzmann's constant.

If the energy E_i is $nh\nu$, then it is very simple to find the average value of the energy or of n, as we have already indicated in Eq. (1-2). We use the weighting factor of Eq. (6-5) and find the weighted mean of the energy. This is

$$\text{Average energy} = \frac{\displaystyle\sum_{n=0}^{\infty} nh\nu \exp\left(-nh\nu/kT\right)}{\displaystyle\sum_{n=0}^{\infty} \exp\left(-nh\nu/kT\right)} \tag{6-6}$$

To evaluate this expression, we note that the denominator is the sum of a geometric series,

$$\sum_{n=0}^{\infty} \exp\left(-nh\nu/kT\right) = 1 + x + x^2 + \cdots$$

$$= \frac{1}{1-x} = \frac{1}{1 - \exp\left(-h\nu/kT\right)} \tag{6-7}$$

where $x = \exp\left(-h\nu/kT\right)$. Similarly the numerator is

$$h\nu(x + 2x^2 + 3x^3 + \cdots) = xh\nu \frac{d}{dx}(1 + x + x^2 + \cdots)$$

$$= xh\nu \frac{d}{dx}(1 - x)^{-1} = \frac{xh\nu}{(1-x)^2} \tag{6-8}$$

Then the average energy of Eq. (6-6) is

$$\text{Average energy} = \frac{xh\nu}{1-x} = \frac{h\nu}{\exp\left(h\nu/kT\right) - 1} \tag{6-9}$$

in agreement with Eq. (1-2). The average value of the quantum number n, or of the number of photons in the mode in question at temperature T, is

$$\text{Average value of } n = \frac{1}{\exp{(h\nu/kT)} - 1} \tag{6-10}$$

If we had used the wave-mechanical value of the energy, $(n + \frac{1}{2})h\nu$, then the average would be the value of Eq. (6-9), increased by $\frac{1}{2}h\nu$.

In Fig. 6-1, we show the average energy, as given by Eq. (6-9), as a function of temperature; we also show the value increased by $\frac{1}{2}h\nu$. It is easy to show, by expanding in power series in $h\nu/kT$, that the energy as given in Eq. (6-9) approaches $kT - \frac{1}{2}h\nu$ at high temperatures; or if we leave the zero-point energy in, so that the average energy is the value

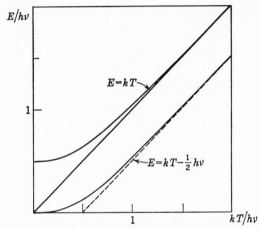

Fig. 6-1. Energy of a linear oscillator as function of temperature. Lower curve, approaching $kT - \frac{1}{2}h\nu$ asymptotically, represents value of Eq. (6-9); upper curve, approaching kT, includes zero-point energy.

given by Eq. (6-9) plus $\frac{1}{2}h\nu$, this average approaches kT at high temperatures. This latter value is the equipartition value given by classical statistics.

6-3. The Distribution of Modes in the Cavity.   To complete our derivation of Planck's law, we must next find the number of resonant modes whose frequency lies between ν and $\nu + d\nu$. According to Eq. (6-1), a resonant mode is described by three positive integers, n_x, n_y, n_z. For each set of n's, there are two independent modes, corresponding to two transverse electromagnetic vibrations. As a first step in finding the number of modes in the frequency range $d\nu$, we find the number $N(\nu)$ whose frequency is less than ν. We set up a three-dimensional space in which n_x, n_y, n_z are rectangular coordinates. The frequency ν is given in terms of the n's by

$$\nu = \frac{\omega}{2\pi} = \frac{c|k|}{2\pi} = \frac{c}{2}\sqrt{\left(\frac{n_x}{X}\right)^2 + \left(\frac{n_y}{Y}\right)^2 + \left(\frac{n_z}{Z}\right)^2} \tag{6-11}$$

If we plot surfaces of constant frequency in the space in which n_x, n_y, n_z are variables, as in Fig. 6-2, the surfaces are ellipsoids with semiaxes $2X\nu/c$, $2Y\nu/c$, $2Z\nu/c$. To find the number of modes whose frequency is less than ν, we must count the number of points corresponding to integral n's within the first octant (since we use only positive n's) and multiply by 2 (since there are two transverse modes for each set of n's). But there is just one point per unit volume, so that if we disregard the error arising from small cubes in Fig. 6-2 which are cut through by the ellipsoidal surface, the number of modes with frequency less than ν will be

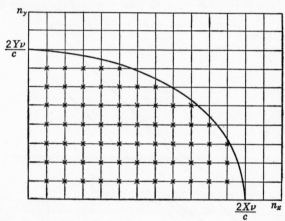

FIG. 6-2. Surface of constant frequency in a space in which n_x, n_y, n_z are variables. All points shown lead to resonant modes, so that the number of resonant modes is approximately found by computing the volume of the first octant enclosed by the ellipsoidal frequency surface.

twice the volume of the first octant enclosed within the ellipsoid, or one-fourth the volume of the ellipsoid. Since the volume of an ellipsoid is $4\pi/3$ times the product of the semiaxes, we have

$$N(\nu) = \frac{1}{4}\frac{4\pi}{3}\frac{8XYZ\nu^3}{c^3} = \frac{8\pi\nu^3}{3c^3}\,V \qquad (6\text{-}12)$$

where $V = XYZ$ is the volume of the cavity. When we differentiate with respect to ν to find the number of modes in $d\nu$, we have

$$dN = \frac{8\pi\nu^2}{c^3}\,V\,d\nu \qquad (6\text{-}13)$$

We can now combine Eq. (6-9) and Eq. (6-13) to derive Planck's law according to the method of Debye. In the frequency range $d\nu$, in unit volume, we have a number of modes equal to $(8\pi\nu^2/c^3)\,d\nu$. Each of these modes has an average energy given by Eq. (6-9). Hence the energy density, the quantity ρ_ν, such that $\rho_\nu\,d\nu$ represents the energy per unit volume in the frequency range $d\nu$, is given by

$$\rho_\nu = \frac{8\pi\nu^2}{c^3} \frac{h\nu}{\exp(h\nu/kT) - 1}$$ (6-14)

or Planck's law, agreeing with Eq. (1-3).

6-4. Einstein's Probabilities and the Equilibrium of Radiation and Matter. Next let us ask how Einstein's probability assumptions, stated in Eqs. (1-9) and (1-10), fit in with our problem of radiation in the cavity. Let us assume that we have an atom in the cavity, which has among other energy levels two, E_1 and E_2, which we shall consider particularly. If E_2 is greater than E_1, as we shall assume, the atom will emit a photon of frequency given by $E_2 - E_1 = h\nu$ when it falls from state 2 to state 1 and will absorb a photon of the same frequency when it is excited from state 1 to state 2. This atom, in other words, is a mechanism for interchanging energy with the particular oscillating modes of the cavity having this frequency. If there are N_1 such atoms in state 1 and N_2 in state 2 and a radiation density ρ_ν at the frequency concerned, then Einstein's assumption is that $N_1 B\rho_\nu$ atoms will rise per second from state 1 to state 2, absorbing photons, and $N_2(A + B\rho_\nu)$ will fall per second from state 2 to state 1, emitting photons. If we consider only these two states and only this transition, we then shall have

$$\frac{dN_1}{dt} = -\frac{dN_2}{dt} = -N_1 B\rho_\nu + N_2(A + B\rho_\nu)$$ (6-15)

since each upward transition results in an increase of unity in the atoms in the excited state and a decrease of unity in the atoms in the lower state, and vice versa.

First let us consider the steady state, in which N_1 and N_2 are independent of time. Then we have

$$N_1 B\rho_\nu = N_2(A + B\rho_\nu) \qquad \frac{N_2}{N_1} = \frac{B\rho_\nu}{A + B\rho_\nu}$$ (6-16)

If we use Eq. (6-14) for ρ_ν, assuming temperature radiation, and if we remember that according to Einstein's assumption of Eq. (1-11) we have $A/B = 8\pi h\nu^3/c^3$, we find from Eq. (6-16)

$$\frac{N_2}{N_1} = \exp\frac{-h\nu}{kT}$$ (6-17)

Since $E_2 - E_1 = h\nu$, Eq. (6-17) states that N_2/N_1 equals the ratio of the Boltzmann factors (6-5) for the two states, so that if the atoms come to a steady state in equilibrium with temperature vibration, their distribution will be governed by the Boltzmann factors, or will be in accordance with statistical theory.

We could equally well proceed in the opposite direction. Whenever there is a process of emitting or absorbing photons, not only does the number of atoms in the states 1 and 2 vary, according to Eq. (6-15), but at the same time the number of photons of the frequency ν varies. If we have atoms maintained at the temperature T, and hence with a distribution given by the Boltzmann factors, the radiation density ρ_ν must come into equilibrium with them. This leads to the same equation, Eq. (6-16), as before; but now we should assume Eq. (6-17) and solve for ρ_ν. Then we should be led to Planck's law. This argument was used by Einstein,[1] in the paper in which he proposed the transition probabilities, and was used as a derivation of Planck's law. It is this argument which tells us that if we have a cavity containing matter which can emit and absorb radiation, and if the matter is at temperature T, the radiation field will automatically come to the same temperature. For this to happen, of course, the matter must be able to emit and absorb radiation of all frequencies, not just of one particular frequency. In the older papers dealing with this subject, this is handled by the postulate that the piece of matter is a small carbon particle, on account of the assumption that a carbon particle, being black, can absorb and therefore emit any wavelength of light.

We must not get the idea that Einstein's assumptions, and the equations like Eq. (6-15) derived from them, are limited to thermal equilibrium; they are intended to apply under any circumstances, and whether or not the energy density ρ_ν is temperature radiation. Suppose, for instance, that we were working at an exceedingly low temperature but that we shone an intense radiation on a group of atoms of just the frequency which they could absorb in going from their ground state, which we now identify with state 1, to an excited state 2. We still shall reach a steady state, as far as the atoms are concerned, in which N_2/N_1 will be given by Eq. (6-16); but we do not need to regard this as being a state of thermal equilibrium. For instance, in microwave resonance problems, we deal with excited states so close to the ground state that the frequency ν is in the microwave part of the spectrum, where the energy density ρ_ν in black-body radiation at an ordinary temperature is negligible. The microwave energy density is not negligible, however, and it is this which would be the ρ_ν in Eq. (6-16). We see that, if ρ_ν were made sufficiently great, the term $B\rho_\nu$ could become large compared with the term A, so that the ratio N_2/N_1 would approach unity, a ratio which could not be reached by thermal means without going to a quite high temperature.

The case we have considered, with only two states, is oversimplified as compared with the situations really met in practice. Ordinarily there are many different states, with the possibility of transitions from one to

[1] A. Einstein, *Physik. Z.*, **18**:121 (1917).

another.   For each state, we have an expression, similar to Eq. (6-15), giving the time rate of change of the number of atoms in this state. This is given as a linear combination of the N's of all states, the coefficients involving $B\rho_\nu$ or $A + B\rho_\nu$ terms, with the energy density of the appropriate frequency.   These equations must be solved as simultaneous equations for the N's, setting the dN/dt's equal to zero, to get the steady-state solution.   In case the external radiation is not temperature radiation, the steady-state values of the N's can be very different from those arising from thermal equilibrium.   It is even possible, in the microwave case, to have larger numbers of atoms in excited states than in lower states.   It is worthwhile, in some such cases, to introduce effective or fictitious temperatures, such that the Boltzmann factors computed for these effective temperatures would lead to the ratios of N's found in the steady-state condition, and in such a case, if there are more atoms in excited than in the ground state, one is led to negative effective temperatures.

We can apply the equations, not only to steady states, but also to transient phenomena.   Thus, for instance, let us take the simple example given in Eq. (6-15), and let us assume that at $t = 0$ the values of N_1 and N_2 do not correspond to thermal equilibrium but that the value of ρ_ν is correct for thermal equilibrium.   Let us then find the time dependence of N_1 and N_2.   We note that the sum of N_1 and N_2 remains fixed in this simple case; let it be N.   We then find that the equilibrium values of N_1 and N_2, which will be reached at infinite value of the time, are

$$N_{1\infty} = N \frac{A + B\rho_\nu}{A + 2B\rho_\nu} \qquad N_{2\infty} = N \frac{B\rho_\nu}{A + 2B\rho_\nu} \qquad (6\text{-}18)$$

These are determined so that their ratio will be given by Eq. (6-16) and so that their sum will be N.   Then Eq. (6-15) can be rewritten in the form

$$\begin{aligned} \frac{d(N_1 - N_{1\infty})}{dt} &= -(A + 2B\rho_\nu)(N_1 - N_{1\infty}) \\ \frac{d(N_2 - N_{2\infty})}{dt} &= -(A + 2B\rho_\nu)(N_2 - N_{2\infty}) \end{aligned} \qquad (6\text{-}19)$$

The solutions of these equations are

$$\begin{aligned} N_1 &= N_{1\infty} + (N_{10} - N_{1\infty}) \exp\left[-(A + 2B\rho_\nu)t\right] \\ N_2 &= N_{2\infty} + (N_{20} - N_{2\infty}) \exp\left[-(A + 2B\rho_\nu)t\right] \end{aligned} \qquad (6\text{-}20)$$

Here N_{10}, N_{20} are the values of these quantities at $t = 0$.   We see that N_1 and N_2 approach their asymptotic values exponentially, and the time in which the exponentials fall to $1/e$ of their initial value is given by $(A + 2B\rho_\nu)^{-1}$.   Similar, but much more complicated, results for the transients will be found in more general cases; as a rule, there will be many exponential terms, with different time constants.   This is the same sort of situation mathematically which one meets in the theory of radioactive decay, where one can have many successive products decaying into each other.

6-5. Quantum Theory of the Interaction of Radiation and Matter.

We have become familiar in the preceding sections with the general approach to the problem of radiation and its interaction with matter as developed by Planck, Debye, and Einstein.   This theory has a great drawback: no method is provided for finding the Einstein probabilities A and B, though their ratio is known.   Bohr endeavored to fill this gap, in the days before the development of wave mechanics, by a method called the correspondence principle, based on analogies between classical mechanics and quantum theory.   We discuss this method in Appendix 10; though it is now supplanted by the wave-mechanical methods, it still is of great importance, particularly for the light it throws on the classical limit of wave mechanics.   The correspondence principle did not give numerical values for the A's and B's, but it could indicate their general orders of magnitude and in particular could show that in some cases they should be zero.   In such a case, the transition cannot occur, and we are said to have a selection rule.   These selection rules are of great importance in the interpretation of spectra.

With the development of wave mechanics, it became clear that for the first time a quantitative method was available for finding the A's and B's from the wave functions.   The first attempts[1] were not entirely successful.   They treated the external electromagnetic field as a perturbative term in the Hamiltonian, depending explicitly on time.   They showed that, under the action of such a field, atomic systems developed polarization charges, oscillating in synchronism with the external fields.   These polarizations acted very much like those which had been postulated in the older classical theory of dispersion.   In the first place, they produced electromagnetic fields which combined with the incident field to account for the phenomenon of dispersion, the existence of an index of refraction different from unity.   In the second place, they led to a calculation of the rate of absorption, and hence to Einstein's coefficients B.   But this theory was not able to account for the existence of Einstein's coefficients A.   It was clearly not a complete theory.   It is, however, extremely useful for those problems which it can handle.

Soon after these attempts to handle the interaction of radiation and matter, Dirac[2] produced an alternative theory, leading to the same values of the B's which had been found by the semiclassical theory, but leading

[1] P. A. M. Dirac, *Proc. Roy. Soc.* (*London*), **A112**:661 (1926); J. C. Slater, *Proc. Natl. Acad. Sci. U.S.*, **13**:7 (1927).

[2] P. A. M. Dirac, *Proc. Roy. Soc.* (*London*), **A114**:243 (1927).

also to the A's and to a complete explanation of Einstein's probabilities. This differed from the earlier theory in that the radiation field was not treated merely as a perturbation; it was considered as part of the system, which consisted of atoms and radiation combined. Dirac started with an unperturbed problem in which the interaction between the atoms and the field was neglected. In this case the radiation field was characterized by the quantum numbers n associated with the various modes of oscillation which we have been setting up in this chapter, and the atomic system was characterized by ordinary atomic quantum numbers. In the absence of interaction, such a system has stationary states, in which each of the n's describing the radiation remains constant and the atoms stay in fixed stationary states.

When the interaction is taken into account, however, one finds nondiagonal matrix components of the Hamiltonian between states with different values of the radiation n's and of the atomic quantum numbers. In other words, we no longer have stationary states of the system of the ordinary sort, and instead we must handle the problem by a perturbation method. A special form of perturbation theory is used, called the method of variation of constants, which leads directly to transitions between stationary states. The result is, as we mentioned earlier, that we find just such probabilities of transition as Einstein had postulated, but with explicit formulas for the A's and B's associated with a transition.

We shall go into both these methods of handling the interaction between radiation and atoms and shall derive the A and B. For practical purposes, however, the single formula for A and B is the essential result of these rather involved calculations, and for the benefit of the reader who wishes only this result, we shall state it here. It is stated in terms of the matrix component of the electric dipole moment of the atomic system, between the two stationary states between which we are finding transition probabilities. The dipole moment of an atom is a vector quantity, whose x component is the sum of the charges of each particle, times their x coordinates, with respect to the nucleus of the atom. This becomes, in wave mechanics, an operator, which we can write as

$$(M_x)_{\text{op}} = \Sigma(j)e_j x_j \qquad (6\text{-}21)$$

where e_j is the charge of the jth particle (ordinarily the electronic charge $-e$, where e is its magnitude) and x_j is the x coordinate of this particle. If we denote the initial atomic wave function as u_1 and the final wave function as u_2, then we have as the matrix component

$$(M_x)_{12} = \int u_1^*(M_x)_{\text{op}} u_2 \, dv \qquad (6\text{-}22)$$

We similarly compute $(M_y)_{12}$ and $(M_z)_{12}$, and

$$|M_{12}|^2 = (M_x)_{12}^*(M_x)_{12} + (M_y)_{12}^*(M_y)_{12} + (M_z)_{12}^*(M_z)_{12} \qquad (6\text{-}23)$$

The formulas for A and B are stated in terms of this quantity. We then find, in terms of the quantity $|M_{12}|^2$, that A and B are given by

$$A = \frac{8\pi h\nu^3}{c^3} \frac{8\pi^3|M_{12}|^2}{(4\pi\epsilon_0)3h^2} \qquad B = \frac{8\pi^3|M_{12}|^2}{(4\pi\epsilon_0)3h^2} \qquad (6\text{-}24)$$

Here ϵ_0 is the constant appearing in the mks system of units, in terms of which these formulas are stated; the corresponding formula in Gaussian units is found by omitting the factor $4\pi\epsilon_0$.

Before we go ahead with the derivation of A and B by wave mechanics, there are interesting comments which can be made about the possibility of handling the electromagnetic field in a classical manner. It is a familiar fact that, in ordinary circuit theory and all the applications of electromagnetic theory to electrical engineering, no difficulties are encountered in using Maxwell's equations and a classical interpretation of electromagnetism. On the other hand, in discussing the photoelectric effect, emission and absorption by atoms, and similar optical problems, we must use the quantum theory of the electromagnetic field. We may well ask why this difference in treatment exists. We shall consider this question in the next section.

6-6. The Classical Limit for Electromagnetic Problems. In Sec. 2-5, we showed that wave mechanics approaches a classical limit when the necessary spread of a wave packet, required by the uncertainty principle, becomes negligible compared with the average dimensions and momenta of the system, and we pointed out that this is equivalent to a statement that classical methods become appropriate in the limit of high quantum numbers. In the same way, in handling the radiation field, we can treat the field classically if the average quantum number of one of the oscillators representing the field, or the average number of photons associated with this oscillator, is large compared with unity. Let us examine this classical limit, first considering thermal radiation.

The average quantum number of an oscillator, at temperature T, in thermal equilibrium, is given by Eq. (6-10) and is

$$(n)_{av} = \frac{1}{\exp{(h\nu/kT)} - 1}$$

We see that this number is small compared with unity if $h\nu/kT$ is large compared with unity, and vice versa. That is, for a given temperature, the low frequencies can be treated by classical theory, since each resonant mode will be excited to a high quantum number, while at high frequencies the average quantum number will be very small, or most of the oscillators will be in their ground state, only a few in the first excited state, and we must use the quantum theory. The dividing line, where $h\nu$ equals kT, comes approximately at the maximum value of ρ_ν as given by Planck's law.   For the lower frequencies, where the classical treatment is correct, we can expand exp $(h\nu/kT)$ in power series and find for the limiting form of Planck's law

$$\rho_\nu = \frac{8\pi\nu^2}{c^3}\,kT$$

the Rayleigh-Jeans law, already given in Eq. (1-1).

For all ordinary temperatures, the frequency given by $h\nu = kT$ lies in the infrared part of the spectrum.   Thus it comes about that there is a dividing line in practice between the frequencies which can be handled classically and those which must be handled quantum-mechanically: those frequencies lower than the infrared, including all those ordinarily met in electrical engineering, even including the whole of the microwave spectrum, can be handled classically, while the visible and everything of higher frequency must be handled by quantum theory.   This is the reason why the quantum theory has developed from a study of optical spectra, where it is absolutely necessary, while the electrical engineers have been able to use the classical Maxwell's equations perfectly properly as the basis of their work, except when they deal with atomic problems.

Let us examine our statements in a little more detail.   First let us consider the visible part of the spectrum.   For ν in the visible, the quantity $h\nu/kT$ is large compared with unity, and we must use the quantum theory, unless the temperature is raised to a good many thousand degrees; this fact is well known from the qualitative fact that the surface temperature of the sun, around 6000°, corresponds approximately to the situation where the maximum of the Planck distribution curve lies in the middle of the visible spectrum, a fact generally related to the sensitivity of the eye, which has developed so as to have its maximum sensitivity where the sunlight is strongest.   We see, then, that, so long as we are dealing with energy densities of radiation in the visible which are less than that present at the surface of the sun in this range of frequencies, we must use the quantum theory.   We realize how very difficult it is in laboratory experiments to build up a radiation density in the visible spectrum comparable with that found at the surface of the sun and can readily see that we are almost always working with energy densities, in this frequency range, where the quantum theory must be used.

The situation is just the opposite in the microwave range, particularly so at the lower frequencies.   Thus, if we take $T = 300°K$, the frequency for which $h\nu/kT = 1$ is about 6×10^{12} cycles/sec, corresponding to a wavelength of 0.05 mm.   At all microwave frequencies we are well on the long-wave side of this value.   Thus, at a wavelength of 1 mm, we have $h\nu/kT = \frac{1}{20}$, at room temperature, corresponding to an average quantum number of about 20 in the oscillators of this frequency, arising from thermal radiation alone.   But this thermal radiation can be shown to be identical with the thermal, or Johnson, noise, familiar in the theory of noise or fluctuations in electrical systems. Any experiment at microwave frequencies deals with power levels which are at least above that of thermal noise and which are ordinarily a good deal above. Hence we see that the classical electromagnetic theory will always be adequate at microwave frequencies. The only exception to this statement might come at the extreme short wavelengths of millimeter waves, in case the system were refrigerated to one of two degrees Kelvin to minimize thermal noise and experiments were carried out with power levels so low as to be comparable with thermal noise at that very low temperature. Then we should be barely on the edge of phenomena where the quantum theory would make appreciable corrections.

In connection with this discussion of the classical limit for electromagnetic phenomena, there is a very interesting way in which we can regard Einstein's probability $A + B\rho_\nu$. If we take account of the ratio between A and B given by Eq. (1-11), we find, using Eqs. (6-10) and (6-14), that

$$A + B\rho_\nu = A[1 + (n)_{av}] \qquad (6\text{-}25)$$

where $(n)_{av}$ is the average quantum number of the oscillators of frequency ν. We see, in other words, that the spontaneous radiation A is only $1/(n)_{av}$ times the induced emission $B\rho_\nu$. In the visible part of the spectrum, where we have seen that $(n)_{av}$ is always small compared with unity, the induced emission is always small compared with the spontaneous emission. On the other hand, in the microwave or radio-frequency range, where $(n)_{av}$ is very large compared with unity, induced emission is large compared with spontaneous emission, and in this range we may disregard spontaneous emission, to the same accuracy to which we can disregard unity in comparison to $(n)_{av}$. This suggests that the induced emission is in a sense a classical type of phenomenon, representing the effect which we find in the limit of high quantum numbers for the radiation, while the spontaneous radiation is a quantum type of phenomenon, which we cannot explain if we treat the radiation in a classical fashion. This makes it seem reasonable that the semiclassical treatment of the interaction of radiation and matter, which we have already mentioned, and which we shall treat in the next section, is able to give a proper explanation of the induced emission and the absorption but fails to explain the spontaneous emission.

6-7. Hamiltonian and Wave-mechanical Treatment of an Atomic System in a Classical Radiation Field. To handle a radiation field in a classical manner, we must find the Hamiltonian of an atomic system in an external electromagnetic field and then use this to set up Schrödinger's equation for the atomic system. We can describe this external field by means of a scalar potential ϕ and a vector potential $\mathbf{A}$, according to the equations

$$\mathbf{E} = -\nabla\phi - \frac{\partial \mathbf{A}}{\partial t} \qquad \mathbf{B} = \nabla \times \mathbf{A} \qquad (6\text{-}26)$$

where $\mathbf{E}$ is the electric field, $\mathbf{B}$ the magnetic induction. Then by the methods of Appendix 4 we show that the Hamiltonian of a system of charges, such as electrons and nuclei, in this external field, and acting on each other by Coulomb forces, is

$$H = \sum (j) \left\{ \frac{[\mathbf{p}_j - e_j\mathbf{A}(\mathbf{r}_j)]^2}{2m_j} + e_j\phi(\mathbf{r}_j) \right\} + V(x_1 \cdots z_N) \qquad (6\text{-}27)$$

where m_j is the mass of the jth particle, e_j its charge, $\mathbf{p}_j$ its momentum, $\mathbf{r}_j$ its vector position, $\mathbf{A}(\mathbf{r}_j)$ and $\phi(\mathbf{r}_j)$ are the vector and scalar potentials at its position, and $V(x_1 \cdots z_N)$ is the potential energy of the Coulomb interactions between the pairs of particles. The first of Hamilton's equations then is

$$\frac{dx_j}{dt} = \frac{\partial H}{\partial p_{x_j}} = \frac{1}{m_j} [p_{x_j} - e_j A_x(\mathbf{r}_j)] \qquad (6\text{-}28)$$

which shows that the momentum, in the presence of a vector potential, is not equal to the mass times the velocity but that rather there is an additional term $e_j A_x$ which must be added to the mass times velocity. The second of Hamilton's equations leads, as we show in Appendix 4, to

$$m_j \frac{d^2x_j}{dt^2} = e_j[\mathbf{E} + (\mathbf{v}_j \times \mathbf{B})]_x \qquad (6\text{-}29)$$

where $\mathbf{E}$ is the value of the electric field at the jth particle, both that arising from the Coulomb interactions with other particles and the external field of Eq. (6-26), and $\mathbf{B}$ is the external magnetic field, arising from Eq. (6-26). The quantity $\mathbf{v}_j$ is the velocity of the jth particle. The force on the right-hand side of Eq. (6-29) is the ordinary Lorentz force. This Hamiltonian is not entirely complete, in that it does not take account of magnetic interactions between the particles of the atomic system, but it is adequate for our present purposes, where the $\mathbf{A}$ comes from an external radiation field.

We shall use the Hamiltonian of Eq. (6-27) to set up the Schrödinger equation for the atomic system in the presence of radiation. Before we do this, however, let us stop to investigate the implications of Eq. (6-28). When we compare it with Eq. (4-52), we see that we have an additional term, in the vector potential. This leads to an additional term in the average value of the velocity, Eq. (4-56), and in the flux, Eq. (4-65).

The flux now becomes

$$\mathbf{f}_i = - \frac{i\hbar}{2m_i} \int \cdots \int (\psi^* \nabla_i \psi - \psi \nabla_i \psi^*) \, dv' - \frac{e_i}{m_i} \int \cdots \int \psi^* \mathbf{A}(\mathbf{r}_i) \psi \, dv'$$
(6-30)

where the notation is the same as in Eq. (4-65). We shall come back in Chap. 23 (Vol. II) to an explanation of the additional term in the flux. We shall see that it is the induced current, set up by ordinary electromagnetic induction in the process of building up the magnetic field.

Now let us return to Eq. (6-27) and Schrödinger's equation. This becomes

$$\sum_{(j)} \left\{ \frac{-\hbar^2}{2m_j} \nabla_j^2 + \frac{ie_j\hbar}{m_j} [\mathbf{A}(\mathbf{r}_j) \cdot \nabla_j] + \frac{e_j^2 A(\mathbf{r}_j)^2}{2m_j} + e_j \phi(\mathbf{r}_j) \right\} \psi + V\psi = i\hbar \frac{\partial \psi}{\partial t}$$
(6-31)

We have three types of terms arising from the external field: the term linear in $\mathbf{A}$, that quadratic in $\mathbf{A}$, and that in ϕ. For discussing interaction with radiation, we do not need the term in ϕ, because the radiation field can be described in terms of a vector potential only. Furthermore, for radiation fields of the size that we need consider, the vector potential is small enough so that the term in A^2 is negligible compared with that in $\mathbf{A}$. Hence the only interaction term which we need consider is the linear term in $\mathbf{A}$. We shall meet other problems in later chapters, however, in which the term in A^2 is essential. This will not come in the interaction with oscillating fields, like a radiation field, but in interaction with static magnetic fields; it is this term, for instance, which is responsible for the phenomenon of diamagnetism.

There is one point to be noticed in connection with the Hamiltonian of Eq. (6-31). We have a term in the classical Hamiltonian given by $-(e_j/m_j)\mathbf{p}_j \cdot \mathbf{A}(\mathbf{r}_j)$. When we convert this into an operator, we are uncertain whether the operator for $\mathbf{p}_j$ should be written before or after $\mathbf{A}(\mathbf{r}_j)$, which is a function of coordinates; in classical mechanics the order of the terms is immaterial, whereas we know that in general it is important in quantum mechanics. However, we can choose the vector potential so that its divergence is zero, and this choice is regularly made in treatments of quantum electrodynamics. We remember the vector relation which states that $\nabla \cdot (\mathbf{A}\psi) = \mathbf{A} \cdot \nabla \psi + \psi(\nabla \cdot \mathbf{A})$. In this case, where $\nabla \cdot \mathbf{A} = 0$, this leads to $\nabla \cdot \mathbf{A}\psi = \mathbf{A} \cdot \nabla \psi$, which shows that the operators $\mathbf{p}$ and $\mathbf{A}$ commute with each other, so that we can write them in either order in setting up the Hamiltonian. As we show in Appendix 7, the Hamiltonian including this term is then Hermitian.

We shall start our calculation of the interaction of radiation and matter by disregarding the coupling term between the two, so that we have the simple Schrödinger equation

$$\sum (j) \frac{-\hbar^2}{2m_j} \nabla_j^2 \psi + V\psi = i\hbar \frac{\partial \psi}{\partial t} \qquad (6\text{-}32)$$

for the atomic system.   We shall assume that this can be solved and that its solutions, for eigenvalues denoted by quantum numbers n, are $u_n \exp(-iE_n t/\hbar)$, in the ordinary way.   The perturbation term will then have matrix components between these functions, which we regard as the unperturbed wave functions of a perturbation calculation.   Such a matrix component, between states denoted by quantum numbers n and m, is

$$H_{nm}^0 = \int u_n^* \sum (j) \left[\frac{ie_j\hbar}{m_j} \mathbf{A}(\mathbf{r}_j) \cdot \nabla_j \right] u_m \, dv \qquad (6\text{-}33)$$

We must now evaluate this matrix component before going further with our calculation.

In the general case, where we have an extended atomic system, we cannot simplify the matrix component (6-33) further.   However, if we are dealing with an atom, whose wave function does not extend very far out from the nucleus, and if the wavelength of the electromagnetic radiation is long compared with atomic dimensions, then we may treat the vector potential $\mathbf{A}$ as being constant over the region where the atomic wave function is different from zero.   This is legitimate if we are dealing with visible light but could not be done with X rays; in that case, in fact, the variation of $\mathbf{A}$ with position within the atom is what leads to the atomic scattering factor, in X-ray scattering.

When we take the factor $\mathbf{A}(\mathbf{r}_j)$ out of the integral and replace it with its value at the nucleus, the remaining integral in Eq. (6-33) is the sum, over all charges, of the product of $-e_j$ and the velocity operator of the corresponding particle, as we see from Eqs. (4-52) and (4-56).   We do not need to worry about the extra term in the vector potential appearing in the velocity operator derived from Eq. (6-28), in the presence of an external field, for this extra term is of a smaller order of magnitude than those which we are retaining in our calculation and can be neglected. We can then use Eq. (4-43) and convert the velocity operator, and its matrix components, into a form involving the matrix components of the displacements of the charged particles.   Thus we have

$$\int u_n^* \sum (j) \frac{ie_j\hbar}{m_j} \frac{\partial}{\partial x_j} u_m \, dv = -\sum (j)e_j \int u_n^* \left(\frac{-i\hbar}{m_j} \right) \frac{\partial}{\partial x_j} u_m \, dv$$

$$= -\sum (j)e_j \int u_n^* \left(\frac{\partial x_j}{\partial t} \right) u_m \, dv$$

$$= -\sum (j)e_j \int u_n^* \frac{i(E_n - E_m)}{\hbar} x_j u_m \, dv$$

$$= \frac{i(E_n - E_m)}{\hbar} \int u_n^* \sum (j)(-e_j x_j) u_m \, dv$$

$$(6\text{-}34)$$

The integral which appears on the right side of Eq. (6-34) is the negative of the component of the dipole moment of the atom, as given in Eq. (6-22)

$$\int u_n^* \Sigma(j) e_j x_j u_m \, dv = (M_x)_{nm} \tag{6-35}$$

Thus finally we have

$$H_{nm}^0 = \frac{i(E_m - E_n)}{\hbar} \, \mathbf{A} \cdot (\mathbf{M})_{nm} \tag{6-36}$$

where $(\mathbf{M})_{nm}$ is the vector whose x component is $(M_x)_{nm}$. We remember that $\mathbf{A}$ is to be computed at the position of the nucleus and that it is supposed to vary so slowly with position that it can be treated as constant over the atom.

Now we must write down the expression for the vector potential, in terms of the modes of oscillation of the cavity, which we have described in Eq. (6-1). We remember that we have many modes, of different frequencies; the number of modes in the frequency range $d\nu$, according to Eq. (6-13), is $dN = (8\pi\nu^2/c^3) V \, d\nu$. Each of these modes can have a different phase and amplitude. We can then write $\mathbf{A}$ as a sum over the modes, of the form

$$\mathbf{A} = \Sigma(\nu) \mathbf{A}_\nu \cos (2\pi\nu t - \alpha_\nu) \tag{6-37}$$

where the direction of $\mathbf{A}_\nu$ is fixed (it must be in the same direction as the vector of components E_x^0, E_y^0, E_z^0 for the mode in question, since in the absence of a scalar potential we have $\mathbf{E} = -\partial\mathbf{A}/\partial t$), but its amplitude and the value of the phase α_ν are arbitrary. We shall later find a relationship between the magnitude of $\mathbf{A}_\nu$ and the energy density in the radiation field.

If we insert Eq. (6-37) into Eq. (6-36), we have our complete assumption as to the nondiagonal matrix components of the Hamiltonian, arising from the coupling between the electromagnetic field and the atomic system. Now we shall proceed to discuss the perturbations produced by these nondiagonal matrix components, using the perturbation method called the method of variation of constants.

6-8. The Method of Variation of Constants for Transition Probabilities. Before going ahead with our radiation problem, we shall explain the method of variation of constants in general terms, then shall show how it is to be applied to our special case. Let us expand the wave function ψ of a quantum-mechanical problem in a series of unperturbed orthonormal functions, in an expansion

$$\psi = \Sigma(k) C_k(t) u_k^0 \tag{6-38}$$

where the u_k^0's are the unperturbed functions, and where the C's, functions of time, would be pure exponentials, $c_k \exp(-iE_k t/\hbar)$, where the c_k's are constants, if the u_k^0's were correct solutions of the problem.

Whether correct or not, we can always make the expansion above, for at any instant ψ can be expressed in series in the orthonormal functions u_k^0, the coefficients being functions of time. If the perturbations are small, we can assume that the exponential behavior of C_k is not far from correct. In other words, if we write

$$C_k(t) = c_k(t) \exp(-iH_{kk}^0 t/\hbar) \qquad (6\text{-}39)$$

where H_{kk}^0 would be the eigenvalue if the unperturbed functions were correct, we may expect that $c_k(t)$ will be a slowly varying function of time. Let us then combine Eqs. (6-38) and (6-39) and substitute into Schrödinger's equation $(H)_{op}\psi = i\hbar \partial \psi/\partial t$ and see what restrictions this imposes on the time dependence of the c_k's.

If we make this substitution, multiply both sides of the equation on the left by u_n^{0*}, and integrate over the volume, we have

$$\int u_n^{0*}(H)_{op} \sum (k)c_k(t) \exp(-iH_{kk}^0 t/\hbar)u_k^0 \, dv$$
$$= i\hbar \int u_n^{0*} \frac{\partial}{\partial t} \sum (k)c_k(t) \exp(-iH_{kk}^0 t/\hbar)u_k^0 \, dv$$

which leads to

$$\sum (k)c_k(t)H_{nk}^0 \exp(-iH_{kk}^0 t/\hbar) = \left(i\hbar \frac{dc_n}{dt} + H_{nn}^0 c_n\right) \exp(-iH_{nn}^0 t/\hbar)$$

and to

$$\frac{dc_n}{dt} = -\frac{i}{\hbar} \sum (k \neq n)c_k(t)H_{nk}^0 \exp[i(H_{nn}^0 - H_{kk}^0)t/\hbar] \qquad (6\text{-}40)$$

These equations are exact, and they show us, as we expected, that the time rates of change of the c_n's are small, since they depend on the non-diagonal matrix components H_{nk}^0 of the Hamiltonian, which are assumed to be small. In our case, they will be given by Eq. (6-36) and are hence proportional to the external field.

The general solution of Eq. (6-40) is very difficult, but we can make a simple and valid approximation, which will allow us to find the transition probabilities we are looking for. We shall assume that at $t = 0$ the system is entirely in a particular state, which we may denote by the subscript m. The time rates of change of the c_n's are small enough so that for some little time c_m will be practically unity, the other c's practically zero. Let us then use Eq. (6-40) for finding the time rate of change of one of the c_n's corresponding to a state for which $n \neq m$, that is, the rate at which a state builds up. On the right side of Eq. (6-40), we can then approximately replace the values $c_k(t)$ which appear inside the summation by their values at $t = 0$; that is, we can replace c_m by unity, the other c's by zero. When we do this, Eq. (6-40) reduces to a single term,

$$\frac{dc_n}{dt} = -\frac{i}{h} H_{nm}^0 \exp\left[i(H_{nn}^0 - H_{mm}^0)t/\hbar\right] \qquad (6\text{-}41)$$

Now we are ready to replace the matrix component H_{nm}^0 of the perturbing Hamiltonian, in Eq. (6-41), by the value found in Eqs. (6-36) and (6-37), for our particular problem. In doing this, it is convenient to expand the cosine in Eq. (6-37) in complex exponential form. When we do so, we find

$$\frac{dc_n}{dt} = -\frac{2\pi^2 \nu_{nm}}{h} \mathbf{M}_{nm} \cdot \sum (\nu)\mathbf{A}_\nu \{\exp(-i\alpha_\nu) \exp[2\pi i(\nu + \nu_{nm})t]$$
$$+ \exp(i\alpha_\nu) \exp[-2\pi i(\nu - \nu_{nm})t]\} \qquad (6\text{-}42)$$

where we have used the definition

$$h\nu_{nm} = H_{nn}^0 - H_{mm}^0 \qquad (6\text{-}43)$$

which is positive if the nth state lies above the mth, negative if it lies below. We now integrate with respect to time, from $t = 0$ to $t = t$, using as an initial condition the requirement that $c_n = 0$ when $t = 0$. We find

$$c_n = \frac{\pi i \nu_{nm}}{h} \mathbf{M}_{nm} \cdot \sum (\nu)\mathbf{A}_\nu \left\{ \exp(-i\alpha_\nu) \frac{\exp[2\pi i(\nu + \nu_{nm})t] - 1}{\nu + \nu_{nm}} \right.$$
$$\left. - \exp(i\alpha_\nu) \frac{\exp[-2\pi i(\nu - \nu_{nm})t] - 1}{\nu - \nu_{nm}} \right\} \qquad (6\text{-}44)$$

Next we are interested in finding $c_n^* c_n$, the probability of finding the system in the nth state, as a function of time. In this, we have a product of two sums over ν, which is, therefore, a double sum. Each such term for which we have different frequencies in the two factors has a term $\exp[i(\pm\alpha_\nu \pm \alpha_{\nu'})]$, which, on account of the random nature of the phases, is as likely to be positive as negative, and which on the average cancels. Thus we are left with only the squares of the individual terms, in which the α's drop out. Further, each of these squares has terms whose denominators are respectively $(\nu + \nu_{nm})^2$, $(\nu + \nu_{nm})(\nu - \nu_{nm})$, $(\nu - \nu_{nm})^2$. The frequency ν_{nm} is so defined that it is positive if the nth state lies above the mth, which we assume to be the case for the moment. When ν becomes nearly equal to ν_{nm}, the term $(\nu - \nu_{nm})^2$ is very small, the term with this as denominator very large. Since ν is always positive, it is not possible for the other terms, involving $\nu + \nu_{nm}$ in the denominator, to become large. To an approximation, then, we neglect all terms except the last, obtaining

$$c_n^* c_n = \frac{4\pi^2 \nu_{nm}^2}{h^2} \sum (\nu)(\mathbf{M}_{nm} \cdot \mathbf{A}_\nu)^2 \frac{\sin^2 \pi(\nu - \nu_{nm})t}{(\nu - \nu_{nm})^2} \qquad (6\text{-}45)$$

If we had taken the other case, where the nth state lies below the mth, we should have kept only the terms for which the denominator is $\nu + \nu_{nm}$ and the result would have been the same as in Eq. (6-45), except that ν_{nm} would be replaced by $|\nu_{nm}|$.

We can now convert the summation in Eq. (6-45) into an integration. We remember that the modes of oscillation of the cavity, of frequency ν, are very closely spaced; the number in a small frequency range $d\nu$ is $(8\pi\nu^2/c^3)V\, d\nu$, so that the average spacing between modes is the recipro- cal of this quantity, $\Delta\nu = [(8\pi\nu^2/c^3)V]^{-1}$. If we now have a function of ν, $F(\nu)$, like the quantity to be summed in Eq. (6-45), we may make a diagram such as that of Fig. 6-3, in which we show the frequency axis subdivided into intervals $\Delta\nu$ by the frequencies for which there are modes

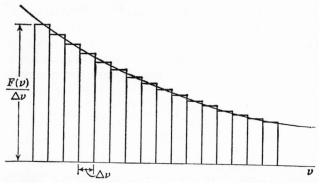

Fig. 6-3. Step function whose integral would equal $\Sigma(\nu)F(\nu)$.

of oscillation. We erect the rectangles shown, of height $F(\nu)/\Delta\nu$, so that each such rectangle has an area of $F(\nu)$. If we integrate the area under the step function, we get the sum of the rectangular areas, or $\Sigma(\nu)F(\nu)$, the summation we wish to evaluate. But we can approximately replace this by the smooth curve drawn, so that the sum is approximately equal to the integral under the smooth curve. In other words, we have approximately

$$\Sigma(\nu)F(\nu) = \int \frac{F(\nu)}{\Delta\nu}\, d\nu \qquad (6\text{-}46)$$

We must now evaluate the function $F(\nu)$, inside the summation of Eq. (6-45). Both magnitudes and directions of the vectors $\mathbf{A}_\nu$ will vary erratically from one mode to the next. On account of the erratic vari- ation of direction, the angle between $\mathbf{M}_{nm}$ and $\mathbf{A}_\nu$ will take on all values with equal probability, and the square of the cosine of this angle will average to $\tfrac{1}{3}$. On account of the erratic variation of the magnitude of $\mathbf{A}_\nu$, different modes will contribute quite differently to the energy density, but nevertheless we must assume that, in the neighborhood of a given frequency ν, there will be an average value of $|A_\nu|^2$ such that the energy density in the mode of frequency ν will, on the average, equal the value $\rho_\nu \, \Delta\nu$. This is necessary so that the total energy density in any range $d\nu$ may be equal to $\rho_\nu \, d\nu$. Let us ask what is the energy density in the mode of frequency ν, with a particular value of the quantity A_ν.

From electromagnetic theory we know that the energy density in a field equals $(\epsilon_0/2)E^2 + (\mu_0/2)H^2$, where E and H are electric- and magnetic-field intensities, ϵ_0 and μ_0 are the fundamental constants; we are using mks units and assuming empty space, without dielectric or magnetic materials. We further know that in such a field the average electric energy equals the average magnetic energy, so that we can get the total energy density by doubling the electric energy. In our case, the vector potential is $A_\nu \cos (2\pi\nu t - \alpha_\nu)$, and the electric field is the negative time derivative of this quantity, or $2\pi\nu A_\nu \sin (2\pi\nu t - \alpha_\nu)$. Its square is $4\pi^2\nu^2 A_\nu^2 \sin^2 (2\pi\nu t - \alpha_\nu)$. Since the time average of the $\sin^2$ is $\frac{1}{2}$, the average electric energy is $(\epsilon_0/2)2\pi^2\nu^2 A_\nu^2$ and the total energy is twice this, or $2\pi^2\nu^2\epsilon_0 A_\nu^2$. This must, from the argument of the preceding paragraph equal $\rho_\nu \, \Delta\nu$. In other words, we may replace the summation of Eq. (6-45) by

$$\int \frac{M_{nm}^2}{3} \frac{\rho_\nu}{2\pi^2\nu^2\epsilon_0} \frac{\sin^2 \pi (\nu - \nu_{nm})t}{(\nu - \nu_{nm})^2} \, d\nu \qquad (6\text{-}47)$$

where we have used Eq. (6-46).

The integration in Eq. (6-47) should be carried out over all frequencies. However, the quantity $\sin^2 \pi(\nu - \nu_{nm})t/(\nu - \nu_{nm})^2$ is large only for a narrow range of frequencies around ν_{nm}. It has a peak, of value $\pi^2 t^2$, at $\nu = \nu_{nm}$ and falls to zero when $(\nu - \nu_{nm})t = 1$, or when $\nu - \nu_{nm} = 1/t$. Outside this range of frequency, the quantity is small. If the time t is long enough to equal many periods of the oscillation of frequency ν_{nm} which we shall assume to be the case, then the frequency range in which the function is large is only a small fraction of ν_{nm}. Over this range of frequencies, we may assume that ρ_ν is practically constant and may take it outside the integral sign. We may also take ν^2 out of the integral replacing it by ν_{nm}^2. We replace $\pi(\nu - \nu_{nm})t$ by a variable x. Then the integral of Eq. (6-47) becomes

$$\frac{M_{nm}^2}{3} \frac{\rho_\nu}{2\pi^2\nu_{nm}^2\epsilon_0} \pi t \int_{-\infty}^{\infty} \frac{\sin^2 x}{x^2} \, dx$$

We use the fact that

$$\int_{-\infty}^{\infty} \frac{\sin^2 x}{x^2} \, dx = \pi$$

and find that

$$c_n^* c_n = \frac{8\pi^3}{3} \frac{M_{nm}^2}{(4\pi\epsilon_0)h^2} \rho_\nu t \qquad (6\text{-}48)$$

The net result of our calculation, then, is that, if the system is in the mth state at $t = 0$, the probability that it will be in the nth state at time t is a constant times t; the constant is ρ_ν times the value of B given in Eq. (6-24). This is just what we should expect according to Einstein's probability method, provided we disregard the spontaneous transitions. For if we start with N_m systems in state m at $t = 0$, and none in state n, Einstein's theory would indicate that the number N_n in state n will be governed by the differential equation

$$\frac{dN_n}{dt} = -\frac{dN_m}{dt} = (-N_n + N_m)B\rho_\nu \qquad (6\text{-}49)$$

analogous to Eq. (6-15). We can set up the general solution of these equations, as in Eqs. (6-18) to (6-20), setting $A = 0$. We have

$$N_{n\infty} = N_{m\infty} = \frac{N}{2}$$

$$N_n = \frac{N}{2}[1 - \exp(-2B\rho_\nu t)] \qquad N_m = \frac{N}{2}[1 + \exp(-2B\rho_\nu t)] \qquad (6\text{-}50)$$

where we assume that at $t = 0$ we have $N_n = 0$, $N_m = N$. For a time small compared with $(2B\rho_\nu)^{-1}$, we can expand the exponentials in power series and use only the linear term, obtaining

$$N_n = NB\rho_\nu t \qquad N_m = N(1 - B\rho_\nu t) \qquad (6\text{-}51)$$

The fraction of atoms in the nth state, N_n/N, is then $B\rho_\nu t$ to this linear approximation, in agreement with Eq. (6-48). We should have been able to get higher approximations, involving higher powers of t, if we had not made the approximation of disregarding all terms in Eq. (6-40) except for $k = m$, but as we can see, this is unnecessary for the determination of B. It is much easier to find B as we have done and then use Einstein's methods, in the form of equations like Eq. (6-15), for carrying the problem to longer time intervals.

There is one question which we should examine: Were we justified, in carrying out the integration of Eq. (6-47), in assuming that we could let be a time of many periods of oscillation of the frequency ν_{nm}? We were not, unless this is compatible with our other approximation, namely, that we may use the linear approximations of Eq. (6-51), which means that is short compared with $(2B\rho_\nu)^{-1}$. Once one has computed B in actual cases, one can check the validity of this approximation and it turns out to be completely justified. The time taken for the N's to build up to half, or to $1/e$, of their final values is ordinarily many million periods of oscillation. Hence one can easily take a time small compared with this time, but still containing many periods.

This is a result of the small interaction between the atomic system and the electromagnetic field. In more advanced study of field theory, this situation is described as saying that there is weak coupling between the atomic system and the electromagnetic field, on account of the numerical values of various physical constants. It is this weak coupling which allows us to carry out our calculations of atomic systems by first assuming that there is no radiation, so that we can find stationary states, and then treating the radiation as a perturbation. If on the contrary there were strong coupling, which would mean that radiation would cause an atomic system to jump from one stationary state to another in a few periods of oscillation, or even more in a fraction of a period, then the concept of stationary states would lose its meaning and we should have to use quite different methods of calculation. Some of the current theories of nuclear behavior involve field theories with strong coupling, and it is natural, for this reason, that they are far more difficult than the electromagnetic problem which we are taking up in the present chapter.

6-9. The Kramers-Heisenberg Dispersion Formula. In the present section we shall consider, not the transitions between stationary states, but rather the induced dipoles set up in an atomic system by an external radiation field.[1] It is these induced dipoles which, according to dispersion theory, are responsible for the fact that the index of refraction of a substance is different from unity. They also are responsible for the scattering of light in an inhomogeneous medium. We shall not go here into these applications but shall content ourselves with finding the induced dipoles and showing the ways in which they resemble the dipoles postulated in the classical theory of dispersion, before the quantum theory was developed.

We may take our external field to be produced by a single component of the vector potential postulated in Eq. (6-37), and our object is now to find the component in the dipole moment which oscillates in synchronism with the field and is proportional to it. On account of the proportionality to the field, we can assume a negligibly small field, small enough so that we can disregard the transitions produced by it. We shall assume the atomic system is in its mth state, as before, and shall look for the component of c_n involving the sinusoidal oscillation with frequency ν. Thus, instead of Eq. (6-44), which satisfied the initial condition that c_n was zero when $t = 0$, we take only the oscillatory terms and have

$$c_n = \frac{\pi i \nu_{nm}}{h} (\mathbf{M}_{nm} \cdot \mathbf{A}_\nu) \left\{ \exp(-i\alpha_\nu) \frac{\exp[2\pi i(\nu + \nu_{nm})t]}{\nu + \nu_{nm}} \right.$$
$$\left. - \exp(i\alpha_\nu) \frac{\exp[-2\pi i(\nu - \nu_{nm})t]}{\nu - \nu_{nm}} \right\} \quad (6\text{-}52)$$

[1] See E. Schrödinger, *Ann. Physik*, **81**:109 (1926), for the first wave-mechanical derivation of the dispersion formula.

We assume that all c_n's are very small, on account of the proportionality with the field, so that to a first approximation c_m is unity. When we substitute these c_n's in Eq. (6-38) and use Eq. (6-39), we find that the perturbed wave function, to the first order of small quantities, is

$$\psi = \exp\left(-iH^0_{mm}t/\hbar\right)\left\{u^0_m + \sum (n \neq m)\,\frac{\pi i \nu_{nm}}{h}\,(\mathbf{M}_{nm} \cdot \mathbf{A}_\nu)u^0_n\right.$$
$$\left.\times\left[\exp\left(-i\alpha_\nu\right)\frac{\exp\left(2\pi i\nu t\right)}{\nu + \nu_{nm}} - \exp\left(i\alpha_\nu\right)\frac{\exp\left(-2\pi i\nu t\right)}{\nu - \nu_{nm}}\right]\right\} \quad (6\text{-}53)$$

We can now set up the probability density $\psi^*\psi$ and find that it has a constant term $u^{0*}_m u^0_m$ and then a series of terms proportional to $\mathbf{A}_\nu$, coming from the products $u^{0*}_m u^0_n$ or $u^{0*}_n u^0_m$. These terms are oscillating with the frequency ν and represent the induced distribution of charge. They will result in an oscillating dipole moment, proportional to the electric field. Let us assume that $\mathbf{A}_\nu$ is a vector in the x direction, for convenience. Then, in the expression $\mathbf{M}_{nm} \cdot \mathbf{A}_\nu$, we are dealing with the x component of the dipole moment $\mathbf{M}_{nm}$. We shall then compute the x component of the induced dipole moment. The possibility is not excluded that there may be y and z components of the induced dipole as well, but we shall perform shortly an average over different orientations of the atom, and when such an average is carried out, all components of the dipole except the x component will disappear, though we shall not discuss these orientational effects here. Let us, then, find the average value of the operator $(M_x)_{\text{op}}$, averaged over the wave function of Eq. (6-53). When we do this, we find that it is

$$(M_x)_{\text{av}} = \int \left\{u^{0*}_m(M_x)_{\text{op}}\sum (n \neq m)\,\frac{\pi i \nu_{nm}}{h}\,(M_{nm})_x A_{\nu x}u^0_n\right.$$
$$\left[\exp\left(-i\alpha_\nu\right)\frac{\exp\left(2\pi i\nu t\right)}{\nu + \nu_{nm}} - \exp\left(i\alpha_\nu\right)\frac{\exp\left(-2\pi i\nu t\right)}{\nu - \nu_{nm}}\right]$$
$$\left. + \text{conjugate}\right\}\,dv$$

$$= \sum (n \neq m)\,\frac{|(M_{nm})_x|^2}{h}\,2\pi\nu_{nm}A_{\nu x}$$
$$\sin\left(2\pi\nu t - \alpha_\nu\right)\left(-\frac{1}{\nu + \nu_{nm}} - \frac{1}{\nu - \nu_{nm}}\right)$$

$$= \sum (n \neq m)\,\frac{|(M_{nm})_x|^2}{h}\,(2\nu_{nm})2\pi\nu A_{\nu x}\sin\left(2\pi\nu t - \alpha_\nu\right)\frac{1}{\nu^2_{nm} - \nu^2}$$

$$= \left[\sum (n \neq m)\,\frac{|(M_{nm})_x|^2}{h}\,\frac{2\nu_{nm}}{\nu^2_{nm} - \nu^2}\right]E \quad (6\text{-}54)$$

where $E = 2\pi\nu A_{\nu x}\sin\left(2\pi\nu t - \alpha_\nu\right)$, the electric field, and where as before $h\nu_{nm} = H^0_{nn} - H^0_{mm}$.

In Eq. (6-54) we have the Kramers-Heisenberg[1] dispersion formula, which was worked out before wave mechanics by means of an argument based on the correspondence principle. It is very similar to the formula worked out in the elementary classical theory of optics. There it is assumed that an electron in an atom is held to a position of equilibrium by a linear restoring force. If its mass is m_0, its charge is e_0, and its natural frequency of vibration is ν_0, the equation of motion in the presence of the external field E is

$$m_0\left(\frac{d^2x}{dt^2} + 4\pi^2\nu_0^2 x\right) = e_0 E \tag{6-55}$$

If we assume that the external field is oscillating with frequency ν and that x oscillates with the same frequency, we have

$$4\pi^2 m_0(-\nu^2 + \nu_0^2)x = e_0 E$$
$$e_0 x = \frac{e_0^2}{4\pi^2 m_0}\frac{1}{\nu_0^2 - \nu^2} E \tag{6-56}$$

Since $e_0 x$ is the induced dipole moment, we see the close resemblance between this classical result and Eq. (6-54). The wave-mechanical result gives a sum of terms of the classical type, one for each transition which is possible from the stationary state m in which the atom is located. On account of the fact that ν_{nm} is positive if the nth state is higher than the mth in energy, negative if it is below, we see that in the quantum-mechanical expression, Eq. (6-54), we can have both terms of the same sign as the classical one, for transitions upward from the mth state, and terms of the opposite sign, called negative dispersion, for transitions downward.

It is a convenient thing to rewrite Eq. (6-54) in a form suggestive of Eq. (6-56), the classical formula. Thus, we can rewrite Eq. (6-54) in the form

$$(M_x)_{\text{av}} = \left[\sum (n \neq m)\frac{e_0^2}{4\pi^2 m_0}\frac{f_{mn}}{\nu_{nm}^2 - \nu^2}\right] E \tag{6-57}$$

where f_{mn}, a dimensionless quantity, is called the oscillator strength of the transition in question. By equating this expression and Eq. (6-54), we see that

$$f_{mn} = \frac{8\pi^2 m_0 \nu_{nm}|(M_{nm})_x|^2}{e_0^2 h} \tag{6-58}$$

If we assume that atoms are equally likely to be oriented in any direction, we shall find that

$$|(M_{nm})_x|^2 = |(M_{nm})_y|^2 = |(M_{nm})_z|^2 = \tfrac{1}{3}|(M_{nm})|^2 \tag{6-59}$$

[1] H. A. Kramers, *Nature*, **113**:673, **114**:310 (1924); H. A. Kramers and W. Heisenberg, *Z. Physik*, **31**:681 (1925).

In terms of this, we can then rewrite Eq. (6-58) in the form

$$f_{mn} = \frac{8\pi^2 m_0 \nu_{nm} |(M_{nm})|^2}{3 e_0^2 h} \qquad (6\text{-}60)$$

In terms of this expression, we can rewrite Eq. (6-24) in the form

$$B = \frac{\pi e_0^2 |f_{mn}|}{m_0 h |\nu_{nm}| (4\pi\epsilon_0)} \qquad (6\text{-}61)$$

The importance of the oscillator strengths is partly that they provide convenient dimensionless quantities proportional to the B's, but partly also on account of an important theorem, the Kuhn-Thomas[1] sum rule. This rule states that

$$\Sigma(n) f_{mn} = N \qquad (6\text{-}62)$$

where the sum is over all final states n, for a given initial state m, transitions to upper states having positive f_{mn}'s, those to lower states having negative f's, and where N is the total number of electrons in the atomic system.   We prove this sum rule in Appendix 11 and show that it follows directly from the commutation rule of Eq. (4-33).   It was originally proved by Kuhn and Thomas before wave mechanics.   They showed that, if the dispersion formula were to reduce properly to the Thomson scattering formula at high frequencies, the rule would have to be obeyed. Heisenberg gave the wave-mechanical proof in terms of Eq. (4-33).   As a matter of fact, the historical importance of the rule is shown by the fact that Heisenberg was led from the existence of the sum rule, as demonstrated by Kuhn and Thomas, to believe that the commutation rule must hold, and this led him, in his first paper on matrix mechanics, to this fundamental postulate of quantum mechanics.

Let us see what is this limiting Thomson scattering formula which led Kuhn and Thomas to the sum rule.   Thomson considered the scattering of X rays by free electrons.   Such an electron would obey Eq. (6-55), with ν_0 equal to zero.   Hence the dipole moment arising from such an electron would be given by Eq. (6-56), again with ν_0 set equal to zero. If there are N electrons in the system, we have N times as great a dipole moment.   But now if the wave-mechanical dipole moment is given by Eq. (6-57), and if we consider frequencies so great that all the ν_{nm}'s can be neglected in comparison with ν, we see when we consider the sum rule, Eq. (6-62), that the result for the dipole moment will be the same as is given by the classical formula.   It is this Thomson scattering formula which we quoted in Sec. 1-2, as an early piece of evidence regarding the number of electrons in an atom.

[1] W. Kuhn, Z. Physik, 33:408 (1925); W. Thomas, Naturwiss., 13:627 (1925); W. Heisenberg, Z. Physik, 33:879 (1925).

6-10. Dirac's Theory of the Interaction of Radiation and Matter. We have seen the shortcoming of the semiclassical method of handling the interaction of radiation and matter, which we have been discussing: it fails to account for the probability A of spontaneous emission. This shortcoming is remedied in Dirac's treatment, which puts radiation theory on a really sound basis. Fortunately, however, the more general theory shows that the results of the semiclassical method are correct as far as they go, and they are considerably simpler to use. We shall go into Dirac's theory in considerable detail in Appendix 12 and shall merely sketch the steps here.

Dirac[1] handled the radiation field quantum-mechanically, as well as the atomic system. He assumed that each mode of oscillation of the electromagnetic field would have a quantum number n, in the absence of coupling between the radiation and the atoms, and that the atomic system would have a set of quantum numbers which we shall now symbolize by p (since we shall be using n for the radiation quantum numbers). Then, when we take account of the interaction between radiation and matter, transitions occur, in which the quantum numbers of the atomic system change, say from p to p', and simultaneously there is a change in quantum numbers of the field, of a sort to indicate the emission or absorption of photons. We calculate the nondiagonal matrix components of the Hamiltonian for such a transition. This Hamiltonian, which we discuss in Appendix 12, is a more general one than we have considered so far and includes the radiation as well as the atoms. We find that the only nonvanishing nondiagonal matrix components come when just one of the radiation modes has a change of quantum number, and its quantum number must change by only ± 1 unit, indicating that in a radiation transition only one photon is emitted or absorbed. The matrix components for these two possibilities prove to be

$$H^0_{n,p;n+1,p'} = \sqrt{\frac{(n+1)h}{8\pi^2\epsilon_0\nu}}\, \frac{i}{\hbar}\,(E_{p'} - E_p)\mathbf{A}\cdot\mathbf{M}_{pp'}$$

$$H^0_{n,p;n-1,p'} = \sqrt{\frac{nh}{8\pi^2\epsilon_0\nu}}\, \frac{i}{\hbar}\,(E_{p'} - E_p)\mathbf{A}\cdot\mathbf{M}_{pp'}$$

$$(6\text{-}63)$$

There are several matters about these formulas which must be explained. The quantum number n is assumed to be that associated with the particular radiation mode which gains or loses a photon in the transition, and the frequency ν is the frequency of this mode. The square roots will be recognized as the matrix components of the linear oscillator, from Eq. (4-46), with ϵ_0 substituted for the mass. They come into the formula since the radiation modes are treated as linear oscil-

[1] P. A. M. Dirac, *Proc. Roy. Soc. (London)*, **A114**:243 (1927).

lators. The remaining factor in the matrix components looks like the matrix component of Eq. (6-36), but there is a fundamental difference which we shall describe, rather than writing in a mathematical formula. The quantity $\mathbf{A}$, which appears in it, looks like the $\mathbf{A}$ of Eq. (6-36), but it is actually quite different, though closely related. It is the value of a vector field, whose dependence on position is like that of $\mathbf{E}$ in Eq. (6-1), but which unlike that vector field is independent of time, and is normalized so that the square of its magnitude, integrated over the volume of the cavity, equals unity.

The transitions produced by these nondiagonal matrix components are treated, as in the semiclassical method, by the method of variation of constants. Here, however, the transitions are those in which the energy of the whole system, radiation plus atoms, is very nearly conserved. We meet a formula which looks superficially like Eq. (6-45); but instead of having $\nu - \nu_{nm}$, we have the energy difference between the initial and final state of the whole system, which is practically zero. We convert the summation into an integration, essentially by Eq. (6-46), and as in Eq. (6-48), we finally end up with $c_{p'}^* c_{p'}$ coming out proportionally to time. The result is as follows:

$$c_{p'}^* c_{p'} = \frac{8\pi^3}{3} \frac{|M_{pp'}|^2}{(4\pi\epsilon_0)h^2} \frac{8\pi h\nu^3}{c^3} [(n)_{av} + 1]t \qquad \text{for emission}$$

$$= \frac{8\pi^3}{3} \frac{|M_{pp'}|^2}{(4\pi\epsilon_0)h^2} \frac{8\pi h\nu^3}{c^3} (n)_{av} t \qquad \text{for absorption} \quad (6\text{-}64)$$

Here the initial atomic state is denoted by p, the final one by p', and the case of emission is that where the energy of the state p' is below that of the state p, while for absorption it is above. The quantity $(n)_{av}$ is the average number of photons in the radiation mode of frequency ν, corresponding to the transition in question. The existence of the terms $(n)_{av} + 1$, $(n)_{av}$ is directly tied up to the square roots in Eq. (6-63). On the other hand, when we examine Eqs. (6-24) and (6-25), we see that Eq. (6-64) gives just what we should have expected, including the term A, which arises from the 1 in the expression $(n)_{av} + 1$. Furthermore, we see that the value of B, arising from Eq. (6-64), is the same one which we have already found by the semiclassical method.

6-11. The Breadth of Spectrum Lines. The spectrum of a radiated spectral line is not infinitely sharp; it has a finite half-breadth, though ordinarily this is only an extremely minute fraction of the frequency. This is a result of the finite time taken to radiate, and consequently the finite length of the wave train. Thus, in Eq. (2-4) and Appendix 3, we have pointed out that the uncertainty in frequency, or breadth, of a spectrum line is of the order of magnitude of the reciprocal of the time taken to emit the radiation. This holds both in the classical and the quantum theory. As a first step in discussing it, let us consider the classical case.

We shall start with the classical equation of motion, Eq. (6-55). However, this equation as it stands is not adequate, for it has no term in it which would result in a damping of the amplitude of oscillation. We must include a resistive term, giving force opposing the motion and proportional to the velocity, to lead to the correct behavior. Thus, let us assume an equation

$$m_0\left(\frac{d^2x}{dt^2} + g\frac{dx}{dt} + 4\pi^2\nu_0^2 x\right) = e_0 E \tag{6-65}$$

where $m_0 g\, dx/dt$ represents the resistive term. If we assume that the oscillator is excited by some sort of collision, and its oscillation then proceeds to decay in the absence of an external field E, we can solve for the damped oscillation in the usual way and find

$$x = x_0 \exp\left[-(g/2)t\right] \exp\left\{2\pi i[\nu_0^2 - (g/4\pi)^2]^{1/2}t\right\} \tag{6-66}$$

a damped oscillation which falls to $1/e$ of its initial amplitude in a time $2/g$. If g is small compared with ν_0, as it is in the cases we are considering, we may neglect $(g/4\pi)^2$ compared with ν_0^2 and write the sinusoidal term as $\exp(2\pi i\nu_0 t)$. We may now expect that the half-breadth of the emitted spectral line will be of the order of magnitude of $g/2$.

We can easily verify that this is actually the case by making a spectral analysis of the disturbance of Eq. (6-66) by Fourier's integral, as in Appendix 3. To find the amplitude of the oscillation of frequency ν in the spectrum, we must multiply the expression of Eq. (6-66) by $\exp(-2\pi i\nu t)$ and integrate over the time when the radiation is being emitted, or from $t = 0$ to ∞. The result is

$$x_0\int_0^\infty \exp\left[-\frac{g}{2} + 2\pi i(\nu_0 - \nu)\right]t\, dt = \frac{x_0}{g/2 - 2\pi i(\nu_0 - \nu)} \tag{6-67}$$

To find the intensity at frequency ν, which is proportional to the square of the amplitude, we multiply the expression of Eq. (6-67) by its complex conjugate to get the square of its magnitude. We have

$$\frac{x_0^2}{4\pi^2(\nu_0 - \nu)^2 + (g/2)^2} \tag{6-68}$$

The half-breadth, or frequency difference between the two frequencies at which this expression has half its maximum value, is

$$\Delta\nu = \frac{g}{2\pi} \tag{6-69}$$

as we see by setting $4\pi^2(\nu_0 - \nu)^2 = (g/2)^2$, so that the half-breadth is of the expected order of magnitude (the uncertainty relations give information only as to order of magnitude, not as to the specific numerical factor). It is convenient to have a normalized form of Eq. (6-68), giving the fraction of the intensity of the line found in the range $d\nu$. This can be found at once by use of the relation that

$$\int_{-\infty}^{\infty} \frac{dx}{x^2 + a^2} = \frac{\pi}{a} \tag{6-70}$$

It is

$$\frac{1}{\pi} \frac{(g/4\pi)\, d\nu}{(\nu_0 - \nu)^2 + (g/4\pi)^2} \tag{6-71}$$

It is now interesting to ask what effect the resistive term in Eq. (6-65) has on the dispersion formula. If we proceed as in the derivation of Eq. (6-56), assuming a sinusoidal external field of frequency ν, varying as $\exp(2\pi i \nu t)$, we find that

$$e_0 x = \frac{e_0^2}{4\pi^2 m_0} \frac{1}{\nu_0^2 - \nu^2 + i\nu g/2\pi} E \tag{6-72}$$

One finds, in studying dispersion theory, that the absorption of light by the atom depends on the imaginary part of the coefficient multiplying E, in Eq. (6-72); this coefficient is the polarizability of the atom, or the ratio of dipole moment to field. If we rewrite this polarizability in terms of its real and imaginary parts, we have

$$\text{Polarizability} = \frac{e_0^2}{4\pi^2 m_0} \frac{(\nu_0^2 - \nu^2) - i\nu g/2\pi}{(\nu_0^2 - \nu^2)^2 + (\nu g/2\pi)^2} \tag{6-73}$$

If the frequency is close to resonance, we may rewrite the expression $\nu_0^2 - \nu^2$ in the denominator, which equals $(\nu_0 - \nu)(\nu_0 + \nu)$, as approximately equal to $2\nu_0(\nu_0 - \nu)$ and we may replace the factor ν, which multiplies g, by ν_0. Thus, approximately, close to resonance, we have

$$\text{Polarizability} = \frac{e_0^2}{4\pi^2 m_0} \frac{1}{2\nu_0} \frac{(\nu_0 - \nu) - ig/4\pi}{(\nu_0 - \nu)^2 + (g/4\pi)^2} \tag{6-74}$$

We now observe the very interesting fact that the imaginary part of Eq. (6-74), which determines the absorption, has the same frequency dependence as Eq. (6-71), expressing the shape of the emission line. This is in accordance with Kirchhoff's law, a fundamental law of radiation, which states that the emission of a body, and its absorption coefficient, must have the same dependence on frequency. Kirchhoff's law is a fundamental result of thermodynamics and as such must hold both in the classical and in quantum theory.

This sketch of the spectral resolution of an emission line in classical theory, and its relation to the absorption coefficient, will prepare us for the situation which is found in wave mechanics. Dirac's radiation theory must be used in studying the shape of the emission line, for we have seen that the semiclassical treatment of radiation cannot account for the spontaneous radiation at all. A study of the shape of an emission line according to Dirac's theory has been made by Weisskopf and Wigner.[1] They proceeded along the general lines sketched in Sec. 6-10 but made two changes in treatment, which allowed them to study this spectral distribution. First, they did not limit themselves to short times during which, as in Eq. (6-48), the quantities $c_n^* c_n$ increased proportionally to the time. Rather, they assumed that they would have solutions for the c_n's which built up according to exponential functions of the time, of the sort suggested by Eq. (6-20), but with the exponential terms undetermined. They substituted these expressions in the equations, similar to Eq. (6-40), which they met in using the method of variation of constants and showed that they could get exact solutions for these equations in this form and that they could determine the constants in the exponential expressions from these equations. The exponentials of course worked out as in Eq. (6-20), thereby justifying our simpler procedure of solving only for a short time, during which $c_n^* c_n$ was building up linearly with time.

The second respect in which Weisskopf and Wigner went beyond our treatment is that they investigated the average quantum numbers or intensities of the modes of radiation, to see which ones had increased in the course of the radiation process. They could find the way the increase of the average quantum number n varied with frequency ν, in the neighborhood of ν_0, the ordinary frequency of the quantum transition, and they found an expression of the general form of Eq. (6-71) for the resulting shape of the spectral line. The interesting feature of their study was the value which they found for the quantum-theory equivalent of the quantity expressed as $g/4\pi$ in Eq. (6-71). For a transition between the nth and mth states, they found

$$g = \text{sum of probabilities of leaving } n\text{th and } m\text{th states} \qquad (6\text{-}75)$$

That is, for instance, in the case which we took up in Eq. (6-20), where the probability of leaving state 1 was $B\rho_\nu$ and that of leaving state 2 was $A + B\rho_\nu$, they would find $g = A + 2B\rho_\nu$.

This symmetrical dependence of the breadth of a spectral line on both initial and final stationary states is required by Kirchhoff's law; it had been pointed out before wave mechanics by the author,[2] using an argu-

[1] V. Weisskopf and E. Wigner, Z. Physik, 63:54 (1930).
[2] J. C. Slater, Phys. Rev., 25:395 (1925).

ment based on the correspondence principle. For it is obvious that, if we must have the same breadth for the emission and absorption lines, then both states must be treated symmetrically, since the state which is the initial state for emission is the final state for absorption, and vice versa.

There is a very interesting interpretation which can be given the law and which was pointed out by Weisskopf and Wigner. We may imagine that each separate energy level is broadened on account of its finite lifetime. That is, if Γ_n is the probability of leaving the nth state, Γ_m the probability of leaving the mth state, then we may assume that the actual energy levels are not sharp but that instead, following Eq. (6-71), there is a sort of continuous distribution of energy levels, the fraction between E and $E + dE$ being

$$\frac{1}{\pi} \frac{(\Gamma_n/4\pi)\, dE/h}{(E_n - E)^2/h^2 + (\Gamma_n/4\pi)^2} \qquad (6\text{-}76)$$

for the nth state, with a corresponding quantity for the mth state. Here E_n is the average energy level of the nth state. Then, in a transition between the nth and mth state, we shall have a situation as shown in Fig. 6-4, where we show a broadened upper and lower level and a possible transition between them. Let us now inquire how much radiation of frequencies between ν and $\nu + d\nu$ will be emitted in the transition. Let E' stand for an energy in the lower band, E'' in the upper, so that $h\nu = E'' - E'$. For a given value of E', the range $d\nu$ corresponds to values of E'' between $E' + h\nu$ and $E' + h(\nu + d\nu)$. The fraction of states of the upper band in this range is

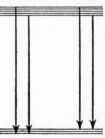

FIG. 6-4. Transitions between broadened levels of an atomic system.

$$\frac{1}{\pi} \frac{(\Gamma_m/4\pi)\, d\nu}{(E_m - E' - h\nu)^2/h^2 + (\Gamma_m/4\pi)^2} \qquad (6\text{-}77)$$

The fraction of states in the lower band between E' and $E' + dE'$ is given by Eq. (6-76), with E' substituted for E. We may then get the fractional amount of radiation emitted in the range $d\nu$ by multiplying these quantities and integrating over dE'.

We thus have as the fraction of radiation in $d\nu$ the quantity

$$\int_{-\infty}^{\infty} \frac{1}{\pi} \frac{\Gamma_m/4\pi}{(E_m - E' - h\nu)^2/h^2 + (\Gamma_m/4\pi)^2} \frac{1}{\pi} \frac{(\Gamma_n/4\pi)\, dE'/h}{(E_n - E')^2/h^2 + (\Gamma_n/4\pi)^2} \qquad (6\text{-}78)$$

This can be integrated, by use of the theorem

$$\int_{-\infty}^{\infty} \frac{a}{\pi} \frac{1}{x^2 + a^2} \frac{b}{\pi} \frac{1}{(x + y)^2 + b^2}\, dx = \frac{a + b}{\pi} \frac{1}{y^2 + (a + b)^2} \qquad (6\text{-}79)$$

which can be proved by expanding the integrand in partial fractions. Then as the fraction of radiation in $d\nu$ we find

$$\frac{1}{\pi} \frac{(\Gamma_n + \Gamma_m)/4\pi \; d\nu}{(\nu_{mn} - \nu)^2 + (\Gamma_n + \Gamma_m)/4\pi^2} \tag{6-80}$$

Here $h\nu_{mn} = E_m - E_n$. We see that Eq. (6-80) is of the form of Eq. (6-71), with g given by Eq. (6-75). The meaning of Eq. (6-80) is the interesting fact that, if two energy levels, of the form given by Eq. (6-71), combine to give an emitted spectrum line, the half-breadth of the line is the sum of the half-breadths of the two levels.

This very simple result, then, expresses the conclusions of Weisskopf and Wigner regarding the broadening of emission lines. It is to be understood that, in the general case, the transition probabilities Γ_n and Γ_m which appear in Eq. (6-80) can include the transition probabilities not merely for making the transitions $n \to m$ or $m \to n$, respectively, but also for making transitions to other quite independent states. Thus it can be that a given energy level n is broadened on account of there being a large transition probability for a transition from this state to a state k, say; this will still have the effect of broadening correspondingly the line emitted in the transition from a state m to the state n. Weisskopf and Wigner have examined such cases and have found the behavior to be in accordance with these statements.

Weisskopf and Wigner did not investigate the corresponding broadening of the absorption lines, and the resulting terms in the polarizability, like those in g in Eq. (6-74); this is a gap in the development of quantum electrodynamics which should be filled in. However, on account of Kirchhoff's law, it is generally assumed that the result will be that the Kramers-Heisenberg dispersion formula, Eq. (6-54), should be supplemented by absorption terms, just as we have found corresponding terms in the classical case, in Eq. (6-72); and it is assumed that the g appearing here, for a given absorption line, should be given by Eq. (6-75), just as it is in the case of emission. Such absorption terms are experimentally found, and their effect on the observed index of refraction and absorption coefficient is well known.

PROBLEMS

1. In classical electromagnetic theory, an electric dipole whose electric moment is $M \cos \omega t$ radiates energy at a rate of [1]

$$\frac{M^2 \omega^4}{3c^3 (4\pi\epsilon_0)}$$

[1] See, for instance, J. C. Slater and N. H. Frank, "Electromagnetism," p. 159, McGraw-Hill Book Company, Inc., New York, 1947.

Set up a differential equation for the time rate of change of energy, and show that this leads to an exponential decay of the energy of the dipole. Find the damping constant, corresponding to g of Sec. 6-11.

2. Use the classical discussion of Sec. 6-11, and the rate of damping given in Prob. 1, to find the breadth of the spectrum line emitted by the classical oscillator damped only by its radiation. This is called its natural line width. Find not only $\Delta\nu$, but also $\Delta\lambda$, where λ is the wavelength, and show that $\Delta\lambda$ is independent of the wavelength of the radiation. Compute its value. Show from this that the natural line width is a more important phenomenon for X rays than for visible radiation.

3. Note that in quantum theory, corresponding to a transition from state 1 to state 2, we have a dipole moment which contains the terms $M_{12} \exp\left[-i(E_2 - E_1)t/\hbar\right]$ and $M_{21} \exp\left[i(E_2 - E_1)t/\hbar\right]$, whose sum is $2M_{12} \cos(E_2 - E_1)t/\hbar$. Suppose you had a classical oscillator with this dipole moment. Find the rate of radiation by the method of Prob. 1. Show that this rate of radiation is $Ah\nu$, where A is determined from M_{12} by Eq. (6-24). This fact was used before Dirac's radiation theory was available, to give a semiclassical treatment of spontaneous radiation.

4. Use the matrix components of x for a linear oscillator given in Sec. 4-6 to find the A, B, and oscillator strength for transitions of a linear oscillator. Use Eq. (6-58) for the oscillator strength, since this is a one-dimensional problem. Verify the sum rule for oscillator strengths.

5. A linear oscillator is in its nth state. Find the rate of spontaneous radiation of energy to the $(n-1)$st state according to the quantum theory, using the value of A found in Prob. 4, and compare with the classical rate of radiation of an oscillator of the same energy.

6. The sodium atom in its ground state has a transition to an excited state at a wavelength of 5,890 angstroms (the D line), which has an oscillator strength very close to unity, all other transitions to excited states having oscillator strengths which are small compared with unity. Find the quantity A for the transition involved in the D line. If we started out at $t = 0$ with an assembly of sodium atoms in the excited state associated with the D line, find the half-life of these excited atoms (the time at which half the atoms have had transitions to the ground state).

7. In a sodium vapor, there is an inert gas present which has the effect of producing a collision with an excited sodium atom after an average time of 10^{-7} sec, interrupting its stationary state and hence broadening the energy level. Work out the half-width of the D line both with and without the inert gas.

8. The polarizability α of an atom equals the dipole moment divided by the electric field. If there are N atoms per unit volume, the dielectric constant equals $1 + (N\alpha/\epsilon_0)$. If the polarizability depends on frequency, this leads to a frequency-dependent dielectric constant. The optical index of refraction n is given by the relation $n^2 =$ dielectric constant. Assume that a crystal contains one atom per cube of linear dimension 3 angstroms. Let each atom have only one important absorption frequency, at an optical wavelength of 2,000 angstroms, and let the oscillator strength corresponding to this transition be unity. Compute the dielectric constant at zero frequency and the index of refraction for radiation of 6,000 and 4,000 angstroms.

9. Assume an upper and a lower energy level each broadened into a Gaussian error curve, rather than into the type of band given in Eq. (6-76), generally called a Lorentzian curve. Apply the same sort of analysis used in the derivation of Eq. (6-80), to show that the width of the emitted spectrum line will equal the sum of the widths of the two levels, the distribution of intensity in the emitted line being Gaussian.

7

The Hydrogen Atom

7-1. Schrödinger's Equation for Hydrogen. In the preceding chapters we have been studying the general principles of wave mechanics. We are now ready to start our main task, the investigation of the structure of atoms. In this chapter we take up the simplest of the atoms, hydrogen, which is not only important in itself, but which furnishes a model for all the others. We have seen in the first chapter that Bohr's success in explaining the structure of hydrogen according to the older quantum theory was the greatest triumph of that theory but that, nevertheless, there were minor features in which it needed correction. When Schrödinger set up his equation, hydrogen was the first problem on which it was tested and here again the success formed a convincing proof of the correctness of the theory. We now proceed to the discussion of the structure of the hydrogen atom on the basis of wave mechanics.

In the hydrogen atom, we have an electron moving in the field of force of the proton, its nucleus. The proton attracts the electron according to the inverse-square law, or Coulomb's law of attraction, met in electrostatics; but many of our results are more general than this law and hold for any central force, that is, any radial force directed toward a center of attraction and depending only on the distance, not on the angle. This is important, for we shall find that we can approximate the general atomic problem by a central field, which, however, differs from an inverse-square field, so that some of the results of the present chapter can be used later. The feature of the present problem which allows us to generalize it is the fact that a central field can exert no torque, or moment of force, on the particle; thus, by Newton's second law, the angular momentum of the particle is constant in classical mechanics, and this has a simple analogue in wave mechanics. This results in simple and important consequences in the quantization of the angular momentum. For generality, we shall treat, not merely hydrogen, but the problem of a single electron moving about a nucleus of charge Ze, where Z is an integer, e the magnitude of the electronic charge. This will allow us to discuss ions of heavier atoms with atomic number Z; it will also prove to give valuable information about the inner electrons of other atoms.

The first thing that we notice about our problem is that the nucleus is very heavy compared with an electron.   Now, if we have a single electron and a single nucleus, exerting forces on each other, we find, in wave mechanics as in classical mechanics, that the center of gravity of the system moves with uniform velocity in a straight line, each particle rotating about the common center of gravity.   We discuss this problem of the nuclear motion by classical mechanics in Appendix 1.   Since the mass of the proton is 1,836 times that of the electron, the center of gravity divides the vector joining nucleus and electron in the ratio of 1:1,836, so that the nucleus executes only a very slight motion and we can almost treat it as being fixed and the electron as moving about a fixed center of attraction at the nucleus.   In Appendix 1 we show that this becomes an exact method of handling the problem of electronic rotation, provided we assign to the electron a so-called reduced mass, μ, slightly different from its true mass, and determined by the equation

$$\frac{1}{\mu} = \frac{1}{m_0} + \frac{1}{M} \qquad \mu = \frac{m_0 M}{m_0 + M} \tag{7-1}$$

where m_0 is the electronic mass, M the mass of the nucleus.   Since M for the proton is approximately $1,836 m_0$, we see that μ is less than m_0 by about one part in 1,836.   It is not hard to show that the same methods can be used in wave mechanics as well.

The problem of the electronic motion, then, is that of an electron of charge $-e$, mass μ, moving in a central field of force.   The attractive force of the nucleus has a potential energy $-Ze^2/4\pi\epsilon_0 r$, in mks units, where we remember that here, and in other cases, we can get the result in nonrationalized Gaussian units by eliminating the factor $4\pi\epsilon_0$.   Thus Schrödinger's equation, with the time eliminated, is

$$(H)_{op} u = \left(-\frac{\hbar^2}{2\mu} \nabla^2 - \frac{Ze^2}{4\pi\epsilon_0 r} \right) u = Eu \tag{7-2}$$

We shall find it convenient in all our atomic problems to introduce at the outset atomic units of distance and energy, which will eliminate the various dimensional constants which we meet in Eq. (7-2).   As the unit of distance, we shall use

$$a_0 = \frac{h^2 (4\pi\epsilon_0)}{4\pi^2 \mu e^2} \tag{7-3}$$

which is the radius of the first Bohr orbit, according to Bohr's theory, as given in Eq. (1-24).   We note that our definition involves μ, slightly different from m_0; the first Bohr radius a_0 would similarly involve μ if we had considered the nuclear motion in the Bohr theory, as we show in

Appendix 1. Similarly for the unit of energy we shall use the Rydberg energy,

$$Ry = \frac{2\pi^2\mu e^4}{(4\pi\epsilon_0)^2 h^2} \tag{7-4}$$

as in Eq. (1-18), except again for using the reduced mass μ, which again appears in the Bohr theory if the nuclear motion is considered. We have, then, slightly different units a_0 and Ry for each nucleus. For anything except quite accurate work, this variation of a_0 and Ry with M can be disregarded, and we can use the values appropriate for the case $M = \infty$.

There is one point to be noticed in connection with our choice of the Rydberg as a unit of energy. Hartree, in his writing on the theory of the self-consistent field, has used a unit of energy twice as great, and the atomic unit of Hartree is used a great deal in the literature. In some respects, Hartree's choice is more convenient than ours when it comes to the method of writing the equations, though there is very small choice between them. However, when it comes to comparing with numerical values, the experimenters almost always use Rydbergs as units of energy, and this seems to the present writer to be a deciding factor in favor of writing the theory in terms of Rydbergs. But the reader is cautioned to be on his guard in comparing our results with those of papers using Hartree's atomic units.

Now we can rewrite Eq. (7-2) in terms of the atomic units. We let new values of the coordinates equal the old values divided by a_0, and a new value of the energy be the old value divided by Ry. We then find that Eq. (7-2) is transformed into

$$\left(-\nabla^2 - \frac{2Z}{r}\right)u = Eu \tag{7-5}$$

where the derivatives are to be taken with respect to the new x, y, z. The coefficient 2 in the potential energy appears in the process of changing variables, the potential energy of two electronic charges being $2/r$ in these units. In contrast, if we had used Hartree's atomic units, we should have had in place of Eq. (7-5) the equation

$$\left(-\tfrac{1}{2}\nabla^2 - \frac{Z}{r}\right)u = Eu \tag{7-6}$$

with a factor $\frac{1}{2}$ in the kinetic energy, rather than a factor 2 in the potential energy.

The next step in solving Schrödinger's equation, Eq. (7-5), is to introduce spherical polar coordinates and carry out the process known as separation of variables. This is a familiar process in mathematical physics, and we give the details in Appendix 13. The result is that we can write u as a product of functions R, Θ, Φ, which are functions, respectively, of r, θ, ϕ, the three spherical coordinates. We can find separate differential equations for these three functions; and these differential equations prove to be

$$\frac{1}{r^2}\frac{d}{dr}\left(r^2\frac{dR}{dr}\right) + \left[E + \frac{2Z}{r} - \frac{l(l+1)}{r^2}\right]R = 0$$

$$\frac{1}{\sin\theta}\frac{d}{d\theta}\left(\sin\theta\frac{d\Theta}{d\theta}\right) + \left[l(l+1) - \frac{m^2}{\sin^2\theta}\right]\Theta = 0 \qquad (7\text{-}7)$$

$$\frac{d^2\Phi}{d\phi^2} + m^2\Phi = 0$$

Here l, m are constants which are introduced in connection with the separation of variables (m is not to be confused with the electronic mass) and which have to be determined from further conditions. The solution of the last equation is obvious: we must have $\Phi = \exp(\pm im\phi)$, or $\cos m\phi$ or $\sin m\phi$. In order to have Φ a single-valued function of ϕ, m must be an integer. The other equations are more complicated.

The equation for Θ in Eq. (7-7) is well known in mathematical physics; it is a form of Legendre's equation, and its solutions are the associated Legendre functions, denoted by $P_l^{|m|}(\cos\theta)$. We solve it by a method which reminds us somewhat of the solution of the problem of the linear oscillator in Sec. 3-7. We make a transformation to the form

$$\Theta = \sin^{|m|}\theta(A_0 + A_1\cos\theta + A_2\cos^2\theta + \cdots) \qquad (7\text{-}8)$$

where the A's are to be determined. When we substitute this series into the differential equation, we get a recursion formula for the A's. This is derived by the same sort of argument used in deriving Eq. (3-56) and is

$$A_k = A_{k-2}\frac{(k + |m| - 1)(k + |m| - 2) - l(l+1)}{k(k-1)} \qquad (7\text{-}9)$$

For integral l's, this series breaks off, the last nonvanishing term being for $k = l - |m|$. This is the reason why we wrote the separation constant in Eq. (7-7) in the form we did. If the series does not break off, it proves to diverge in the limit where $\cos\theta = 1$, the function going infinite, in much the same way that we found divergence in the problem of the linear oscillator if we allowed the series to continue. Since we cannot allow our solution to be infinite when $\cos\theta = 1$, this means that we must choose l to be an integer. In order for the series to break off, we see from Eq. (7-9) that l must be greater than or equal to $|m|$. Furthermore, if $l - |m|$ is even, it is only the expansion in even powers which will break off, so that we must set $A_1 = 0$, while if $l - |m|$ is odd, only the expansion in odd powers will break off, and we must set $A_0 = 0$.

The functions resulting in this way, and expressed in a standard form, with suitably chosen values of the coefficients, are the associated Legendre functions. They are ordinarily expressed, not as in Eq. (7-8) in a series of increasing powers of cos θ, but in a series of descending powers, starting with the term of highest power. In this form, they are defined as

$$P_l^m(\cos\theta) = \frac{\sin^m\theta(2l)!}{2^l l!(l-m)!}\left[(\cos\theta)^{l-m} - \frac{(l-m)(l-m-1)}{2(2l-1)}(\cos\theta)^{l-m-2}\right.$$
$$+ \frac{(l-m)(l-m-1)(l-m-2)(l-m-3)}{2\cdot4\cdot(2l-1)(2l-3)}(\cos\theta)^{l-m-4} - \cdots$$
$$+ \frac{(-1)^p(l-m)(l-m-1)\cdots(l-m-2p+1)}{2\cdot4\cdots(2p)(2l-1)(2l-3)\cdots(2l-2p+1)}(\cos\theta)^{l-m-2p}$$
$$\left.- \cdots\right] \quad (7\text{-}10)$$

where m is zero or a positive integer. To show the identity of this expression with that of Eq. (7-8), we need merely show that the ratio of successive coefficients is as given in Eq. (7-9). To do this, we may identify the term in $(\cos\theta)^{l-m-2p}$ in Eq. (7-10) with the term in $(\cos\theta)^{k-2}$ in Eq. (7-8) and the term in $(\cos\theta)^{l-m-2p+2}$ in Eq. (7-10) with that in $(\cos\theta)^k$ in Eq. (7-8). When we do this and take the ratio of coefficients from Eq. (7-10), we find that it is the same as given in Eq. (7-9), so that Eq. (7-10) forms a legitimate way of writing the solution of Eq. (7-8). The constant factor multiplying the series in Eq. (7-10) is chosen so as to simplify certain formulas.

The associated Legendre functions have many important properties, some of which are given in Appendix 14, but for our present purposes the most useful ones are their orthogonality and normalization relations. It can be proved that

$$\int_{-1}^1 P_l^m(x)\,P_{l'}^m(x)\,dx = \int_0^\pi P_l^m(\cos\theta)\,P_{l'}^m(\cos\theta)\sin\theta\,d\theta$$
$$= 0 \qquad\qquad \text{if } l \neq l'$$
$$= \frac{2}{2l+1}\frac{(l+m)!}{(l-m)!} \quad \text{if } l = l' \qquad (7\text{-}11)$$

In this formula, as in others in which we have not written $|m|$ with absolute value signs, it is understood that m is zero or a positive integer; the associated Legendre functions are not defined for negative values of m.†

7-2. The Radial Wave Function for Hydrogen. We have considered the nature of the angular dependence of the wave function for hydrogen and shall examine it in more detail in Sec. 7-3. Before doing so, let us consider the radial wave equation from Eq. (7-7) and the related wave function R. This equation becomes simplified if we introduce the quan-

† Some writers define associated Legendre functions for negative m's, but this is likely to lead to confusion, and we shall not do so.

tity $P(r) = rR(r)$.   It is unfortunate to use the symbol $P(r)$ for this function, along with the symbol $P_l^m(\cos \theta)$ for the associated Legendre function, but it is standard practice, which we shall adhere to.   When we assume this definition, the radial equation from Eq. (7-7) is transformed into

$$\frac{d^2P(r)}{dr^2} + \left[E + \frac{2Z}{r} - \frac{l(l+1)}{r^2} \right] P(r) = 0 \qquad (7\text{-}12)$$

Let us first consider the general nature of Eq. (7-12).   We see that it resembles the Schrödinger equation of a particle moving in one dimension, under the influence of a potential energy $-2Z/r + l(l+1)/r^2$. Let us ask what is the physical interpretation of the term $l(l+1)/r^2$, which at first sight might seem peculiar.   The kinetic energy of a particle of mass m can be written in terms of two components of momentum: p_r, along the radius, and p_l, at right angles to the radius.   The radial part of the kinetic energy is $p_r^2/2m$, whereas the angular part is $p_l^2/2m$. We can rewrite this latter term in the form $(p_l r)^2/2mr^2$, where the quantity $p_l r$ is the angular momentum.   Then we write the classical equation of conservation of energy in the form

$$\frac{p_r^2}{2m} + \frac{(p_l r)^2}{2mr^2} - \frac{Ze^2}{4\pi\epsilon_0 r} = \text{energy} \qquad (7\text{-}13)$$

But by the law of conservation of angular momentum, the quantity $p_l r$ remains constant provided there is no torque acting on the particle. Thus Eq. (7-13) is like the law of conservation of energy for a particle in one-dimensional motion along r, subject to a potential energy which consists, not merely of the Coulomb energy $-Ze^2/4\pi\epsilon_0 r$, but also of the term $(p_l r)^2/2mr^2$, which may be interpreted as the potential energy associated with the fictitious centrifugal force which we must insert if we wish to treat the problem as a one-dimensional one.

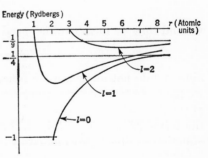

FIG. 7-1.   Effective potential energy $-2/r + l(l+1)/r^2$ for the hydrogen problem.

Now we shall show in the next section that the angular momentum is given by the relation

$$(p_l r)^2 = l(l+1)\hbar^2 \qquad (7\text{-}14)$$

If we insert this value in Eq. (7-13) and transform to atomic units, we find just the term $l(l+1)/r^2$ which is present in Eq. (7-12).

We see, then, that our radial problem is like a one-dimensional problem with the potential energy $-2Z/r + l(l+1)/r^2$.   In Fig. 7-1 we show this potential energy, for the case $Z = 1$, as a function of r, for various values of l. We also draw lines at constant energy, corresponding to the actual energy levels of the problem, which prove to be given, in wave mechanics as in Bohr's theory, by $-Ry/n^2$, where n is an integer. We see that in the case of each value of l horizontal lines corresponding to those energy levels for which n is equal to or greater than $l + 1$ will cross the potential-energy curve twice. Between two limiting values of r, the points where the curves cross, the classical kinetic energy is positive, and the wave function behaves in a more or less sinusoidal fashion. Outside this range the classical kinetic energy is negative, and the wave function rapidly decreases to zero. We see that the sinusoidal ranges rapidly increase in size as n increases. In Fig. 7-2, we show radial wave functions $P(r)$, for a number of values of n and l, for hydrogen. If we examine these functions carefully, we see that each function behaves in a sinusoidal fashion just in the range of r indicated in Fig. 7-1, starting to decrease rapidly outside that range.

Let us now start to consider the behavior of the wave function analytically. Its behavior for small and for large r, outside the sinusoidal region, can be determined by general arguments. For very small r, the term in $1/r^2$ in Eq. (7-12) is large compared with the terms E and $2Z/r$. If we disregard the two latter terms, so that we have

$$\frac{d^2P(r)}{dr^2} - \frac{l(l + 1)}{r^2}\, P(r) = 0 \tag{7-15}$$

we find that we have two independent solutions,

$$P(r) = r^{l+1},\, r^{-l} \tag{7-16}$$

Since we do not allow a wave function which becomes infinite at $r = 0$, we have the former type of behavior, so that $P(r)$ must behave like r^{l+1} at small r. Next we consider the case of very large values of r, for which the terms $2Z/r$ and $-l(l + 1)/r^2$ can be neglected, and the differential equation can be approximated by

$$\frac{d^2P(r)}{dr^2} + EP(r) = 0 \tag{7-17}$$

whose solutions are

$$P(r) = \exp\left(\pm \sqrt{-E}\, r\right) \tag{7-18}$$

If E is negative, the positive exponential will lead to a function becoming infinite at infinity, which we must discard, so that our wave function must behave like the negative exponential. This is the case leading to discrete eigenvalues. On the other hand, for positive E, the solution is sinusoidal for large r, and any positive energy gives an allowed solution, just as we found in Chap. 3 for the case of the potential well.

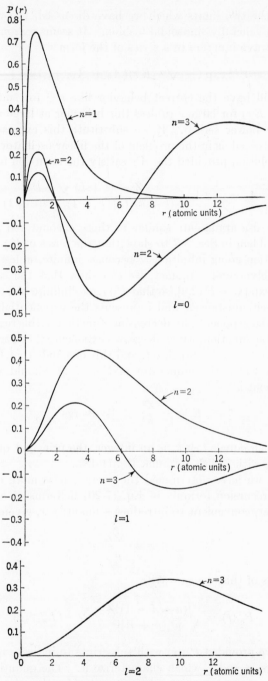

Fig. 7-2. Radial wave functions $P(r)$ for hydrogen.

173

Between the two limits which we have discussed, the wave function behaves in a generally sinusoidal fashion. It seems reasonable to try to expand the wave function in a series of the form

$$P(r) = r^{l+1} \exp{(-\sqrt{-E}\,r)}(A_0 + A_1 r + A_2 r^2 + \cdots) \qquad (7\text{-}19)$$

since this will have the correct behavior like r^{l+1} for small r and like $\exp{(-\sqrt{-E}\,r)}$ for large r (unless this behavior at large r is interfered with by the power series). If we substitute this expression into Eq. (7-12) and proceed as in the problem of the linear oscillator, we find that we have a solution provided the A's satisfy the recursion formula

$$A_k = -2A_{k-1}\frac{Z - (l+k)\sqrt{-E}}{(l+k)(l+k+1) - l(l+1)} \qquad (7\text{-}20)$$

We can now use arguments similar to those encountered in the linear-oscillator problem in Sec. 3-7 to show that the series of Eq. (7-20) represents a function going infinite as r becomes infinite, unless it breaks off to form a polynomial. In fact, we can show that the series becomes infinite like $\exp{[\sqrt{-E}\,(2r)]}$, so that $P(r)$ goes infinite like $\exp{(\sqrt{-E}\,r)}$ under these circumstances, and represents the exponentially increasing, rather than the exponentially decreasing, function in this region of large r. To get a usable function, which decreases exponentially to zero for large r, we must have the series break off, and this demands that there be some integer k for which the numerator of Eq. (7-20) should vanish. This will come about if

$$E = -\frac{Z^2}{n^2} \qquad \text{Rydbergs} \qquad (7\text{-}21)$$

where n, which equals $l + k$, is an integer, the principal quantum number, agreeing with Bohr's formula, Eq. (1-18).

Now that we have determined the energy, it is more convenient to express the recursion formula of Eq. (7-20) in terms of n. It is, as a matter of fact, convenient to introduce a quantity x, given by

$$x = \frac{2Zr}{n} \qquad (7\text{-}22)$$

and, in terms of this, we can write

$$P_{nl}(r) = \sqrt{\frac{(n-l-1)!Z}{n^2[(n+l)!]^3}}\; x^{l+1} e^{-x/2}\, L_{n+l}^{2l+1}(x) \qquad (7\text{-}23)$$

Here we have provided $P_{nl}(r)$ with subscripts to indicate the two quantum numbers, n and l, which characterize it. The quantity $L_{n+l}^{2l+1}(x)$ is called a Laguerre polynomial. It is described by the relations

$$L_{n+l}^{2l+1}(x) = B_0 + B_1 x + B_2 x^2 + \cdots + B_{n-l-1} x^{n-l-1}$$

$$B_k = -B_{k-1} \frac{n - l - k}{(l + k)(l + k + 1) - l(l + 1)} \qquad (7\text{-}24)$$

$$B_{n-l-1} = (-1)^{n+l} \frac{(n + l)!}{(n - l - 1)!}$$

where $n - l - 1$ must be zero or positive, so that $n = l + 1, l + 2, \ldots$, or where $l = 0, 1, \ldots, n - 1$.

The function $P_{nl}(r)$ defined by Eq. (7-23) is normalized, in the sense that

$$\int_0^\infty [P_{nl}(r)]^2 \, dr = 1 \qquad (7\text{-}25)$$

We recall that r is here measured in atomic units. If we wish to set up a function expressed in terms of ordinary units, we let $x = 2Zr/a_0 n$, and we must insert an extra factor $a_0^{-\frac{1}{2}}$ in $P_{nl}(r)$ to compensate for the use of ordinary units in the element of length. We can prove that the $P_{nl}(r)$'s are orthogonal in the sense that

$$\int_0^\infty P_{nl}(r) P_{n'l}(r) \, dr = 0 \qquad \text{if } n \neq n' \qquad (7\text{-}26)$$

This fact can be proved directly from Eq. (7-12), by the same methods used in Sec. 4-2. There are many other important properties of these radial wave functions, which we take up in Appendix 15.

It is interesting to consider specifically the behavior of the wave function for small and for large values of r, which we have already considered in a general way in Eqs. (7-16) and (7-18). For small r, P goes as r^{l+1}. That is, the greater l is, the more rapidly the function approaches zero as r approaches zero. This is natural from Fig. 7-1, for we see that, the larger l is, the greater is the effective potential energy near the origin, and hence the greater the negative kinetic energy. This corresponds to the classical situation. In Appendix 1, we saw that classical orbits of large angular momentum (there denoted by kh) did not penetrate close to the nucleus, while those of small angular momentum penetrated very close. We shall see that k is equivalent to $l + 1$, so that these results are consistent with our present observations that the wave functions are large near the nucleus for small l values, small for large l values.

For large values of r, the limit to the classical motion is set mostly by the total energy, or by n, the principal quantum number. The greater n is, the larger the classical orbit. Corresponding to this, the Schrödinger wave function has large values farther out, for large n values. It is easy to find approximately how large the orbit is. For large values of r, the most important term in the function P is that in the highest power of r. From Eq. (7-23) we see that the highest power of r is n, so that for large r the function P approaches $r^n \exp(-Zr/n)$. We can now find the value of r at which this quantity has its maximum; this will give us a certain measure of the size of the orbit. We find at once that the radius is n^2/Z, measured in atomic units. This is the same as the radius of the corresponding circular orbit in Bohr's theory.

We have now determined completely the solutions of the hydrogen problem associated with negative energy. We have found an infinite number of eigenvalues, given by Eq. (7-21), for all integral values of n. For a given n, we have wave functions, given by Eq. (7-23), for $l = 0$, $1, 2, \ldots, n - 1$, since it is only for these values of l that the Laguerre polynomial exists, according to Eq. (7-24). We have degeneracy, all the states of the same n value, but different l and m, having the same energy.

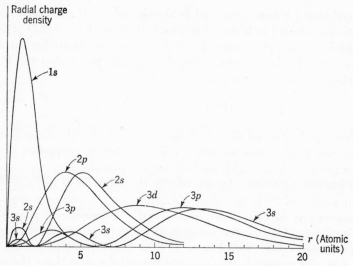

FIG. 7-3. Radial charge density for hydrogen.

We have illustrated the general form of the wave functions in Fig. 7-2. It is interesting to plot not only the wave function itself, but also the quantity P^2. The reason is that this is proportional to the density of charge per unit range of r. If we wish to find the amount of charge contained between r and $r + dr$, we must multiply R^2, which is proportional to the density of charge, by the volume of the shell between r and $r + dr$, which is $4\pi r^2\, dr$. The quantity $P^2 = r^2 R^2$ is often called the radial charge density, and it is plotted for several stationary states in Fig. 7-3. Plots of this sort are valuable in discussing the structure of other atoms besides hydrogen. It is clear that the maximum charge density coincides with the maximum value of P, which we used earlier in deriving an effective radius for an orbit. In these plots the fact that the outer maximum is more important than the inner ones is exaggerated as compared with the plots of the wave function itself.

As the energy goes through smaller and smaller negative values to zero, the principal quantum number n becoming larger and larger, the orbits get larger and larger and for positive energies they extend to infinity. At the same time, the motion ceases to be quantized, and we have a continuous spectrum. This is similar to the case taken up in Sec. 3-5, where we showed a potential well leading to quantized energy levels for small energies, and a continuous spectrum for high energy. The continuous spectrum is observed in experiments on the hydrogen atom. An electron can absorb energy sufficient to raise it from a low energy level, such as the ground state (with $n = 1$), to the continuous band of energies, and as a result, it can absorb any frequency greater than that corresponding to the series limit (that is, to the energy sufficient to raise it to the state $E = 0$, or $n = \infty$). At the same time, the electron becomes free, or ionized; the potential corresponding to the energy necessary to raise the electron to the series limit is the ionization potential.

7-3. The Angular Momentum; Dependence of the Wave Function on Angles. We have already mentioned that the classical kinetic energy can be written $p_r^2/2m + (p_l r)^2/2mr^2$. The corresponding operator in wave mechanics, as we find it in Appendix 13, is

$$-\frac{\hbar^2}{2mr^2}\frac{\partial}{\partial r}\left(r^2\frac{\partial}{\partial r}\right) - \frac{\hbar^2}{2mr^2}\left[\frac{1}{\sin\theta}\frac{\partial}{\partial\theta}\left(\sin\theta\frac{\partial}{\partial\theta}\right) + \frac{1}{\sin^2\theta}\frac{\partial^2}{\partial\phi^2}\right] \quad (7\text{-}27)$$

By comparison, it seems reasonable that the operator for $(p_l r)^2$ is

$$(p_l r)^2_{\text{op}} = -\hbar^2\left[\frac{1}{\sin\theta}\frac{\partial}{\partial\theta}\left(\sin\theta\frac{\partial}{\partial\theta}\right) + \frac{1}{\sin^2\theta}\frac{\partial^2}{\partial\phi^2}\right] \quad (7\text{-}28)$$

We shall get a more formal proof of this fact in Sec. 11-1. But now from the differential equations for Θ and Φ, Eq. (7-7), we easily have, using this operator,

$$(p_l r)^2_{\text{op}} u = l(l + 1)\hbar^2 u \quad (7\text{-}29)$$

That is, $(p_l r)^2_{\text{op}}$ has a diagonal matrix, since $(p_l r)^2_{\text{op}} u$ is a constant times u, without any terms in other characteristic functions, and the diagonal value is $l(l + 1)\hbar^2$, so that the total angular momentum is constant, as it must be in the absence of torques. We can also easily find the component of angular momentum along the z axis. The angular momentum along this axis is the momentum conjugate to the angle ϕ of rotation about this axis, so that its operator is $-i\hbar\,\partial/\partial\phi$. Now take the solutions where ϕ enters into the wave function as the exponential $\exp(im\phi)$. Then we have

$$-i\hbar\frac{\partial u}{\partial\phi} = m\hbar u \quad (7\text{-}30)$$

This again is diagonal, showing that the component of angular momentum along the axis remains constant and that its component is $m\hbar$.

We thus see that our quantum number l takes the place of the quantum number k of Bohr's theory, discussed in Sec. 1-7. It is called the azimuthal quantum number, and it measures in a way the total angular momentum of the electron, in units $\hbar$. More specifically, the magnitude of the angular momentum, from Eq. (7-29), is $\sqrt{l(l+1)}\,\hbar$, slightly different from $l\hbar$. Since k takes on the values 1, 2, . . . , n, while l goes from 0 to $n - 1$, we see that l is one unit less than k. There is a convention which grew up long ago in spectroscopy, according to which the various l values are known by certain symbols, whose meaning will be described later. These symbols are

$$
\begin{aligned}
l = 0, &\ s \\
1, &\ p \\
2, &\ d \\
3, &\ f \\
4, &\ g \\
5, &\ h \\
6, &\ i \\
7, &\ k \\
&\ \cdot \cdot \cdot
\end{aligned}
$$

We use a simple symbol to denote the n and l values of a state, consisting of the value of n and the symbol for l. Thus, for instance, a state with $n = 3$, $l = 0$, is called a $3s$ state, and one with $n = 2$, $l = 1$, is a $2p$, and so on. We note that on account of the limitation on values of l, according to which it can take on values 0, 1, . . . , $n - 1$, the lowest s state is $1s$, the lowest p is $2p$, and so on; that is, the lowest state with any value of l is given by $n = l + 1$.

The quantum number m, which as we have seen measures the component of angular momentum along the axis, can take on values l, $l - 1$, $l - 2$, . . . , $-l$, according to the properties of the associated Legendre functions. We can interpret these different values of m in terms of space quantization, as in the Bohr theory, and as we illustrated in Fig. 1-1. However, we cannot draw unique conclusions from such a diagram, for it would imply that the orbit lay in a plane normal to the vector representing the angular momentum, whereas, on account of the principle of uncertainty, the real orbit does not lie in a plane but is spread out in space. We can get a more useful picture of the distribution of the wave functions in angle by showing polar diagrams of the functions of angle, plotting the square of the function $P_l^{|m|}(\cos \theta)$ as a function of angle. This is done in Fig. 7-4, for $l = 1$, $m = 1$ and 0, and $l = 2$, $m = 2$, 1, 0 ($l = 0$ does not depend on angle). If we imagine these figures rotated about the axes, we see that for $m = l$ the figure indicates that most of the density is near the plane normal to the axis but a considerable part

is out of the plane.   For $l = 2$, $m = 1$, for instance, the density lies near
a cone, as if the plane of the orbit took up all directions whose normal
made the proper angle with the axis.

A very important property of the quantum number m is that the
energy does not depend on it.   We can see this directly from the equation for the radial part of the wave function, in Eq. (7-7), which determines the energy: this equation does not contain the number m.   The
physical explanation of this fact is of course that m measures in a sense
the orientation of the orbit in space, and for a spherically symmetrical
problem, the energy cannot depend on this orientation.   Hence, since
there are $2l + 1$ different values of m for each value of n and l, we see
that each such energy level must be $(2l + 1)$-fold degenerate.   This is in

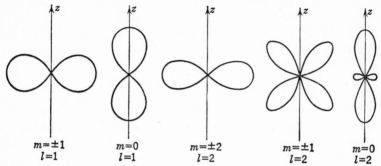

$$m=\pm 1 \qquad m=0 \qquad m=\pm 2 \qquad m=\pm 1 \qquad m=0$$
$$l=1 \qquad l=1 \qquad l=2 \qquad l=2 \qquad l=2$$

Fig. 7-4. Dependence of wave functions on angle. $(P_l^{|m|})^2$ plotted in polar diagram.

addition to the degeneracy by which states with the same n, but different l, are degenerate.   This latter degeneracy is peculiar to the hydrogen
problem and is in a sense accidental.   The degeneracy by which all states
of the same l value, but different m, have the same value is on the contrary common to all solutions of the central-field problem and depends
only on the spherical symmetry.

We have now discussed the nature of the functions of r, θ, and ϕ for
the hydrogen problem, and it is useful to write down the normalized
wave functions of the problem.   These can be set up in the form

$$u_{nlm}(r,\theta,\phi) = \frac{(-1)^{(m+|m|)/2}}{(4\pi)^{\frac{1}{2}}} \sqrt{\frac{(2l+1)(l-|m|)!}{(l+|m|)!}} \, R_{nl}(r) P_l^{|m|}(\cos\theta)$$

$$\times \exp\,(im\phi) \quad (7\text{-}31)$$

where
$$R_{nl}(r) = \frac{P_{nl}(r)}{r} \qquad (7\text{-}32)$$

and $P_{nl}(r)$ is defined in Eq. (7-23).   The proof that these functions are
normalized, when integrated over all space, follows from Eqs. (7-11) and
(7-25), and the orthogonality of functions which differ from each other
in at least one of the three quantum numbers n, l, or m follows from Eqs.

(7-11) and (7-26). The choice of the sign for the function, in Eq. (7-31), is made for a purpose which will become clear in Sec. 11-1. It corresponds to the rule that we use a positive sign for negative m, and even positive m, but a minus sign for odd positive m.

Table 7-1. Angular Wave Functions, for s, p, and d Functions

s: $l = 0, m = 0$: 1

p: $l = 1, m = \pm 1$: $\sqrt{3/2} \sin \theta \exp (\pm i\phi)$

  $m = 0$: $\sqrt{3} \cos \theta$

d: $l = 2, m = \pm 2$: $\sqrt{15/8} \sin^2 \theta \exp (\pm 2i\phi)$

  $m = \pm 1$: $\sqrt{15/2} \sin \theta \cos \theta \exp (\pm i\phi)$

  $m = 0$: $\sqrt{5/4} (3 \cos^2 \theta - 1)$

It is interesting to consider a little more in detail the s, p, and d wave functions, which are very important in molecular binding, and which we have already illustrated in polar diagrams in Fig. 7-4. In Table 7-1 we give the values of the functions

$$\sqrt{\frac{(2l + 1)(l - |m|)!}{(l + |m|)!}} \; P_l^{|m|}(\cos \theta) \exp (im\phi) \qquad (7\text{-}33)$$

which we see from Eq. (7-31) are proportional to the angular part of the normalized wave function, for the various states for $l = 0, 1$, and 2. The functions as they stand are not very easy to visualize, since they represent complex functions. However, we can make simple real linear combinations of them. Thus, we can take the sum of functions for a positive and an equal negative m and divide by $\sqrt{2}$, or we can take the difference and divide by $i \sqrt{2}$. These functions will be real and will be normalized and orthogonal, so that this transformation represents a unitary transformation. The resulting functions take a simpler form if we express them in terms of the rectangular coordinates, $x = r \sin \theta \cos \phi$, $y = r \sin \theta \sin \phi$, $z = r \cos \theta$. We then find the functions given in Table 7-2.

Table 7-2. Real Normalized Angular Wave Functions, for s, p, and d Functions

s: $m = 0$: 1

p: $|m| = 1$: $\sqrt{3} \dfrac{x}{r}$, $\sqrt{3} \dfrac{y}{r}$

  $m = 0$: $\sqrt{3} \dfrac{z}{r}$

d: $|m| = 2$: $\sqrt{\dfrac{15}{4}} \dfrac{(x^2 - y^2)}{r^2}$, $\sqrt{15} \dfrac{xy}{r^2}$

  $|m| = 1$: $\sqrt{15} \dfrac{xz}{r^2}$, $\sqrt{15} \dfrac{yz}{r^2}$

  $m = 0$: $\sqrt{5} \dfrac{z^2 - \frac{1}{2}(x^2 + y^2)}{r^2}$

We can indicate the behavior of these angular functions by considering the behavior of their nodal surfaces. The three p functions, in the order in which they are given in Table 7-2, obviously have an x, y, z type of symmetry and are often denoted by p_x, p_y, p_z, respectively. Their nodes are the planes $x = 0$, $y = 0$, $z = 0$. The nodal surfaces of the d functions arising from $|m| = 2$ are two planes passing through the z axis and at right angles to each other; for the first of the two functions they are the planes $x = y$ and $x = -y$ [since $x^2 - y^2$ factors into $(x - y)(x + y)$], and for the second of the two functions they are the planes $x = 0$ and $y = 0$. For the d functions arising from $|m| = 1$ we again have two nodal planes, in the first case the planes $x = 0$, $z = 0$,

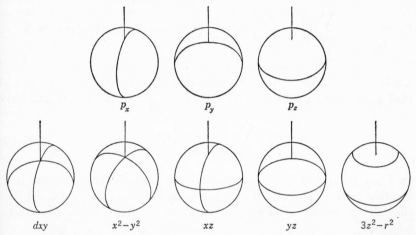

FIG. 7-5. Angular dependence of p and d wave functions, indicated by nodal surfaces on a sphere.

and in the second case the planes $y = 0$, $z = 0$. The d function with $m = 0$ is different: the nodal surface is a conical surface making an angle given by $3 \cos^2 \theta = 1 = 0$. We show these nodal surfaces by means of their intersections with a sphere in Fig. 7-5.

We have noted that the three p functions in Table 7-2 show an x, y, z type of symmetry. Three of the five d functions clearly show a similar type of symmetry: $\sqrt{15}\, yz$, $\sqrt{15}\, zx$, $\sqrt{15}\, xy$, in which we go from one function to the next by a cyclic advancement of the letters, as we do with x, y, and z. The other two functions, however, do not at first sight show any simple form of symmetry. This is only apparent, however, as we can show by considering the three functions $x^2 - y^2$, $y^2 - z^2$, $z^2 - x^2$, which do show such a symmetry, and of which the first is proportional to one of the two functions. We cannot use the other two functions, for we note that the sum of the three functions above is zero, so that they are not linearly independent and cannot be orthogonal to each other.

We can form only one linear combination of the second and third functions $y^2 - z^2$ and $z^2 - x^2$ which is orthogonal to $x^2 - y^2$, and it proves to be the function $z^2 - 1/2(x^2 + y^2)$ which we meet for $m = 0$.

There is one very interesting general theorem regarding the angular dependence of the wave functions: if we add the squares of the magnitudes of all the angular wave functions corresponding to a given l value, the result is independent of orientation. Thus, for the p states, we see at once that the sum of squares is $3(x^2 + y^2 + z^2)/r^2 = 3$. For the d functions, it is a little more complicated, but we find that the sum of squares equals 5. To get a general proof, we can use a well-known theorem generally called the addition theorem of spherical harmonics:

$$P_l(\cos \gamma) = \sum_{m=-l}^{l} \frac{(l - |m|)!}{(l + |m|)!} P_l^{|m|}(\cos \theta_1) P_l^{|m|}(\cos \theta_2) \exp [im(\phi_1 - \phi_2)]$$

$$(7\text{-}34)$$

where γ is the angle between the direction given by the angles θ_1, ϕ_1 and that given by θ_2, ϕ_2. We set $\theta_1 = \theta_2$, $\phi_1 = \phi_2$, so that $\gamma = 0$, and have

$$P_l(1) = \sum_{m=-l}^{l} \frac{(l - |m|)!}{(l + |m|)!} [P_l^{|m|}(\cos \theta)]^2 \qquad (7\text{-}35)$$

In Eqs. (7-34) and (7-35), $P(\cos \gamma)$ is the ordinary Legendre function, identical with $P_l^0(\cos \gamma)$. These Legendre functions are so defined that they all equal unity when $\gamma = 0$, or $\cos \gamma = 1$. When we use these facts, we have

$$\sum_{m=-l}^{l} \frac{(2l + 1)(l - |m|)!}{(l + |m|)!} [P_l^{|m|}(\cos \theta) \exp (im\phi)]^* [P_l^{|m|}(\cos \theta) \exp (im\phi)]$$

$$= 2l + 1 \quad (7\text{-}36)$$

As we see from Eq. (7-36), this leads to just the result we wished, namely, that the sum over m of the squares of the magnitudes of the wave functions of all states with the same l value, but different m's, is independent of angle; furthermore, we check the result we found by direct calculation, namely, that the sum was 3 for a p state, 5 for a d state. The importance of the result we have just proved will be seen later, when we talk about the structure of complicated atoms.[1]

7-4. Series and Selection Rules. We have mentioned that all the states for a given value of l and n, but different m, have the same function

---

[1] This theorem is generally called Unsöld's theorem. See A. Unsöld, *Ann. Physik*, **82**:355 (1927).

of r and the same energy. Thus we often group together the various substates with the same l and n, but different m, regarding them as constituting a single degenerate state with a $(2l + 1)$-fold degeneracy. It is convenient to group all the states of the same l value, but different n, together to form a series, since they are closely connected physically, having the same functions of angle. The series of different l values, as we have already mentioned, are denoted by the letters s, p, d, f, etc., derived from spectroscopy.

The classification into series becomes important when we consider the transition probabilities from one level to another. We recall that these are determined by the matrix components of the electric moment between the states in question. When these components are computed, it is found that there are certain selection rules:

1. The component is zero unless the l's of the two states differ by ± 1 unit.

2. The component is zero unless the m's differ by 0 or ± 1 unit.

This latter rule is easily proved. For suppose we compute the matrix components of $x + iy$, $x - iy$, and z, which are simple combinations of x, y, z, the three components of displacement. If we find the matrix components of all three of these to be zero for a given transition, the transition will be forbidden. Now these three quantities, in polar coordinates, are $r \sin \theta \exp (i\phi)$, $r \sin \theta \exp (-i\phi)$, and $r \cos \theta$, respectively. If u is $R\Theta \exp (im\phi)$, we have

$$(x + iy)u = rR \sin \theta \, \Theta \exp [i(m + 1)\phi] \qquad (7\text{-}37)$$

showing that this quantity has a matrix component only to states having the quantum number $m + 1$, since the quantity on the right could be expanded in series of functions with many values of n and l, but only the one value $m + 1$. Similarly $(x - iy)u = rR \sin \theta \, \Theta \exp [i(m - 1)\phi]$, allowing transitions only from m to $m - 1$, and $zu = rR \cos \theta \, \Theta \exp (im\phi)$, allowing transitions in which m does not change. The proof of the selection principle for l is slightly more difficult, involving the theorem that $\sin \theta \, P_l^{|m|}(\cos \theta)$ or $\cos \theta \, P_l^{|m|}(\cos \theta)$ can be expanded in spherical harmonics whose lower index is $l + 1$ or $l - 1$ only. We shall go into these selection rules in detail later, in Chap. 25 (Vol. II).

The selection rules have the following results: If we arrange the series in order, s, p, d, f, . . . , a level of one series can have transitions only to the immediately adjacent series. This gives us the transitions indicated in Fig. 7-6 (all the transitions between upper states are not indicated; merely some of the more important ones down to lower states). The series of lines arising from transitions of the p states to the $1s$ is called the principal series; from the s terms to $2p$, the sharp series; from the d terms to $2p$, the diffuse series; from the f terms to $3d$, the fundamental series. These names were given by the spectroscopists to the corresponding transitions, and term values, in the spectra of the alkalies, which have a similar classification of levels, long before the quantum theory was worked out, and the letters s, p, d, f are the initials of the various series. On account of the degeneracy in l in hydrogen, the various series are not separated in this spectrum, but they are in the alkali atoms, as we shall see in the next chapter.

When we look into the theory of the hydrogen spectrum with more care than we have done so far, we find several types of corrections, which

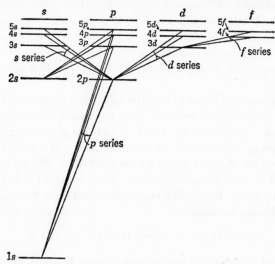

FIG. 7-6. Energy levels and allowed transitions and series in hydrogen.

have the effect of slightly displacing the energy levels, so that the degeneracy is removed and levels with the same n value, but different l's, no longer exactly coincide. The resulting splitting of the energy levels is referred to as fine structure. It is on such a small scale that it is hard to observe, but still measurable, and capable of shedding light on further refinements of the theory. One of the perturbations, the one which has been studied longest, is the relativistic correction. The electrons in hydrogen travel rather slowly compared with the velocity of light, but still they approach close enough to it so that corrections to their motion on account of the theory of relativity are barely detectable. Sommerfeld[1] many years ago worked out a relativistic theory of the fine structure which, remarkably enough, agreed very closely with the experiments. This was remarkable, because several other perturbing effects have been discovered since then, each of which modified the theory, but in just such

[1] A. Sommerfeld, *Ann. Physik*, **51**:1 (1916).

a way as to leave the net result very close to the original prediction of Sommerfeld.

The most important of these effects is the electron spin. It was discovered by Uhlenbeck and Goudsmit,[1] guided by the theory of more complicated spectra than that of hydrogen, that the electron itself possesses a magnetic moment and an angular momentum, quite aside from its rotation in an orbit. This intrinsic spin must be considered in the theory of atomic spectra, and we shall meet it many times in our future work. As far as its effect on the hydrogen spectrum is concerned, it produces perturbations of the same order of magnitude as the relativity correction. In the first place, there proves to be a space quantization of the electronic spin with respect to the orbital angular momentum, resulting in most cases in a doubling of the number of energy levels. These energy levels are split apart by the magnetic energy associated with the magnetic interaction between the magnetic moments of orbital motion and of spin. By extraordinary coincidence, as we have mentioned, the net result of this splitting and displacement of levels is to have new levels, with a different interpretation from the old ones, nevertheless lying at just the same energies that Sommerfeld predicted. We shall not go further into this effect here, since it is relatively unimportant in hydrogen, whereas we shall later find it to be of great importance in discussing the heavier atoms. We shall take it up first in Chap. 10, and then in greater detail in Chaps. 23 and 24 and Appendix 29 (Vol. II).

There is a final type of perturbation, recently discovered, called the Lamb-Retherford[2] shift, resulting from a higher-order interaction term in the energy, involving interaction between electrostatic energy and radiation energy. This involves quantum electrodynamics, in forms which we hardly touched on in the preceding chapter, and while it is of considerable theoretical interest, it is of small practical importance. We shall not consider it further in this volume.

In addition to these small perturbative effects in the hydrogen spectrum, which occur in the absence of external field, there are, of course, perturbations produced by external magnetic or electric fields. We have already mentioned in Chap. 1 the Zeeman effect, the effect of an external magnetic field, producing displacement of the levels by an amount proportional to the field strength and to the magnetic quantum number m. This effect is greatly complicated by the electronic spin, and we postpone its discussion until Chap. 10, where we shall take up the general theory of multiplet structure and the Zeeman effect. Similarly an external

[1] G. E. Uhlenbeck and S. Goudsmit, *Naturwiss.*, **13**:953 (1925); *Nature*, **117**:264 (1926).

[2] W. E. Lamb and R. C. Retherford, *Phys. Rev.*, **79**:549 (1950); **81**:222 (1951); **85**:259 (1952); **86**:1014 (1952).

electric field produces a perturbation, the Stark effect, which is interesting in some connections, but which we shall not discuss further.

PROBLEMS

1. Carry out the solution of the radial wave equation for hydrogen, deriving Eq. (7-20), following the method outlined in the text, and verifying that, if the series does not break off, it represents a function which becomes infinite as r approaches infinity.

2. Assume that the solution of Schrödinger's equation for hydrogen, Eq. (7-12), can be expressed in the form $P = r^n \exp(-ar)(1 + A_1/r + A_2/r^2 + \cdots)$. Find the recursion formula for the A's, and the value of a. Find the condition that the series break off. Show that the resulting function is the same as that found in ascending powers of r in the text.

3. The solution of the preceding problem can be used to discuss the outer part of the wave function of a nonhydrogenic problem in which the potential energy is $2Z/r$ in the outer part of the orbit but deviates further in. In such a case the energy levels will be different from the hydrogen values. Consider the nature of the solution for an arbitrary energy value. Show that as $r \to 0$ the series diverges. This does not interfere with this use of the solution, in which the potential departs from the hydrogenic value for small r, so that we do not use the solution in this region.

4. Set up the solution of the radial Schrödinger equation for hydrogen by the WKB method. Carry the solution as far as you can, and compare with the exact solution.

5. Apply the variation method to the determination of the wave function for the ground state of hydrogen, in the following way: Assume that the wave function is a constant times $\exp(-ar)$, where a is an arbitrary parameter to be determined. Compute the average energy for this function, vary a to minimize the energy, and show that the minimum is found for that value of a which makes the solution agree with the exact solution of Schrödinger's equation.

6. One can obtain a fairly good, though far from perfect, approximation to the wave function of the ground state of hydrogen in the form of a Gaussian function, a constant times $\exp(-ar^2)$. Apply the variation method to this function, varying a to minimize the energy. Find the average energy corresponding to this value, and show that it lies above the true energy of the ground state. Compare the resulting wave function graphically with the true wave function.

7. Work out the angular functions for $l = 3$, and draw diagrams from them similar to Fig. 7-4.

8. Prove from the differential equation that the associated Legendre functions are orthogonal. Verify this for the cases of $l = 1$ and 2.

9. Draw an energy-level diagram in which the substates of different m's are shown, drawing them as if slightly separated, including states $1s$, $2s$, $3s$, $2p$, $3p$, $3d$. Indicate all transitions allowed by the selection rules for l and m, as in Fig. 7-6.

10. Set up the angular part Θ of the wave function corresponding to $l = 0$, $m = 0$; $l = 1$, $m = 0$; $l = 2$, $m = 0$; $l = 3$, $m = 0$. Then investigate the selection rule for l by showing that $\cos\theta\, \Theta_l$ can be expanded in terms of Θ_{l-1} and Θ_{l+1}, so that there are only transitions for which $l \to l \pm 1$. Carry out for $l = 1, 2$.

11. Set up normalized hydrogen wave functions corresponding to $n = 2$, $l = 1$, $m = 1, 0, -1$, and $n = 1$, $l = 0$. Find the matrix components of electric moment for the transitions from the $n = 2$ levels to the ground state $n = 1$. Compute Einstein's A and B coefficients for these transitions.

12. Set up Schrödinger's equation for a particle moving in an electric and a magnetic field, using the Hamiltonian of Eq. (A4-32). Work out the special case of this for a particle acted on by a spherically symmetrical potential $V(r)$ and a constant magnetic field along the z axis.

13. Use the Schrödinger equation derived in Prob. 12 to discuss the Zeeman effect in hydrogen. Disregard the electron spin, and proceed by perturbation theory. Use the ordinary hydrogen wave functions as set up in this chapter as unperturbed wave functions, and find the average value of the perturbed Hamiltonian, including magnetic terms, over these unperturbed wave functions. Show that there are two sorts of terms: terms proportional to the magnetic field, and to the magnetic quantum number; and terms proportional to the square of the magnetic field, and to the mean value of the quantity $x^2 + y^2$ over the orbit. The terms of the first sort are those concerned in the ordinary Zeeman effect, and we shall later find that those of the second sort explain the phenomenon of diamagnetism.

8

The Central-field Model for Atomic Structure

8-1. Introduction. The hydrogen atom is a simple mathematical problem in wave mechanics, but any atom with more than one electron is so difficult that an exact solution is impossible. For the two-electron atom, helium, very elaborate approximate solutions of Schrödinger's equation have been set up, by Hylleraas[1] and others, which give results agreeing with experiment within experimental error. This agreement has convinced physicists that Schrödinger's equation for the many-body problem provides the correct starting point for a study of more complicated atoms. But the methods used for helium are too complicated to apply to atoms with more than two electrons, and we are forced to rely on simpler approximations for their treatment.

Fortunately we have approximations which are good enough to give very good qualitative, and quite good quantitative, agreement with experiment, though with far larger errors than for the helium calculations we have just quoted. These approximations will occupy us for most of the rest of this volume. They are divided into two parts. First, we find that a good starting point is provided by assuming that each electron moves in a central, or spherically symmetrical, force field, produced by the nucleus and the other electrons. This is a good enough approximation to account for the periodic system of the elements and the general size and energies of the atoms. For the atoms of the alkalies, it is good enough to explain the spectrum in fair detail. The second part of the approximate theory deals with complex multiplet structure, which is a feature of the spectra of all atoms more complicated than the alkalies. It arises on account of torques exerted by one electron on another, which are neglected in the central-field model.

In the present and the following chapters, we shall handle the central-field approximation, then shall go on in subsequent chapters to the multiplet theory. The central-field model was worked out during the 1920s,

[1] E. A. Hylleraas, *Z. Physik*, **54**:347 (1929); T. Kinoshita, *Phys. Rev.*, **105**:1490 (1957); C. L. Pekeris, *Phys. Rev.*, **112**:1649 (1958).

starting with Bohr's[1] first proposals for the explanation of the periodic table, in 1922, supplemented by the discovery of the electron spin by Uhlenbeck and Goudsmit[2] and of the exclusion principle by Pauli,[3] both in 1925, and completed with Hartree's[4] proposal of the method of the self-consistent field in 1928 and with the so-called Hartree-Fock[5] method in 1930.   The structures of many atoms have been worked out since then, but by use of principles which have been known since 1930 (see Appendix 16 for references).   The development of the postulates of the method was a difficult and confusing process, and rather than carrying the reader through the rather puzzling steps, we shall start by stating the general outline of the scheme as it was finally worked out and then shall show how the type of evidence available leads to a verification of the method.

8-2. The Postulates of the Central-field Method.   There are three ingredients going into the central-field method.   One of these follows from wave mechanics as we have already described it and is merely an approximate method of solving Schrödinger's equation for the many-body problem of Z electrons moving about a nucleus of charge Z units.   The other two are extensions of the wave-mechanical principles we have described.   These are the postulate of the electron spin and of the Pauli exclusion principle.   We shall now describe these three ingredients in succession.

First we have the central-field approximation itself, which really is practically identical with the method of the self-consistent field.   In this method, we replace the instantaneous action of all the electrons of an atom on one of their number, which would result in a mechanical problem so difficult that it could not be solved, by the much simpler problem in which each electron is assumed to be acted on by the averaged charge distribution of each other electron, averaged by taking the quantity $\psi^*\psi$ for the corresponding wave function.   This charge distribution, summed over the electrons of an atom, is very nearly spherically symmetrical, and in the central-field approximation, one takes a spherical average, so that the potential arising from this spherically averaged charge distribution, and from the nucleus, is itself spherically symmetrical, or is a central field.

Then, following Hartree, we proceed in the following fashion: We assume that each electron moves in such an averaged potential arising from the other electrons.   We solve Schrödinger's equation for an elec-

---

[1] N. Bohr, *Z. Physik*, **9**:1 (1922).

[2] G. E. Uhlenbeck and S. Goudsmit, *Naturwiss.*, **13**:953 (1925); *Nature*, **117**:264 (1926).

[3] W. Pauli, Jr., *Z. Physik*, **31**:765 (1926).

[4] D. R. Hartree, *Proc. Cambridge Phil. Soc.*, **24**:89, 111 (1928).

[5] V. Fock, *Z. Physik*, **61**:126 (1930), **62**:795 (1930).

tron moving in that potential, a simple problem on account of the spherical symmetry. We choose the wave function of the desired quantum number in that potential and assume that this wave function ψ is to be used in finding the charge density arising from the particular electron in question. We build up the total charge density arising from the electrons present in the atom, find the potential arising from this charge density by electrostatics, and then make the requirement of self-consistency; this final potential must agree with the initial one which had been assumed in setting up Schrödinger's equation.

This type of approximation is not unfamiliar: we meet essentially the same thing in the theory of the space charge in a vacuum tube. There we have a very great number of electrons acting on each other. Instead of trying to handle the interaction in detail, we replace the electrons by a continuous density of space charge, find a potential from this space charge by Poisson's equation, find the motion of electrons in this potential by Newtonian mechanics, find the current density and charge density arising from these electrons, and apply the condition of self-consistency, that this charge density be identical with that which we had assumed at the outset. In a simple case, such as the familiar Child-Langmuir equation for space-charge-limited emission of a cathode, these conditions can be combined into a single equation, which results in the familiar law that the emitted current is proportional to the $\frac{3}{2}$ power of the voltage.

In the case of the self-consistent field in an atom, the problem is much more complicated, partly because the motion of the electrons must be handled by wave mechanics rather than by classical mechanics, and we cannot get a direct and straightforward solution as in the space-charge case. However, Hartree found that he could set up a very manageable procedure for determining his self-consistent field, based on a method of iteration, or successive approximations. He started by assuming trial wave functions, which he hoped were fairly near the final ones. From these functions he determined charge densities, potentials, solved Schrödinger's equation, and came out with final wave functions. Since he could not have expected to have achieved self-consistency, these final functions would not agree with the initial ones. But then he started a new cycle of operation, using the final functions of one step as the starting functions of the next step, finding charge densities, potentials, and so on, from them, and proceeding just as before. Fortunately he found that this process converged; by carrying through a number of cycles, he came out with wave functions which were self consistent, to a very good approximation.

The wave function of an electron in such a spherical field is very similar to the hydrogenic function given in Eq. (7-31). Its dependence on angle is exactly the same, and the only difference is in the radial function $R_{nl}(r)$.

It is then characterized by the same three quantum numbers, the principal quantum number n, the azimuthal quantum number l, and the magnetic quantum number m. As before, l determines the total angular momentum of the electron, in the sense given in Eq. (7-29); the operator representing the square of the angular momentum is diagonal, with a diagonal matrix component equal to $l(l + 1)\hbar^2$. The quantum number m, as before, determines the component of angular momentum along the axis of coordinates, which is $m\hbar$, where m can take on the values $l, l - 1, \ldots, -l$. We shall examine later the detailed nature of the radial wave function and of the energy levels. As with hydrogen, the energy is independent of m, but unlike the case of hydrogen, the energy depends on l as well as on n.

Next we must consider the electron spin. As we have mentioned briefly in Sec. 7-4, the electron is found to have an intrinsic spin, corresponding to an azimuthal quantum number of $\frac{1}{2}$; that is, the operator representing the square of its angular momentum has a diagonal matrix component equal to $(\frac{1}{2})(\frac{3}{2})\hbar^2$, and the component of angular momentum along the axis is $m_s\hbar$, where the quantum number m_s can take on just the two values $\frac{1}{2}, -\frac{1}{2}$. To distinguish the quantum number m from m_s, it is customary to denote the quantum number which we have so far called m by the symbol m_l, which we shall henceforth do. The angular momentum described by l is called the orbital angular momentum, to distinguish it from the spin angular momentum. The evidence for the existence of the electron spin comes from a study of complex spectra, and we shall therefore put off a discussion of this evidence until later.

We are now in a position to state the third postulate of the central-field method, the Pauli exclusion principle. This states that no two electrons in the same atom can have the same values of all four quantum numbers, n, l, m_l, m_s. Since m_l can take on the values $l, l - 1, \ldots, -l$, or $2l + 1$ values in all, and m_s can take on the values $\frac{1}{2}, -\frac{1}{2}$, or two values, we see that there are $2(2l + 1)$ different states, with different values of the m's, for a given set of values of n and l, or a given (nl) value, as we may express it. These states will all have the same energy, or will be degenerate, since the energy does not depend on m_l or on m_s, in a central-field problem. In an atom, we can then have anywhere from zero to $2(2l + 1)$ electrons of a given (nl) value. If we have the full number, $2(2l + 1)$, we shall refer to them as a completed group, or a closed shell, of (nl) electrons; if there are fewer, we have an incompleted group, or partially filled shell. Pauli's principle was formulated as a result of the study of the periodic table of the elements, principally by Bohr, during the years from 1920 to 1925. We shall now go into the structure of the periodic table and into the types of experimental information about the atoms which have contributed to our understanding of the central-field model.

8-3. The Periodic Table of the Elements.   Two main types of information, chemical and spectroscopic, have led to our interpretation of the periodic table.   Mendelyeev, in the latter half of the nineteenth century, discovered that, if the elements were arranged in the order of atomic weight (or, as we now realize, in order of atomic number), their chemical properties showed a regular behavior which was very striking and which led to the concept of the periodic table.   This regularity is now more easily understood than it was in Mendelyeev's time, since we now know all the inert gases, helium, neon, argon, krypton, xenon, and radon, with atomic numbers 2, 10, 18, 36, 54, and 86, which were not known to Mendelyeev, and which really form the key to the periodic system.   The atoms with one more electron than the inert gases, namely, lithium, sodium, potassium, rubidium, and cesium, and the unfamiliar element francium, with atomic numbers 3, 11, 19, 37, 55, and 87, are the alkalies, having a single easily detachable electron, so that they easily form singly charged positive ions.   Those with two electrons more than the inert gases, namely, beryllium, magnesium, calcium, strontium, barium, and radium, with atomic numbers 4, 12, 20, 38, 56, and 88, are the so-called alkaline earths and have two easily removable electrons, forming doubly charged positive ions.   Similar situations hold for the next few elements in each row of the periodic table.   On the other hand, the elements with one less electron than the inert gases, namely, fluorine, chlorine, bromine, iodine, and the unfamiliar element astatine, with atomic numbers 9, 17, 35, 53, and 85, are the halogens, and they readily form singly charged negative ions, attracting to themselves an extra electron.   In a similar way the elements two places before the inert gases, oxygen, sulfur, selenium, tellurium, and polonium, with atomic numbers 8, 16, 34, 52, and 84, form doubly charged negative ions, with attachment of two extra electrons.

These facts, or as many of them as were known, convinced the chemists that the inert gases had particularly stable electronic configurations, since, in all the ions we have mentioned, enough electrons were removed or added to produce the same electronic configuration as for an inert gas. During the period from 1916 to 1919, Kossel,[1] Lewis,[2] and Langmuir[3] speculated a great deal about the probable meaning of these stable inert-gas structures.   Langmuir particularly noted the way in which the addition of eight electrons to helium produces neon and addition of eight to neon produces argon.   This led him to postulate a particularly stable

[1] W. Kossel, *Ann. Physik*, **49**:229 (1916).
[2] G. N. Lewis, *J. ACS*, **38**:762 (1916).
[3] I. Langmuir, *J. ACS*, **41**:868 (1919).

structure of eight electrons, which he called an octet. It was natural to think of these groups of electrons as shells of some sort and to think that one shell was completed at helium, consisting of two electrons; a second shell of eight, one of Langmuir's octets, would be completed at neon, a third shell at argon, and so on. This would imply that the inner shells remained in the heavier atoms, presumably shrinking in size so that they could be accommodated in the interior of the atom.

These simple and fundamental facts about the periodic system found their explanation, as Bohr[1] showed in 1922, in terms of the central-field model of the atom, coupled with the restriction on the number of electrons accommodated in a completed group, which was later formulated as Pauli's exclusion principle. We shall shortly look into the energy levels of an electron in such a central field as we find in an atom, and we shall find that the order of the energy levels, starting with the most tightly bound, is $1s$, $2s$, $2p$, $3s$, $3p$, $3d$, $4s$ (though for a number of atoms the $3d$ and $4s$ have almost identical energies, and in some cases $4s$ is more tightly bound than $3d$), $4p$, $4d$, $5s$ (though here again the $4d$ and $5s$ have almost identical energies for some atoms), $5p$, $6s$, $4f$, $5d$, $6p$, $7s$, $5f$, $6d$. Then one gets an essentially complete explanation of the periodic system by assuming that the electrons of any atom go into the lowest energy levels available for them, filling them up until they form completed groups. Let us see how this explains the shells of electrons, and the inert gases.

We give in Fig. 8-1 the periodic system of the elements, in essentially the form used by Bohr. Starting from the beginning, hydrogen has one $1s$ electron, and helium has two, thus completing the group of $1s$ electrons, and forming an inert gas. Lithium has one $2s$ electron outside the closed shell of $1s$ electrons. This $2s$ is easily detached, as we shall see when we study the energy values, and is the valence electron of lithium. Beryllium has two $2s$'s, boron has in addition a $2p$, and we go on to neon, $Z = 10$, with six $2p$'s. We indicate the number of electrons in such an atom by a symbol such as $(1s)^2(2s)^2(2p)^6$. Such an assignment of electrons to quantum numbers is called a configuration.

After neon, we add one $3s$ electron in sodium; two $3s$'s in magnesium; a $3p$ in aluminum; and so on, until we have argon, $Z = 18$, with the configuration $(1s)^2(2s)^2(2p)^6(3s)^2(3p)^6$. We see, in other words, that Langmuir's octets consisted of the eight electrons $(2s)^2(2p)^6$ or $(3s)^2(3p)^6$. We shall see shortly that the $2s$ and $2p$ are approximately equally tightly bound, and similarly the $3s$ and $3p$, so that there is no break in properties, or formation of an inert gas, at the point where the $2s$ or $3s$ group is completed, namely, at beryllium or magnesium.

[1] Bohr, *loc. cit.*

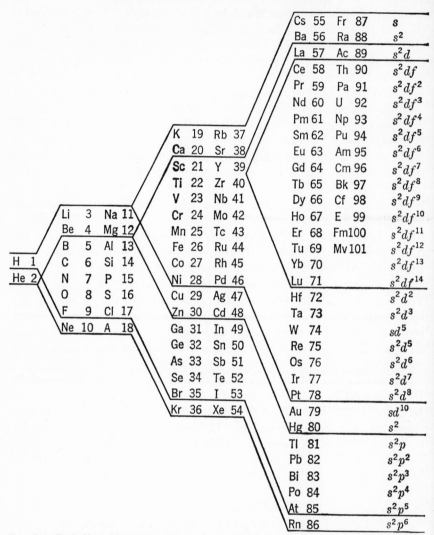

Cs 55	Fr 87		s
Ba 56	Ra 88		s^2
La 57	Ac 89		s^2d
Ce 58	Th 90		s^2df
Pr 59	Pa 91		s^2df^2
Nd 60	U 92		s^2df^3
Pm 61	Np 93		s^2df^4
Sm 62	Pu 94		s^2df^5
Eu 63	Am 95		s^2df^6
Gd 64	Cm 96		s^2df^7
Tb 65	Bk 97		s^2df^8
Dy 66	Cf 98		s^2df^9
Ho 67	E 99		s^2df^{10}
Er 68	Fm 100		s^2df^{11}
Tu 69	Mv 101		s^2df^{12}
Yb 70			s^2df^{13}
Lu 71			s^2df^{14}
Hf 72			s^2d^2
Ta 73			s^2d^3
W 74			sd^5
Re 75			s^2d^5
Os 76			s^2d^6
Ir 77			s^2d^7
Pt 78			s^2d^8
Au 79			sd^{10}
Hg 80			s^2
Tl 81			s^2p
Pb 82			s^2p^2
Bi 83			s^2p^3
Po 84			s^2p^4
At 85			s^2p^5
Rn 86			s^2p^6

FIG. 8-1. Periodic table of the elements, with electron configurations of the lowest states. The electron configurations do not in every case represent the absolutely lowest state, but in every case the state indicated at least is very close to the ground state. The lines are drawn to indicate chemically similar elements.

After argon, one $4s$ electron is added in potassium, and two in calcium; for these elements, the $4s$ is more tightly bound than the $3d$. But next we start a set of elements called a transition group, quite different in properties from those which come earlier in the periodic table. Here the $3d$ electrons begin to be bound into the atom. We start with scandium, with the configuration $(1s)^2(2s)^2(2p)^6(3s)^2(3p)^6(4s)^23d$, then titanium with

$(4s)^2(3d)^2$ outside the inner shells, which we shall no longer bother to repeat each time, and so on, to iron, with the configuration $(4s)^2(3d)^6$, cobalt with $(4s)^2(3d)^7$, and nickel with $(4s)^2(3d)^8$. As a matter of fact, the relative energies of $4s$ and $3d$ shift about at this point, and actually the configuration $(4s)(3d)^9$ of nickel lies slightly below $(4s)^2(3d)^8$. It is these elements, iron, cobalt, and nickel, which show the most conspicuous magnetic properties in the periodic table, and it is the incomplete group of $3d$ electrons which proves to be responsible for this magnetism. Also, the ions of the elements in this neighborhood tend to be brilliantly colored in solution, and this also is ascribed to the incomplete group of $3d$'s. These experimental facts were pointed out by Bohr in his first study of the periodic table, though the complete explanation waited for a long time before it could be given.

In the next element, copper, the ground state has the configuration $(4s)(3d)^{10}$, so that with this element the $3d$ group is completed. Copper has a slight chemical resemblance to the alkalies, having one easily detachable $4s$ electron outside completed groups of electrons, and having a tendency to form a singly charged positive ion. However, the last $3d$ electron is also easily detached, and copper often loses this electron as well, forming a divalent positive ion. Beyond copper we have zinc, with two $4s$ electrons, resembling an alkaline earth.

With the next element, gallium, which is quite similar in some ways to aluminum, we start adding $4p$'s, and this process is completed at krypton, the next inert gas. Then we start the same process all over again. The $5s$, $4d$, and $5p$ electrons resemble closely the $4s$, $3d$, and $4p$ in their general energy relationship, and all are more tightly bound than the $4f$. Thus, in the elements from rubidium to xenon, we go through another transition group, in which the $4d$ electrons are being added, including such an important metal as molybdenum. The element palladium resembles nickel, and the element silver, with one $5s$, resembles copper. After that we add electrons until we have a complete inert-gas configuration in xenon, with two $5s$'s and six $5p$'s.

Following after xenon, we add a $6s$ electron in cesium and another in barium, similar to rubidium and strontium. Then in lanthanum the first $5d$ electron is added. But at this point, something new happens: the $4f$ level, which previously had been less tightly bound than the others, becomes more tightly bound, and we have a series of 14 elements in which $4f$ electrons are added, one by one, with in each case three other electrons (two $6s$ and one $5d$, or one $6s$ and two $5d$). These 14 elements are the rare earths. Their outer electrons, which are mostly responsible for their chemical properties, are the same for each. They differ only in the number of $4f$ electrons, whose orbits are far inside the atom, even though they are not tightly bound. It is for this reason that the rare earths are so hard to separate chemically.   Also, having partly filled inner shells, they have interesting magnetic and optical properties, like the iron group. After the rare earths are completed, at lutecium, the $5d$ shell begins to be filled again, and we go through the elements from hafnium to platinum, similar to the group ending with palladium.   Gold, similar to copper and silver, comes next, with one $6s$ electron, and we go through another series of elements ending with the inert gas radon, with two $6s$'s and six $6p$'s.

Finally, we start to build up the $7s$ and $6d$ shells, radium having two $7s$ electrons and being an alkaline earth.   Actinium has one $6d$ electron; but immediately beyond that point, the $5f$ electrons become more stable, as the $4f$'s did in the rare earths, and we start a new series of rare earths, which includes thorium, protactinium, uranium, and the radioactive transuranic elements neptunium, plutonium, and so on, stretching up slightly beyond atomic number 100.   This is as far as the periodic table goes, not for lack of electronic orbits, but because the nuclei become so unstable that they do not last long enough to be examined.   It is likely that a few additional ones may be found; but there are good reasons for thinking that they will rapidly get more unstable with further increase in atomic number.

Here, then, we have the outline of the periodic system of the elements. The general interpretation was worked out by Bohr on the basis of chemical evidence and the postulate about the number of electrons that could be accommodated in a completed group of electrons.   Spectroscopic evidence, however, was extremely useful as well, and in the next section we turn to the spectra, both optical and X-ray, and the information which they give regarding the periodic system and the nature of the elements.

8-4. Spectroscopic Evidence for the Central-field Model.   The principal types of atomic spectra are of two sorts, the optical spectra, lying in the visible or near ultraviolet or infrared parts of the spectrum, and the X-ray spectra.   The optical spectra have been known for longer, since they were investigated extensively in the nineteenth century and early twentieth century.   It was found that these showed a close correlation to the chemical behavior of the atoms.   The alkalies have by far the simplest spectra, and the spectra of the various alkalies resemble each other very strongly and have a rather close resemblance to the hydrogen spectrum.   Their terms fall into series, with energies given rather accurately by a law discovered by Rydberg,

$$E = -\frac{1}{(n - d)^2} \qquad \text{Rydbergs} \qquad (8\text{-}1)$$

where n is an integer, d a constant called the quantum defect.   The close resemblance of this to the hydrogenic case convinced physicists that a theory similar to that of hydrogen must underlie the structure of the alkali atoms.   However, as soon as one goes beyond these atoms, the spectra become bewilderingly complicated.   It seems very clear that a single electron outside an inert-gas structure behaves very simply, almost as simply as the single electron in the hydrogen atom, but that, if we have more than one electron outside the inert-gas core, they interact with each other in a very complicated manner.

The X-ray spectra were discovered in the years immediately following 1912.   In that year, it occurred to von Laue that X rays must have

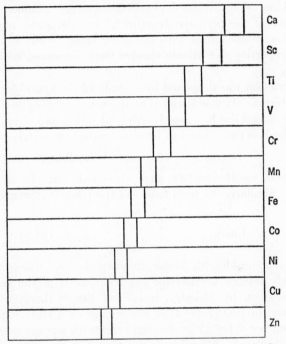

FIG. 8-2. K X-ray lines of a number of successive elements, as obtained by Moseley and other workers.

wavelengths of the same order of magnitude as the spacings between atoms in a crystal, and that consequently it might be possible to diffract X rays by passing them through a crystal.   This proved to be the case, and in that way two new fields were opened up, the study of crystal structure, and of X-ray spectra.   W. H. and W. L. Bragg, father and son, devised practical methods of handling the X rays, including the design of an X-ray spectrometer.   Their principal research was in the crystal-structure aspect of the problem, which we shall not go into here, but as far as X-ray spectra were concerned, they were studied in great detail, first by Moseley,[1] who was killed in the First World War very

[1] H. G. J. Moseley, *Phil. Mag.*, **26**:1024 (1913).

shortly afterward, then by a number of other investigators, of whom the best known was Siegbahn. It was found that, in contrast to the case of the optical spectra, the X-ray spectra showed great simplicity, and in particular the spectra of successive elements were very similar to each other, with no trace of the periodicity which is shown in the optical spectra or in the chemical properties. Thus, in Fig. 8-2, we show the lines of one of the X-ray series, the K series, for the atoms from calcium, $Z = 20$, to zinc, $Z = 30$. The regular progression from one atom to the next is striking. This simple dependence on atomic number, and relative independence of the periodic structure of the elements, suggested that the X rays were concerned with the inner shells of electrons, while the chemical properties and atomic spectra were concerned with the outermost shells.

This conviction was deepened by a study of the actual term values of the X-ray terms. It was found that there were several series of terms, which were named the K series, L series, M series, and so on. The term values of the K series proved to be given rather accurately by

$$\text{Energy} = -(Z - s)^2 \quad \text{Rydbergs} \qquad (8\text{-}2)$$

where s was a small quantity, depending only slightly on the atomic number Z. Similarly the term values of the L series were given approximately by

$$\text{Energy} = -\frac{(Z - s')^2}{4} \quad \text{Rydbergs} \qquad (8\text{-}3)$$

where s' was a considerably larger quantity than s. These simple laws, rather closely related to laws for the frequencies of the emitted lines which were given by Moseley, resembled Bohr's theory of hydrogen. We have seen in Eq. (7-21) that the energy of a state with principal quantum number n, for a one-electron atom with nuclear charge Z units, is $-Z^2/n^2$ Rydbergs. This suggested that the K series of terms was similar to a hydrogenic problem with $n = 1$, the L series to a hydrogenic problem with $n = 2$. Similarly the M series appeared related to $n = 3$, and so on.

It was then necessary to explain the quantities s and s'. Naturally an electron, in a neutral atom, is acted on, not only by the nucleus, but by the other electrons as well. These other electrons will partly shield the nuclear attraction. Thus a single electron near the nucleus will feel the whole nuclear charge of Z units, whereas if it is in the outer part of the atom, the remaining $Z - 1$ electrons will shield the nucleus, and it will feel only a net charge of 1 unit. The field felt by an electron, then, would be expected to vary from that of a charge of Z units when it is very close to the nucleus, down to a charge of 1 unit when it is far outside. It was naturally assumed that the quantities $Z - s$ and $Z - s'$, of Eqs. (8-2) and (8-3), represented the effective charges which an electron felt at the radius of the orbit in question. The quantity s or s' would represent the shielding effect of the electrons, and for this reason it was called a shielding constant. The fact that s' was greater than s was connected with the larger orbit which an electron with $n = 2$ would have as compared with one with $n = 1$.

It was found experimentally that, though the K level was single, there were in fact three closely spaced L levels, five M levels, and so on. This did not agree with what one might have anticipated from our explanation of these levels. We might well expect two L levels, coming from the $2s$ and $2p$ levels in a central-field problem, and three M levels, coming from $3s$, $3p$, and $3d$. It was for some time a puzzle why the observed number of levels was greater than this. The puzzle was later removed when the effect of the electron spin was better understood: it was found that it resulted in a doubling of all levels except s levels, so that the $2p$, $3p$, and $3d$ levels were all double. The doubling of the levels finds a counterpart in the doubling of all optical levels of an alkali spectrum except the s levels; here again the explanation comes from the electron spin, as we shall see later.

8-5. An Example of Atomic Spectra: the Sodium Atom. Let us now look more closely at a particular case, to understand the type of information which the optical and X-ray spectra are able to give regarding the structure of the atom and of the periodic table. We shall choose an alkali atom, for it is only the alkalies that show simple spectra; in particular we shall choose sodium, on which a great deal of work was done during the 1920s, to test the general concept of the central field. We recall that, according to Bohr's explanation of the periodic table, the ground state of sodium has the configuration $(1s)^2(2s)^2(2p)^63s$. First let us consider the information given about this atom from X-ray spectra. Actually some of the transitions which in heavier atoms would come in the X-ray part of the spectrum are in the far ultraviolet for sodium, but we shall treat them as if they were observed by X-ray techniques.

The X-ray term values of an atom are observed experimentally in two different ways. First, one can bombard the atom with electrons of controlled energy and try to remove one of the X-ray electrons from the atom. Unless the bombarding electrons have enough energy to remove one of the electrons from the atom, nothing happens, except an elastic collision, but above a sharply defined energy value, we find ionization of the electron in question. The energy of the bombarding electrons required to produce ionization can be accurately measured, and in this way one finds the ionization potentials, or term values. One finds in this way that to remove a $1s$ electron from the sodium atom requires an energy which, expressed in Rydbergs, is 79.4 Rydbergs; to remove a $2s$ requires 5.2

Rydbergs, and to remove a 2p requires 2.80 Rydbergs. Hence the energy of a 1s electron in the atom is −79.4 Rydbergs, that of a 2s is −5.2 Rydbergs, and of a 2p it is −2.80 Rydbergs. (These statements should really be qualified. In the first place, not all these values are actually observed for sodium; for some of them, we must deduce the numbers by extrapolation from neighboring elements. Second, on account of the doubling of the 2p level, the value we have quoted is a suitable average of the two levels. Third, the observations are made using metallic sodium, and an attempt has been made, in the quoted values, to correct for this, and to give the values which would be observed in an isolated sodium atom, if such experiments could be carried out on it.)

The second way in which the X-ray term values are observed is from the X-ray emission spectrum. If a K, or 1s, electron has been removed, by bombardment by an electron which has given up an energy of 79.4 Rydbergs to the atom, there is a vacancy in the 1s shell. An outer electron can then fall down into the vacant 1s location. The selection principle, which forbids transitions unless the azimuthal quantum number l changes by ±1 unit, prevents a transition of a 2s electron to the vacant 1s state, but a 2p electron can fall to the 1s state. After this transition has occurred, the atom is left in just the same state as if a 2p electron had been removed from a neutral atom. We have seen that the energy of this state is −2.80 Rydbergs. In other words, the energy liberated when a 2p electron falls to a 1s level should be

$$79.4 - 2.80 = 76.6 \qquad \text{Rydbergs}$$

This energy will be liberated in a photon, corresponding to an X-ray line in the so-called K series of X rays. We should then observe this frequency in the X-ray spectrum of sodium. Such frequencies are observed for the atoms (though, in the specific case of sodium, the observation has not been made), and they agree very accurately with the values predicted from the term values as determined from electronic bombardment.

For sodium, we then deduce in this way that the energy required to remove a 1s electron, or its ionization potential, is 79.4 Rydbergs, that for 2s is 5.2 Rydbergs, and for 2p it is 2.80 Rydbergs. These are the electrons in the inner shells of the atom. The remaining electron in the ground state of the atom is the 3s, the valence electron, which we assume to be much more easily removed. This is actually the case: the ionization potential of the 3s electron can be found by electron-bombardment experiments, and it is found to be 0.38 Rydberg. From optical spectroscopy, one can observe the energies of a great many levels aside from the 3s. For the valence electron can be excited from its ground state, the 3s, to many different excited states and can have transitions from one to another of these states. These transitions result in the emission of spectrum lines in the visible or neighboring parts of the spectrum, which are observed by the spectroscopists, so that they can determine the positions of the levels.   Thus, in Fig. 8-3 we show the observed energy levels of the sodium atom and some of the transitions allowed by the selection principle.   Such a diagram is called a Grotrian diagram, from the spectroscopist[1] who introduced its use.

In Fig. 8-3a we see the X-ray levels of sodium, as we have just described them, with allowed transitions from $2p$ to $1s$, $3p$ to $1s$ (these two transitions give rise to the K series), and from $2p$ to $2s$ and from $3s$ to $2p$ (leading to the L series).   In (b) we show the optical levels, which demand a very different scale of energy.   We see the $3s$ level, which is occupied by one electron in the ground state, but also the $4s$, $5s$, . . . ; $3p$, $4p$, . . . ; $3d$, $4d$, . . . ; etc.   These are excited states, normally unoccupied, but states into which the $3s$ electron can be excited.   We show many of the allowed transitions between these levels.   The transitions from the (np) levels to the $3s$ are called the lines of the principal series; those from (ns) to $3p$ form the sharp series; those from the (nd) to $3p$ form the diffuse series; those from (nf) to $3d$ form the fundamental series.   As we have mentioned earlier, these names were given to the series by the spectroscopists long before their interpretation in terms of quantum theory was understood, and they are not particularly appropriate.   However, their initials, s for sharp, p for principal, d for diffuse, f for fundamental, have persisted in the notation which we still use for the terms of various l values.   As a matter of interest, the transition from $3p$ to $3s$ is the familiar D line of sodium, in the yellow part of the spectrum.   It is a familiar fact that this line is double, with components of wavelength 5,890 and 5,896 angstroms.   (The doubling arises from the $3p$ level and comes from the electron spin, as we have mentioned earlier.)   A suitable average of these two wavelengths leads to a wave number (reciprocal of the wavelength) of 16,967.6 cm^{-1}, or 0.154624 Rydberg (the Rydberg for sodium, taking account of the reduced mass, is 109,734.8 cm^{-1}).   Since the energy level of the $3s$ state is found to be -0.377726 Rydberg, this means that that of the $3p$ state is -0.223102 Rydberg.   In this sort of way one can find the various energy levels in Fig. 8-3.

In Table 8-1, we give the observed energy levels of sodium, as shown in Fig. 8-3.   We also give several other pieces of information.   First, we give quantum defects for the optical energy levels.   These are the numbers d, from Eq. (8-1).   Thus, we see that for the s levels the d's are approximately constant, varying from 1.37 to 1.35.   For the p levels they run from 0.88 to 0.85, for the d levels they are about 0.01, and for

[1] W. Grotrian, "Graphische Darstellung der Spektren von Atomen," Springer-Verlag OHG, Berlin, 1928.

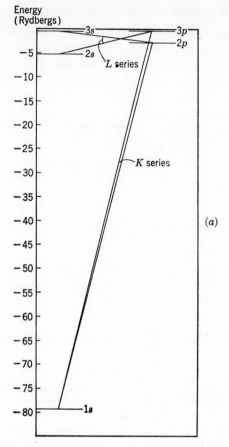

(a)

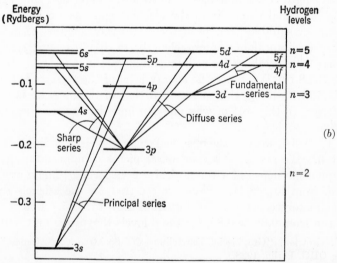

(b)

Fig. 8-3. Energy levels of the sodium atom.   (a) X-ray levels;   (b) optical levels.

the f levels they are much smaller than that. The fact that they vary slightly with principal quantum number shows that Rydberg's law, Eq. (8-1), is not an exact law, but their approximate constancy shows that nevertheless it is a rather accurate approximation to the facts. We shall consider later the question as to why the quantum defect d decreases in this way with increasing azimuthal quantum number.

A second piece of information in Table 8-1 is labeled Effective Z for Energy. This is the value of $Z - s$ or $Z - s'$ which must be used in Eq. (8-2) or (8-3) to reproduce properly the observed X-ray term value. We see that for the $1s$ level, where $Z = 11$, $Z - s = 8.91$, we have $s = 2.09$. For the $2s$, $Z - s' = 4.56$, so that $s' = 6.44$, and for the $2p$,

Table 8-1. Observed and Calculated Energy Levels of the Sodium Atom in Rydbergs

Observed energies from optical and X-ray spectra. Calculated energies from V. Fock and M. Petrashen, *Physik. Z. Sowjetunion*, **6**:368 (1934). Quantum defects d are from Rydberg law, energy $= -1/(n - d)^2$. Effective Z for energy is given by the equation, energy $= -Z_{\text{eff}}^2/n^2$. Effective Z for wave function is value used in hydrogenic function; values from Fock and Petrashen, who have determined them by variation method.

State	Energy observed	Energy calculated	Quantum defect	Effective Z for energy	Effective Z for wave function
$1s$	-79.4	-81.2		8.91	10.68
$2s$	$- 5.2$	$- 6.0$		4.56	8.44
$3s$	$- 0.377726$	$- 0.372$	1.3729		
$4s$	$- 0.143162$	$- 0.1406$	1.3571		
$5s$	$- 0.075172$		1.3527		
$6s$	$- 0.046266$		1.3509		
$7s$	$- 0.031326$		1.3500		
$2p$	$- 2.80$	$- 3.66$		3.35	6.98
$3p$	$- 0.223102$	$- 0.2188$	0.8829		
$4p$	$- 0.101873$		0.8669		
$5p$	$- 0.058393$		0.8617		
$6p$	$- 0.037840$		0.8593		
$3d$	$- 0.111877$		0.0103		
$4d$	$- 0.062887$		0.0123		
$5d$	$- 0.040214$		0.0133		
$6d$	$- 0.027907$		0.0140		
$4f$	$- 0.062524$		0.00077		
$5f$	$- 0.040024$		0.00150		
$6f$	$- 0.027790$		0.00132		
$5g$	$- 0.040000$		0.00000		

$Z - s' = 3.35$, and $s' = 7.65$.   We see, then, the way in which the s' for
the L electrons is much greater than the s for the K electrons, as we
mentioned earlier.   We shall comment later on the column headed
Effective Z for Wave Function.

Bohr, in his treatment of the structure of the periodic table, worked out
syntheses of the type we have described for the various atoms, deducing
the quantum numbers appropriate for the optical term values.   Before
his explanation, this had not been at all clear.   The Rydberg formula,
Eq. (8-1), does not uniquely determine the value of n from the observed
spectrum.   Thus, if one knows the optical energy levels of the sodium
atom, as given in Fig. 8-3b, but does not know how to assign the values
of n, there is no way to tell whether the ground state should be $3s$, with
$d = 1.37$, or $2s$, with $d = 0.37$, or $1s$, with $d = -0.63$, or even $4s$, with
$d = 2.37$, etc.   Any of these possibilities would lead to the same value of
$n - d$, and hence to the same term value.   Uncertainties of this sort
persisted in the interpretation of the spectra of the alkalies, until Bohr
resolved them by showing the way in which the lower n values of each
series belonged to the X-ray levels, and the higher n values to the optical
values, so that the lower levels could be described by formulas of the type
of Eqs. (8-2) and (8-3), the higher levels by Eq. (8-1).

Once it was clear that we had in a diagram like that of Fig. 8-3 a complete set of energy levels for such an atom as sodium, it was naturally a
matter of great interest to ask whether these energy levels could really
be described in terms of a central field.   During the years from 1921 to
1924, a number of workers, among them Schrödinger, Hartree, and
Lindsay,[1] undertook to work backward from the observed energy levels
of sodium and to find whether a central field could be found in which
the energy levels would have the values found experimentally.   They
were, of course, using the Bohr theory for the motion of an electron in a
central field, rather than wave mechanics, but the results are not greatly
different.   The conclusion to which these workers came was that such a
potential could be set up and that it could reproduce fairly well the
observed energy levels.   This clearly gave a very useful verification of
Bohr's ideas.

Once wave mechanics came along, and Hartree's formulation of the
method of the self-consistent field, one could find the central field appropriate for sodium by direct application of Hartree's method, rather than
by working backward from the observed spectrum.   In Table 8-1, we
give calculated energies for a number of the terms, found in this way.

[1] E. Schrödinger, Z. Physik, **4**:347 (1921); E. Fues, Z. Physik, **11**:364 (1922);
12:1 (1922); D. R. Hartree, Proc. Cambridge Phil. Soc., **21**:625 (1923); **22**:409 (1924);
A. Th. van Urk, Z. Physik, **13**:268 (1923); R. B. Lindsay, J. Math. and Phys., **3**:191
(1924).

These were not, as a matter of fact, found by Hartree's original method, but by the improved Hartree-Fock method, which we have mentioned, and which we shall take up in Chap. 17 (Vol. II); this case of sodium was the one chosen by Fock and Petrashen for the first test of the Hartree-Fock method.   One can see, by inspection of Table 8-1, that most of the energy levels calculated by Fock and Petrashen show remarkably close agreement with the observations, though there are some rather bad discrepancies.   At any rate, the agreement is good enough so that there is no doubt that we are on the right track in our interpretation of the sodium spectrum and of the periodic table of the elements.   We have used sodium as an example here, for the reason that it was studied more intensively in the 1920s than any other element, but now we have self-consistent-field calculations of many atoms, and the agreements in general are just as good as for sodium.   In Appendix 16 we give references to the literature for the cases which have been calculated.

There is an alternative, simpler, and less accurate method of approach to the potential and charge density within an atom, called the Thomas-Fermi[1] method.   We shall not describe it here, but we discuss it in Appendix 17.   It is very useful as a first approximation and directly yields values of the potential within any atom.   It has been suggested that a first step toward the solution of the Hartree problem, for the many atoms for which that problem has not been solved, might be to find the wave functions of an electron satisfying Schrödinger's equation in a Thomas-Fermi potential.[2]   Such a program has been carried through by Latter.[3]   He has made calculations for a large number of atoms scattered through the periodic table.   The accuracy of these results is not as good as for the Hartree method but is not very much poorer. Results like these tell us that, while these approximations are not perfect, still they form a very good first approximation to the solution of the problem of atomic structure.

8-6. Optical and X-ray Energy Levels of the Atoms.   We have gone in detail through the example of sodium to show the type of experimental information which is found from the X-ray and optical spectra of the elements.   Now we shall give information of the same sort, for all the lighter atoms.   Before giving this information, there is one comment which should be made.   It is only for the alkalies that the optical spectrum has the simple form which we have been describing.   For the other atoms, the spectrum is very much more complicated.   Instead of having

[1] L. H. Thomas, *Proc. Cambridge Phil. Soc.*, **23**:542 (1927); *J. Chem. Phys.*, **22**:1758 (1954).   E. Fermi, *Atti. accad. nazl. Lincei*, **6**:602 (1927); **7**:342 (1928); *Z. Physik*, **48**:73 (1928), **49**:550 (1928).

[2] M. G. Mayer, *Phys. Rev.*, **60**:184 (1941).

[3] R. Latter, *Phys. Rev.*, **99**:510 (1955).

Table 8-2. Experimental Values of the X-ray and Optical Terms in the Lighter Atoms, in Rydbergs

Taken from J. C. Slater, *Phys. Rev.*, **98**:1039 (1955), where detailed references are given. One-electron energies are the negatives of the values tabulated.

		$1s$	$2s$	$2p$	$3s$	$3p$	$3d$	$4s$	$4p$	$4d$	$5s$
H	1	1.00									
He	2	1.81									
Li	3	4.77	0.40								
Be	4	8.9	0.69								
B	5	14.5	1.03	0.42							
C	6	21.6	1.43	0.79							
N	7	30.0	1.88	0.95							
O	8	39.9	2.38	1.17							
F	9	51.2	2.95	1.37							
Ne	10	64.0	3.56	1.59							
Na	11	79.4	5.2	2.80	0.38						
Mg	12	96.5	7.0	4.1	0.56						
Al	13	115.3	9.0	5.8	0.83	0.44					
Si	14	135.9	11.5	7.8	1.10	0.57					
P	15	158.3	14.1	10.1	1.35	0.72					
S	16	182.4	17.0	12.5	1.54	0.86					
Cl	17	208.4	20.3	15.3	1.86	1.01					
A	18	236.2	24.2	18.5	2.15	1.16					
K	19	266.2	28.2	22.2	3.0	1.81		0.32			
Ca	20	297.9	32.8	26.1	3.7	2.4		0.45			
Sc	21	331.1	37.3	30.0	4.2	2.6	0.59	0.55			
Ti	22	366.1	42.0	34.0	4.8	2.9	0.68	0.52			
V	23	402.9	46.9	38.3	5.3	3.2	0.74	0.55			
Cr	24	441.6	51.9	43.0	6.0	3.6	0.75	0.57			
Mn	25	482.0	57.7	47.8	6.6	4.0	0.57	0.50			
Fe	26	524.3	63.0	52.8	7.3	4.4	0.64	0.53			
Co	27	568.3	69.0	58.2	8.0	4.9	0.66	0.53			
Ni	28	614.1	75.3	63.7	8.7	5.4	0.73	0.55			
Cu	29	662.0	81.3	69.6	9.6	6.1	0.79	0.57			
Zn	30	712.0	88.7	76.2	10.5	7.0	1.28	0.69			
Ga	31	764.0	96.4	83.0	11.8	7.9	1.6	0.93	0.44		
Ge	32	818.2	104.6	90.5	13.5	9.4	2.4	1.15	0.55		
As	33	874.5	113.0	98.5	15.4	10.8	3.4	1.30	0.68		
Se	34	932.6	122.1	106.8	17.3	12.2	4.5	1.54	0.80		
Br	35	993.0	131.7	115.6	19.9	13.8	5.6	1.80	0.93		
Kr	36	1,055.5	142.0	124.7	22.1	15.9	7.1	2.00	1.03		
Rb	37	1,120.1	152.7	134.5	24.3	18.3	8.7	2.7	1.56		0.31
Sr	38	1,186.7	163.7	144.6	26.8	20.5	10.4	3.3	2.0		0.42
Y	39	1,255.3	175.1	155.0	29.4	22.7	12.0	3.7	2.3	0.48	0.64
Zr	40	1,325.9	186.7	165.5	32.0	24.8	13.6	4.1	2.3	0.61	0.54
Nb	41	1,398.9	199.3	176.9	35.1	27.6	15.8	5.0	3.1		0.58

simple energy levels associated with each configuration, with only the doubling observed in the alkalies, we find that a given configuration results in many different energy levels, falling into groups of closely spaced levels which we shall refer to as multiplets.[1] One can, however, as we shall explain in Secs. 14-2 and 15-6, find a suitable average of the levels arising from a given configuration, which amounts to averaging over different orientations of the angular momenta of the various electrons. This represents the equivalent of the energy level which would be found for the atom in question if one used the central-field approximation, without taking account of the torques exerted by one electron on another. We shall use these averages of the energy levels in a configuration for the purpose of the present discussion.

With this simplification, we now give in Table 8-2 the term values as determined experimentally for both X-ray and optical terms in the lighter atoms. Among the optical terms, we include only those levels which are occupied in the ground state of the atom. These same results are shown graphically in Fig. 8-4. There we have plotted the results in the form of $\sqrt{-E/Ry}$. That is, we have taken the negative of the energy, or the ionization potential, expressed in Rydbergs, and then have taken its square root, which would be equal to $(Z - s)/n$, where s is the shielding constant, n the principal quantum number, if Eq. (8-2) or (8-3) were correct. Thus, we might expect these curves to be linear functions of atomic number, with a slope of unity for the K series, a slope of $\frac{1}{2}$ for the L series, and so on. Such diagrams were given, by Bohr and Coster,[2] in the original papers in which the correlation between the X-ray levels and the structure of the periodic table was explained.

These diagrams give very complete information about the nature of the periodic table. In the first place, we notice that each type of electron first puts in its appearance at the element where it would be expected

---

[1] There is not complete agreement concerning the nomenclature regarding multiplets. The name was introduced by M. A. Catalan, *Phil. Trans. Roy. Soc. (London),* **223**:127 (1922), to describe the array of spectrum lines arising from transitions between two closely spaced groups of energy levels of the type we have just mentioned. Many writers, such as E. U. Condon and G. H. Shortley, "Theory of Atomic Spectra," Cambridge University Press, New York, 1935, continue to use this notation and refer to such a closely spaced group of levels as a term. In the present work, however, we have preferred to refer to the groups of levels themselves as multiplets, a notation used by some other writers, as, for instance, R. F. Bacher and S. Goudsmit, "Atomic Energy States," McGraw-Hill Book Company, Inc., New York, 1932 (see p. 7). Since we refer to these groups of levels as singlets, doublets, triplets, etc., the name multiplets seems an appropriate generic name for them, whereas the expression term does not suggest the multiplicity. Since we shall be referring in a very large majority of the cases to energy levels, and only occasionally to the lines arising from transitions between these levels, our use of the word multiplet will hardly result in confusion.

[2] N. Bohr and D. Coster, *Z. Physik,* **12**:342 (1922).

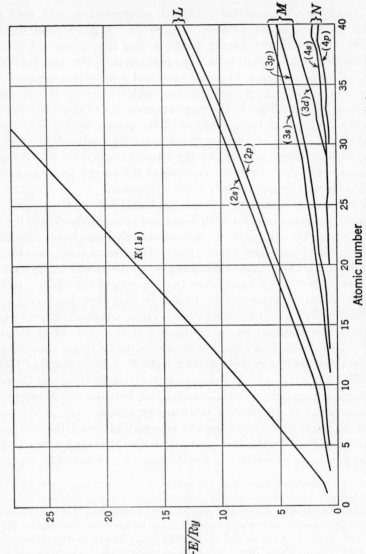

FIG. 8-4. Experimental values of $\sqrt{-E/Ry}$ for X-ray and optical terms of the lighter atoms.

according to Bohr's theory: the 2s at lithium, $Z = 3$; the 2p at boron, $Z = 5$; the 3s at sodium, $Z = 11$; the 3p at aluminum, $Z = 13$; the 4s at potassium, $Z = 19$; the 3d at scandium, $Z = 21$; the 4p at gallium, $Z = 31$; the 5s at rubidium, $Z = 37$. Similar situations are found for the heavier atoms, which we have not included in our table and figure. We observe furthermore that the value of the energy is such that the lowest levels are occupied in the ground state, agreeing with the fundamental postulate underlying the theory of the periodic table. We note that, in the transition group from scandium to nickel, the 3d and 4s electrons are bound with practically equal tightness, as we have mentioned before. We notice furthermore that those electrons which are easily removed from atoms to form positive ions, like the valence electrons in the alkali and alkaline-earth atoms, have small ionization potentials, while the outermost electron in an inert gas, for instance, requires very much more energy to ionize.

8-7. Dimensions of Electronic Wave Functions in Atoms. As we have stated, the self-consistent-field method results in central fields in which the energy levels reproduce these experimental values, with approximately the same accuracy as in sodium. In the next chapter we shall go into the details of that method. There is one result which we may well give here, however, rather than waiting until we have discussed the method in detail, and that relates to the sizes of the atoms. We realize, of course, that there is no definite meaning to the question as to how large an atom is, or how large is the wave function of any (nl) value, or any shell of electrons. The reason is that the radial wave function is a continuous function of r, and charge is distributed all the way from $r = 0$ to infinity. However, a good measure of the size of any particular shell of electrons is given by the radius at which the quantity $P = rR$ of the electron in question has its maximum; as we saw in Sec. 7-2, in the discussion of Fig. 7-3, this is the radius at which the radial charge density of the electron in question has its maximum. In Table 8-3 we give the radius, as determined by the method of the self-consistent field, for the maximum radial charge density for the various electrons of the lighter atoms. Since only a relatively small fraction of the atoms have been worked out by this method, a great deal of interpolation has been required to set up the values in this table, but they are believed to be relatively accurate.

There are a number of interesting consequences to be noticed from this table. First, of course, we notice how the size of any particular wave function decreases as we go to heavier and heavier atoms. This is a consequence of the Bohr theory of hydrogen, in which we find that the size of the orbit of an electron of given quantum numbers, in the field of a nucleus of charge Z units, is inversely proportional to Z. This comes

Table 8-3

Radius of maximum radial charge density for the various wave functions of the light atoms as determined by self-consistent-field calculations. Since such calculations have been made for relatively few atoms, many of the values tabulated are interpolated but are believed to be fairly accurate. Values are given in angstroms.

	$1s$	$2s$	$2p$	$3s$	$3p$	$3d$	$4s$	$4p$
H	0.53							
He	0.30							
Li	0.20	1.50						
Be	0.143	1.19						
B	0.112	0.88	0.85					
C	0.090	0.67	0.66					
N	0.080	0.56	0.53					
O	0.069	0.48	0.45					
F	0.061	0.41	0.38					
Ne	0.055	0.37	0.32					
Na	0.050	0.32	0.28	1.55				
Mg	0.046	0.30	0.25	1.32				
Al	0.042	0.27	0.23	1.16	1.21			
Si	0.040	0.24	0.21	0.98	1.06			
P	0.037	0.23	0.19	0.88	0.92			
S	0.035	0.21	0.18	0.78	0.82			
Cl	0.032	0.20	0.16	0.72	0.75			
A	0.031	0.19	0.155	0.66	0.67			
K	0.029	0.18	0.145	0.60	0.63		2.20	
Ca	0.028	0.16	0.133	0.55	0.58		2.03	
Sc	0.026	0.16	0.127	0.52	0.54	0.61	1.80	
Ti	0.025	0.150	0.122	0.48	0.50	0.55	1.66	
V	0.024	0.143	0.117	0.46	0.47	0.49	1.52	
Cr	0.023	0.138	0.112	0.43	0.44	0.45	1.41	
Mn	0.022	0.133	0.106	0.40	0.41	0.42	1.31	
Fe	0.021	0.127	0.101	0.39	0.39	0.39	1.22	
Co	0.020	0.122	0.096	0.37	0.37	0.36	1.14	
Ni	0.019	0.117	0.090	0.35	0.36	0.34	1.07	
Cu	0.019	0.112	0.085	0.34	0.34	0.32	1.03	
Zn	0.018	0.106	0.081	0.32	0.32	0.30	0.97	
Ga	0.017	0.103	0.078	0.31	0.31	0.28	0.92	1.13
Ge	0.017	0.100	0.076	0.30	0.30	0.27	0.88	1.06
As	0.016	0.097	0.073	0.29	0.29	0.25	0.84	1.01
Se	0.016	0.095	0.071	0.28	0.28	0.24	0.81	0.95
Br	0.015	0.092	0.069	0.27	0.27	0.23	0.76	0.90
Kr	0.015	0.090	0.067	0.25	0.25	0.22	0.74	0.86

in wave mechanics from Eq. (7-22), in which the wave function is a function of $x = 2Zr/n$, so that the radius is inversely proportional to Z. With the shielding taken into account, we should expect that the size of the orbit should be equal to that of a corresponding hydrogenic orbit, divided by $Z - s$, where s is a shielding constant. In Table 8-1, we have given in the column Effective Z for Wave Function values of $Z - s$ which determine the scale of the orbits in this way, for the $1s$, $2s$, and $2p$ orbits of sodium.   We notice that they are quite different from the effective Z for energy, and we shall comment on the explanation of this discrepancy in the next chapter.   Nevertheless, this does not affect the fact that in general the orbit of a given type has a radius which is approximately proportional to $1/(Z - s)$, where s is a suitably chosen shielding constant.   This means that, by the time we get to $Z = 100$, the size of the $1s$ orbit, instead of being 1 atomic unit as in hydrogen, has shrunk to about 0.01 atomic unit.

A result of the shrinkage of the orbits, as we go to higher atomic number, is that more electrons can be accommodated inside an atom of about the same size.   The radius of the outermost electronic shell of the alkali atoms, for example, increases only slightly as we go from lithium to sodium, potassium, rubidium, and cesium.   In other words, the atoms increase only slightly in size as we go up the periodic table.   Nevertheless the number of electrons increases greatly; this is possible because they are packed more tightly into the atom.   The same thing is observed when the sizes of atoms are studied in other ways.   For instance, in a solid, we can estimate the sizes of the atoms by assuming that they act like rigid spheres and pack closely together.   The estimates of atomic sizes we get in this way do not, of course, agree with the figures of Table 8-3, which give the radii of maximum radial charge density, but nevertheless there is a good parallelism between them, and the radii observed from crystal structure show the same feature as the radii of Table 8-3, namely, that they do not increase nearly as fast, in going from light to heavy atoms, as we might have supposed from the great increase in number of electrons.

There is one final, rather specialized observation which we can make from Table 8-3.   This is the fact that the radii of maximum radial charge density for the $3d$ electrons, in the elements from scandium to nickel or copper, are much smaller than those for the $4s$, even though the energies are about the same.   This is contrary to the usual trend, which is that, the more tightly bound an electron is, the smaller is its radius.   The reason for the discrepancy comes in the very different shape of the wave functions for the $3d$ and $4s$.   We shall give examples later to show the different shapes.   A result of this is that the d electrons, in the transition groups of elements, in many ways act as inner electrons, even though they are easily removed from the atom.

PROBLEMS

1. The helium atom, with two electrons, can be approximated fairly well by the self-consistent-field method, replacing the wave function of each electron by a hydrogen-

like function exp $(-\alpha r)$, where α is a parameter to be determined by the variation principle. The present problem and the three following show how the calculation is to be made. First normalize the wave function; then use this normalized function to compute the potential energy of one electron in the field of the nucleus and of the other electron. Show that this potential energy, in atomic units, is $-(2/r)[1 + (1 + \alpha r) \exp (-2\alpha r)]$. *Hint:* The potential is the sum of that arising from the nucleus, and the other electron. A charge q (in atomic units), distributed over the surface of a shell of radius r_1, has a potential energy, at a point whose distance from the origin is r, equal to $2q/r$ if $r > r_1$ and $2q/r_1$ if $r < r_1$; that is, the shell acts at exterior points as if the charge were concentrated at the origin, whereas the potential is constant inside the shell.

2. Let one electron have a charge distribution arising from the wave function exp $(-\alpha_2 r)$, so that the potential energy of an electron in the electrostatic field of the nucleus and this electron, by Prob. 1, is $-(2/r)[1 + (1 + \alpha_2 r) \exp (-2\alpha_2 r)]$. Find the average potential energy of an electron whose wave function is exp $(-\alpha_1 r)$ in the field of this other electron.

3. Find the average kinetic energy of an electron whose wave function is exp $(-\alpha_1 r)$, and hence its total energy, using the result of Prob. 2 for the potential energy. Now vary α_1 to minimize this total energy, keeping α_2 fixed. This gives the best approximation to a 1s solution of Schrödinger's equation for the potential in question.

4. After performing the variation of Prob. 3, set $\alpha_2 = \alpha_1$, to achieve self-consistency, and find the resulting energy of the helium 1s electron in the field of the other. Compare with the experimental value of -1.81 Rydbergs.

5. Use the wave function of Prob. 4 to find the radius of maximum radial charge density in the helium atom, and compare with the radius given in Table 8-3.

6. It is often convenient to write the potential energy of an electron in the field of the nucleus and the other electrons as $-2Z_p/r$, so that, in the case taken up in Prob. 1, $Z_p = 1 + (1 + \alpha r) \exp (-2\alpha r)$. Compute and plot this function Z_p as a function of r. Also compute and plot the Z_p which would arise if all the charge were concentrated on the surface of a spherical shell whose radius is that found in Prob. 5. Compare these two functions Z_p, and show that the Z_p derived from the spherical shell model forms a crude approximation to that arising from the hydrogenic wave function.

7. The result of Prob. 6 suggests a simplified method of getting at an approximate self-consistent-field potential for any atom. Carry this approximation out for the potential energy acting on the valence electron of sodium, in the following way. Assume that there are two 1s electrons on the surface of a sphere of radius 0.050 angstrom (as given in Table 8-3), two 2s electrons on the surface of a sphere of radius 0.32 angstrom, and six 2p's on the surface of a sphere of radius 0.28 angstrom. Find Z_p as a function of r, and plot the resulting function.

8. The potential found in Prob. 7 is that of a sodium ion lacking a 3s electron. The potential of a neutral sodium atom would be given by adding also a 3s electron, which may be approximated as if it were on a shell of radius 1.55 angstroms. Compute and plot the Z_p arising in this way for the sodium atom.

9. In Appendix 17 is given the Thomas-Fermi approximate formula for Z_p as a function of r, for any neutral atom. Compute Z_p for sodium from that formula, and compare with the value found in Prob. 8.

9

The Self-consistent-field Method

9-1. Hartree's Assumption for the Atomic Wave Function. In Sec. 8-2, we have studied the general principles underlying Hartree's method of the self-consistent field. Now we shall go into the details of the method. First we ask ourselves: What type of wave function for the atom does Hartree's method presuppose? He starts by assuming that each electron moves in a central field, produced by the nucleus, and the spherically averaged potential fields of each other electron. We have already pointed out that the angular dependence of the solution of Schrödinger's equation in an arbitrary central field is the same as that for hydrogen, and as given in Eq. (7-31). The reason is that the separation of variables, as discussed in Appendix 13, goes through just the same when the potential is a general function of r as it does for the Coulomb potential, and the equations for the functions of θ and ϕ are the same as in hydrogen. Hence we may start our discussion by using Eq. (7-31) for the one-electron wave functions, with the understanding that the radial wave functions $R_{nl}(r)$ will have a different form from what they do in hydrogen but that the normalization factors, and angular functions, as given in Eq. (7-31), still apply in the present case. That is, we assume that the one-electron wave functions, or orbitals as we shall call them, have the form

$$u_{nlm_l}(r,\theta,\phi) = \frac{(-1)^{(m_l+|m_l|)/2}}{\sqrt{4\pi}} \sqrt{\frac{(2l+1)(l-|m_l|)!}{(l+|m_l|)!}}$$
$$\times R_{nl}(r)P_l^{|m_l|}(\cos\theta)\exp(im_l\phi) \quad (9\text{-}1)$$

where
$$R_{nl}(r) = \frac{P_{nl}(r)}{r} \quad (9\text{-}2)$$

and where R_{nl}, or P_{nl}, is normalized so that

$$\int_0^\infty [P_{nl}(r)]^2\,dr = 1 \quad (9\text{-}3)$$

213

Next we inquire how a wave function for the N-electron atom can be constructed out of these one-electron orbitals. Each electron is supposed to move quite independently of the others, being acted on by the others only in an averaged manner. Hence the quantity $\psi^*\psi$, the probability density, where ψ is the N-electron wave function, should be a product of probability densities for the various electrons, as we should have for independent motion. This implies that the wave function ψ should be a product of functions of the various electrons. In other words, we start by assuming a wave function of the form

$$\psi(r_1\theta_1\phi_1 \cdots r_N\theta_N\phi_N) = u_{n_1l_1ml_1}(r_1\theta_1\phi_1) \cdots u_{n_Nl_Nml_N}(r_N\theta_N\phi_N) \quad (9\text{-}4)$$

where the u's on the right side of Eq. (9-4) are orbitals of the type of Eq. (9-1), each one a function of the coordinates of a single electron. We assign the quantum numbers $n_1l_1ml_1 \cdots n_Nl_Nml_N$ of the various electrons according to the configurations in which we expect the atom to be found, as discussed in the preceding chapter. The wave function, in the method we are using at the moment, does not depend on the spin quantum number m_s, but in accordance with Pauli's exclusion principle, we may assign no more than two electrons to a given set of (nlm_l) values, of which we assume that one has $m_s = \frac{1}{2}$, the other has $m_s = -\frac{1}{2}$.

We can now go through the postulates of Hartree's method, find the spherically averaged potential arising from the nucleus and all electrons but one, set up Schrödinger's equation for an electron moving in this potential, and assume that each of the orbitals satisfies such a Schrödinger equation. Before we are through, we shall write down those equations. But it must occur to the reader that there should be another way of deriving these equations. The function of Eq. (9-4) is not an exact solution of Schrödinger's equation for the atom; it is an approximate function, containing the undetermined radial functions $R_{n_1l_1}(r)$, $R_{n_2l_2}(r)$, . . . , $R_{n_Nl_N}(r)$ as quantities which we may vary. Why do we not use the variation method,[1] varying these radial functions so as to minimize the energy of the atom, as computed from the approximate wave function of Eq. (9-4)? We can carry through this variation problem, and the wave functions prove to be very nearly those of Hartree's method. If we modify the calculation very slightly, we get just Hartree's equations: we modify it by computing the average energy, not exactly, but by making the spherical average of the potential of an electron which underlies Hartree's approximation. Later, in Chap. 17 (Vol. II), when we discuss the Hartree-Fock method, we shall remove this limitation, computing the energy exactly, and shall find that this makes a very slight correction to the results of Hartree's method.

---

[1] See J. C. Slater, *Phys. Rev.*, **35**:210 (1930), for suggestion of this method.

Since this variation procedure is a satisfying method of deriving Hartree's equations, showing that they are not simply the result of intuition, we shall derive them in this way and after we have derived them, we shall show that they have the interpretation which Hartree gave to them.

9-2. The Average Hamiltonian for an Atom. The first step in applying the variation method to Hartree's wave function is to compute the average value of the Hamiltonian for the wave function of Eq. (9-4), making the approximation of spherical averaging. The Hamiltonian for an N-electron atom, with atomic number Z (by allowing N to be different from Z we give the possibility of handling ions as well as atoms), is

$$(H)_{op} = - \sum (i)\nabla_i^2 - \sum (i)\frac{2Z}{r_i} + \sum (\text{pairs } i,j) \frac{2}{r_{ij}} \qquad (9\text{-}5)$$

where the summation over i is over all N electrons, that over pairs is over each pair counted once, excluding the case $i = j$. The first term in Eq. (9-5) is the sum of the kinetic energies of all electrons, the second is the potential energy in the field of the nucleus, r_i being the distance from the nucleus to the ith electron, and the last is the repulsive Coulomb potential of interaction between the ith and jth electrons, r_{ij} being the distance between the ith and jth electrons. We understand that we are to perform a spherical average of this repulsive interaction. The Hamiltonian of Eq. (9-5) is in atomic units. It is convenient to rewrite this Hamiltonian in the form

$$(H)_{op} = \Sigma(i)f_i + \Sigma(\text{pairs } i,j)g_{ij} \qquad (9\text{-}6)$$

where
$$f_i = -\nabla_i^2 - \frac{2Z}{r_i} \qquad g_{ij} = \frac{2}{r_{ij}} \qquad (9\text{-}7)$$

The characteristic of the f_i's is that each operates on the coordinates of only one electron, while each g_{ij} operates on the coordinates of two electrons; consequently they are called one-electron and two-electron operators, respectively.

We now let the operator of Eq. (9-5) or (9-6) operate on the wave function of Eq. (9-4), multiply by the conjugate of the wave function, and integrate over all values of the coordinates. First we consider one of the one-electron operators f_i. It operates only on the orbital $u_{n_i l_i m_{l_i}}(r_i\theta_i\phi_i)$. In integrating over the coordinates of the electrons, we can integrate first over the coordinates of all electrons except the ith, each such integral giving unity on account of the normalization of the orbitals. Hence the contribution of an operator f_i to the average value of the Hamiltonian is

$$\int u_{n_i l_i m_{l_i}}^*(r_i\theta_i\phi_i)f_i u_{n_i l_i m_{l_i}}(r_i\theta_i\phi_i) \, dv_i = (i/f/i) \qquad (9\text{-}8)$$

where the expression $(i/f/i)$ is an abbreviation for the integral. Next we consider one of the two-electron operators g_{ij}. It operates on two orbitals, with indices i and j. We can then integrate first over the coordinates of all electrons except these two and find as the contribution of this operator g_{ij} to the average Hamiltonian

$$\int [u^*_{n_i l_i m_{l_i}}(r_i \theta_i \phi_i) u^*_{n_j l_j m_{l_j}}(r_j \theta_j \phi_j) g_{ij} u_{n_i l_i m l_i}(r_i \theta_i \phi_i)$$
$$\times\ u_{n_j l_j m_{l_j}}(r_j \theta_j \phi_j)]_{\mathrm{av}}\ dv_i\ dv_j = (ij/g/ij)_{\mathrm{av}} \quad (9\text{-}9)$$

where the subscript av refers to the spherical average which we are to perform, and where $(ij/g/ij)$ is a notation for the integral of Eq. (9-9), without any spherical average.

We then may combine these results, and we find that

$$(H)_{\mathrm{av}} = \Sigma(i)(i/f/i) + \Sigma(\text{pairs } i,j)(ij/g/ij)_{\mathrm{av}} \quad (9\text{-}10)$$

where we have defined the integrals in Eqs. (9-8) and (9-9). We shall now go on in the next section to the evaluation of these integrals, for wave functions of the type given in Eq. (9-1).

9-3. Energy Integrals for the Hartree Calculation. The operator $-\nabla^2$, met in the kinetic-energy part of f_i, is found in Eq. (7-27), though that equation is stated in terms of ordinary rather than atomic units. We allow the corresponding operator in atomic units to operate on a function of the type given in Eq. (9-1) and use the equation satisfied by $P_l^{|m_l|}(\cos\theta)$, namely, Eq. (7-7). We proceed as in deriving Eq. (7-12) and find

$$-\nabla^2 u = \frac{(-1)^{(m_l+|m_l|)/2}}{\sqrt{4\pi}} \sqrt{\frac{(2l+1)(l-|m_l|)!}{(l+|m_l|)!}}$$
$$P_l^{|m_l|}(\cos\theta) \exp(im_l\phi) \frac{1}{r}\left[-\frac{d^2}{dr^2} + \frac{l(l+1)}{r^2} \right] P_{nl}(r) \quad (9\text{-}11)$$

where u, n, l, m_l, r, θ, ϕ stand for u_i, n_i, l_i, m_{l_i}, r_i, θ_i, ϕ_i if we are dealing with the function u_i. We multiply by u_i^* and integrate over coordinates, making use of the properties of the associated Legendre functions given in Eq. (7-11). We then find

$$\int u^*_{n_i l_i m_{l_i}}(r_i \theta_i \phi_i)(-\nabla_i^2) u_{n_i l_i m_{l_i}}(r_i \theta_i \phi_i)\ dv_i$$
$$= \int_0^\infty P_{n_i l_i}(r_i)\left[-\frac{d^2}{dr_i^2} + \frac{l_i(l_i+1)}{r_i^2} \right] P_{n_i l_i}(r_i)\ dr_i \quad (9\text{-}12)$$

As for the term $-2Z/r_i$ in the operator f_i, we can carry out immediately the integration over angles and are left with a radial integration only. Hence we arrive at the result

$$(i/f/i) = \int_0^\infty P_{n_i l_i}(r_i)\left[-\frac{d^2}{dr_i^2} + \frac{l_i(l_i+1)}{r_i^2} - \frac{2Z}{r_i} \right] P_{n_i l_i}(r_i)\ dr_i \quad (9\text{-}13)$$

We shall denote this one-electron integral by

$$(i/f/i) = I(n_i l_i) \tag{9-14}$$

which indicates the quantum numbers on which it depends; we observe it does not depend on m_{l_i}. In Chap. 13 we shall indicate several alternative forms for the integral, which are sometimes more convenient for actual calculation.

Next we consider the two-electron integral of Eq. (9-9). This represents the Coulomb interaction energy between a charge distribution

$$u_{n_i l_i m_{l_i}}^*(r_i \theta_i \phi_i) u_{n_i l_i m_{l_i}}(r_i \theta_i \phi_i)$$

and another charge distribution

$$u_{n_j l_j m_{l_j}}^*(r_j \theta_j \phi_j) u_{n_j l_j m_{l_j}}(r_j \theta_j \phi_j)$$

where it is understood that we are to perform a spherical average of the charges or potentials. We know from electrostatics that rather than carry out the integral over the coordinates of both electrons, as in Eq. (9-9), we can regard our problem in a different light. We can first compute the quantity

$$\int u_{n_j l_j m_{l_j}}^*(r_j \theta_j \phi_j) u_{n_j l_j m_{l_j}}(r_j \theta_j \phi_j) \left(\frac{2}{r_{ij}}\right) dv_j \tag{9-15}$$

This is the electrostatic potential (in atomic units) of the charge distribution of the jth electron, at the position of the ith. Then we multiply this by the charge distribution $u_{n_i l_i m_{l_i}}^*(r_i \theta_i \phi_i) u_{n_i l_i m_{l_i}}(r_i \theta_i \phi_i)$ of the ith electron and integrate over dv_i. This is exactly what Eq. (9-9) says, but it amounts to giving a physical interpretation to each step of the process.

In addition to this, we must perform a spherical average. Electrostatic theory shows that the spherical average of such a potential as is given in Eq. (9-15) is identical with the potential of the spherically averaged charge density. Let us then find this spherical average of the charge density of the jth electron. We must take the total charge enclosed in a spherical shell bounded by spheres of radii r_j, $r_j + dr_j$, and we are to replace the actual charge by a charge distribution in which this same charge is uniformly distributed through the shell. Now the charge located in the volume bounded by r_j, $r_j + dr_j$, θ_j, $\theta_j + d\theta_j$, ϕ_j, $\phi_j + d\phi_j$ is the volume element $r_j^2 \sin \theta_j \, dr_j \, d\theta_j \, d\phi_j$ times the product of the wave function of Eq. (9-1) and its conjugate (times, of course, the electronic charge $-e$, if we are using ordinary units). Hence the charge located in the spherical shell will be the integral of this quantity over θ and ϕ, or

$$\frac{1}{\pi} \frac{(2l_j + 1)(l_j - |m_{l_j}|)!}{(l_j + |m_j|)!} P_{n_j l_j}^2(r_j) \, dr_j \int_0^{2\pi} d\phi_j$$
$$\times \int_0^{\pi} [P_{l_j}^{|m_{l_j}|}(\cos \theta_j)]^2 \sin \theta_j \, d\theta_j \tag{9-16}$$

again times $-e$ if we are using ordinary units. The integral over θ_j is given in Eq. (7-11). The integral over ϕ_j is 2π. When we combine these facts, we find that the charge located in the shell between r_j and $r_j + dr_j$ is

$$P^2_{n_j l_j}(r_j) \, dr_j \qquad (9\text{-}17)$$

times $-e$. In other words, as far as the spherical average is concerned the result is just as if we had disregarded the functions of angles in Eq. (9-1) and used $P^2_{n_j l_j}$ directly as the radial charge density.

To find the electrostatic potential of Eq. (9-15), we now wish to find the potential energy of an electron at distance r_i from the origin, in the presence of a shell of radius r_j and of charge equal to $P^2_{n_j l_j}(r_j) \, dr_j$, using atomic units in which the potential energy of interaction between two electrons at a distance r is $2/r$. By elementary principles of electrostatics a spherical shell of charge has a potential at external points equal to that of a point charge of the same total charge concentrated at the origin, and at points inside the shell the potential is constant, equal to its value at the surface of the shell. (This fact has already been used in the problems for Chap. 8.) Then the potential energy of the electron at distance r_i from the origin, in the presence of the shell, is

$$\frac{2}{r_i} P^2_{n_j l_j}(r_j) \, dr_j \qquad \text{if } r_i > r_j$$
$$\frac{2}{r_j} P^2_{n_j l_j}(r_j) \, dr_j \qquad \text{if } r_i < r_j \qquad (9\text{-}18)$$

The total potential energy of the electron at distance r_i from the origin, in the presence of the electron whose wave function is given by $P_{n_j l_j}(r_j)$, is then

$$\text{Potential energy} = \frac{2}{r_i} Y_0(n_j l_j, n_j l_j / r_i) \qquad (9\text{-}19)$$

where

$$Y_0(n_j l_j, n_j l_j / r_i) = \int_0^{r_i} P^2_{n_j l_j}(r_j) \, dr_j + \int_{r_i}^{\infty} P^2_{n_j l_j}(r_j) \left(\frac{r_i}{r_j} \right) dr_j \qquad (9\text{-}20)$$

The notation $Y_0(nl, nl/r)$ was introduced by Hartree and is a special case of a more general notation which we shall meet later in Chap. 17 (Vol. II), and which is used in finding the potential arising from a distribution which is not necessarily spherically symmetric.

To evaluate the integral of Eq. (9-9), we must next multiply this potential energy by the spherically averaged charge distribution of the ith electron and integrate over the coordinates of that electron. The result, which we shall denote as $F^0(n_i l_i; n_j l_j)$, is

$$F^0(n_i l_i; n_j l_j) = \int_0^{\infty} P^2_{n_i l_i}(r_i) \left(\frac{2}{r_i} \right) Y_0(n_j l_j, n_j l_j / r_i) \, dr_i$$
$$= \int_0^{\infty} \int_0^{\infty} P^2_{n_i l_i}(r_i) P^2_{n_j l_j}(r_j) \frac{2}{r(b)} \, dr_i \, dr_j \qquad (9\text{-}21)$$

where $r(b)$ is the larger of the two variables r_i, r_j; that is, when $r_i > r_j$, $r(b) = r_i$, and when $r_i < r_j$, $r(b) = r_j$.

We now have found the values of the various integrals involved in the average value of the Hamiltonian, and Eq. (9-10) can be rewritten in the form

$$(H)_{av} = \Sigma(i)I(n_il_i) + \Sigma(\text{pairs } i,j)F^0(n_il_i;n_jl_j) \qquad (9\text{-}22)$$

This gives the total energy, as computed subject to Hartree's assumption of spherical averaging.

9-4. The Hartree Equations as Determined by the Variation Method. We are now ready to carry out our variation of the one-electron orbitals, so as to minimize the average Hamiltonian of Eq. (9-22). Since we wish to minimize this Hamiltonian with respect to variation of each one of the radial wave functions, we can handle these functions separately: $(H)_{av}$ must be a minimum as a particular function $P_{n_il_i}$ is varied. The terms of Eq. (9-22) which depend on this function are

$$(H_i)_{av} = I(n_il_i) + \Sigma(j \neq i)F^0(n_il_i;n_jl_j) \qquad (9\text{-}23)$$

Let us now vary this quantity, subject to the condition that the normalization integral $\int_0^\infty P_{n_il_i}^2(r_i)\,dr_i$ should remain equal to unity. We use the method of undetermined multipliers, as in Eq. (5-7), and following our experience there, we shall let the multiplier λ be written as $-\epsilon_{n_il_i}$, where $\epsilon_{n_il_i}$ is the eigenvalue of the problem. That is, we shall assume that

$$\delta(H_i)_{av} - \epsilon_{n_il_i}\delta \int_0^\infty P_{n_il_i}^2(r_i)\,dr_i = 0 \qquad (9\text{-}24)$$

We must then compute the variation of the integrals concerned.

First, we have

$$\delta I(n_il_i) = \int_0^\infty \delta P_{n_il_i}\left[-\frac{d^2}{dr_i^2} + \frac{l_i(l_i+1)}{r_i^2} - \frac{2Z}{r_i}\right]P_{n_il_i}\,dr_i$$
$$+ \int_0^\infty P_{n_il_i}\left[-\frac{d^2}{dr_i^2} + \frac{l_i(l_i+1)}{r_i^2} - \frac{2Z}{r_i}\right]\delta P_{n_il_i}\,dr_i$$
$$= 2\int_0^\infty \delta P_{n_il_i}\left[-\frac{d^2}{dr_i^2} + \frac{l_i(l_i+1)}{r_i^2} - \frac{2Z}{r_i}\right]P_{n_il_i}\,dr_i \qquad (9\text{-}25)$$

where the last step follows as in Eq. (5-4), and where the integral is real, so that it equals its own conjugate. Next, we have

$$\delta F^0(n_il_i;n_jl_j) = 2\int_0^\infty\int_0^\infty \delta P_{n_il_i}(r_i)P_{n_il_i}(r_i)P_{n_jl_j}^2(r_j)\frac{2}{r(b)}\,dr_i\,dr_j$$
$$= 2\int_0^\infty \delta P_{n_il_i}(r_i)P_{n_il_i}(r_i)\frac{2}{r_i}Y_0(n_jl_j,n_jl_j/r_i)\,dr_i \qquad (9\text{-}26)$$

Last we have

$$\delta \int_0^\infty P_{n_il_i}^2\,dr_i = 2\int_0^\infty \delta P_{n_il_i}P_{n_il_i}\,dr_i \qquad (9\text{-}27)$$

Then, when we insert these values in Eq. (9-24), we have

$$2 \int_0^\infty \delta P_{n_i l_i}(r_i) \left[-\frac{d^2}{dr_i^2} + \frac{l_i(l_i+1)}{r_i^2} - \frac{2Z}{r_i} \right.$$
$$\left. + \sum (j \neq i) \frac{2}{r_i} Y_0(n_j l_j, n_j l_j / r_i) - \epsilon_{n_i l_i} \right] P_{n_i l_i}(r_i) \, dr_i = 0 \quad (9\text{-}28)$$

We can now proceed as in Sec. 5-1: the integral of Eq. (9-28) must be zero for any value of the variation function $\delta P_{n_i l_i}(r_i)$, which means that the remaining part of the integrand must be zero. Hence we have

$$\left[-\frac{d^2}{dr_i^2} + \frac{l_i(l_i+1)}{r_i^2} - \frac{2Z}{r_i} + \sum (j \neq i) \frac{2}{r_i} Y_0(n_j l_j, n_j l_j / r_i) \right] P_{n_i l_i}(r_i)$$
$$= \epsilon_{n_i l_i} P_{n_i l_i}(r_i) \quad (9\text{-}29)$$

In Eq. (9-29) we have the fundamental equation of the Hartree method. It is to be combined with Eq. (9-20) defining $Y_0(n_j l_j, n_j l_j / r_i)$. Now that we have derived it from the variation method, we can see that its interpretation is very simple. It is the radial wave equation for an electron moving in a spherical potential produced by the nuclear charge of Z units and by the spherically averaged charge distributions of all other electrons. In other words, we are led to precisely the set of equations which would be derived from Hartree's original, intuitively derived postulate of the self-consistent field.

It is often convenient to rewrite the potential energy in the form $-2Z_{pi}/r_i$, where

$$Z_{pi} = Z - \Sigma(j \neq i) Y_0(n_j l_j, n_j l_j / r_i) \quad (9\text{-}30)$$

so that the Hartree equations become

$$\left[-\frac{d^2}{dr_i^2} + \frac{l_i(l_i+1)}{r_i^2} - \frac{2Z_{pi}}{r_i} \right] P_{n_i l_i}(r_i) = \epsilon_{n_i l_i} P_{n_i l_i}(r_i) \quad (9\text{-}31)$$

This is just the radial part of the general Schrödinger equation for the orbital $u_{n_i l_i m_{li}}(r_i \theta_i \phi_i)$ in the self-consistent field, which is

$$\left(-\nabla^2 - \frac{2Z_{pi}}{r_i} \right) u_{n_i l_i m_{li}}(r_i \theta_i \phi_i) = (H_i)_{op} u_{n_i l_i m_{li}}$$
$$= \epsilon_{n_i l_i m_{li}} u_{n_i l_i m_{li}} \quad (9\text{-}32)$$

where in Eq. (9-32) we have defined our one-electron operator as $(H_i)_{op}$. This is the one-electron Hamiltonian of an electron moving in the field of the nucleus, and all other electrons than the ith, spherically averaged.

Hartree's equations are of a form called integrodifferential equations: the unknown function $P_{n_i l_i}(r)$ appears both in the ordinary way found in a differential equation and also in terms of certain integrals, the Y_0's. As we have indicated, the only practical method of solving the set of simultaneous equations for the occupied orbitals is a method of iteration, or successive approximations. We take the P's determined from one stage of the approximation and use them to calculate the Y_0's. We then insert these values into Eq. (9-29) and solve these equations in the usual way. From these solutions we determine new P's. We then use these as the starting point of the next stage of approximation, calculating Y_0's from them, and so on.

As for the actual method used in the solution, the solution of Eq. (9-29) must be made by numerical integration, as described in Sec. 3-8. We start the numerical integration from $r = 0$, starting by using the expansion $P_{n_i l_i}(r) = r_i^{l+1}$ for small r's. We assume a trial value of $\epsilon_{n_i l_i}$, the

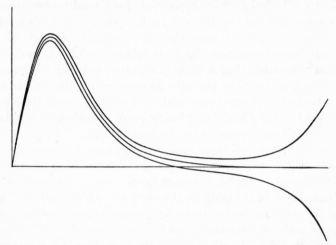

FIG. 9-1. Trial integrations of the radial wave equation, for various trial values of $\epsilon_{n_i l_i}$.

eigenvalue of the one-electron problem, and integrate outward. The solution will, in general, become exponentially infinite as r becomes infinite. The calculation is carried out for a number of closely spaced values of $\epsilon_{n_i l_i}$, and if these values are properly chosen, the functions will behave as shown in Fig. 9-1, some functions rising exponentially, others falling exponentially. By interpolation, it is possible to estimate the value of $\epsilon_{n_i l_i}$ for which the function will decrease exponentially to zero, as accurately as desired. Another procedure for finding the eigenvalues is to integrate outward from $r = 0$, and also inward from infinite r, for the same energy value, using the exponentially decreasing function of the type of Eq. (7-18) for large r. Then, at a predetermined value of r, we find the ratio $(1/P) \, dP/dr$ for the functions starting out from $r = 0$ and from infinite r. If we have an eigenvalue, these will agree; ordinarily, in fact, they will not, and by using a number of trial values of $\epsilon_{n_i l_i}$, we can determine the value for which these ratios agree, so that the same function will behave properly both at $r = 0$ and at infinite r. This latter procedure is recommended by Hartree.

It is possible, in other words, to calculate the wave functions with quite moderate effort. They must be normalized, which can be done by Simpson's rule, and we then have the functions $P_{n_i l_i}(r_i)$ for one stage of the approximation. We next carry out the integrations necessary to get the functions $Y_0(n_j l_j, n_j l_j / r_i)$ from Eq. (9-20), by using Simpson's rule, and are ready to start another stage of the process. Detailed techniques for handling this procedure have been described by Hartree.[1] As we have stated before, the process can be made to converge by a considerable but quite finite amount of labor, and as we have indicated in Chap. 8 and Appendix 16, calculations have been made for a good many atoms, both by this method and by the Hartree-Fock method, which we have mentioned earlier, and which is somewhat more accurate, though not different in its fundamental concepts from the scheme we have been describing.

We must remember that a slightly different Schrödinger equation is solved for each orbital: the potential in each case is that of the nucleus and the spherically averaged potential of all orbitals except the one which is being calculated. Thus the ordinary proof of orthogonality does not apply. Two u_i's corresponding to different l values will automatically be orthogonal on account of their functions of angle, but functions of the same l value will not be quite orthogonal. For some purposes involving the calculation of multiplet structure, according to methods which we shall discuss later, it is highly desirable to use orthogonal orbitals. In this case, the usual method of procedure, not an entirely satisfactory one, has been to make orthogonal linear combinations of the Hartree functions, using the Schmidt orthogonalization technique. For instance, for the s functions, one uses the $1s$ function; a linear combination of $1s$ and $2s$, chosen to be orthogonal to $1s$; a linear combination of $1s$, $2s$, and $3s$, chosen to be orthogonal to $1s$ and $2s$; and so on. This difficulty is not met with the Hartree-Fock method. In that method, though, as with Hartree's method each electron still moves in a different potential, nevertheless things are so arranged that the orbitals are automatically orthogonal to each other.

9-5. Examples of Calculation by the Self-consistent-field Method. We now wish to illustrate the sort of results obtained by the self-consistent-field method, and as an example, we give in Fig. 9-2 the radial wave functions calculated by the Hartree-Fock method for Cu^+, by Hartree and Hartree.[2] This is the heaviest atom for which the Hartree-Fock calculation has been carried out. For comparison, in Fig. 9-3 we

[1] D. R. Hartree, "The Calculation of Atomic Structures," John Wiley & Sons, Inc., New York, 1957.

[2] D. R. Hartree and W. Hartree, *Proc. Roy. Soc. (London)*, **A157**:490 (1936).

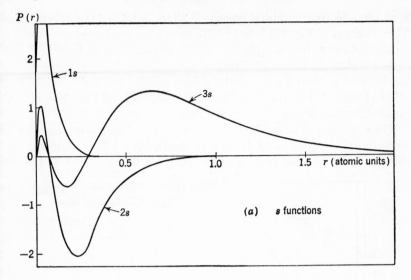

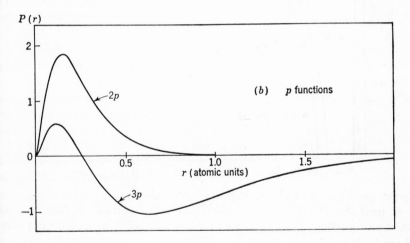

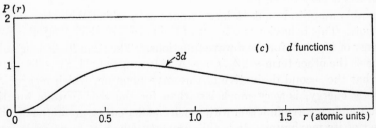

FIG. 9-2. Radial wave functions $P_{nl}(r)$ for Cu^+, as determined by the Hartree-Fock method by Hartree and Hartree.

give the effective potential energy $-2Z_p/r + l(l + 1)/r^2$ for this case. This diagram of Fig. 9-3 is not really complete: we should properly have a different curve for each electron of the atom. The Z_p used in Fig. 9-3 is that giving the potential acting on the valence electron, which is missing in the Cu$^+$ ion; we should be using slightly different curves for the other electrons, but the difference is not enough to interfere with the qualitative description of the situation.

The wave functions of Fig. 9-2 to a first approximation resemble hydrogenic functions, with suitably chosen effective Z's. If we attempt to fit them with hydrogenic functions, however, we find that the fit is rather

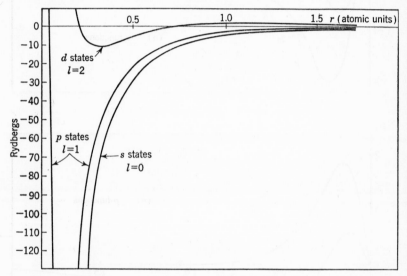

Fig. 9-3. Effective potential energy $-2Z_p/r + l(l + 1)/r^2$ for Cu$^+$ ion.

poor, good enough to be useful in a first very rough approximation, but not further. Particularly interesting in Fig. 9-2 is the behavior of the 3d wave function, as compared with the 3s and 3p. We notice that these have their maxima at about the same values of r; but the 3d wave function has a very much longer tail than the others and extends with considerable amplitude out to large values of r, which the other functions do not. This behavior is a result of the nature of the effective potential energy of Fig. 9-3, for the d wave functions. The term $l(l + 1)/r^2$ almost cancels the other term $-2Z_p/r$ over a wide range of r, for the d functions, so that the second derivative of the wave function, which measures the kinetic energy, is very much less than for the s or p wave functions, resulting in a wave function with much smaller curvature in the neighborhood of its maximum. It is this property which is responsible for the long tail. The small ionization potential of the 3d electron, in comparison with the $3s$ and $3p$, is a result also of the nature of the effective potential energy.

It is interesting in this connection to study the way in which the $3d$ function becomes bound into the atom, as we go through the transition elements, from potassium to copper. In Fig. 9-4, we give the effective potential energy for d electrons for the K^+ and Cu^+ ions; the second curve is identical with the corresponding one from Fig. 9-3. We see that the minimum of the curve is much shallower for K^+, at the beginning of the transition group, than for Cu^+, at its end. This is a result of the

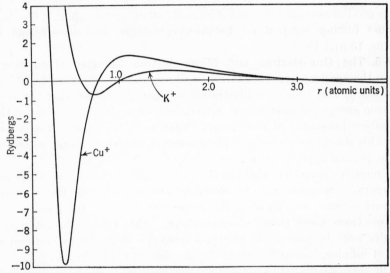

FIG. 9-4. Effective potential energy for d states, for K^+ and Cu^+ ions.

increasing value of Z_p as the nuclear charge increases. The deeper minimum in Cu^+ results in a wave function more concentrated in the inner part of the atom. As one goes a few units of atomic number beyond Cu^+, the minimum of the effective potential energy for the d electrons rapidly becomes deeper and their energy rapidly decreases, as we see in Fig. 8-4 and Table 8-2. This process of binding the $3d$ electron into the atom is one of the most interesting features of the periodic table. It also results in considerable difficulty in carrying out the self-consistent-field calculation: the $3d$ electrons prove to be very sensitive in the sense that it requires many iterations to achieve self-consistency.

We have already seen in Chap. 8 that the energy values found for the various electrons in the self-consistent calculation agree rather well with the X-ray and optical term values. In Table 8-1 we have given calculated and observed term values for sodium. In Table 9-1 we give similar calculated and observed values for Cu^+. We see that here again there is

Table 9-1. Calculated and Observed Term Values for Cu$^+$, in Rydbergs

	Calculated	Observed
1s	658.4	662.0
2s	82.30	81.3
2p	71.83	69.6
3s	10.651	9.6
3p	7.279	6.1
3d	1.613	0.79

quite good agreement between calculated and observed values. We shall discuss further comparisons between calculation and observation in Chaps. 15 and 16.

9-6. The One-electron and Many-electron Energies of an Atom. From the agreement of calculations and experiment which we have just mentioned, and which we illustrated in Chap. 8, we see that the one-electron energy parameters $\epsilon_{n_i l_i}$ agree quite well with the negatives of the ionization potentials of the various electrons in the atom. Let us see why this should be the case. The energy of the whole atom, according to the present approximation, is given by Eq. (9-10) or Eq. (9-22). This is a negative quantity; the kinetic energy and the repulsive Coulomb interactions between pairs of electrons are positive, but the negative attractive terms coming from the interaction between the nucleus and the electrons more than outweigh them. This means that it would require work to remove the electrons from the atom and leave them at rest at infinity, just as it does in the simplest atom, hydrogen.

The energy required to remove a single electron from the atom is then equal to the energy of the ion formed by removing this electron, minus the energy of the atom. We could calculate this ionization energy by solving the self-consistent-field problem for the ion, then for the atom, and subtracting their energies. In most cases, this has not been done, though we shall give examples of this method in Chap. 16, and we ask: Can we not compute the ionization energies somehow from the solution for the atom alone? We can, if we are willing to approximate the wave function of the ion as a product of orbitals of the atom, of the form of Eq. (9-4), for those electrons present in the ion, assuming that the change in each orbital between the atom and the ion is small. This is not a very good approximation, but because of the minimum principle, the use of a wave function for the ion that is incorrect by a small quantity of the first order will make only a second-order error in the energy. But the energy of the ion, as calculated from a wave function made up of the orbitals of the atom, would have just the form of Eq. (9-22), except that it would lack all those terms associated with the electron which has been removed. It is just these terms which form the quantity $(H_i)_{\text{av}}$ of Eq. (9-23). Hence we conclude that the ionization energy, as determined by this method, is the negative of $(H_i)_{\text{av}}$. But from Eq. (9-32), we find that $(H_i)_{\text{av}}$ equals $\epsilon_{n_i l_i}$, as we can see by multiplying that equation on both sides by $u^*_{n_i l_i m_{l_i}}$ and integrating. Hence we have verified our statement that the $\epsilon_{n_i l_i}$ measures to a good approximation the negative of the ionization potential of the ith electron.

It is important to notice that the sum $\Sigma(i)\epsilon_{n_i l_i}$ of the one-electron energies is not equal to the total energy of the atom, as we might be tempted to suppose. When we use Eqs. (9-22) and (9-23) and remember that $(H_i)_{\text{av}} = \epsilon_{n_i l_i}$, we find

$$\begin{aligned} \Sigma(i)\epsilon_{n_i l_i} &= \Sigma(i)I(n_i l_i) + 2\Sigma(\text{pairs } i,j)F^0(n_i l_i; n_j l_j) \\ &= (H)_{\text{av}} + \Sigma(\text{pairs } i,j)F^0(n_i l_i; n_j l_j) \end{aligned} \qquad (9\text{-}33)$$

The reason for the factor 2 in the summation over pairs is that, if we sum $(H_i)_{\text{av}}$ of Eq. (9-23) over i, we have a double sum over i and j of the terms $F^0(n_i l_i; n_j l_j)$, so that each pair of indices i and j is counted twice, instead of once as in Eq. (9-22). Hence we see that the sum of the one-electron energies lies higher on an energy scale by the amount of the double sum, which is the total repulsive interaction energy of the electrons.

Let us inquire why there should be this difference, from physical rather than mathematical arguments. One of the $-\epsilon_{n_i l_i}$'s is the energy required to remove the ith electron from a neutral atom. On the other hand, $-(H)_{\text{av}}$ is the sum of the energies required to remove the electrons, in succession, from more and more highly ionized atoms, leaving the nucleus with all electrons removed. To remove a given electron from a positive ion requires more work than to remove it from a neutral atom, because the nuclear attraction is less shielded by the cloud of electrons surrounding it. Thus the sum of successive ionization potentials from the ions in successively higher stages of ionization must be greater than the sum of the ionization potentials required to remove each one of the electrons from the neutral atom. This is the difference which we have shown is equal to the total Coulomb repulsive interaction between pairs of electrons.

9-7. Inner and Outer Shielding. In Sec. 8-4 we have introduced shielding constants s, and effective nuclear charges $Z - s$, such that the energy of an X-ray term value was approximately $-(Z - s)^2/n^2$. In Table 8-1 we gave values of such effective Z's for the $1s$, $2s$, and $2p$ electrons, called Effective Z for Energy. We also gave in Table 8-1 quantities labeled Effective Z for Wave Function, on which we have not yet commented: these are effective Z's such that a hydrogen wave function, using this effective Z, would give as good a fit as possible to the calculated self-consistent-field wave function. These two sets of effective Z's, the first for energy, the second for wave function, do not agree at all well. We are now in a position to discuss the effective Z's and to explain this apparent discrepancy.

We can rewrite the expression of Eq. (9-30) in the form

$$Z_{pi}(r_i) = Z - \int_0^{r_i} \sum (j \neq i) P^2_{n_j l_j}(r_j)\, dr_j$$
$$- \int_{r_i}^{\infty} \sum (j \neq i) P^2_{n_j l_j}(r_j)\, \frac{r_i}{r_j}\, dr_j \quad (9\text{-}34)$$

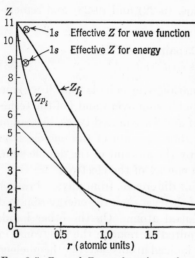

FIG. 9-5. Z_{p_i} and Z_{f_i}, as functions of r_i, for the potential in which the $1s$ electron moves in the sodium atom, as determined by Fock and Petrashen.

Here Z minus the first integral represents the total charge inside the sphere of radius r_i, arising both from the nucleus and from the other electrons. This effect of the electrons inside the sphere is called inner shielding. The remaining term arises from the electrons outside the sphere and is called outer shielding. If we were computing, not the potential energy of an electron in the field of the others, but the electrostatic field, we should not have the outer-shielding term. For we remember that, according to electrostatics, a spherical shell of charge exerts a field at external points as if it were concentrated at the center of the sphere but exerts no field at internal points. Thus the field at any radius r_i would be that of a charge $Z_{f_i}e$ at the origin, where

$$Z_{f_i} = Z - \int_0^{r_i} \sum (j \neq i) P^2_{n_j l_j}(r_j)\, dr_j \quad (9\text{-}35)$$

The quantities Z_{f_i} and Z_{p_i} can be quite different. Thus, in Fig. 9-5, we show the values of Z_{p_i} and Z_{f_i} as functions of r, for the potential and field in which the $1s$ electron moves, in sodium. The difference between these curves, for a definite r value, is a measure of the outer shielding.

The inner and outer shielding appear in quite different ways if we compute the potential energy of the electron, rather than Z_{p_i}. Thus we have

$$\text{Potential energy} = -\frac{2}{r_i}\left[Z - \int_0^{r_i} \sum (j \neq i) P^2_{n_j l_j}(r_j)\, dr_j \right]$$
$$+ \int_{r_i}^{\infty} \sum (j \neq i) P^2_{n_j l_j}(r_j)\, \frac{2}{r_j}\, dr_j \quad (9\text{-}36)$$

If we happened to be at a value of r_i where $\Sigma(j \neq i)P_{n_jl_j}^2(r_i)$ was small, so that the integrals were almost independent of r_i, we should then see that the potential energy was like a hydrogenic potential energy with an effective Z of Z_{f_i}, plus an almost constant correction term in the energy arising from the outer shielding. If we had this situation, the wave function would be hydrogenic, with an effective Z given by Z_{f_i}; for the almost constant correction term arising from the outer shielding would not affect the shape of the wave function, but only its total energy. The energy level, on the contrary, would have the outer shielding effect added in, so that it would be given more nearly by a hydrogenic formula with the effective Z equal to Z_{p_i}. We can show that this is approximately the case by plotting points giving effective Z for energy and effective Z for wave function, from Table 8-1, on the curves of Fig. 9-5, using a value of r equal to the radius of maximum radial charge density for this electron, as given in Table 8-3. We do this in Fig. 9-5 for the sodium $1s$ electron and find as we should expect that the effective Z for energy lies very nearly on the Z_{p_i} curve and the effective Z for wave function very nearly on the Z_{f_i} curve. Such a calculation is only qualitative and suggestive, but it does tell us why the two types of effective Z's given in Table 8-1 are so different.

There is a simple relation between Z_{p_i} and Z_{f_i}. We can get at it from the fact that

$$-\frac{d}{dr}\left(\frac{Z_{p_i}}{r}\right) = \frac{Z_{f_i}}{r^2} = \frac{Z_{p_i}}{r^2} - \frac{1}{r}\frac{dZ_{p_i}}{dr} \qquad (9\text{-}37)$$

which must be true since the potential energy Z_{p_i}/r results in the field Z_{f_i}/r^2. Equation (9-37) leads to

$$Z_{p_i} - r\frac{dZ_{p_i}}{dr} = Z_{f_i} \qquad (9\text{-}38)$$

As a consequence of this equation, we see that there is a geometric relationship between the curves of Z_{p_i} and Z_{f_i}, illustrated in Fig. 9-5: the tangent to the Z_{p_i} curve, projected backward to the vertical axis, intersects it at a height equal to Z_{f_i}.

9-8. Interpretation of the Rydberg Formula.

In the preceding section we have seen that the inner and outer shielding give us an understanding of the nature of the shielding constants for the X-ray energy levels. Now we should consider why it is that Rydberg's law, Eq. (8-1), holds for the outer, optical energy levels, in particular for the alkalies. We note in the first place that, for an alkali atom, the valence electron moves in the field of the inner, filled shells. Their charge density, according to Eq. (7-36), is rigorously spherically symmetrical, since the sum of the charge distributions of all wave functions with different m_l's, and the same l is independent of angle. This result, Unsöld's theorem, already mentioned in Sec. 7-3, shows that Hartree's procedure is more accurate for the alkalies than in other cases, in that the averaging procedure is not really necessary: we should get the same result, for the potential acting on the valence electron, if we had not carried it out. Furthermore, the motion of the inner electrons is almost precisely independent of the behavior of the outer electron, which can result only in an outer-shielding effect on the inner electrons and therefore cannot affect their wave functions or charge distributions. Therefore we are justified in using the same potential field for describing the valence electron, not merely in its ground state, but in any excited state; this potential is that arising from the nucleus and the spherically symmetrical charge distributions of the closed shells forming the inert gas core of the alkali atom. Hence our problem of interpreting Rydberg's law is rigorously that of investigating the excited energy levels of an electron in a central field of the type we meet in an alkali ion.

The value of Z_{p_i} in which the valence electron moves, in sodium, is nearly enough like that of Fig. 9-5 so that we do not have to give another figure to illustrate it. We note that, for r greater than about 1.5 atomic units, Z_p becomes practically equal to unity. That is, for all larger values of r, the potential is exactly hydrogenic. The energies, however, as we see from Table 8-1, are not characteristic of hydrogen. We can describe the outer part of the orbital by a solution of the hydrogen radial wave equation, corresponding to the actual energy, but reducing to zero at infinity. If we used this energy in a radial wave equation which was hydrogenic for all values of r, the wave function which behaved properly at infinity would become infinite as r approached zero, behaving according to Eq. (7-16) like r^{-l} as r approached zero. However, we may not use this solution for r's smaller than about 1.5 units. We must instead join the solution at this point onto a solution of the actual problem, with Z_{p_i} similar to that of Fig. 9-5, which behaves properly at the origin.

Now this actual solution for small r's is very nearly independent of energy, over the narrow range of energies covered by the excited states (in our case, the range from -0.377 Rydberg to zero). We can see this from Fig. 9-6, in which we have plotted the calculated 3s and 4s wave functions in this range, with such multiplying factors that they agree with each other as closely as possible. The reason for this approximate independence of energy is that in this range of r the quantity $2Z_{p_i}(r)/r - l_i(l_i + 1)/r^2$ is very large numerically compared with $\epsilon_{n_i l_i}$, so that small variations in $\epsilon_{n_i l_i}$ make very small relative changes in the classical kinetic energy, or in the quantity $d^2 P_{n_i l_i}/dr^2$ of Eq. (9-31), and hence in the wave function. Put more physically, when the electron penetrates into the interior of the atom, it speeds up so much on account of the nuclear attraction that its motion is almost independent of the very small amount of kinetic energy which it had when it entered the atom.

We see, then, that we can build up a good approximation to the true wave function of an excited state, by joining a hydrogenic function of adjustable energy to such a wave function as shown in Fig. 9-6, at a distance such as 1.5 atomic units, which may be considered to be the boundary of the atom. We must now ask for what energies this can be done. We can describe the hydrogenic function by an effective quantum number n^*, defined by the relation $\epsilon_{n_i l_i} = -1/n^{*2}$ Rydbergs. We ask how the wave function which behaves properly at infinity varies as n^* changes. Every time n^* takes on an integral value, we have a real solution of the hydrogen problem. Each increase of n^* by unity then adds

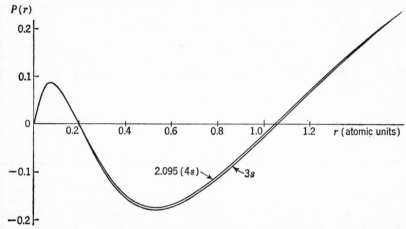

FIG. 9-6. Calculated $3s$ and $4s$ radial wave functions for sodium, from calculations of Fock and Petrashen. The $4s$ function is multiplied by 2.095 to produce the best agreement with the $3s$ function for small r's.

an additional node to the wave function, the extra loop being for larger and larger r's, and certainly for r greater than our value of 1.5 atomic units. As we go through this unit increase of n^*, the phase of the wave function at $r = 1.5$ will go through all possible values, in the process of adding the extra node. Thus somewhere in this interval the hydrogenic wave function will have just such a phase that it can join smoothly onto the correct wave function for smaller r's. We conclude, then, that one eigenvalue of the general central-field problem will come between each pair of eigenvalues of the hydrogen problem. It is clear from Fig. 8-3 that this is equivalent to the type of behavior actually found. The Rydberg law merely states that each integral increment of n^* brings us back to substantially the same type of behavior in the neighborhood of the boundary of the atom, so that eigenvalues come at approximately $n^* = n - d$, where d is independent of n.

We understand from this argument the general explanation of the Rydberg formula, but we should also consider the rapid decrease of the quantum defect d with increasing l value. Thus, we have found for sodium that it is about 1.35 for s levels, 0.86 for p levels, but very small for the other levels. The point is that the magnitude of the quantum defect depends on the amount of penetration of the orbit into the interior of the atom. If we plot d and f wave functions, in the manner of Fig. 9-6, we find that they are very small in the region for r less than 1.5 atomic units. Hence their boundary condition is very nearly that they should go to zero at the value $r = 1.5$, and this is substantially the same condition which we should have for hydrogen itself. This is the reason why the energy levels are almost exactly as in hydrogen. As a simple rule, we can state that those l values for which there are no occupied states in the atom will have nonpenetrating wave functions, and their energies will be almost hydrogenic. As we go from these l values to the lower ones for which there are occupied states, the quantum defect very rapidly increases.

PROBLEMS

1. Assume that the wave function for the two electrons in the ground state of the helium atom is proportional to exp $[-\alpha(r_1 + r_2)]$, where r_1, r_2 are the distances to the two electrons from the nucleus and α is a parameter to be determined by the variation method. Set up the average energy of the atom, using this approximate wave function, and vary α to minimize the energy. Show that the resulting value of α is the same as that determined in Prob. 4, Chap. 8.

2. Take the average energy of the helium atom, as found in Prob. 1, subtract from it the energy of the He^+ ion lacking an electron, and hence derive a value for the ionization potential of helium, and compare it with the observed ionization potential, 1.81 Rydbergs. Compare the value with the one-electron energy derived in Prob. 4, Chap. 8. Explain why these two values do not agree with each other.

3. In Prob. 1, Chap. 8, we give the potential acting on a helium $1s$ electron, using a hydrogenic approximation. Use this potential in Schrödinger's equation, and solve the radial Schrödinger's equation numerically, so as to get a better wave function than the hydrogenic value. Integrate for a number of values of energy near the experimental value, so as to be able to find the eigenvalue and eigenfunction. Compare the resulting eigenvalue with that found in Prob. 4, Chap. 8, and compare the wave function with the exponential function used in that chapter.

4. Carry out numerical integration for the same potential as in Prob. 3, for the $2s$ and $3s$ wave functions. Compare the eigenvalues with the experimental values of the energies of the $1s2s$ and $1s3s$ configurations in helium, namely, -0.336 Rydberg and -0.134 Rydberg, respectively. (*Note:* For the benefit of the reader who has read ahead and realizes that the $1s2s$ and $1s3s$ configurations have both a singlet and a triplet state, we mention that the experimental values quoted are the weighted means of these two multiplets.)

5. Find how closely the observed $1s^2$, $1s2s$, and $1s3s$ energies of the helium atom fit a Rydberg formula.

6. Use the same method employed in Prob. 1 to find the wave functions and energy of the Li$^+$, Be^{++}, B^{3+}, . . . ions.   Compare the energies with the experimental values given in Table 15-2.

7. Use the approximate value of Z_p for sodium found in Prob. 7, Chap. 8, to set up a radial wave equation for the $3s$ orbital.   Solve Schrödinger's equation using this potential, for the $1s$, $2s$, $3s$, and $4s$ wave functions, and compare their energies with the experimental values of Table 8-1.

8. The Z_p for sodium used in the preceding problem is meant to be used for the $3s$ orbital but is not exactly right for the $1s$ or $2s$.   Set up instead the appropriate Z_p for the $1s$, integrate Schrödinger's equation for this potential, and find how much error was involved in using the incorrect potential of Prob. 7.

9. Carry out a calculation like that of Prob. 7, for the $2p$ and $3d$ wave functions of sodium, comparing the eigenvalues with the observed energies.

10

The Vector Model of the Atom

10-1. Multiplets in Complex Spectra. In the early days of spectroscopy, the spectra of hydrogen, of the alkalies, and of copper, silver, and gold stood out as almost the only simple ones. The others showed a bewildering complexity of energy levels, which seemed hopeless to understand. The spectrum of iron, for example, was regarded as an utterly confusing set of lines, filling up the whole spectrum. It is one of the very great triumphs of twentieth-century science that these complex spectra have been worked out and completely explained. A large part of the pioneering work was done during the period from 1920 to 1926; the main features of the theory of complex spectra were worked out before wave mechanics was developed. On the other hand, there were great puzzles in the theory at this period, which were explained only by means of wave mechanics. The general picture which proved capable of untangling the complications of these spectra was based on the interaction of the angular-momentum vectors of the various electrons in the atom; for this reason, we can describe it in terms of a vector model of the atom. We shall start by describing this model in the semiclassical language which was used in the early 1920s, for this gives us a more physical picture of the situation than the wave-mechanical explanation which came later.

The first key to the understanding of the spectra came from the fact that the alkalies and copper, silver, and gold had simple spectra, while all others were complicated. It was this fact which really led to the central-field model, which we have been discussing in the two preceding chapters. It certainly appeared that these spectra could be described in terms of a single electron moving in a central field. But these were spectra in which we had a single electron outside closed shells: in the case of the alkalies, a closed shell of s and p electrons, and in the case of copper, silver, and gold, closed shells of s, p, and d electrons. This suggested very clearly that these closed shells acted on the electrons outside them like spherical force fields. We have seen the explanation of this in terms of wave mechanics: on account of Unsöld's theorem, mentioned in

Secs. 7-3 and 9-8, the charge distribution of a closed shell is really spherically symmetrical, so that Hartree's model becomes very appropriate in such cases. This wave-mechanical explanation was not available in the early 1920s, but it gradually came to be realized that the fact was true, that the inner, closed shells of the atom did not contribute to the complexity of the spectrum, but only to the absolute position of the terms, through their effect on the shielding constants or the quantum defects.

It was then an obvious deduction that the complexity of the other spectra arose because the electrons outside the closed shells exerted torques on each other, thereby destroying the applicability of the central-field model. It was a further deduction that only those electrons outside the closed shells had to be considered in discussing the vector model or the interaction of angular-momentum vectors; those in the closed shells acted on those outside only as central fields. Thus, for instance, all atoms with two electrons outside closed shells showed similar spectra: the alkaline earths, beryllium, magnesium, calcium, strontium, and barium, and the elements zinc, cadmium, and mercury, with two electrons outside completed d shells. Again, all atoms with three electrons outside closed shells had similar spectra, and so on. A related fact came from the spectra of positive ions: the general nature of the spectrum of a positive ion was found to be similar to that of an atom with the same number of electrons, and hence with the same number outside closed shells. Thus, for instance, the singly charged positive ions of the alkaline earths have the same simple type of spectrum that the neutral alkalies have. It was naturally supposed that the two-electron

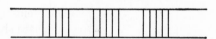

Fig. 10-1. Schematic representation of a typical Zeeman pattern.

spectra would be simplest to interpret, and in fact it was the study of the calcium spectrum, by Russell and Saunders,[1] which contributed as much as any to the understanding of complex spectra.

It would have been almost hopeless to unravel any of these complex spectra, however, if it had not been for a number of very useful experimental facts relating to them. Foremost among these was the Zeeman effect. In a magnetic field, a spectrum line becomes split into a number of closely spaced components, so close that it requires a high magnetic field, and a spectrograph of very high resolution, to observe it properly. We show in Fig. 10-1 a typical Zeeman pattern. A theory had been worked out on classical lines by Lorentz,[2] before the quantum theory had been applied to such problems, which predicted that a Zeeman

[1] H. N. Russell and F. A. Saunders, Astrophys. J., 61:38 (1925).

[2] H. A. Lorentz, "The Theory of Electrons," Teubner Verlagsgesellschaft, Leipzig, 2d ed., 1916.

pattern should consist of three lines. In a few cases this was observed, but much more commonly the patterns were complicated, as in Fig. 10-1, and many different types were observed. A great deal of effort was put into both the measurement and the interpretation of these Zeeman patterns, and a theory due to Landé[1] showed that one could interpret them, in a way which made them of the greatest value in understanding the spectra.

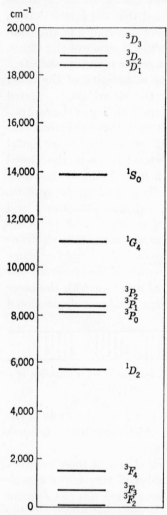

FIG. 10-2. Energy levels in a typical two-electron spectrum, Zr III.

There are several other facts which gradually became clear from the empirical study of the spectra. The lines proved to be grouped into closely spaced sets which were called multiplets, relatively widely separated from other lines. When the observed lines were interpreted in terms of energy levels, the levels themselves showed this grouping into multiplets. A given type of spectrum showed definite multiplicities, that is, definite numbers of levels associated into multiplets. Thus, one-electron spectra showed doublets (two closely spaced levels). Two-electron spectra showed singlets (single levels) and triplets (three closely spaced levels). Three-electron spectra showed doublets and quartets (four closely spaced levels), four-electron spectra showed singlets, triplets, and quintets, and so on. In Fig. 10-2 we show some observed energy levels in a typical two-electron spectrum, showing singlets and triplets.

When the energy levels of a multiplet were deduced from the spectrum and their resulting lines were observed, not all possible transitions were found. There seemed, instead, to be selection rules in operation. These selection rules could be stated, first empirically and then in terms of partially adequate theory, in terms of a quantum number called J, named

[1] A. Landé, Z. Physik, **5**:231 (1921); **7**:398 (1921); **11**:353 (1922); **15**:189 (1923); **19**:112 (1923).

the inner quantum number,[1] which the spectroscopists found would characterize each level. This quantum number could be described most clearly in terms of the Zeeman effect. In a magnetic field, each level splits into a certain number of equally spaced components, the spacing being proportional to the magnetic field. The number of such components was defined as $2J + 1$, as if we had an angular momentum characterized by the quantum number J [or such that the square of its magnitude, according to results like Eq. (7-29), would be $J(J + 1)\hbar^2$], whose component along an axis was $M\hbar$, where $M = J, J - 1, \ldots, -J,$

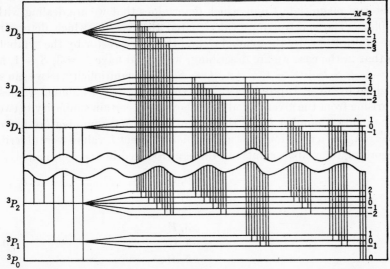

Fig. 10-3. Schematic description of allowed transitions from levels of one multiplet to those of another, both with and without magnetic fields.

similar to the m of Sec. 7-3. In the presence of a magnetic field, it was assumed that the energy of each such state had a term proportional to M and to the magnetic field. Then in terms of the J so defined, which could be determined unambiguously for a given term from the Zeeman effect, it was found empirically that a selection rule held, such that the only allowed transitions were those in which J changed to $J \pm 1$ or to J. There was a further selection rule in the Zeeman effect: the quantum number M could change only in a transition from M to $M \pm 1$ or M. In Fig. 10-3, we show schematically the levels of two multiplets, both with and without magnetic fields, and the allowed transitions between them. It is clear that, once the selection rule was established, it provided a valuable check on the values of J determined from the Zeeman effect. As a matter of fact, this method is even more valuable than it

[1] A. Sommerfeld, *Ann. Physik,* **70**:32 (1923).

seems, for the Zeeman effect is so difficult to observe that many spec-troscopists were forced to deduce the J values of spectral terms without use of the Zeeman effect, or with only partial use of it.

The spectroscopists went further than we have described in their attempts to assign quantum numbers to the various levels of a spectrum. Suppose, for instance, that they found a triplet with values of J equal to 4, 3, and 2. They found it useful to assume that these formed the resultants of two vectors of magnitudes 3 units and 1 unit, respectively, which could form resultants equal to all integrally spaced values between the sum (4) and the difference (2) of the vectors. In this case, it is the vector of magnitude 1 unit which determines that we are dealing with a triplet. The spectroscopists designated this vector, which determined the multiplicity, by the symbol S, and the other vector by the symbol L, so that in the case we are describing, we should have $L = 3$, $S = 1$, and $J = L + S, L + S - 1, \ldots, |L - S|$. The multiplicity, as we can see, is given by $2S + 1$; provided $L \geq S$, there are $2S + 1$ different values of J arising from the given L and S. They saw a certain similarity between the quantum number L and the azimuthal quantum number l of a single electron, and a notation grew up in which different L values were described according to symbols similar to those introduced in Sec. 7-3, namely,

$$
\begin{aligned}
L = 0, &\ S \\
1, &\ P \\
2, &\ D \\
3, &\ F \\
4, &\ G \\
5, &\ H \\
6, &\ I \\
7, &\ K \\
8, &\ L \\
&\ \cdots
\end{aligned}
\tag{10-1}
$$

They introduced symbols for a given level, in which the multiplicity was indicated by a superscript ahead of a letter, given by Eq. (10-1), denoting the value of L, while a subscript after the letter gave the value of J. Thus a level with $S = 1$, $L = 4$, $J = 5$, would be denoted as $^3G_5$.

All this notation, with the assignment of quantum numbers to levels, grew up in the years following 1920. Then, in the interpretation of two-electron spectra, it first began to be clear what the real interpretation of the quantum numbers L and S was in terms of the angular momenta of the electrons. This interpretation was known as the Russell-Saunders coupling scheme, after the two workers who introduced these concepts in the interpretation of the spectrum of calcium. We shall see that the interpretation depends essentially on the existence of the electron spin, which was not understood at the time the spectra were first analyzed. The reader can well imagine that the whole situation was very much more puzzling then than it now seems in retrospect. It was really in order to resolve the puzzles arising from these complex spectra that Uhlenbeck and Goudsmit suggested the existence of the electron spin. Now we can hardly conceive of any other way of explaining the complex spectra, and we shall start our more detailed description, in the next section, by postulating its existence.

10-2. The Russell-Saunders Coupling Scheme. The fundamental idea with which Russell and Saunders started was that of the coupling of two vectors, representing angular momenta. We have seen in the preceding section how it was useful to postulate two vectors $\mathbf{L}$ and $\mathbf{S}$, which could be coupled to give a vector $\mathbf{J}$, whose magnitude could have any one of the values $L + S, L + S - 1, \ldots, |L - S|$. In the same way Russell and Saunders assumed that we could describe the coupling of any two vectors in the same way. This concept of the coupling of vectors is one which we shall later examine in much more detail, on the basis first of classical mechanics and then of wave mechanics, but for the moment we shall merely introduce it in a rather empirical fashion, much as it was understood in the days in which it was first being applied to the description of spectra. Let us now ask ourselves: What vectors are there to be coupled, in a two-electron spectrum such as calcium, the case with which Russell and Saunders were concerned?

The calcium atom, with $Z = 20$, has in its ground state the configuration $(1s)^2(2s)^2(2p)^6(3s)^2(3p)^6(4s)^2$. This ground state is not as interesting as the excited states, however, and to get an example of the general situation which Russell and Saunders faced, let us consider an excited configuration such as $(1s)^2(2s)^2(2p)^6(3s)^2(3p)^6 3d4p$, which we may abbreviate $3d4p$, omitting the notation for the inner, completed groups of electrons, which are always present in calcium. We then have two electrons, the $3d$ and $4p$, outside closed shells. Each of these has an orbital angular momentum, which we may call l_1 and l_2, equal to 2 units and 1 unit, respectively. Each also has a spin angular momentum, of magnitude $\frac{1}{2}$ unit, according to the postulate of Uhlenbeck and Goudsmit. These four vectors, then, are to be combined according to the vector coupling method.

The main feature of the Russell-Saunders coupling scheme was the prescription of the method which was to be used in coupling these four vectors. It was arrived at empirically: if one proceeded as they did, one found a satisfying explanation of the calcium spectrum. Since then we have learned how to justify the scheme, but we shall present it simply as a postulate, as Russell and Saunders did.

Their first step was to couple the two orbital angular-momentum vectors to form a resultant **L**. This vector **L** could then have possible magnitudes L equal to $l_1 + l_2$, $l_1 + l_2 - 1$, . . . , $|l_1 - l_2|$, or in the present case $L = 3, 2$, and 1. Their second step was to couple the two spin angular-momentum vectors to form a resultant **S**. With two spins, the magnitude S of the vector **S** could be either 1 or 0. These, they postulated, were the values of L and S which would arise from the configuration $3d4p$. Then, in terms of the discussion of the preceding section, we should find from this configuration the multiplets ^3F, ^3D, ^3P, ^1F, ^1D, ^1P. In similar ways Russell and Saunders could predict the

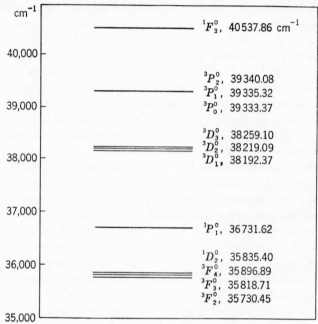

FIG. 10-4. Energy levels from $3d4p$ configuration of calcium.

multiplets which should arise from each of the low configurations which might plausibly occur in the calcium spectrum. When they looked at the observed spectra, they found that they had the multiplets which would be expected, in reasonable parts of the spectrum. Thus, in Fig. 10-4, we show the observed multiplets arising from the $3d4p$ configuration of calcium, according to the analysis of Russell and Saunders. Similar groups of multiplets were found arising from the other configurations which might be expected from calcium. It is now clear why atoms like this have such complicated spectra: each configuration, instead of having only one level, really has quite a number of multiplets, and when they are all taken together, we have a very great number of levels in the spectrum.

The scheme as we have described it holds for two-electron atoms. However, similar methods were extended, almost immediately after this work, to cases of atoms with more electrons outside closed shells, and they proved just as successful in these more general cases. The general scheme was equally simple. First, we take the l's of each electron and form them into vector sums L; then the spins of each electron (we may call them s's) and form them into sums S; finally we couple each L and S, as in the preceding section, to form J, and to lead to a multiplet. We may well ask, however, just how to proceed in coupling the three or more l's or s's into their resultants. Let us describe this process first in connection with the s's.

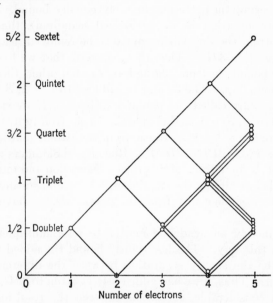

FIG. 10-5. The branching diagram.

The way Russell and Saunders proceeded was to couple the vectors one at a time. Thus, with three s's, we start by coupling two of them, to get $S = 1$ or 0. Then we couple an additional s of $\frac{1}{2}$ to each of these S's. Thus, if we couple $s = \frac{1}{2}$ to $S = 1$, we can have $S = \frac{3}{2}, \frac{1}{2}$; if we couple $\frac{1}{2}$ to 0, we can have $\frac{1}{2}$. In other words, by adding $s = \frac{1}{2}$ to any value of S, we get two new S's, one a half unit greater, the other a half unit less, than the original S (unless the original S is zero, in which case we can have only the half unit greater). We see from this example that for three electrons we can have $S = \frac{1}{2}$ or $\frac{3}{2}$, or doublets and quartets, which agrees with our earlier statement. More generally, we have what is called the branching diagram, shown in Fig. 10-5, in which each line indicates the way in which an S value appropriate to one number of electrons splits into two values when the number of electrons is increased by unity.

In a similar way, Russell and Saunders coupled the l's one at a time. Here, however, the process was less obvious: which ones should one take first? The answer which they gave to this question depended on studying the spectrum, not only of the neutral atom, but of its various ionized states. Thus, for instance, suppose we are interested in the configuration $3d4s5p$ of the scandium atom, which has one more electron than calcium. From our knowledge of the tightness of binding of the various electrons, as found in the preceding two chapters, we know that the $5p$ electron will be much less tightly bound than the $3d$ or $4s$, which in a transition element like scandium are approximately equally bound. Then, if we go to the Sc$^+$ ion (that is, singly ionized scandium), the most easily removed electron, the $5p$, will presumably be removed, leaving the Sc$^+$ in the configuration $3d4s$. This, then, suggests that we first couple the more tightly bound electrons, $3d$ and $4s$, to each other, then couple the less tightly bound $5p$. The $3d$ and $4s$ will lead to $L = 2$, $S = 1, 0$, or to ^3D, ^1D. These are called the parent multiplets. If we start with the ^3D, or with $L = 2$, $S = 1$, and couple the $5p$ electron to it, we shall have $L = 3, 2, 1$ and $S = \frac{3}{2}, \frac{1}{2}$. Hence from the parent multiplet $3d4s\ ^3D$, we shall have ^4F, ^4D, ^4P, ^2F, ^2D, ^2P. Russell and Saunders would denote these as $3d4s(^3D)5p\ ^4F$, etc., giving the configuration and multiplet of the parent state before adding the remaining electron and stating its resulting multiplet. In a similar way from the parent ^1D, we have $3d4s(^1D)5p$ ^2F, ^2D, ^2P.

It is not merely an academic matter to refer multiplets to parent multiplets in this way. The less tightly bound the added electron, the smaller will be the energy separation between the different multiplets arising from it. Thus, if we had added a $4p$ electron to $3d4s$, there would have been a considerable separation between the resulting multiplets ^4F, ^4D, ^4P, ^2F, ^2D, ^2P, arising from the ^3D. This separation would be less if we added a $5p$, still less if we added a $6p$, and so on. On the other hand, the separation between the ^3D and ^1D of the parent configuration is a fixed thing, and as we add a less tightly bound outer electron, the energy levels of all the multiplets arising from a given parent tend to cluster round the energy of the parent multiplet. In Fig. 10-6, we show an example of this, in which we can actually approach a series limit as we go to higher and higher principal quantum numbers of the added electron. The terms in this case approach as series limits the parent terms in the spectrum of the ion.

This concept of the parentage of terms is clear-cut if the electron which is last added is definitely less tightly bound than the others, but it is less clear if several electrons are approximately equally tightly bound. Even in such a case, it does no harm to use it. We can show that the same multiplets will be predicted, irrespective of the order in which the electrons are coupled. Thus, in the case we have been considering, the configuration $3d4s5p$, we could first have coupled the $3d$ and $5p$, arriving at ^3F, ^3D, ^3P, ^1F, ^1D, ^1P, and then have coupled the $4s$ to these. Each of the triplets, in accordance with the branching diagram, will give rise to a doublet and a quartet, and each of the singlets to a doublet, so that the final set of multiplets is the same as before.

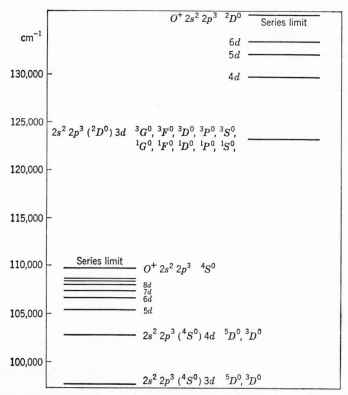

Fig. 10-6. Energies of configurations $1s^22s^22p^3(^4S^o)nd$ and $1s^22s^22p^3(^2D^o)nd$ of oxygen, illustrating the way in which the levels approach two series limits, namely, the levels $1s^22s^22p^3$ $^4S^o$ and $1s^22s^22p^3$ $^2D^o$ of O$^+$. The separations of the various multiplets associated with each configuration are too small to show on this graph.

If we have two or more equivalent electrons—that is, electrons with the same (nl) values—the situation is, however, quite different. We certainly cannot distinguish between the two electrons as to their tightness of binding, so that we cannot determine the parentage of terms in the same simple way. But, much more serious, we shall find later that in such cases the exclusion principle has profound effects on the spectrum, excluding completely certain multiplets which would be allowed according to the vector model. Thus, for instance, two nonequivalent p electrons, such as $2p$ and $3p$, will give rise to the multiplets ^3D, ^3P, ^3S, ^1D, ^1P, ^1S. We shall show later, however, that if they are equivalent, for example if both are $2p$, the ^3D, ^3S, and ^1P multiplets do not exist, and we have only the ^3P, ^1D, and ^1S. This fact cannot be derived in any simple manner from the type of vector model we have described so far, and we shall have to use quite different methods in Sec. 13-2 to lead to the prediction of such excluded multiplets. Since they are of very great importance in the understanding of spectra, we must realize that the simple rules stated in this section are by no means complete. However, for nonequivalent electrons, they predict correctly the multiplets which will be observed, and they have been of enormous value in the interpretation of the observed spectra.

In our description of the Russell-Saunders coupling scheme, we have said nothing so far about the selection rules which are found to occur, aside from the rules stated in Sec. 10-1, namely, that J changes in a transition by ±1 or 0 unit, and similarly M changes by ±1 or 0 unit. Several other selection rules are found to apply, some exactly, some only approximately. The first of these rules is that, to an approximation, the only allowed transitions are between configurations which differ in the l of only one electron, and this l must change by ±1 unit in the transition. These are the same transitions which would be allowed according to the central-field approximation. As we have larger and larger deviations from the central-field model, this selection rule becomes less completely obeyed but there is a closely related rule which is rigorously true. This is based on what is called the parity of a configuration. If we add the l's of all the electrons, the parity is said to be even if the sum is even and odd if the sum is odd. Then it is a rigorous selection rule that we can have transitions only between a configuration of even parity and one of odd parity. Since this is a very fundamental principle, it is common to denote all multiplets of odd parity by a superscript o following the L symbol. Thus a ^3P multiplet arising from the configuration $2s2p$ has odd parity and would be denoted $^3P^o$, while one arising from the configuration $2p3p$ would have even parity and would be denoted ^3P. Even this selection rule is rigorous only in a certain sense: as long as we are considering the interaction between radiation and the atom only by means of the electric dipole moment, as in Chap. 6, the rule is rigorous, but there are other terms in the interaction between radiation and atoms, which we did not consider in that chapter, arising from magnetic dipoles and electric quadrupoles. When we consider these terms, transitions between two states of even parity or between two states of odd parity are allowed, though the transition probability is very small compared with the probabilities of allowed electric dipole transitions.

The other selection rules which hold in Russell-Saunders coupling are that L can change by only ± 1 unit or 0 unit, and S does not change, so that we do not have transitions between states of different multiplicities. Neither of these rules is rigorous. They both hold in the limiting case where the energy separations between the various levels of a multiplet are very small compared with the energy differences between the multiplets. If this is the case, the orbital and spin angular momenta, given by L and S, have very small torques acting on them and they are approximately constant. If the interaction between L and S is very large, however, resulting in a large separation between levels of different J in the same multiplet, this means that there is a large torque between L and S, so that these two quantities no longer remain constant. As one says, they are no longer good quantum numbers and any selection rule based on them breaks down. Now the interaction energy between L and S proves to be of magnetic origin and to increase rapidly as we go to heavier atoms. Hence these selection rules for L and S hold quite accurately for light atoms but not at all well for heavy atoms.

For heavy atoms for which the interaction between L and S becomes large, the whole concept of Russell-Saunders coupling breaks down. In such cases, one approaches what is called j-j coupling. This is the case where the interaction between the l and s of a single electron is much greater than between the l's of different electrons or between the s's of different electrons. In this case, it proves to be nearer the truth first to couple the l and s of each electron together to form a j and then to couple the j's of the various electrons to form J. The whole spectrum in this case becomes much more complicated, and we shall not go further into j-j coupling at this point.

10-3. The Classical Mechanics of Vector Coupling. We have seen in preceding sections that the vector model of the atom is based on the concept of the coupling together of two vectors to form a resultant. This is a concept which becomes much clearer if we investigate the classical behavior of angular-momentum vectors acted on by torques. We shall therefore proceed to the treatment of these problems by classical mechanics, as a preliminary to our later treatment of them by wave mechanics. As a first step, we consider the behavior of a single classical angular-momentum vector such as the orbital angular momentum of an electron in a central field, when it is acted on by an external torque such as arises from an impressed magnetic field.

The treatment is based on Newton's second law of motion, which takes the form that the time rate of change of the angular momentum equals the torque acting on it. This is a vector equation. The angular momentum has direction as well as magnitude; and the torque is defined as a vector whose magnitude is the moment of the external force and whose direction is the axis about which it is trying to produce rotation. In the case in which we are interested, the direction of the torque is at right angles to the angular-momentum vector, and in this case its effect is, not to change the magnitude of the angular velocity, but rather to change the direction of the angular-momentum vector, keeping its magnitude fixed, leading to a type of motion called precession. This is illustrated in Fig. 10-7, where we show an angular momentum vector $L\hbar$; a torque at right angles to $L\hbar$, in the horizontal plane; and the resulting motion of $L\hbar$, taking up successive positions on a cone with a vertical axis. This is the type of motion which a symmetric rigid body, like a spinning top,

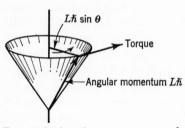

FIG. 10-7. Angular momentum and torque for precessing motion of symmetrical rigid body.

undergoes when a gravitational torque acts on it, trying to pull the axis of the top downward.

We meet such a case in atomic physics when we deal with the Zeeman effect, and we shall use this as a quantitative example. We have pointed out in Sec. 1-7 that, in a magnetic field B along the z axis, an electron with magnetic quantum number m will have an energy $m\mu_B B$, where μ_B is the Bohr magneton, equal to $e\hbar/2m_0$, where e is the magnitude of the electronic charge and m_0 is the electronic mass. Stated otherwise, the energy is $m\hbar(eB/2m_0)$, where $m\hbar$ is the component of angular momentum along the axis and $eB/2m_0$ is a quantity of the dimensions of an angular frequency, which we shall denote by ω_0. We shall later show that the same formula holds in wave mechanics. Let us handle our angular-momentum vectors according to classical mechanics, and let us consider the whole orbital angular momentum of an atom, which may contain one or more electrons. We shall let $L\hbar$ be the vector angular momentum and shall let its component along the z axis be $L\hbar \cos \theta$, so that the energy is $L\hbar \cos \theta \, \omega_0$. The magnitude of the torque is the negative derivative of the energy with respect to the angle; that is, it is $L\hbar \sin \theta \, \omega_0$. Let us set up the torque in vector language. If ω_0 is a vector whose magnitude is ω_0, pointing along the z axis, then the vector $\omega_0 \times L\hbar$ has a magnitude $L\hbar \sin \theta \, \omega_0$ and has the direction of the torque, so that we have

$$\text{Torque} = \omega_0 \times L\hbar \qquad (10\text{-}2)$$

We can now state Newton's second law in vector language; it is

$$\frac{d\mathbf{L}}{dt} = \omega_0 \times \mathbf{L} \qquad (10\text{-}3)$$

We can solve this simple differential equation at once, by the assumptions

$$L_x = L \sin \theta \cos (\omega_0 t - \alpha)$$
$$L_y = L \sin \theta \sin (\omega_0 t - \alpha) \qquad (10\text{-}4)$$
$$L_z = L \cos \theta$$

where $L\hbar$ is the magnitude of the angular momentum, ω_0 is the magnitude of the vector ω_0, or $eB/2m_0$, and α is an arbitrary phase. This motion, in which L_z stays constant while L_x and L_y vary as sinusoidal functions of time, 90° apart from each other in phase, is a precession. It is indicated in Fig. 10-7 by a motion of the angular-momentum vector about the cone shown in the figure. The angular frequency of precession, $\omega_0 = eB/2m_0$, is called the Larmor frequency. Larmor and Lorentz deduced this precession, from purely classical arguments, before the quantum theory was proposed. Lorentz derived from this a classical theory of the Zeeman effect, as we mentioned in Sec. 10-1. He showed that, if in the absence of a magnetic field an electron was executing an oscillation about a position of equilibrium with an angular frequency ω_1, then in the presence of the field the whole orbit would precess with the angular frequency ω_0, and this would result in the appearance of three frequencies in the spectrum, ω_1, and $\omega_1 \pm \omega_0$.

Next we shall apply the same sort of analysis to the classical motion of two angular-momentum vectors, $L\hbar$ and $S\hbar$, coupled together by an interaction energy $\Gamma(\mathbf{L} \cdot \mathbf{S})$, proportional to the cosine of the angle between the vectors, where Γ is a constant. This is the assumption which proved to be appropriate, in the vector model, for the interaction of the vectors $L\hbar$ and $S\hbar$; they proved to be coupled to each other by a magnetic torque which had this type of interaction energy. If there is no external field, the torques produced by this interaction will be internal to the system, no torque will act on the system as a whole, and the total angular momentum, the resultant of $L\hbar$ and $S\hbar$, will stay constant. This resultant then furnishes a fixed axis in space: if we show the two vectors, as in Fig. 10-8, adding vectorially to form a constant resultant, the only motion possible to the vectors is for the plane containing them to rotate round the fixed axis of total angular momentum.

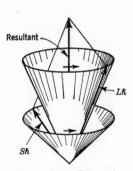

Fig. 10-8. Precession of two angular-momentum vectors about their resultant.

We can analyze the classical motion by using the same methods we have just employed. Let us consider specifically the case where one vector is $L\hbar$, the other $S\hbar$ (we shall use $\mathbf{L}$ and $\mathbf{S}$ as vectors, of magnitude L and S, pointing in the directions of the appropriate angular momenta).

We assume the interaction energy $\Gamma(\mathbf{L} \cdot \mathbf{S})$. Then, by methods like those we have just used, the torque acting on $\mathbf{S}$ will be $\Gamma(\mathbf{L} \times \mathbf{S})$, and that on $\mathbf{L}$ will be $\Gamma(\mathbf{S} \times \mathbf{L})$. These are equal and opposite, so that there is no torque on the system as a whole, and the resultant $\mathbf{J} = \mathbf{L} + \mathbf{S}$ will remain constant. We can write the equations of motion, analogous to Eq. (10-3), in the form

$$\hbar \frac{d\mathbf{L}}{dt} = \Gamma(\mathbf{S} \times \mathbf{L}) \qquad \hbar \frac{d\mathbf{S}}{dt} = \Gamma(\mathbf{L} \times \mathbf{S}) \qquad (10\text{-}5)$$

which can be rewritten in the form

$$\frac{d\mathbf{L}}{dt} = \frac{\Gamma}{\hbar}(\mathbf{J} \times \mathbf{L}) \qquad \frac{d\mathbf{S}}{dt} = \frac{\Gamma}{\hbar}(\mathbf{J} \times \mathbf{S}) \qquad (10\text{-}6)$$

where $\mathbf{J} = \mathbf{L} + \mathbf{S}$ and $\mathbf{L} \times \mathbf{L} = \mathbf{S} \times \mathbf{S} = 0$. Comparison with Eqs. (10-3) and (10-4) shows that $\mathbf{L}$ and $\mathbf{S}$ will both precess about the axis of the resultant $\mathbf{J}$ with the angular frequency $\Gamma J/\hbar$.

Now let us assume that our system of two coupled vectors is in an external field, such as a magnetic field, which exerts a torque on it. The exact solution of the problem of the motion of the two vectors in this field is difficult; but we can get a simple approximate solution in case the precessional frequency $\Gamma J/\hbar$ of the two vectors about their resultant is large compared with the Larmor frequency. The reason for the simplification is the following: Actually the external magnetic field will exert independent torques on the vectors $\mathbf{L}$ and $\mathbf{S}$, and these torques will depend on the phase of the precession of $\mathbf{L}$ and $\mathbf{S}$ about $\mathbf{J}$. This is seen in Fig. 10-9, where we show $\mathbf{L}$ and $\mathbf{S}$ precessing about $\mathbf{J}$ and $\mathbf{J}$ itself precessing in an external field: it is clear that, as $\mathbf{L}$ and $\mathbf{S}$ precess about $\mathbf{J}$, their angles to the external field will vary. But the components of $\mathbf{L}$ and $\mathbf{S}$ at right angles to $\mathbf{J}$ will average to zero over one period of the precession, and the average values of $\mathbf{L}$ and $\mathbf{S}$ over a period will be merely the components of these vectors along $\mathbf{J}$.

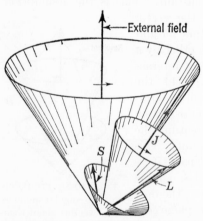

Fig. 10-9. L and S precessing about J; J precessing around external field.

If this period is small compared with the Larmor period (that is, if the frequency of precession is large compared with the Larmor frequency), we can replace the magnetic moments arising from $\mathbf{L}$ and $\mathbf{S}$ by their average values, as if they pointed along $\mathbf{J}$, so that there will be an interaction energy between the magnetic moments and the external field proportional to the cosine of the angle between **J** and the field, and the whole system will precess in the external field just as we have described in Eqs. (10-3) and (10-4). This type of motion suggested to Landé certain formulas for multiplet separation and for Zeeman effect which he proposed with great success before wave mechanics. We shall describe these formulas in the next section.

10-4. Landé's Theory of Multiplet Separation and the Zeeman Effect. Landé's theory of multiplet separation was based on the assumption that the interaction energy between the angular momenta **L** and **S** could be given by the formula $\Gamma(\mathbf{L} \cdot \mathbf{S})$, which we have just been assuming, and which, as he showed, was reasonable if the interaction energy between them arose from magnetic coupling between the magnetic moments of the orbital and spin angular momenta. Since $\mathbf{J} = \mathbf{L} + \mathbf{S}$, we can square this vector relation, obtaining

$$J^2 = L^2 + 2(\mathbf{L} \cdot \mathbf{S}) + S^2 \qquad (10\text{-}7)$$

where J^2, L^2, S^2 are the squares of the respective vectors. From this we have

$$\Gamma(\mathbf{L} \cdot \mathbf{S}) = \frac{\Gamma}{2}(J^2 - L^2 - S^2) \qquad (10\text{-}8)$$

This suggested, then, the form of dependence of the energy on J, L, and S resulting from this magnetic interaction. However, Landé found that this did not agree with experiment; to get agreement, he had to modify it to the form

$$\Gamma(\mathbf{L} \cdot \mathbf{S}) \rightarrow \frac{\Gamma}{2}[J(J+1) - L(L+1) - S(S+1)] \qquad (10\text{-}9)$$

At the period when Landé made this modification, it was not obvious why it should be done. We can now see it much more clearly, on the basis of wave mechanics. As we shall see later, we are to regard $(\mathbf{L} \cdot \mathbf{S})$ as an operator and must consider Eq. (10-8) as an operator equation. Then Eq. (10-9) represents the diagonal matrix component of the operator in question, and the diagonal matrix components of the squares of the various angular-momentum operators proved to be given by relations like Eq. (7-29). The fact that Eq. (10-9) had been established empirically was a valuable verification of Eq. (7-29) when it was first derived from wave mechanics.

The form in which Landé's relation of Eq. (10-9) proved to be most useful is in what is called Landé's interval rule. This is the formula giving the energy separation between the state with a given J and that with the value $J - 1$. From Eq. (10-9), this is

$$\frac{\Gamma}{2}[J(J+1) - (J-1)J] = \Gamma J \qquad (10\text{-}10)$$

which proves to be rather well obeyed in many observed multiplets.

In addition to the multiplet separations, Landé suggested a treatment of the Zeeman effect which proved to be correct. In the first place, he argued, as we did at the end of the preceding section, that we could compute the energy of the atom in the magnetic field by using only the average values of **L** and **S**, averaged over the period of their precession about their resultant **J**. These average values, as we have seen, are simply their components along **J**, which in vector language are

$$(\mathbf{L})_{\text{av}} = \frac{\mathbf{J}(\mathbf{L} \cdot \mathbf{J})}{J^2} \qquad (\mathbf{S})_{\text{av}} = \frac{\mathbf{J}(\mathbf{S} \cdot \mathbf{J})}{J^2} \qquad (10\text{-}11)$$

Next, Landé assumed that the energy of the orbital angular momentum, in the presence of the external magnetic field, was the value we have stated earlier, namely, $\mu_B B$ times the component of the orbital angular momentum along the axis. If **J** is space-quantized, with component M along the axis, this implies that the energy of the orbital magnetic moment in the external field, as we see from Eq. (10-11), is

$$\text{Magnetic energy of } L = \frac{M(\mathbf{L} \cdot \mathbf{J})}{J^2} \mu_B B \qquad (10\text{-}12)$$

For the spin angular momentum, however, he found that he had to use a different formula, to get agreement with experiment: he had to assume that the magnetic energy of a spin angular momentum in the presence of the field was twice as great as that of an orbital angular momentum of equal value. That is, he assumed

$$\text{Magnetic energy of } S = \frac{M(\mathbf{S} \cdot \mathbf{J})}{J^2} 2\mu_B B \qquad (10\text{-}13)$$

There was no theoretical reason at the time for using this factor 2; it was done purely from empirical reasons. We must remember that at that time, 1921 to 1923, it was not even understood that S came from electron spins, or in fact that spins existed; the spectroscopists were merely manipulating vectors and quantum numbers in a way to get agreement with experiment. Now, however, this assumption of Landé's is built into our theories of the magnetic spin: it is assumed that each electron spin, though its angular momentum is only $\frac{1}{2}\hbar$, nevertheless has a magnetic moment of 1 Bohr magneton, twice as big as we should anticipate for such an angular momentum. As we shall see later, in Chap. 23 (Vol. II), Dirac's[1] theory of the spinning electron, based on relativistic principles, automatically leads to this result, but that was not known until 1928, a number of years after Landé's work in the early 1920s.

---

[1] P. A. M. Dirac, *Proc. Roy. Soc. (London)*, **A117**:610 (1928); **A118**:351 (1928)

Landé's arguments immediately led to the result that the magnetic energy of the whole atom was

$$\text{Magnetic energy} = \frac{M[(\mathbf{L} + 2\mathbf{S}) \cdot \mathbf{J}]}{J^2} \mu_B B = gM\mu_B B \quad (10\text{-}14)$$

where g, known as Landé's g factor, is a dimensionless quantity given by

$$g = \frac{(\mathbf{L} + 2\mathbf{S}) \cdot \mathbf{J}}{J^2} \quad (10\text{-}15)$$

When we remember that vectorially $\mathbf{L} + 2\mathbf{S} = \mathbf{J} + \mathbf{S}$, we can rewrite Eq. (10-15) in the form

$$g = 1 + \frac{\mathbf{S} \cdot \mathbf{J}}{J^2} = 1 + \frac{J^2 - L^2 + S^2}{2J^2} \quad (10\text{-}16)$$

where we have used $\mathbf{L} = \mathbf{J} - \mathbf{S}, L^2 = J^2 - 2(\mathbf{S} \cdot \mathbf{J}) + S^2$. Just as with the multiplet-separation formula, Landé found that, to get agreement with experiment, Eq. (10-16) had to be modified to the form

$$g = 1 + \frac{J(J + 1) - L(L + 1) + S(S + 1)}{2J(J + 1)} \quad (10\text{-}17)$$

As with Eq. (10-9), we know now that this has to be done because Eq. (10-16) is an operator equation, and the average value, or diagonal matrix component, is given by Eq. (10-17).

This formula of Eq. (10-17) proves to give correctly the g factors of the energy levels of multiplets in Russell-Saunders coupling, and its usefulness in checking the quantum numbers of multiplets, in experimental spectroscopy, is very great. It proves to be the case that the magnetic energy follows Eq. (10-14), varying linearly with the magnetic field, only provided the magnetic splitting of a level is small compared with the separation of the various levels of the multiplet, associated with different J values. This is equivalent to the statement that it is correct only when the magnetic precession frequency is small compared with the precession frequency of the two vectors $\mathbf{L}$ and $\mathbf{S}$ about their resultant $\mathbf{J}$, which we earlier saw to be necessary for the justification of the classical model on which Eq. (10-14) is based. For higher magnetic fields, there are deviations from the formula, as we shall see later, called the Paschen-Back effect. These effects are also observed experimentally, and they are found to agree well with the theory, which we shall present later.

As a result of the fact that the Landé g factor is different from unity, we see that the precession of the J vector in a magnetic field does not take place with the Larmor frequency, but rather with g times this frequency. It is this which results in the complicated nature of the Zeeman patterns, as shown in Fig. 10-1. The factor g is, as we can see, proportional to the ratio of magnetic moment to angular momentum; for a very simple argument shows that the magnetic moment of the atom, as well as its component along the axis, is equal to $ge/2m_0$ times the angular momentum. This ratio of magnetic moment to angular momentum is often called the gyromagnetic ratio, and this name is sometimes used to refer to the g factor itself.

10-5. General Survey of Wave-mechanical Theory of Multiplet Structure. We must now start a treatment of the vector model and multiplet theory, using the methods of wave mechanics, instead of the semiclassical arguments which we have been using in the preceding sections and which were all that was available in the early 1920s. Those simple arguments lead correctly to the classification of the multiplets, with their various quantum numbers, and to a fairly complete understanding of multiplet separations and of the Zeeman effect. They furnish no method, however, for calculating the energy separation between the various multiplets arising from a given configuration. The magnitudes of these separations, as we see from Figs. 10-2 and 10-4, are far greater than would be explained by magnetic terms in the energy; for the magnetic terms prove to be of the right order of magnitude to explain the much smaller separations between the various J values in a single multiplet. It seems plausible that the torques responsible for coupling of the l's of the various electrons together should be electrostatic; the charge density of an electron will certainly depend on its m value, whether we interpret it in terms of Bohr's orbits or in terms of wave functions, and we should expect that there would be an interaction energy between two orbits, depending on their m values or on the resultant angular momentum L. But no attempt was made to calculate these torques, or the resulting energy values, until after wave mechanics came along.

Much more puzzling is the dependence of the energy on S, or on the relative orientation of the spins. From Fig. 10-4, for instance, we see that the separations between multiplets with the same L, but different S, are of the same order of magnitude as those between states with the same S, but different L. In other words, the empirical evidence indicates that these separations also are of electrostatic origin, for this is the only type of energy of the required order of magnitude. But why should different orientations of the electron spin result in large electrostatic terms in the energy? This puzzle remained until wave mechanics was developed, when Heisenberg[1] and Dirac[2] made a proposal relating to the symmetry of the wave function which tied together this aspect of multiplet structure, the nature of the electron spin, and the Pauli exclusion principle

[1] W. Heisenberg, Z. Physik, **38**:411 (1926); **39**:499 (1926); **41**:239 (1927).
[2] P. A. M. Dirac, Proc. Roy. Soc. (London), **A112**:661 (1926).

in a way which really furnished the basis for the whole wave-mechanical theory of atomic structure.

In the meantime, however, a great deal of work had been applied to the problem of the wave-mechanical treatment of angular-momentum vectors. This work started before the development of wave mechanics, by use of the correspondence principle, which we have described in Appendix 10. In turn, this led Heisenberg[1] to propose the concept of matrix components, and Born, Heisenberg, and Jordan[2] developed a complete treatment of angular-momentum vectors in 1925, before the development of wave mechanics. It turns out to be more convenient to handle angular-momentum vectors directly by matrix methods, rather than through wave functions and wave mechanics, and as a result, we find that later work, such as a fundamental paper by Güttinger and Pauli[3] in 1931, which was the first one giving many of the details of the vector-coupling scheme of two vectors, still uses matrix methods. These matrix methods are adaptable to treating, not only angular-momentum vectors, but also the matrix components of the electric moment, required for studying the selection principles.

The whole study of complex spectra by wave-mechanical methods, involving the angular-momentum vectors, the symmetry properties of the wave function, and its relation to multiplet structure, is a complicated theory which will take us several chapters to describe fully. We shall start our discussion, in the next chapter, with the matrix properties of the angular-momentum vectors, then shall go on in Chap. 12 to the symmetry properties of the wave function, and shall only then be prepared, in Chap. 13, to calculate the matrix components of the Hamiltonian between the unperturbed wave functions which we shall be using and to solve the secular problem involved in expanding the wave functions of the problem in terms of unperturbed wave functions.

Even then we shall be only part way through our task, for we shall have to describe many applications which have been made of the method, which has now been carried to the point where it can handle almost all of even the most complicated multiplet problems. This will all be done with only a superficial treatment of the spinning electron and its magnetic properties; and we shall have to work out later, in Chaps. 23 and 24 (Vol. II), the correct theory of electronic structure, as derived by Dirac from relativistic theory. Then we must apply our methods, not only to the positions of the energy levels, but to the transition probabilities

[1] W. Heisenberg, *Z. Physik*, **33**:879 (1925).

[2] M. Born and P. Jordan, *Z. Physik*, **34**:858 (1925); M. Born, W. Heisenberg, and P. Jordan, *Z. Physik*, **35**:557 (1926); W. Heisenberg and P. Jordan, *Z. Physik*, **37**:263 (1926).

[3] P. Güttinger and W. Pauli, *Z. Physik*, **67**:743 (1931).

between them, which we have merely stated without proof in the present chapter. Finally we shall come to hyperfine structure, the interaction between the angular-momentum vectors of the electronic part of the atom with the angular-momentum vectors of the nucleus, which we have been neglecting. All this forms an ambitious program, which will occupy us for much of the second volume of this work.

PROBLEMS

1. Prove that an S level, no matter what the multiplicity, has only one sublevel (one J value) and that a P level never has more than three sublevels.

2. Consider the transitions from the various J values of a $^3P^o$ multiplet to a ^3D. Assume that the total width of the ^3D multiplet is 20 per cent less than the total width of the $^3P^o$ and that Landé's interval rule is obeyed in each case. Draw a diagram showing the levels, indicating the allowed transitions, and work out the relative frequencies of the various spectral lines of the multiplet arising from these transitions. Show the spectrum graphically, as it would be observed in a spectrometer.

3. Find the Landé g values for the various levels of a $^3P^o$ and ^3D multiplet, as indicated in Prob. 2.

4. Find the way in which the levels $^3D_3$ and $^3P^o_2$ are split up in a magnetic field, using the values of the g factors worked out in Prob. 3. Draw a diagram of the sublevels into which these two levels split, and indicate the allowed transitions, using the fact that the selection principle for M is $\Delta M = \pm 1, 0$. Find the relative frequencies of the various spectrum lines, and show the Zeeman pattern graphically.

5. Proceed as in Prob. 4, with the remaining spectrum lines arising in Prob. 2.

6. The D lines of sodium come from the transition $3p\ ^2P_{\frac{1}{2},\frac{3}{2}} \to 3s\ ^2S_{\frac{1}{2}}$. Work out the Zeeman patterns for the levels, including the g values, and from this deduce the Zeeman patterns of the resulting spectrum lines.

11

The Behavior of Angular-momentum
Vectors in Wave Mechanics

11-1. The Angular Momentum of an Electron in a Central Field. In Sec. 7-3 we have given a very brief discussion of the angular momentum of an electron in a central field, according to wave mechanics. In Sec. 10-3 we have shown how a single angular-momentum vector behaves in classical mechanics and how we treat the coupling of two angular-momentum vectors. Our first step in going further with the problem will be to amplify those discussions. In quantum mechanics, of course, we treat the angular momentum as an operator; since it is a vector, we have three operators, representing the x, y, and z components. We deal with the matrix components of these operators, with respect to wave functions of the type we have found in Eq. (7-31), characterized by the quantum numbers n, l, m_l. Our first task will be to discuss the angular momentum of a single electron in a central field, according to these methods. Later we shall find that the discussion is much more general than this example would suggest: the behavior of any angular-momentum operator which would remain constant in classical mechanics, or on which no torques act, is practically identical to that of a single electron. Thus we can use the same principles to discuss the total orbital angular momentum of an atom or its total spin angular momentum, provided the spin-orbit interaction is small enough so that there is no appreciable torque between them; or we can use them for the total angular momentum, orbital plus spin, even if there is a spin-orbit interaction. Let us then begin this discussion.

First, what is the operator giving the angular momentum of an electron in wave mechanics? The classical angular momentum of a particle is $\mathbf{r} \times \mathbf{p}$, where $\mathbf{r}$ is the radius vector, $\mathbf{p}$ the momentum vector; it is a vector at right angles to both the radius vector and the momentum, whose magnitude is the magnitude of the momentum, times the projection of the radius vector perpendicular to the momentum, or times the

255

lever arm. Consequently the operator associated with the angular momentum is in ordinary units $-i\hbar(\mathbf{r} \times \nabla)$, or in atomic units, in which $\hbar$ is the unit of angular momentum,

$$(\mathbf{L})_{op} = -i(\mathbf{r} \times \nabla) \tag{11-1}$$

whose components are

$$(L_x)_{op} = -i\left(y \frac{\partial}{\partial z} - z \frac{\partial}{\partial y}\right)$$

$$(L_y)_{op} = -i\left(z \frac{\partial}{\partial x} - x \frac{\partial}{\partial z}\right) \tag{11-2}$$

$$(L_z)_{op} = -i\left(x \frac{\partial}{\partial y} - y \frac{\partial}{\partial x}\right)$$

Since the wave function is expressed in spherical polar coordinates, we wish to express these three operators in spherical polar coordinates. It is a straightforward problem in changing variables in partial differentiation to do this, and we find

$$(L_x)_{op} = i\left(\sin \phi \frac{\partial}{\partial \theta} + \cot \theta \cos \phi \frac{\partial}{\partial \phi}\right)$$

$$(L_y)_{op} = i\left(-\cos \phi \frac{\partial}{\partial \theta} + \cot \theta \sin \phi \frac{\partial}{\partial \phi}\right)$$

$$(L_z)_{op} = -i \frac{\partial}{\partial \phi} \tag{11-3}$$

$$(L^2)_{op} = -\frac{1}{\sin \theta} \frac{\partial}{\partial \theta}\left(\sin \theta \frac{\partial}{\partial \theta}\right) - \frac{1}{\sin^2 \theta} \frac{\partial^2}{\partial \phi^2}$$

From these operators and the properties of the associated Legendre functions, we prove at once that

$$(L_z)_{op}u_{nlm} = mu_{nlm}$$
$$(L^2)_{op}u_{nlm} = l(l+1)u_{nlm} \tag{11-4}$$

in agreement with Eqs. (7-29) and (7-30). Thus we find that $(L_z)_{op}$ and $(L^2)_{op}$ have diagonal matrices, since operating on the wave function with them gives a constant times the wave function. Hence they represent constant quantities, and m (times the unit $\hbar$, if we are using ordinary units) measures the component of the angular momentum along z, and $l(l+1)$ (times $\hbar^2$ in ordinary units) measures the square of the absolute value of the angular momentum, so that l is closely related to the magnitude of the angular momentum. More properly we should use $\sqrt{l(l+1)}$ to measure this quantity, so that the interpretation which we gave earlier of the rule that $|m|$ could not be greater than l is not quite as simple as we indicated.

For future use, we shall need also the matrix components of $(L_x)_{op}$ and $(L_y)_{op}$, which are somewhat more troublesome to compute. In working them out, we must differentiate the Legendre function $P_l^m(\cos \theta)$ with respect to θ. In doing this, we make use of the following mathematical relations, which are among those tabulated in Appendix 14,

$$\frac{dP_l^m(\cos \theta)}{d\theta} = -P_l^{m+1}(\cos \theta) + m \cot \theta \, P_l^m(\cos \theta) \tag{11-5}$$

$$m \cot \theta \, P_l^m(\cos \theta) = \tfrac{1}{2}[P_l^{m+1}(\cos \theta) + (l + m)(l - m + 1)P_l^{m-1}(\cos \theta)] \tag{11-6}$$

where Eq. (11-6) holds only for $m > 0$, whereas Eq. (11-5) holds for any positive value of m and for zero. When we make use of these equations and consider separately the positive and negative values of m, which is necessary on account of the absolute value signs in Eq. (7-31), we find the following equations:

$$(L_x)_{op}u_{nlm} = \tfrac{1}{2}[\sqrt{(l - m)(l + m + 1)} \, u_{n,l,m+1} + \sqrt{(l - m + 1)(l + m)} \, u_{n,l,m-1}]$$

$$(L_y)_{op}u_{nlm} = \frac{i}{2}[- \sqrt{(l - m)(l + m + 1)} \, u_{n,l,m+1} + \sqrt{(l - m + 1)(l + m)} \, u_{n,l,m-1}] \tag{11-7}$$

$$(L_x + iL_y)_{op}u_{nlm} = \sqrt{(l - m)(l + m + 1)} \, u_{n,l,m+1}$$

$$(L_x - iL_y)_{op}u_{nlm} = \sqrt{(l - m + 1)(l + m)} \, u_{n,l,m-1}$$

$$(L_z)_{op}u_{nlm} = mu_{nlm}$$

We can use the same formulas for both positive and negative m's. The reason for the peculiar choice of signs in the definition of our wave functions, in Eq. (7-31), was in order to get these convenient formulas for the matrix components of $(L_x)_{op}$ and $(L_y)_{op}$.†

We now notice a significant fact about $(L_x)_{op}$ and $(L_y)_{op}$: these operators, operating on a wave function, give us a linear combination of just two wave functions, namely, those with the same n and l values, but with m values equal to the original value ± 1, and $(L_x \pm iL_y)_{op}$ each gives a single wave function, whose m is greater or less than the original value by one unit, respectively. For this reason, $(L_x + iL_y)_{op}$ and $(L_x - iL_y)_{op}$ are called step-up and step-down operators, respectively, since when they operate on a wave function they increase or decrease m by one unit, depending on the sign of the term $\pm i(L_y)_{op}$.

We can write the matrix components of $(L_x)_{op}$, $(L_y)_{op}$, $(L_z)_{op}$ from Eq. (11-7), multiplying on the left by the conjugate of one of the wave functions, integrating over the coordinates, and taking advantage of the orthonormal properties of the u's. We find that these components can

† See E. U. Condon and G. H. Shortley, "Theory of Atomic Spectra," Cambridge University Press, New York, 1935, for further information regarding this point and regarding many other matters treated in this text.

all be combined into the equations

$$(L_x)_{m,m+1} = (L_x)_{m+1,m} = -i(L_y)_{m,m+1} = i(L_y)_{m+1,m}$$
$$= \tfrac{1}{2} \sqrt{(l-m)(l+m+1)} \tag{11-8}$$
$$(L_z)_{m,m} = m$$

In these expressions, it is understood that the n and l values are identical in initial and final states and only the m changes as indicated.

11-2. The Precession of the Angular-momentum Vector. We have found the matrix components of Eq. (11-7) or (11-8) by straightforward calculation from the wave function. Let us now inquire what is their significance and how they describe in wave-mechanical language the same precession of the angular-momentum vector which we have been considering classically in Sec. 10-3. In the first place, L_z has a diagonal matrix, according to Eq. (11-7) or (11-8). This ties in with the constancy of the z component of angular momentum according to Eq. (10-4); and the diagonal matrix component m, or $m\hbar$, from Eq. (11-8), is just what would be indicated by Eq. (10-4), where we find that L_z equals $L \cos \theta$, or the projection of L along the axis.

The nondiagonal nature of the matrix components of L_x and L_y, from Eq. (11-7) or (11-8), is related to the precession, the fact that L_x and L_y according to Eq. (10-4) vary sinusoidally with the time. If we have a perturbative term in the energy, of the form $m\mu_B B$, as discussed in Sec. 10-3, the various states of the same l, but different m, will have different energy, so that in the expressions for the average values of L_x and L_y, averaged over the wave function, as in Eq. (4-28), but not over time, we shall have terms varying sinusoidally with time. Thus, from that equation we have

$$(L_x + iL_y)_{\text{av}} = \Sigma(m',m) C_{m'}^* C_m (L_x + iL_y)_{m'm} \exp [i(E_{m'} - E_m)t/\hbar] \tag{11-9}$$

where m', m are two quantum numbers. Now from Eq. (11-7) we find that the only nonvanishing matrix component of $(L_x + iL_y)$ is of the type

$$(L_x + iL_y)_{m+1,m} = \sqrt{(l-m)(l+m+1)} \tag{11-10}$$

Thus we can handle all terms if we convert the double sum in Eq. (11-9) into a single sum over m, letting $m' = m + 1$. Furthermore, we have $E_{m'} - E_m = (m+1)\mu_B B - m\mu_B B = \mu_B B$. Thus we have

$$(L_x + iL_y)_{\text{av}} = \Sigma(m) C_{m+1}^* C_m \sqrt{(l-m)(l+m+1)} \exp (i\omega_0 t) \tag{11-11}$$

where $\omega_0 = \mu_B B/\hbar = eB/2m_0$, the Larmor frequency defined in Sec. 10-3.

This expression of Eq. (11-11) is to be compared with the expression

$$L_x + iL_y = L \sin \theta \exp [i(\omega_0 t - \alpha)] \qquad (11\text{-}12)$$

which follows from Eq. (10-4). Here $L \sin \theta = \sqrt{l^2 - m^2}$, if l is the azimuthal quantum number and m is the magnetic quantum number. In the limit of large quantum numbers, in which we expect to get a parallelism between wave mechanics and classical mechanics, this is approximately equal to $\sqrt{(l - m)(l + m + 1)}$, since in that limit we can disregard unity compared with l or m. In the case of large quantum numbers, we can set up a wave packet: we can choose the C_m's to vary smoothly with m, but to be large only when m is near a certain specified value. Then in the summation of Eq. (11-11) we may take the square root and the exponential outside the summation, being left with $\Sigma(m)C_{m+1}^* C_m$. But by hypothesis in our wave packet the C's vary slowly with m, so that this is nearly the same as $\Sigma(m)C_m^* C_m$, which is unity. Hence Eq. (11-11) becomes approximately equivalent to Eq. (11-12), except for the absence of the phase factor $\exp (i\alpha)$, which we could have obtained by a slightly different assumption regarding the C's. In other words, we see that the nondiagonal matrix components of L_x and L_y are just what are needed to describe the precession of the angular-momentum vector, as described classically in Eq. (10-4).

11-3. General Derivation of Matrix Components of Angular Momentum. We have so far proceeded by quite elementary methods, working directly from the wave functions of the central-field problem, and using properties of the associated Legendre functions. It was shown, however, by Born, Heisenberg, and Jordan, in the papers quoted in Sec. 10-5, that these same results can be derived from much more general points of view, without using the formulas for the properties of the associated Legendre functions. These general derivations are particularly important when we come to consider atoms containing more than one electron, for this general derivation can be used in these more complicated cases just as well as for the single electron, but no such simple derivation as we have used so far, in terms of the associated Legendre functions, can conveniently be given.

We shall find that it is very helpful to consider the commutation properties of the operators representing the three components of angular momentum. In classical mechanics, the angular momentum of a particle acted on by a central force, or with a potential energy depending on r only, stays constant, since no torques act. Correspondingly we should expect that, in quantum mechanics, the angular-momentum operators would commute with the Hamiltonian, provided we are neglecting any such torques as those arising from external magnetic fields, since we have seen that this is the characteristic of a quantity which stays constant.

To demonstrate that this is true, let us first consider the Laplacian, or kinetic energy. We have

$$\left(y\frac{\partial}{\partial z} - z\frac{\partial}{\partial y}\right)\nabla^2 u = y\nabla^2\left(\frac{\partial u}{\partial z}\right) - z\nabla^2\left(\frac{\partial u}{\partial y}\right)$$

$$\nabla^2\left(y\frac{\partial u}{\partial z} - z\frac{\partial u}{\partial y}\right) = y\nabla^2\left(\frac{\partial u}{\partial z}\right) + 2\frac{\partial^2 u}{\partial y\,\partial z} - z\nabla^2\left(\frac{\partial u}{\partial y}\right) - 2\frac{\partial^2 u}{\partial z\,\partial y} \quad (11\text{-}13)$$

From Eq. (11-13), we see that

$$\left(y\frac{\partial}{\partial z} - z\frac{\partial}{\partial y}\right)\nabla^2 u = \nabla^2\left(y\frac{\partial}{\partial z} - z\frac{\partial}{\partial y}\right)u \quad (11\text{-}14)$$

or the Laplacian commutes with $(L_x)_{op}$. An equally simple proof holds for any spherically symmetrical potential energy $V(r)$, so that each component of the angular momentum commutes with the Hamiltonian.

On the other hand, though each component of $(L)_{op}$ commutes with the energy, we find that the components do not commute with each other but that rather we have the commutation relations

$$(L_y)_{op}(L_z)_{op} - (L_z)_{op}(L_y)_{op} = i(L_x)_{op}$$
$$(L_z)_{op}(L_x)_{op} - (L_x)_{op}(L_z)_{op} = i(L_y)_{op} \quad (11\text{-}15)$$
$$(L_x)_{op}(L_y)_{op} - (L_y)_{op}(L_x)_{op} = i(L_z)_{op}$$

where we are using atomic units, as in Eq. (11-2). Since these operators do not commute with each other, they cannot be simultaneously diagonalized, though any one of them can be diagonalized. This is the reason why we found in Sec. 11-1 that $(L_z)_{op}$ has a diagonal matrix, whereas $(L_x)_{op}$ and $(L_y)_{op}$ have not. However, as we saw in Eq. (4-40), any quantity whose operator commutes with the Hamiltonian can have nondiagonal matrix components only between states of the same energy, which explains why we have found nonvanishing matrix components of $(L_x)_{op}$ and $(L_y)_{op}$ only between states of the same n and l values, but different m. Even though $(L_x)_{op}$, $(L_y)_{op}$, and $(L_z)_{op}$ do not all commute with each other, nevertheless one can prove that each one commutes with the square of the angular momentum, $(L^2)_{op} = (L_x^2)_{op} + (L_y^2)_{op} + (L_z^2)_{op}$. This square also commutes with the energy. It is for this reason that we can find a set of wave functions which have diagonal matrices for $(L^2)_{op}$ as well as $(L_z)_{op}$.

We have calculated the matrix components of the angular-momentum vector by direct evaluation from the Schrödinger wave functions. We have stated, however, that these matrix components were found by Born, Heisenberg, and Jordan in 1925 from the matrix mechanics which preceded wave mechanics. They were derived only from the commutation rules and follow uniquely (except for ambiguity of signs) from these commutation rules. We shall now show how this calculation can be made.   The importance of this method of derivation, as we have mentioned above, will become evident when we come to the many-electron atom; for the one-electron problem it is not appreciably simpler than that making use of the Schrödinger operator method.   For the many-electron case, however, we shall still find that the operator representing the total angular momentum of the electrons will commute with the Hamiltonian, since that is merely an expression of the constancy of the angular momentum of the whole atom, when no torques act on it.   Furthermore, we shall be able to prove even in this general case that the commutation rules of Eq. (11-15) hold for the total angular momentum.   Since we are now going to show that the matrix components of angular momentum follow from these facts alone, this allows us to use the matrix method directly for investigating the angular-momentum properties in a many-electron atom, whereas for this case, unlike the one-electron problem, the wave functions are quite complicated, and the evaluation of the matrix components from the Schrödinger operator method involves considerable difficulties.

Let us start our discussion by assuming that $(L_z)_{op}$ has a diagonal matrix; since it commutes with the energy, we can certainly achieve this. We know that $(L_x)_{op}$ and $(L_y)_{op}$ do not commute with $(L_z)_{op}$, and hence they cannot have diagonal matrices, provided we are dealing with degenerate states.   On account of Eq. (4-40), however, since $(L_x)_{op}$ and $(L_y)_{op}$ commute with the energy, they can have nondiagonal matrix components only between states of the same energy.   Let m be a quantum number denoting the various wave functions of this degenerate set between which $(L_x)_{op}$ and $(L_y)_{op}$ have nondiagonal matrix components.   Let us assume that we are dealing with a finite set of degenerate states, consisting of $2l + 1$ different states, where l is an integer (or an integer plus $\frac{1}{2}$, a possibility which did not occur in our earlier discussion).   We shall choose the numbers m to run by unit steps from $-l$ to l.   Then $(L_x)_{op}$, $(L_y)_{op}$ will have matrix components between states of different m value, so that we shall have finite matrices for them.

Let us now write the m, m' component of the first two equations of Eq. (11-15) in matrix form, making use of the fact that $(L_z)_{op}$ has a diagonal matrix.   We have

$$(L_y)_{mm'}(L_z)_{m'm'} - (L_z)_{mm}(L_y)_{mm'} = (L_y)_{mm'}[(L_z)_{m'm'} - (L_z)_{mm}]$$
$$= i(L_x)_{mm'} \qquad (11\text{-}16)$$

and similarly

$$(L_x)_{mm'}[(L_z)_{m'm'} - (L_z)_{mm}] = -i(L_y)_{mm'} \qquad (11\text{-}17)$$

Both Eqs. (11-16) and (11-17) give values for the ratio $(L_x)_{mm'}/(L_y)_{mm'}$. If we equate these values, we have an equation for L_z; it is

$$[(L_z)_{m'm'} - (L_z)_{mm}]^2 = 1 \qquad (11\text{-}18)$$

It is legitimate to write such an equation only for two states mm' between which $(L_x)_{op}$ and $(L_y)_{op}$ have nondiagonal matrix components, for otherwise the ratio $(L_x)_{mm'}/(L_y)_{mm'}$ is indeterminate. We then find from Eq. (11-18) that the difference of diagonal matrix components of L_z, between two states between which L_x and L_y have nondiagonal matrix components, must be ± 1.

This gives us two pieces of information: the differences between the diagonal matrix components of L_z must be integers, and L_x and L_y can have nondiagonal components only between states differing by a single unit. Since the states are numbered by means of the quantum number m, we can write the diagonal matrix components of L_z as m, thereby achieving the correct differences between the L_z values of successive states. We remember that we have assumed that m runs from $-l$ to l, which means that we are implying that $(L_z)_{mm}$ also runs from $-l$ to l, so that for every state with a given $(L_z)_{mm}$ there is another state with the negative of this value. We must, as a matter of fact, make this assumption, for we shall see later that, unless we have this sort of symmetry between positive and negative m's, we cannot satisfy the required conditions for the matrix components of L_x and L_y.

Now that we have established the value of $(L_z)_{mm}$, we can use either Eq. (11-16) or (11-17) to show that

$$\frac{(L_x)_{m,m\pm1}}{(L_y)_{m,m\pm1}} = \mp i \qquad (11\text{-}19)$$

where the upper or lower signs are to be used together, respectively. This shows that, if, for instance, the matrix components of L_x are real, those of L_y are imaginary. We shall choose this case; if we had made the opposite choice, the eventual results for any physically observable quantity would be the same. It follows from Appendix 7 that the matrices of L_x and L_y are Hermitian; thus we can conclude that

$$(L_x)_{m,m+1} = (L_x)_{m+1,m} = -i(L_y)_{m,m+1} = i(L_y)_{m+1,m} \qquad (11\text{-}20)$$

We can now use the third equation of Eq. (11-15) to establish the common value of these matrix components. We use the formulas for a matrix product and set up this equation for the mm component. We have

$$(L_x)_{m,m+1}(L_y)_{m+1,m} + (L_x)_{m,m-1}(L_y)_{m-1,m} - (L_y)_{m,m+1}(L_x)_{m+1,m}$$
$$- (L_y)_{m,m-1}(L_x)_{m-1,m} = i(L_z)_{mm} = im \qquad (11\text{-}21)$$

If we use Eq. (11-20), this is transformed into

$$[(L_x)_{m,m+1}]^2 - [(L_x)_{m,m-1}]^2 = -\frac{m}{2} \qquad (11\text{-}22)$$

The maximum value of m is l, so that there is no matrix component of L_x corresponding to a transition from l to $l + 1$.   Hence we have

$$[(L_x)_{l,l-1}]^2 = \frac{l}{2} \tag{11-23}$$

Then we can use Eq. (11-22) to get successive values of the squares of the matrix components of L_x.   We have

$$
\begin{aligned}
[(L_x)_{l-1,l-2}]^2 &= [(L_x)_{l,l-1}]^2 + \tfrac{1}{2}(l - 1) \\
&= \tfrac{1}{2}[l + (l - 1)] \\
[(L_x)_{l-2,l-3}]^2 &= \tfrac{1}{2}[l + (l - 1) + (l - 2)] \\
&\cdot\cdot\cdot\cdot\cdot\cdot\cdot\cdot\cdot\cdot\cdot\cdot\cdot\cdot\cdot\cdot\cdot\cdot \\
[(L_x)_{m+1,m}]^2 &= \tfrac{1}{2}[l + (l - 1) + (l - 2) + \cdot\cdot\cdot + (m + 1)] \\
&= \tfrac{1}{4}(l - m)(l + m + 1)
\end{aligned} \tag{11-24}
$$

If we take the square root of this and combine with Eq. (11-20), we arrive at Eq. (11-8).   We note that Eq. (11-24) automatically makes the matrix component zero between the state with $m = -l$ and $m = -l - 1$, which is necessary in order that the series break off and give us a finite number of states.   We should not have had this situation for the negative m's unless we had the type of symmetry between positive and negative m's which we have achieved by having l an integer or an integer plus $\tfrac{1}{2}$.   Our derivation, then, has resulted in the same formulas for matrix components which we found by direct use of the Schrödinger wave functions.   Thus we verify our earlier statement that these matrix components follow directly from the commutation rules.

We note that there is one feature in which our present derivation is more general than the earlier one: we can have a solution if l is an integer plus $\tfrac{1}{2}$, and similarly the m's are integers plus $\tfrac{1}{2}$, as well as when they are integers.   There are no wave functions in the form of Legendre functions which lead to such matrix components of the angular momentum, but we see that they are consistent with the commutation rules.   We meet these matrix components when we study the electron spin.   We have already indicated that Uhlenbeck and Goudsmit's hypothesis that the electron had an intrinsic angular momentum of magnitude $\hbar/2$ led to an understanding of many previously puzzling features of atomic spectra. This would correspond to $l = \tfrac{1}{2}$.   Pauli[1] suggested soon after that we could describe this spin angular momentum by using two wave functions, one connected with the quantum number $m_s = \tfrac{1}{2}$, the other with $m_s = -\tfrac{1}{2}$, and that the matrix components of the spin angular momentum, which we can denote by S, between these wave functions, were

[1] W. Pauli, Z. Physik, **43**:601 (1927).

given by

$$(S_x)_{\frac{1}{2},-\frac{1}{2}} = (S_x)_{-\frac{1}{2},\frac{1}{2}} = -i(S_y)_{-\frac{1}{2},\frac{1}{2}}$$
$$= i(S_y)_{\frac{1}{2},-\frac{1}{2}} = \frac{1}{2}$$

$$(S_z)_{\frac{1}{2},\frac{1}{2}} = \frac{1}{2} \qquad (S_z)_{-\frac{1}{2},-\frac{1}{2}} = -\frac{1}{2}$$

(11-25)

which follows directly from Eq. (11-8), if we set $l = \frac{1}{2}$.

11-4. Application of Angular-momentum Properties to Complex Atoms.
Any angular momentum on which no torques act behaves like that
described in the previous section; for if no torques act, its time derivative
is zero and this means, according to Eq. (4-45), that it commutes with
the Hamiltonian. Let us then make three different applications of these
methods to the case of complex atoms in Russell-Saunders coupling.
First, if the spin-orbit interaction is negligible, the total orbital angular
momentum and the total spin angular momentum will have no torques
acting on them. Then each one must behave according to the results of
the preceding section. There must be a quantum number L, such that
the operator representing the square of the orbital angular momentum
operating on the wave function gives $L(L + 1)$ times the wave function
(in atomic units), and a quantum number M_L, which can take on all
values from $-L$ to L, such that the operator representing the z component of orbital angular momentum operating on the wave function gives
M_L times the wave function. The x and y components of orbital angular
momentum must have matrix components between the states characterized by different values of M_L, given by Eq. (11-8), in which we replace
l and m by L and M_L. The states of different M_L, but the same L, must
have the same energy. In other words, we are led to the wave-mechanical
justification of the quantum number L introduced in Chap. 10. In a
similar way we must have quantum numbers S and M_S characterizing
the spin angular momentum. The existence of these quantum numbers
depends on two things which seem plausible, but which should be proved:
the operators representing the orbital and spin angular momenta should
have the same commutation rules which we have demonstrated in Eq.
(11-15) for the angular-momentum operator of a single electron, and they
should commute with the Hamiltonian; these are the only postulates
which went into the demonstration of Sec. 11-3. In Appendix 18 we
prove that they actually satisfy these commutation relations.

If there is a spin-orbit interaction, such as the term $\Gamma(\mathbf{L} \cdot \mathbf{S})$, which we
discussed in Chap. 10, the separate angular-momentum vectors of orbital
and spin motion will no longer stay constant, or commute with the
Hamiltonian; in Appendix 18 we prove that neither will the operator
arising from L or from S commute with the quantity $\Gamma(\mathbf{L} \cdot \mathbf{S})$. Hence we
can no longer prove in this case that the orbital and spin angular momenta
separately are quantized; the quantities L and S are no longer good quan-

tum numbers.   But the resultant angular momentum still is constant, or commutes with the Hamiltonian, as we prove in Appendix 18, so that we can introduce a quantum number J, such that the operator representing the square of the total angular momentum, orbital plus spin, is diagonal, with matrix component $J(J + 1)$, and its component along z is also diagonal, with matrix component M, which can go from J to $-J$. We can thus demonstrate the existence of these various quantum numbers directly from the properties of the angular-momentum operators.

We have to look more closely, however, into the rules for finding the vector sums of various vectors.   How do we know that, if L and S are coupled to give J, the values of J can run from $L + S$ to $|L - S|$ or, if we couple two l vectors of two electrons together to give L, we can have L going from $l_1 + l_2$ to $|l_1 - l_2|$?   We shall look into this matter next; it gives us a good deal of insight into the type of calculation which we make when we consider the coupling of angular-momentum vectors, according to wave mechanics.   To have a specific example in mind, we shall assume that the spin-orbit interaction can be neglected, so that the orbital and spin angular momenta can be separately quantized, and we shall consider the orbital angular momentum arising from two electrons, showing that the value of L can go from $l_1 + l_2$ to $|l_1 - l_2|$.   To be even more specific, we shall assume that the two electrons being coupled together are p electrons, say a $2p$ and a $3p$ (we wish for the moment to avoid possible difficulties with the exclusion principle, so that we do not wish to have two $2p$ electrons, which might involve such problems).

Our problem is then straightforward.   We start with a $2p$ and a $3p$ electron moving in a central field; they might well be moving in the central field arising from the Hartree method, as described in Chap. 9. We are now interested, however, in a better approximation than we were making in the central-field method.   The charge distributions of the $2p$ and $3p$ orbitals are not spherically symmetrical; they have instead the angular dependence described in Sec. 7-3.   Hence they will exert torques on each other.   We shall later calculate the electrostatic interaction energy between them and find the actual quantitative values of these torques.   In the presence of these torques, the separate angular momenta of the two electrons will no longer be quantized; their l's cease to be good quantum numbers, but their resultant L should be quantized, and by the methods of Chap. 10, we expect that this L can be 2, 1, or 0 units, since it is the resultant of l_1 and l_2, each of which is of unit magnitude.   Let us now ask how we can describe this situation in terms of the perturbation theory.

We have seen in Chap. 9 that Hartree's wave functions can be written as products of one-electron wave functions or orbitals of the various electrons.   In our case, where we have two electrons, we have products of two such orbitals. If we denote the $2p$ orbital by $u_{2p,m_{l1}}$ and the $3p$ by $u_{3p,m_{l2}}$, where m_{l1} and m_{l2} are the values of the magnetic quantum numbers in the two cases, such a wave function is

$$u_{2p,m_{l1}}(r_1\theta_1\phi_1)u_{3p,m_{l2}}(r_2\theta_2\phi_2) \qquad (11\text{-}26)$$

We can set up nine such wave functions, for m_{l1} and m_{l2} can each take on the three values 1, 0, -1, and these can be combined in any way; more generally, with any two electrons, we can set up $(2l_1 + 1)(2l_2 + 1)$ wave functions if l_1 and l_2 are the azimuthal quantum numbers of the two electrons. If we were dealing only with central fields, each of these nine wave functions would have the same energy. However, in the presence of the torque between the electrons, they will have different diagonal matrix components of the energy, and there will be nondiagonal matrix components between various ones of these wave functions. It is natural, then, to assume that linear combinations of these nine functions, regarded as unperturbed wave functions, would give better approximations to the true eigenfunctions than the functions (11-26) themselves. In other words, we have a secular problem, with a 9×9 secular equation [more generally one with $(2l_1 + 1)(2l_2 + 1)$ rows and columns] which we must solve. Let us inquire whether the angular-momentum properties can help us in carrying out the solution.

As a first step, we shall find the matrix components of the z component of orbital angular momentum, with respect to the functions of Eq. (11-26). The angular-momentum operator is the sum of the operators for the two electrons. The angular-momentum operator of the first electron, acting on the function (11-26), gives m_{l1} times the function, and that of the second electron gives m_{l2} times the function. Hence the z component of angular momentum of the two electrons, operating on the function (11-26), gives $m_{l1} + m_{l2}$ times the function, showing that this operator is diagonal. We expect to find such a diagonal operator after we have solved Schrödinger's equation and shall name it M_L. We see, then, that the functions (11-26) are already chosen to diagonalize the z component of angular momentum and that the corresponding quantum number is given by

$$M_L = m_{l1} + m_{l2} \qquad (11\text{-}27)$$

On the other hand, if we were to set up the operator representing the square of the angular momentum of the two electrons and let it operate on the function (11-26), we should find that it was not diagonal.

We shall next show that Eq. (11-27) allows us to make a very important statement about the matrix component of the Hamiltonian: if we compute the matrix components of the Hamiltonian (including the interaction between the two electrons) between the functions of Eq. (11-26), we shall find no nondiagonal matrix components, except between two states for which M_L, or $m_{l1} + m_{l2}$, has the same value. This very greatly limits the number of nondiagonal matrix components. Let us see how we prove this statement.

The first point is that the total angular-momentum operator of the two electrons commutes with the Hamiltonian, even when we are including the interactions between the two electrons. This arises physically because the torques they exert on each other are internal to the system, leaving the vector sum of the angular momenta constant. We prove it for a similar case in Appendix 18. Let us call the operator representing the z component of angular momentum, whose eigenvalues are M_L, by the notation $(L_z)_{op}$. Then our statement is that

$$(L_z)_{op}(H)_{op} - (H)_{op}(L_z)_{op} = 0 \qquad (11\text{-}28)$$

Let us now take the matrix component of the operator equation (11-28) between two of the unperturbed functions (11-26) corresponding to different M_L, say M_L and M'_L. When we remember the fact that $(L_z)_{op}$ is diagonal with eigenvalues M_L, the result is

$$(M_L - M'_L)H^0_{ML,ML'} = 0 \qquad (11\text{-}29)$$

where $H^0_{ML,ML'}$ is the nondiagonal matrix component of the Hamiltonian between unperturbed functions characterized by quantum numbers M_L, M'_L. The consequence of Eq. (11-29) is that the nondiagonal matrix component of the Hamiltonian is zero, unless $M_L = M'_L$, which we wished to prove.

The result of this fact is very important. We can make linear combinations of just those unperturbed functions with a given M_L value and diagonalize the matrix of the Hamiltonian with respect to the functions of this particular M_L. In this way the process of solving the secular equation breaks up into separate problems, one for each M_L value, so that it is really very much simpler than it might seem at first sight. In the case we are dealing with, for instance, we shall find that the worst secular equation we meet is 3×3, instead of 9×9. Furthermore, in making linear combinations, we are combining unperturbed functions all of which have the same diagonal matrix component of the diagonal operator $(L_z)_{op}$. Any linear combination of functions of the same M_L will still diagonalize this operator, with the same value of M_L. In other words, $(L_z)_{op}$ will automatically be diagonal in the final functions which we arrive at by diagonalizing the Hamiltonian. Since in solving a secular equation we always end up with as many functions as we start with, we see that the number of states with a given value of M_L in the final result equals the number of unperturbed functions with the same M_L value. We can then make an immediate check as to whether we have the correct number of functions of each M_L value to agree with our vector model, in which the values of the quantum number L should run from $l_1 + l_2$ to $|l_1 - l_2|$. Let us carry out this check for our case of two p electrons.

In Table 11-1 we show the nine unperturbed wave functions, indicated by giving the m_{l1} and m_{l2} values, and the corresponding value of M_L. We see that we have one unperturbed function with $M_L = 2$, two with $M_L = 1$, three with $M_L = 0$, and so on. But if we have the case $L = 2$, we should have $M_L = 2, 1, 0, -1, -2$; for $L = 1$ we should have $M_L = 1, 0, -1$; and for $L = 0$ we should have $M_L = 0$. We have just the right number of states of each M_L. It is easy to show that the same result holds in the general case of two azimuthal quantum numbers l_1 and l_2.

We can draw further conclusions. From our discussion of Sec. 11-3, we know that, after we have solved Schrödinger's equation, we shall find that, not only are $(H)_{op}$ and $(L_z)_{op}$ diagonal, but also $(L^2)_{op}$. Furthermore, we know that for each L value we have a set of $2L + 1$ degenerate states, characterized by values of M_L running from L to $-L$. Hence we may conclude that the following things will be true in the case we are considering: The first state in Table 11-1, corresponding to $M_L = 2$, must arise from $L = 2$. Since there is no secular equation to be solved

Table 11-1. Unperturbed States for Combination of Two p Electrons

M_L	m_{l1}	m_{l2}
2	1	1
1	1	0
1	0	1
0	1	-1
0	0	0
0	-1	1
-1	0	-1
-1	-1	0
-2	-1	-1

in this case, it must be that $(L^2)_{op}$ is diagonal for this unperturbed wave function, its eigenvalue being $L(L + 1) = 2(3) = 6$. Furthermore, if we find the diagonal matrix component of the Hamiltonian for this state, this must give us the energy of the state $L = 2$, or the D state. Next, with the two states with $M_L = 1$, we must solve a secular equation with two rows and columns to diagonalize the Hamiltonian. When we have done this, we shall also automatically diagonalize $(L^2)_{op}$ and one of the states must have an eigenvalue for this operator of $2(3)$, while the other must have an eigenvalue of $1(2)$, corresponding to the case $L = 1$. The eigenvalue of the Hamiltonian for the first of these two states, that with $L = 2$, must be identical with the energy of the state $L = 2$, and $M_L = 2$. The eigenvalue of the other state must be that of the P state, with $L = 1$.

We could find these two perturbed states by solving a quadratic secular equation; but this is not necessary, if we wish only to find the energies. For we can use the diagonal sum rule, Eq. (5-39). It is easy to compute the diagonal matrix components of the Hamiltonian for the two unperturbed states with $M_L = 1$. But the sum of these two matrix components must equal the sum of the eigenvalues of the states for $L = 2$ and $L = 1$. Since we have already found the eigenvalue of the state for $L = 2$ from the state with $M_L = 2$, we can subtract and find the eigenvalue of the other state, with $L = 1$. If we wish to find the eigenfunctions as well as the eigenvalues, we must really set up the proper linear combinations of the two states with the same M_L to diagonalize the Hamiltonian; but it is a great help in doing this to know the eigenvalues to start with, which we do from the sum rule. We shall find that one linear combination of the two unperturbed states corresponds to $L = 2$, another to $L = 1$; we cannot assume that either unperturbed state by itself is connected with a given L value.

We can proceed in a similar way with the three states for $M_L = 0$. After the secular problem between these states is solved and the matrix of the Hamiltonian is diagonalized, one of the states must correspond to $L = 2$, one to $L = 1$, and one to $L = 0$. Since we know the eigenvalues of the Hamiltonian for $L = 2$ and $L = 1$, we can use the sum rule to find that for $L = 0$, so that the cubic secular equation does not have to be solved if we are interested only in the eigenvalues. If we have found the eigenfunctions as well, we shall find that they diagonalize $(L^2)_{op}$ as well as $(H)_{op}$, having eigenvalues of $(L^2)_{op}$ of $2(3)$, $1(2)$, and $0(1)$, respectively.

The fact that $(L^2)_{op}$ as well as $(H)_{op}$ is diagonal for the final eigenfunctions allows us to find the eigenfunctions in a way which is sometimes simpler than diagonalizing the Hamiltonian: if we diagonalize $(L^2)_{op}$ instead, we must come out with the same eigenfunctions.[1] We can regard this in a slightly different light. We may write the vector equation $\mathbf{L} = \mathbf{l}_1 + \mathbf{l}_2$, where $\mathbf{l}_1$ and $\mathbf{l}_2$ now represent the vector angular momenta of the two electrons and $\mathbf{L}$ represents their resultant. We then have

$$L^2 = l_1^2 + l_2^2 + 2(\mathbf{l}_1 \cdot \mathbf{l}_2) \qquad (11\text{-}30)$$

We can convert this into an operator equation and allow it to operate on the wave functions of the type of Eq. (11-26). Since $(l_1^2)_{op}$ operates only on the wave function of the first electron, we find that it is diagonal, multiplying the wave function by $l_1(l_1 + 1)$, and similarly $(l_2^2)_{op}$ is diago-

[1] See M. H. Johnson, Jr., *Phys. Rev.*, **39**:197 (1932), for suggestion and application of this method.

nal, with an eigenvalue of $l_2(l_2 + 1)$. These diagonal values are independent of m_{l1} and m_{l2} and hence hold for any one of our $(2l_1 + 1)(2l_2 + 1)$ unperturbed functions or for any linear combination of them. When we are dealing with the unperturbed functions, $(L^2)_{op}$ is not diagonal and consequently $(l_1 \cdot l_2)_{op}$ is not diagonal. After we have diagonalized $(L^2)_{op}$, however, Eq. (11-30) shows us that $(l_1 \cdot l_2)_{op}$ will also be diagonal. The matrix components of $(l_1 \cdot l_2)_{op}$ for a set of functions like those of Eq. (11-26) are simpler to set up than those of the Hamiltonian, and it is often more convenient to diagonalize this operator than the Hamiltonian; once the linear combinations have been found which diagonalize $(l_1 \cdot l_2)_{op}$, they will diagonalize the Hamiltonian as well. This does not imply at all that the interaction between the two electrons has the simple form $(l_1 \cdot l_2)$, proportional to the cosine of the angle between the angular momenta. It does imply, however, that any internal torque will have an energy which is some function of the angle between the angular momenta, so that, if the Hamiltonian is diagonalized, the cosine of the angle will also be diagonal.

There are still further uses which can be made of the angular momentum, resulting from the step-down operators of Eq. (11-7). We can set up a step-down operator related to the total angular momentum, not merely to that of a single electron. Such an operator, operating, for instance, on the function for $M_L = 2$, $L = 2$, of Table 11-1, will give the function for $M_L = 1$, $L = 2$ directly. We do not need to solve any secular equation at all to find this eigenfunction. Similarly, if we operate on this function for $M_L = 1$, $L = 2$, we can get that for $M_L = 0$, $L = 2$, and so on. Thus we can find all the functions of a given L value, once one of them is known. We can then proceed easily to find the functions for $L = 1$. Out of the two functions for $M_L = 1$, the step-down operator has given us that corresponding to $L = 2$. But there can be only two eigenfunctions for this M_L value, orthogonal to each other, and linear combinations of the original unperturbed functions. If we then look for a linear combination of these two functions orthogonal to the known function for $L = 2$, it must be that of $L = 1$. We can then apply step-down operators to this function to find the functions for $L = 1$, $M_L = 0$, and $M_L = -1$. Finally we can find a linear combination of the three functions for $M_L = 0$, orthogonal to the known functions for $L = 2$ and $L = 1$; it must give the function for $L = 0$.†

We have sketched very briefly a number of the uses of angular-momentum operators in solving such problems as we have in the coupling of two angular-momentum vectors. There are still other, very powerful applications. We shall, however, postpone the use of these angular-momen-

† See N. M. Gray and L. A. Wills, *Phys. Rev.*, **38**:248 (1931), for suggestion and applications of this method.

tum methods until Chap. 20 (Vol. II), where we explain and illustrate them and give references to the literature. The simple diagonal sum method applied to the problem of diagonalizing the Hamiltonian will give us the energy values of the multiplets, in a great majority of the cases we are interested in, and we shall concentrate on the use of that method for a number of chapters, using it to derive as many results as possible, before we come back to these more powerful methods based on angular-momentum vectors, in the second volume.

11-5. The Nature of Spin-orbitals. In the preceding section, we have been considering the coupling of two orbital angular-momentum vectors, without speaking about the spin. The case of orbital angular momentum is simple and straightforward: we know how to calculate the matrix components of angular momentum, we can understand why the Hamiltonian should depend on the angle between the two angular-momentum vectors, and there are no unfamiliar problems connected with the solution. On the other hand, so far we have not explained enough properties of the spin to allow us to carry out the corresponding operations with the spin angular momentum. We shall not go into all the details of the spin until Chap. 23 (Vol. II), where we discuss Dirac's theory of the electron, which gives a thorough explanation of the properties of the spin. In the meantime, we must anticipate and state the properties which we wish to use more or less in the form of postulates, expecting to justify them later on the basis of Dirac's theory.

Before we go further, we must ask how to incorporate the existence of the spin into the wave function for a single electron. The first thing to notice in this connection is that there are really four things to be measured in order to determine an electron's behavior: not merely the coordinates x, y, and z, but also the component of spin along a fixed axis. This is shown particularly clearly by the famous Stern-Gerlach[1] experiment of atomic beams. These workers, in the early 1920s, wished to demonstrate the space quantization of atoms experimentally. They produced a beam of atoms of silver vapor, by evaporating them from an oven and suitably collimating the beam of relatively slow atoms. They then passed these atoms through a transverse magnetic field, which would be expected to space-quantize the angular momenta transverse to the direction of motion, and then through a transverse inhomogeneous magnetic field in the same direction, which would exert a transverse force on each atom, since its north pole would be in a stronger field than its south pole, or vice versa. Atoms with space quantization in opposite directions would be accelerated in opposite directions, and they were observed to split into two beams, which could be detected separately, after traveling

[1] O. Stern, Z. *Physik*, **7**:249 (1921); W. Gerlach and O. Stern, Z. *Physik*, **8**:110 (1922); **9**:349, 353 (1922).

a sufficiently long distance. This experiment provides a method of observing separately the atoms with different orientations of their magnetic moments. In silver, where the only electron outside closed shells is an s electron, we are observing directly the spin orientation in this way.

We have, then, a method of observing which direction the spin is oriented in. We could, for instance, let one of the two beams pass through a small aperture, and on the far side we should have a wave packet consisting of atoms all located in a small region of space, and at the same time with a given spin orientation. We must then enlarge our ideas of the wave function: the wave function must be a function, not only of the coordinates, but also of the orientation of the spin. Thus, in the Stern-Gerlach experiment, the wave function associated with upward-pointing spins is large in that region of space where the beam formed from upward-pointing spins is located, while that associated with downward-pointing spins is large in the region of space where the beam of downward-pointing spins is located. It is useful to employ a wave function for a single electron which is a function of four variables: x, y, z, the ordinary space coordinates, and a fourth quantity which we shall call s, which can take on only two values, one associated with upward-pointing spins, the other with downward-pointing spins. If these two values are called $\frac{1}{2}$ and $-\frac{1}{2}$, respectively (the angular momenta of the electron along the axis in the two cases, in multiples of $\hbar$), we may say that the wave function is $\psi(x,y,z,s)$, which really consists of two separate functions of x, y, z, namely, $\psi(x,y,z,\frac{1}{2})$ and $\psi(x,y,z,-\frac{1}{2})$. As we have just seen, we interpret $\psi^*(x,y,z,\frac{1}{2})\psi(x,y,z,\frac{1}{2})\,dx\,dy\,dz$ as giving the probability of finding the electron with upward-pointing spin in $dx\,dy\,dz$ and $\psi^*(x,y,z,-\frac{1}{2})\psi(x,y,z,-\frac{1}{2})\,dx\,dy\,dz$ as the probability of finding the electron with downward-pointing spin in $dx\,dy\,dz$. Since the probability of finding the electron somewhere with some spin is unity, the normalization condition must be

$$\Sigma(s)\int\psi^*(x,y,z,s)\psi(x,y,z,s)\,dx\,dy\,dz = 1 \qquad (11\text{-}31)$$

where the summation is over the two values $s = \frac{1}{2}$, $-\frac{1}{2}$.

Now let us ask what type of function $\psi(x,y,z,s)$ we should expect for an electron moving in a central field, with no spin-orbit interaction or other magnetic forces. Since there is no interaction between the coordinates and the spin, we should expect that the wave function would separate into the product of a function of coordinates and a function of spin. The function of coordinates would be expected to be the usual type, $u_{nlm_l}(r\theta\phi)$. As for the function of spin, we should expect it to have a quantum number m_s, which can take on the values $\frac{1}{2}$, $-\frac{1}{2}$. Let us denote this function of spin by the symbol $v_{m_s}(s)$. What, then, do we expect the function $v_{\frac{1}{2}}(s)$ to represent? If $m_s = \frac{1}{2}$, we certainly expect that the spin orientation will be along the $+z$ axis. In other words, we expect to find

$$v_{1/2}(1/2) = 1 \qquad v_{1/2}(-1/2) = 0 \qquad (11\text{-}32)$$

so that in this case the wave function $u_{nlm_l}(r\theta\phi)v_{1/2}(s)$ will be zero if $s = -1/2$, indicating no chance of finding the electron with spin pointing down, whereas if $s = 1/2$ and the spin points upward, the wave function equals $u_{nlm_l}(r\theta\phi)$, which leads to the probability of finding the electron, with spin $1/2$, at given points of space. Similarly we expect to have

$$v_{-1/2}(1/2) = 0 \qquad v_{-1/2}(-1/2) = 1 \qquad (11\text{-}33)$$

so that, if $m_s = -1/2$, there is certainty that the spin orientation is along $-z$. Following Pauli, we often use the notation

$$v_{1/2}(s) = \alpha(s) \qquad v_{-1/2}(s) = \beta(s) \qquad (11\text{-}34)$$

The type of central-field wave function which we expect to use is then given by

$$u_{nlm_l}(r\theta\phi)v_{m_s}(s) \qquad (11\text{-}35)$$

where v is defined in Eqs. (11-32) and (11-33). A function like that of Eq. (11-35) is called a spin-orbital. It represents a stationary state in which the quantum numbers n, l, m_l of the orbital motion are definitely known, and in which the quantum number m_s is determined as well. We should then properly build up a wave function for an atom, not merely as a product of orbitals such as is given in Eq. (11-26), but as a product of spin-orbitals. And in studying a configuration, we are interested in all the product functions corresponding to different values, not merely of the m_l's of the various electrons, but also of the m_s's. We see, then, that our treatment of Sec. 11-4 was incomplete, in that we took no account of the spin functions.

We can now understand the interpretation of Eqs. (11-25), giving the matrix components of the x, y, and z components of the spin angular momentum of a single electron. They are to be interpreted in terms of spin operators, operating on the functions α and β. Thus, by analogy with Eq. (11-7), we expect to find

$$
\begin{aligned}
(S_x)_{op}\alpha(s) &= \tfrac{1}{2}\beta(s) & (S_x)_{op}\beta(s) &= \tfrac{1}{2}\alpha(s) \\
(S_y)_{op}\alpha(s) &= \frac{i}{2}\beta(s) & (S_y)_{op}\beta(s) &= -\frac{i}{2}\alpha(s) \\
(S_z)_{op}\alpha(s) &= \tfrac{1}{2}\alpha(s) & (S_z)_{op}\beta(s) &= -\tfrac{1}{2}\beta(s) \\
(S_x + iS_y)_{op}\alpha(s) &= 0 & (S_x + iS_y)_{op}\beta(s) &= \alpha(s) \\
(S_x - iS_y)_{op}\alpha(s) &= \beta(s) & (S_x - iS_y)_{op}\beta(s) &= 0
\end{aligned}
\qquad (11\text{-}36)
$$

To derive the first equation of Eq. (11-36), for example, we start with the first equation of Eq. (11-7), replace l by $1/2$, m by $1/2$, u_{nlm} by $\alpha(s)$, and u_{nlm-1} by $\beta(s)$. The other equations follow in similar ways.

We can follow the general lead of Eq. (11-31) and set up a rule for finding the matrix component of an operator which may involve both orbital and spin parts, between two spin-orbitals. This rule is

$$F_{nlm_lm_s, n'l'm_l'm_s'} = \Sigma(s) \int u^*_{nlm_l}(r\theta\phi) v^*_{m_s}(s)$$
$$\times (F)_{op} u_{n'l'm_l'}(r\theta\phi) v_{m_s'}(s) \, dx \, dy \, dz \quad (11\text{-}37)$$

In applying this rule, we have to know how to find the effect of operating with $(F)_{op}$ on the spin function as well as on the orbital function. For the case of the spin angular-momentum operators, we have just set up the definition, in Eq. (11-36). We shall be able to work out the other operators we shall meet, by use of Eq. (11-36).

Let us then apply Eq. (11-37), and Eq. (11-36), and see how to interpret Eq. (11-25). For instance, let us find the matrix component of $(S_x)_{op}$ between two states. Since this operator affects only the spin function, we see that Eq. (11-37) can be rewritten in the form

$$(S_x)_{nlm_lm_s, n'l'm_l'm_s'} = \int u^*_{nlm_l}(r\theta\phi) u_{n'l'm_l'}(r\theta\phi) \, dx \, dy \, dz$$
$$\times \Sigma(s) v^*_{m_s}(S_x)_{op} v_{m_s'} \quad (11\text{-}38)$$

The integral is zero unless $n' = n$, $l' = l$, $m_{l'} = m_l$, on account of orthogonality of the space orbitals, in which case it is unity. This is a special example of the general relation that an operator affecting only the spins has no nonvanishing matrix components except between two states for which the orbital quantum numbers are identical. We then have the case

$$(S_x)_{nlm_l\frac{1}{2}, nlm_l-\frac{1}{2}} = \Sigma(s) \alpha^*(s)(S_x)_{op}\beta(s)$$
$$= \Sigma(s) \alpha^*(s)\frac{1}{2}\alpha(s) = \frac{1}{2} \quad (11\text{-}39)$$

where, in the sum over s, we note that, when $s = \frac{1}{2}$, $\alpha(s) = 1$ and, when $s = -\frac{1}{2}$, $\alpha(s) = 0$, so that the latter case does not contribute to the summation. Thus this result agrees with Eq. (11-25).

From the result we have just proved we note that

$$\Sigma(s) \alpha^*(s)\alpha(s) = 1 \quad (11\text{-}40)$$

so that in a sense the functions v_{m_s} are normalized. Also, we see at once from Eqs. (11-32) and (11-33) that

$$\Sigma(s) \alpha^*(s)\beta(s) = 0 \quad (11\text{-}41)$$

so that the functions α and β are orthogonal. As a result of this, two spin-orbitals corresponding to opposite spins are automatically orthogonal to each other. These results can be combined in the statement

$$\Sigma(s) v^*_{m_s}(s) v_{m_s'}(s) = \delta_{m_sm_s'} \quad (11\text{-}42)$$

11-6. Use of Angular-momentum Operators in Cases Including Spins.
We have now learned the general rules for incorporating the spin into

the one-electron functions, rules which we shall justify later in terms of Dirac's electron theory. Now let us use these methods to study the coupling of angular-momentum vectors, including spins, in complex atoms. There are several rules regarding the commutation of angular-momentum operators, and of the Hamiltonian, which we can prove very simply, and which we need in our discussion. If we have a Hamiltonian involving the coordinates only, independent of spins, as we shall have if all magnetic effects are disregarded, then the Hamiltonian will commute with all spin angular-momentum operators. If the Hamiltonian involves no external torques, then as before it will commute with the orbital angular-momentum operator of the whole atom. Furthermore, the orbital and spin angular-momentum operators will commute with each other. Thus in this case, where we are disregarding spin-orbit coupling, we can simultaneously quantize the orbital and spin angular-momenta separately. That is, we have, not only the quantum numbers L, M_L, which we discussed in Sec. 11-4, but also S, M_S. There will be matrix components of the orbital angular-momentum operators only between two wave functions with identical values of the spin quantum numbers of each electron and matrix components of the spin angular-momentum operators only between two wave functions with identical values of the orbital quantum numbers of each electron. The matrix components will have the form already given in Eq. (11-8), with the same form for those representing the total spin angular momentum of the whole atom. The Hamiltonian will have nonvanishing matrix components only between two states which have not only the same M_L value, as in Eq. (11-29), but also the same M_S value. We find, then, that if we analyze the many-electron wave functions according to both their M_L and M_S values, we break down the secular equation into a great many separate equations and can use the diagonal sum rule very effectively in finding the energies of the various multiplets. We shall now give examples of how these methods can be used in the configurations found in actual spectra. We shall confine ourselves to two-electron atoms, but the same methods can be extended easily to cases with more than two electrons.

The first example which we shall take is the very simple configuration $2s2s$, which according to the vector model leads to ^1S and ^3S. This is particularly simple because there is no orbital angular momentum to be considered. Let us make a table like Table 11-1 to justify the rule of vector addition in this case, in which the two spins of $\frac{1}{2}$ unit each combine to give $S = 1, 0$. We have only four unperturbed functions given by the four combinations of $m_{s1} = \pm\frac{1}{2}$, $m_{s2} = \pm\frac{1}{2}$. These four functions are shown in Table 11-2. For $M_S = 1$ we have one state, for $M_S = 0$ we have two, and for $M_S = -1$ one. This is what would be expected for the two vectors with $S = 1$ and 0. The state with $M_S = 1$

Table 11-2. Unperturbed States for Configuration 1s2s

M_S	m_{s1}	m_{s2}
1	$\frac{1}{2}$	$\frac{1}{2}$
0	$\frac{1}{2}$	$-\frac{1}{2}$
0	$-\frac{1}{2}$	$\frac{1}{2}$
-1	$-\frac{1}{2}$	$-\frac{1}{2}$

must belong to the triplet, $S = 1$. The diagonal matrix component of the Hamiltonian for this state will give the triplet energy. The two states for $M_S = 0$ must lead to the states of $S = 1$ and 0 with $M_S = 0$. Hence, by the sum rule, the sum of the diagonal matrix components of these states must equal the sum of the triplet and singlet energies, from which the singlet energy can be found by subtraction.

A slightly more complicated case is that of a configuration 1s2p. In this case we have 12 unperturbed states, as shown in Table 11-3. We

Table 11-3. Unperturbed States for Configuration 1s2p

M_L	M_S	m_{l2}	m_{s1}	m_{s2}
1	1	1	$\frac{1}{2}$	$\frac{1}{2}$
1	0	1	$\frac{1}{2}$	$-\frac{1}{2}$
1	0	1	$-\frac{1}{2}$	$\frac{1}{2}$
1	-1	1	$-\frac{1}{2}$	$-\frac{1}{2}$
0	1	0	$\frac{1}{2}$	$\frac{1}{2}$
0	0	0	$\frac{1}{2}$	$-\frac{1}{2}$
0	0	0	$-\frac{1}{2}$	$\frac{1}{2}$
0	-1	0	$-\frac{1}{2}$	$-\frac{1}{2}$
-1	1	-1	$\frac{1}{2}$	$\frac{1}{2}$
-1	0	-1	$\frac{1}{2}$	$-\frac{1}{2}$
-1	0	-1	$-\frac{1}{2}$	$\frac{1}{2}$
-1	-1	-1	$-\frac{1}{2}$	$-\frac{1}{2}$

now have both M_L and M_S to consider, though M_L arises from one elec-tron only. The vector model tells us that we should have ^3P and ^1P multiplets arising from this configuration. The ^3P should have nine components, with $M_L = 1, 0, -1, M_S = 1, 0, -1$, combined in any way and ^1P should have three, with $M_L = 1, 0, -1$ and $M_S = 0$. In Table 11-3 we have just the right number of states for each set of values of M_L, M_S. The sum rule would allow us very easily to find the energies of both multiplets. Thus, for instance, the state with $M_L = 1, M_S = 1$ must belong to ^3P. There is only one state with these M's, and conse-quently the diagonal matrix component of the Hamiltonian for this state must give the ^3P energy. Again, the two states with $M_L = 1, M_S = 0$

must result in components of both ^3P and ^1P.   We can find the sum of the diagonal matrix components of the Hamiltonian for these two unperturbed states, subtract the known energy of ^3P, and get that of ^1P. There are numerous other combinations which could be used, and each must give the same result.

In Chap. 13, we shall go over these examples, and other more complicated ones, and shall really carry them through, computing the matrix components of the Hamiltonian, and finding the energies of the various multiplets.   Before we do this, however, there is a situation to be considered which we shall take up in the next chapter.   We can point out this situation by considering the configuration $1s2s$, treated in Table 11-2. Here we have four unperturbed wave functions, differing only in the spin functions.   But the Hamiltonian depends only on coordinates.   Hence, if we proceed according to the methods we have outlined, we should find the same diagonal matrix component of the Hamiltonian for each of the four functions; in applying Eq. (11-37) to the calculation of the diagonal matrix component, the spin functions will drop out, and the energy will come only from an integral over the functions of coordinates, which will be identical in each of the four cases.   Hence we should conclude that the ^1S and ^3S multiplets should have the same energy.   This is only natural; why should they differ in energy, when the only difference between them is the orientation of the spins, and the energy does not depend on the spins?   This paradox could not be resolved in the older quantum theory, where it was an outstanding puzzle why the energy should depend strongly on the spin orientation, as we have seen it to do in Fig. 10-4.   The paradox was removed in an unexpected way in wave mechanics by study of the symmetry properties of the wave function, and we take up these properties in the next chapter, using our case of $1s2s$ as an illustration.

PROBLEMS

1. Consider three p functions, corresponding to the same n value and to $m_l = 1$, 0, -1; denote these by u_1, u_0, u_{-1}, respectively.   Use Eq. (11-7) to find the effect of operating with $(L_x)_{op}$, $(L_y)_{op}$, $(L_z)_{op}$ on each of these.   Then use the law of matrix multiplication to find the effect of operating with $(L^2)_{op} = (L_x^2)_{op} + (L_y^2)_{op} + (L_z^2)_{op}$ on each of these.   Prove in this way that these functions diagonalize the operator $(L^2)_{op}$, with a diagonal matrix component $l(l + 1) = 1(2) = 2$.

2. Proceed in the same way as in Prob. 1, with the five d functions corresponding to $m_l = 2, 1, 0, -1, -2$.

3. Consider the unperturbed wave functions for the case of two nonequivalent p electrons, as given in Table 11-1.   Denote these functions by two subscripts, as u_{11}, u_{10}, u_{01}, ...   Use Eq. (11-7) to find the effect on these functions of the operators $(L_x)_{op} = (L_{x1} + L_{x2})_{op}$, $(L_y)_{op} = (L_{y1} + L_{y2})_{op}$, $(L_z)_{op} = (L_{z1} + L_{z2})_{op}$, where $(L_{x1})_{op}$ is the operator corresponding to the first electron, $(L_{x2})_{op}$ to the second elec-

tron, etc. Find the effect of each of these operators on the functions u_{11}, u_{10}, u_{01}
Use this information to find the effect of operating with $(L^2)_{op}$ on the function u_{11}
and prove that this function is an eigenfunction of the operator, with the eigenvalue
$L(L + 1) = 2(3) = 6$ characteristic of a D function, with $L = 2$.

4. Set up a step-down operator which, operating on the first function of Table 11-1
u_{11}, which is the eigenfunction of the D state, $L = 2$, corresponding to $M_L = 2$, will
yield the D function for $M_L = 1$. Show that this resulting function is a linear com
bination of the functions u_{10} and u_{01} of Table 11-1.

5. Set up a combination of the functions u_{10} and u_{01} of Table 11-1 which is orthogo
nal to the function for $L = 2$, $M_L = 1$, described in Prob. 4. This must be an eigen
function of the operator $(L^2)_{op}$ corresponding to a P state, or $L = 1$. Prove that this
is the case.

6. Apply the step-down operator to the function for $L = 1$, $M_L = 1$, determined in
Prob. 5, and also to the function for $L = 2$, $M_L = 1$, to get the functions for $L =$
and 2, $M_L = 0$. Set up a linear combination of the three functions for $M_L = 0$ from
Table 11-1, orthogonal to the functions so obtained for $L = 1, 2$. This must be the
eigenfunction for the S state, $L = 0$. Prove that it diagonalizes $(L^2)_{op}$, with an eigen
value appropriate to an S state.

7. A sum rule applies to the operator $(L^2)_{op}$: the sum of the diagonal matrix com
ponents of this operator is not affected by making a unitary transformation. Check
this sum rule by the functions of Table 11-1, and the functions found in Prob. 6, for
$M_L = 0$; that is, prove that the sum of the diagonal matrix components of the operator
for the three functions of Table 11-1 for $M_L = 0$ equals the sum of the eigenvalues
$2(3) + 1(2) + 0(1)$, found from the eigenfunctions of the D, P, and S states.

8. Use the spin operators on the functions of Table 11-2 to prove that the first and
fourth functions are triplets and to set up the linear combinations of the second and
third functions to give the eigenfunctions for the triplet and singlet states.

9. Use both orbital and spin angular-momentum operators, as in the preceding
problems, to set up the linear combinations of the unperturbed states for the con
figuration $1s2p$, given in Table 11-3, corresponding to the ^3P, ^1P functions for the
various M_L, M_S values.

12

Antisymmetry of Wave Functions and the Determinantal Method

12-1. Wave Functions and Matrix Components of the Hamiltonian for the Two-electron System. We have mentioned at the end of the preceding chapter that there is a very important part of atomic theory which we have not yet touched on at all. It relates to the symmetry properties of many-electron wave functions, when the coordinates of two electrons are interchanged. This in turn is closely connected with Pauli's exclusion principle, as was realized very early in the development of wave mechanics by Heisenberg[1] and Dirac.[2] Furthermore, it leads to the understanding of the way in which spin angular-momentum vectors can interact by means of torques of electrostatic origin. We shall discuss these interrelated problems in the present chapter.

We start, in the present section, with the construction of wave functions for a two-electron atom, as a simple case, and the actual calculation of the matrix components of the Hamiltonian for these wave functions. As an example to introduce the ideas, we take the configuration $1s2s$, leading to multiplets ^1S and ^3S, which we have been discussing in Sec. 11-6, and particularly in Table 11-2. For the electron with quantum numbers $1s$, we can have m_s equal to either $\frac{1}{2}$ or $-\frac{1}{2}$. We can, then, build up two spin orbitals for this electron: $u_{1s}(r)\alpha(s)$ and $u_{1s}(r)\beta(s)$, where we symbolize the $1s$ wave function by u_{1s}, and where we use Pauli's notation for the spin function. Similarly for the $2s$ electron we have two spin-orbitals, $u_{2s}(r)\alpha(s)$ and $u_{2s}(r)\beta(s)$. We can combine these in four ways, as in Table 11-2. We start with the approximation in which the two electrons move independently of each other and then introduce their interaction as a perturbation. We recall that, if we have two independent systems, the wave function describing them both is the product of the individual wave functions. That is, for our combined sys-

---

[1] W. Heisenberg, *Z. Physik*, **38**:411 (1926); **39**:499 (1926); **41**:239 (1927).
[2] P. A. M. Dirac, *Proc. Roy. Soc. (London)*, **A112**:661 (1926).

tem we can use wave functions like, for instance, $u_{1s}(r_1)\alpha(s_1)u_{2s}(r_2)\alpha(s_2)$. We can make up four such functions, in which the electron of coordinates r_1 is in the $1s$ state, that with coordinates r_2 is in the $2s$ state with the four possible spin combinations. But in addition, corresponding to each of these functions, there is another equally valid function entirely disregarded in Chap. 11, in which the electron of coordinates r_1 is in the $2s$ state, that of coordinates r_2 in the $1s$ state. Thus, if the function written above is called U_1, we have a related function U_2, given by

$$U_1 = u_{1s}(r_1)\alpha(s_1)u_{2s}(r_2)\alpha(s_2)$$
$$U_2 = u_{2s}(r_1)\alpha(s_1)u_{1s}(r_2)\alpha(s_2) \qquad (12\text{-}1)$$

We have in all eight unperturbed functions, not four as before. We must now set up matrix components of the Hamiltonian between these eight functions and find linear combinations of them which will diagonalize the Hamiltonian matrix.

We shall assume the Hamiltonian of Eq. (9-6), containing terms arising from the kinetic energy of each electron, their potential energy in the field of the nucleus of charge Z units, and their repulsive Coulomb interaction with each other. In atomic units, this is

$$(H)_{\text{op}} = -\nabla_1^2 - \nabla_2^2 - \frac{2Z}{r_1} - \frac{2Z}{r_2} + \frac{2}{r_{12}}$$
$$= f_1 + f_2 + g_{12} \qquad (12\text{-}2)$$

where $\qquad f_1 = -\nabla_1^2 - \dfrac{2Z}{r_1} \qquad f_2 = -\nabla_2^2 - \dfrac{2Z}{r_2} \qquad g_{12} = \dfrac{2}{r_{12}}$

Here the Laplacian ∇_1^2 operates on the coordinates of the first electron, ∇_2^2 on those of the second, r_1 and r_2 are the distances of each electron from the nucleus, and r_{12} is the distance between the electrons. The characteristic of the f's is that each one depends on the coordinates of a single electron only, whereas g depends on the coordinates of a pair of electrons. We note that the Hamiltonian of Eq. (12-2) includes only electrostatic terms, not magnetic and spin-orbit interaction terms; we shall disregard these magnetic and spin-orbit effects in the present chapter and shall concentrate on the electrostatic part of the energy.

Let us now apply our rule of Eq. (11-37) for calculating the matrix components of various operators. We start by finding H_{11}, the diagonal matrix component of energy for the first state of Eq. (12-1). This is

$$\Sigma(s_1,s_2)\int u_{1s}^*(r_1)\alpha^*(s_1)u_{2s}^*(r_2)\alpha^*(s_2)(H)_{\text{op}}u_{1s}(r_1)\alpha(s_1)$$
$$\times u_{2s}(r_2)\alpha(s_2)\ dv_1\ dv_2 \qquad (12\text{-}3)$$

where the integration is over the coordinates of the two electrons and the summation is over their spins. We may remove the factor $\alpha^*(s_1)\alpha^*(s_2)\alpha(s_1)\alpha(s_2)$ from under the integral sign and perform the sum mation over s_1 and s_2 separately, since $(H)_{op}$ does not operate on the spin functions. We get a contribution only from the case where $s_1 = \frac{1}{2}$, $s_2 = \frac{1}{2}$, in which case we have unity. Then H_{11} reduces to an integral over coordinates, which is

$$H_{11} = \int u_{1s}^*(r_1) u_{2s}^*(r_2)(f_1 + f_2 + g_{12}) u_{1s}(r_1) u_{2s}(r_2) \, dv_1 \, dv_2 \quad (12\text{-}4)$$

The operator f_1 operates only on the coordinates of the first electron; hence, in the contribution from this term, the integration over the coordinates of the second electron can be carried out separately, and on account of the normalization of the u's, we find that this term in the operator contributes to the integral the amount

$$\int u_{1s}^*(r_1) f_1 u_{1s}(r_1) \, dv_1 = (1s/f/1s) \quad (12\text{-}5)$$

where $(1s/f/1s)$ is a convenient symbol for this integral, already used in Eq. (9-8). Similarly the term f_2 contributes

$$\int u_{2s}^*(r_2) f_2 u_{2s}(r_2) \, dv_2 = (2s/f/2s) \quad (12\text{-}6)$$

The function arising from g_{12} cannot be further simplified and may be abbreviated

$$\int u_{1s}^*(r_1) u_{2s}^*(r_2) g_{12} u_{1s}(r_1) u_{2s}(r_2) \, dv_1 \, dv_2 = (1s,2s/g/1s,2s) \quad (12\text{-}7)$$

as in Eq. (9-9). Then we have

$$H_{11} = (1s/f/1s) + (2s/f/2s) + (1s,2s/g/1s,2s) \quad (12\text{-}8)$$

We readily find that H_{22} has the same value.

Let us next consider the nondiagonal matrix component of energy, H_{12}. We find that the spin summation can be carried out as before, and we are left with

$$H_{12} = \int u_{1s}^*(r_1) u_{2s}^*(r_2)(H)_{op} u_{2s}(r_1) u_{1s}(r_2) \, dv_1 \, dv_2 \quad (12\text{-}9)$$

When we substitute the value of $(H)_{op}$ from Eq. (12-2), we see that the terms f_1 and f_2 contribute nothing, for we shall assume that u_{1s} and u_{2s} are orthogonal to each other, as we have mentioned in Sec. 9-4. Thus, for f_1, we have

$$\int u_{1s}^*(r_1) f_1 u_{2s}(r_1) \, dv_1 \int u_{2s}^*(r_2) u_{1s}(r_2) \, dv_2 \quad (12\text{-}10)$$

in which the second factor is zero. We are left only with the term arising from g_{12}, which is

$$H_{12} = \int u_{1s}^*(r_1) u_{2s}^*(r_2) g_{12} u_{2s}(r_1) u_{1s}(r_2) \, dv_1 \, dv_2$$
$$= (1s,2s/g/2s,1s) \quad (12\text{-}11)$$

An integral of the form of Eq. (12-11), in which the order of the one-electron functions is interchanged on the right side of the integral from what it is on the left, is called an exchange integral.

It is worthwhile inquiring about the physical meaning of the various terms in our matrix components. Thus, $(1s/f/1s)$ is the sum of the kinetic energy of the $1s$ orbital and its potential energy in the field of the nucleus; similarly with $(2s/f/2s)$. The expression $(1s,2s/g/1s,2s)$ is the Coulomb interaction energy of a distribution of charge given by $u_{1s}^*(r_1)u_{1s}(r_1)$ with another distribution given by $u_{2s}^*(r_2)u_{2s}(r_2)$; we find the integral by taking the charge from the first distribution located in dv_1, multiplying by the charge of the second distribution located in dv_2, dividing by the distance between, and integrating, which is just the way to compute the electrostatic repulsive energy. It is ordinarily called a Coulomb integral. In a similar way the exchange integral of Eq. (12-11) is the electrostatic interaction of the charge density $u_{1s}^*(r_1)u_{2s}(r_1)$, which is called the exchange charge, with the distribution $u_{2s}^*(r_2)u_{1s}(r_2)$, which is the complex conjugate of the first charge distribution, or in the present case, where the u's are real, which equals the first charge distribution. It is interesting to point out that such an exchange integral must always be positive. In electrostatics, we can convert the electrostatic interaction of a charge distribution with itself into the integral over all space of the square of the electric field arising from this charge distribution, which necessarily is positive. This represents merely a transformation of the integral by integration by parts, and we show in Appendix 19 that this same argument can be applied here, to prove that the exchange integral is positive.

We now have found the matrix components H_{11}, H_{12}, H_{22} of the Hamiltonian between the two functions of Eq. (12-1), which differ from each other by a transposition of the electron coordinates. We could go on to find all the matrix components between the eight unperturbed functions, but this does not prove to be the most useful step to take next. It proves to be the case that if we set up linear combinations of U_1 and U_2 which diagonalize the Hamiltonian, proceed similarly with the next two functions U_3 and U_4, and so on, then the whole problem of solving the secular equations with eight unperturbed functions is greatly simplified. Let us then proceed with this problem of two rows and two columns, using U_1 and U_2 as unperturbed functions.

12-2. Symmetric and Antisymmetric Wave Functions, and Pauli's Exclusion Principle. To set up a secular equation with two rows and columns between the first two functions U_1 and U_2, we can use the methods of Sec. 5-3, and since the diagonal matrix components of the Hamiltonian for the two states are equal, we have the case of degeneracy given in Eqs. (5-27) and (5-28). That is, we find that the functions which diagonalize the Hamiltonian are $(2)^{-\frac{1}{2}}(U_1 \pm U_2)$, with energies

$H_{11} \pm H_{12}$.   If we write out the wave functions, they are

$$(2)^{-\frac{1}{2}}[u_{1s}(r_1)u_{2s}(r_2) \pm u_{2s}(r_1)u_{1s}(r_2)]\alpha(s_1)\alpha(s_2) \qquad (12\text{-}12)$$

with energies

$$(1s/f/1s) + (2s/f/2s) + (1s,2s/g/1s,2s) \pm (1s,2s/g/2s,1s) \quad (12\text{-}13)$$

The first of the two functions in Eq. (12-12) is symmetric in the coordinates and spins of the electrons: if we interchange r_1, s_1 with r_2, s_2, the function is unchanged.   The second function is antisymmetric in interchange of the electrons: it changes sign when we interchange r_1, s_1 with r_2, s_2.

From each of the four starting functions, corresponding to each of the arrangements of the spins of the two electrons, we can proceed as we have done with the functions U_1 and U_2, and in each case, if we diagonalize the Hamiltonian with respect to the two functions obtained by permuting the electron coordinates and spins, we find that we are led to two linear combinations, one symmetric and one antisymmetric with respect to interchange of the electron coordinates and spins.   The resulting wave functions are

$$
\begin{aligned}
u_1^{\pm} &= (2)^{-\frac{1}{2}}[u_{1s}(r_1)\alpha(s_1)u_{2s}(r_2)\alpha(s_2) \pm u_{2s}(r_1)\alpha(s_1)u_{1s}(r_2)\alpha(s_2)] \\
u_2^{\pm} &= (2)^{-\frac{1}{2}}[u_{1s}(r_1)\alpha(s_1)u_{2s}(r_2)\beta(s_2) \pm u_{2s}(r_1)\beta(s_1)u_{1s}(r_2)\alpha(s_2)] \\
u_3^{\pm} &= (2)^{-\frac{1}{2}}[u_{1s}(r_1)\beta(s_1)u_{2s}(r_2)\alpha(s_2) \pm u_{2s}(r_1)\alpha(s_1)u_{1s}(r_2)\beta(s_2)] \\
u_4^{\pm} &= (2)^{-\frac{1}{2}}[u_{1s}(r_1)\beta(s_1)u_{2s}(r_2)\beta(s_2) \pm u_{2s}(r_1)\beta(s_1)u_{1s}(r_2)\beta(s_2)]
\end{aligned}
\qquad (12\text{-}14)
$$

Each of the four functions of Eq. (12-14) really represents two different functions, on account of the $\pm$ sign; we can denote them as u_1^+, u_1^-, for example.

We can now find the matrix components of the Hamiltonian with respect to these wave functions.   We find in the first place that there are no nondiagonal matrix components between a symmetric and an antisymmetric wave function.   It is obvious from elementary principles that this must be the case.   If we have, for instance, the integral $\int u_i^{+*}(H)_{op}u_j^-\, dv$, where i and j are two of the indices $1 \cdots 4$, and where the integration includes a summation over spins, and if we interchange the spatial and spin coordinates of the two electrons, the integral cannot be altered, since we are merely interchanging the names of the variables of integration.   On the other hand, when we do this, u_i^{+*} will be unchanged and u_j^- will change sign.   Since $(H)_{op}$, as given in Eq. (12-2), depends in a symmetrical way on the coordinates of the two electrons, $(H)_{op}u_j^-$ will also change sign.   Then the integral must change sign.   But an integral cannot simultaneously remain unchanged and change sign unless it is zero.

Our secular problem with eight rows and columns is then reduced to two problems, each with four rows and columns, one for the symmetric and one for the antisymmetric wave functions. Each of these problems is entirely analogous to that discussed earlier in connection with Table 11-2. We find without trouble that the nonvanishing matrix components are the following:

$$
\begin{aligned}
H_{11} = H_{44} &= (1s/f/1s) + (2s/f/2s) \\
&\qquad + (1s,2s/g/1s,2s) \pm (1s,2s/g/2s,1s) \\
H_{22} = H_{33} &= (1s/f/1s) + (2s/f/2s) + (1s,2s/g/1s,2s) \\
H_{23} &= \pm (1s,2s/g/2s,1s)
\end{aligned}
\tag{12-15}
$$

where as in Eq. (12-14) the upper signs refer to the symmetric, the lower to the antisymmetric functions. It is now simple to solve the secular problem. We note that there are no nondiagonal matrix components between the states u_1, u_4 and any others, as we should conclude from our discussion of Table 11-2; the state u_1 has $M_S = 1$, u_4 has $M_S = -1$. The only secular problem remaining is that between u_2 and u_3, each having $M_S = 0$. These are degenerate, so that the resulting eigenfunctions are then $(2)^{-\frac{1}{2}}$ times their sum and difference, and we find the eigenfunctions, which diagonalize the Hamiltonian for the complete problem of eight unperturbed states, and eigenvalues, as given in Table 12-1.

In Table 12-1, we have denoted the states by the symbols of spectrum theory, namely, ^1S, ^3S, with M_S taking on appropriate values. We shall justify these notations in the next section, where we show that the functions diagonalize the operators $(S^2)_{op}$ and $(S_z)_{op}$, with eigenvalues indicating the quantum numbers consistent with the spectral notation. Hence we have found, corresponding to each type of symmetry, a singlet and a triplet state, with energies differing by twice the exchange integral

Table 12-1

Energies and wave functions arising from the secular problem of Eq. (12-14). Upper signs refer to symmetric, lower to antisymmetric, eigenfunctions.

^1S: *Energy* $= (1s/f/1s) + (2s/f/2s) + (1s,2s/g/1s,2s) \mp (1s,2s/g/2s,1s)$
Wave function, $M_S = 0$:

$$(2)^{-\frac{1}{2}}[u_{1s}(r_1)u_{2s}(r_2) \mp u_{2s}(r_1)u_{1s}(r_2)](2)^{-\frac{1}{2}}[\alpha(s_1)\beta(s_2) - \beta(s_1)\alpha(s_2)]$$

^3S: *Energy* $= (1s/f/1s) + (2s/f/2s) + (1s,2s/g/1s,2s) \pm (1s,2s/g/2s,1s)$
Wave function, $M_S = 1$:

$$(2)^{-\frac{1}{2}}[u_{1s}(r_1)u_{2s}(r_2) \pm u_{2s}(r_1)u_{1s}(r_2)]\alpha(s_1)\alpha(s_2)$$

$M_S = 0$:

$$(2)^{-\frac{1}{2}}[u_{1s}(r_1)u_{2s}(r_2) \pm u_{2s}(r_1)u_{1s}(r_2)](2)^{-\frac{1}{2}}[\alpha(s_1)\beta(s_2) + \beta(s_1)\alpha(s_2)]$$

$M_S = -1$:

$$(2)^{-\frac{1}{2}}[u_{1s}(r_1)u_{2s}(r_2) \pm u_{2s}(r_1)u_{1s}(r_2)]\beta(s_1)\beta(s_2)$$

$(1s,2s/g/2s,1s)$. This result disagrees with experiment, as we shall now show, and it illustrates the reason which led Heisenberg and Dirac to assume fundamental relations between the symmetry of the wave function and the exclusion principle, which we have mentioned in Sec. 12-1.

It is found in experimental spectroscopy that the $1s2s$ configuration of a two-electron atom, which we are considering, leads to only one singlet and one triplet, the energy of the triplet lying lower than that of the singlet; the rule according to which the multiplet of higher multiplicity generally has a lower energy than one of lower multiplicity is known as Hund's rule and is generally obeyed experimentally. This behavior would be characteristic of the antisymmetric solution of Table 12-1, which leads to only one singlet and one triplet, the triplet lying below the singlet by the amount $2(1s,2s/g/2s,1s)$. It thus seems that there is no place for the symmetric solution in ordinary spectrum theory. This conclusion is reinforced if we consider the case where both electrons are in $1s$ states, so that we encounter the operation of the exclusion principle. If we change u_{2s} into u_{1s}, we find that the function $u_{1s}(r_1)u_{1s}(r_2) - u_{1s}(r_1)u_{1s}(r_2)$ is obviously zero. That is, the ^1S of the symmetric functions and the ^3S of the antisymmetric would be excluded, leaving only the antisymmetric ^1S and the symmetric ^3S arising from the configuration $1s^2$. But we know that this case, met in the ground state of helium, experimentally leads only to a state ^1S. This again agrees with the hypothesis that there is no place in the spectrum for the symmetric solution.

These facts, and others like them, led Heisenberg and Dirac to the fundamental postulate that only the antisymmetric solution existed in nature and that the symmetric solution represented a solution which we do not find in the ordinary universe. And they pointed out that, if we make this assumption, it automatically leads to Pauli's exclusion principle in its elementary form. If we have two spin-orbitals, ψ_1 and ψ_2, and denote the spatial and spin coordinates by the symbols 1 and 2, the antisymmetric function can be written as $(2)^{-\frac{1}{2}}[\psi_1(1)\psi_2(2) - \psi_2(1)\psi_1(2)]$. It is obvious that if $\psi_1 = \psi_2$, as will be the case if the spatial and spin quantum numbers of the spin-orbitals are identical, the antisymmetric function will automatically vanish. That is, no antisymmetric function can be set up which disobeys Pauli's exclusion principle, which is then seen to be a consequence of the more fundamental postulate of antisymmetry. As for the explanation of that postulate, however, we must realize that it does not follow from any principles of quantum mechanics but must be accepted as an additional assumption, justified because it leads to results in agreement with experiment. As for its validity, we should point out that we shall later prove rigorously, not merely by use of approximations as we have done here, that all solutions of the two-electron problem must be either antisymmetric or symmetric, so that we are on sound ground in accepting only the antisymmetric functions as existing in nature.

12-3. Spin Coupling in the Two-electron System. Before we go on to consider problems with more than two electrons, let us consider more carefully the interaction of the spins in the problem we have been taking up. Our four antisymmetric functions, from Table 12-1, are

^1S, $M_S = 0$:
$$(2)^{-\frac{1}{2}}[u_{1s}(r_1)u_{2s}(r_2) + u_{2s}(r_1)u_{1s}(r_2)](2)^{-\frac{1}{2}}[\alpha(s_1)\beta(s_2) - \beta(s_1)\alpha(s_2)]$$
^3S, $M_S = 1$:
$$(2)^{-\frac{1}{2}}[u_{1s}(r_1)u_{2s}(r_2) - u_{2s}(r_1)u_{1s}(r_2)]\alpha(s_1)\alpha(s_2)$$
^3S, $M_S = 0$:   (12-16)
$$(2)^{-\frac{1}{2}}[u_{1s}(r_1)u_{2s}(r_2) - u_{2s}(r_1)u_{1s}(r_2)](2)^{-\frac{1}{2}}[\alpha(s_1)\beta(s_2) + \beta(s_1)\alpha(s_2)]$$
^3S, $M_S = -1$:
$$(2)^{-\frac{1}{2}}[u_{1s}(r_1)u_{2s}(r_2) - u_{2s}(r_1)u_{1s}(r_2)]\beta(s_1)\beta(s_2)$$

Let us first show how to justify our assignment of S values to these wave functions, by showing that the operator $(S^2)_{op}$ is diagonal for these functions, where it represents the square of the total spin angular momentum, and that the diagonal matrix component is $S(S + 1)$, or $1(2) = 2$ for the triplets, $0(1) = 0$ for the singlet.

The method we use is similar to that found in Prob. 8, Chap. 11. However, a slight modification of that method leads to the most convenient way to carry out this calculation. The problem is simplified if we use the identity

$$(S^2)_{op} = (S_x + iS_y)_{op}(S_x - iS_y)_{op} + (S_z^2)_{op} - (S_z)_{op} \qquad (12\text{-}17)$$

which holds for any angular-momentum operator satisfying the commutation rules of Eq. (11-15), as we can readily prove directly from those commutation rules. It is simpler to apply, on account of its use of step-up and step-down operators, than the more obvious relationship that $(S^2)_{op} = (S_x^2)_{op} + (S_y^2)_{op} + (S_z^2)_{op}$. We then combine Eq. (12-17) with Eq. (11-36), and with the result that the spin angular momentum of the two-electron system is the sum of the angular momenta of the two electrons. Let us show, for instance, how we prove that the first function of Eq. (12-16) represents a singlet.

The spin operators have no effect on the function of coordinates, so that we can get our desired information by finding

$$(S^2)_{op}[\alpha(s_1)\beta(s_2) - \beta(s_1)\alpha(s_2)]$$

allowing the operator to operate only on the spin part of the wave function. Let us first find the effect of operating on the function with $(S_x - iS_y)_{op} = (s_{x1} + s_{x2} - is_{y1} - is_{y2})_{op}$, where, for instance, $(s_{x1})_{op}$ is the corresponding operator for the first electron. We use Eq. (11-36) and have

$$(s_{x1} - is_{y1})_{op}[\alpha(s_1)\beta(s_2) - \beta(s_1)\alpha(s_2)] = \beta(s_1)\beta(s_2) \qquad (12\text{-}18)$$

Similarly we have

$$(s_{x2} - is_{y2})_{op}[\alpha(s_1)\beta(s_2) - \beta(s_1)\alpha(s_2)] = -\beta(s_1)\beta(s_2) \qquad (12\text{-}19)$$

Hence the effect of operating on the wave function with the operator $(S_x - iS_y)_{op}$ is to give zero. Similarly $(S_z)_{op}$ operating on the wave function gives zero, and so does $(S_z)_{op}(S_z)_{op} = (S_z^2)_{op}$. Hence we verify that $(S^2)_{op}$ operating on this wave function gives zero, which establishes the fact that it is a singlet. Similar steps applied to the other functions lead to a verification that they are triplet functions.

We understand, then, the spin dependence of the singlet and triplet wave functions in Eq. (12-16). Now let us consider the more interesting question: why the energies of the states differ by an electrostatic integral, the exchange integral $(1s,2s/g/2s,1s)$. This is the phenomenon which was incomprehensible in the older vector model of the atom before the development of wave mechanics, and the phenomenon which Heisenberg explained in terms of an argument similar to the one we are giving here. The reason is to be found in the way in which the antisymmetry postulated by Heisenberg and Dirac has resulted in different orbital parts of the wave function for the singlet and the triplet: the orbital function is a symmetric function of r_1 and r_2 for the singlet, and antisymmetric for the triplet; the antisymmetry of the wave function as a whole is provided by the fact that the spin function is antisymmetric in interchange of s_1 and s_2 for the singlet, symmetric for the triplet. These different orbital wave functions, in turn, result in different average values for the Coulomb interaction between the two electrons, and hence in different energies for the singlet and triplet.

We can follow rather closely the feature of the wave function which produces the difference of energy. We have pointed out that the triplet will lie below the singlet in energy; the reason is that the exchange integral $(1s,2s/g/2s,1s)$ is positive, and it is subtracted in the triplet, added in the singlet. Now, if we look at the orbital part of the wave function for the triplet, $u_{1s}(r_1)u_{2s}(r_2) - u_{2s}(r_1)u_{1s}(r_2)$, we note that it goes to zero when $r_1 = r_2$. In other words, as a result of our antisymmetry, the probability of finding two electrons of the same spin at the same point of space is zero. There is no such situation for the singlet, where the wave function $u_{1s}(r_1)u_{2s}(r_2) + u_{2s}(r_1)u_{1s}(r_2)$ does not go to zero when $r_1 = r_2$. Now, when the two electrons are at the same point of space, the Coulomb repulsion between them is positively infinite, and when they are nearby, it is very large and positive. They can get close together in the singlet,

but not in the triplet. Hence the singlet has a positive contribution to
its potential energy which the triplet does not have (the integral is finite,
though the integrand is infinite when the two electrons are at the same
position), and consequently the energy of the singlet is higher than that
of the triplet. We shall find that this same general situation holds
throughout our work, explaining how it can be that merely changing the
orientation of the spins of the various electrons can make large changes
in the energy.

12-4. The Antisymmetric Wave Function in the N-electron Case.
The symmetry problem in the N-electron case is very much more complicated than in the two-electron case. If we start with N spin-orbitals,
all different (on account of the exclusion principle), which we may symbolize as $u_1 \cdots u_N$, where the subscripts stand for sets of quantum
numbers, and with electrons whose space and spin coordinates are symbolized by $1, 2, \ldots, N$, we may set up a function like the U_1 of Eq.
(12-1) in the form

$$U_1 = u_1(1)u_2(2) \cdots u_N(N) \qquad (12\text{-}20)$$

But now, instead of having only two such functions, we have $N!$, since
any permutation of the subscripts of the u's, or of the arguments of the
electrons, will lead to such a function, and there are $N!$ permutations.
If we tried to solve the secular problem between these $N!$ functions
directly, we should have an exceedingly complicated problem.

By means of the group theory, we can show that, after this secular
problem has been solved, each of the resulting linear combinations of the
U's will have a particular type of symmetry. In particular, there will be
one symmetric combination, which is simply the sum of all the U's.
There will be one antisymmetric combination, which is a linear combination of the U's with coefficients which are either 1 or -1, depending
on whether an even or an odd number of transpositions of pairs of subscripts must be made to transform the U in question into U_1. In addition, there will be many combinations with much more complicated
symmetry properties. In Chap. 19 (Vol. II), where we discuss the group
theory and its application to wave mechanics, we shall give examples of
these more complicated types of symmetry.

Fortunately, the postulate of antisymmetry of Heisenberg and Dirac
makes a very great simplification at this point, as was pointed out by
the author;[1] we need consider only the single antisymmetric combination.
Group theory can prove that the nondiagonal matrix component of the
Hamiltonian between an antisymmetric function and a function of any
other symmetry type is zero, so that we need deal only with the antisymmetric functions and shall never be called on to investigate any of

[1] J. C. Slater, *Phys. Rev.*, **34**:1293 (1929).

the other symmetry types. Such an antisymmetric function can be written in the form of a determinant. It is

$$(N!)^{-\frac{1}{2}} \begin{vmatrix} u_1(1) & u_1(2) & \cdots & u_1(N) \\ u_2(1) & u_2(2) & \cdots & u_2(N) \\ \cdots & \cdots & \cdots & \cdots \\ u_N(1) & u_N(2) & \cdots & u_N(N) \end{vmatrix} \qquad (12\text{-}21)$$

The factor $(N!)^{-\frac{1}{2}}$ is added for normalization purposes, as we shall explain in the next section.

Let us inquire why this determinant forms the desired antisymmetric combination of the $N!$ unperturbed functions. We recall the definition of a determinant. It is a linear combination of the $N!$ products of elements, choosing only one factor from each row, one from each column, in each product. The coefficients are ± 1, $+1$ if it requires an even number of transpositions of subscripts of the u's to bring the product to the principal diagonal, -1 if it requires an odd number of transpositions. Thus, the product of terms on the principal diagonal, $u_1(1)u_2(2) \cdots u_N(N)$, has a coefficient 1. Such a term as $u_2(1)u_1(2)u_3(3) \cdots u_N(N)$, which differs from the product of principal diagonal terms only by the single transposition of the subscripts of the first two functions, has the coefficient -1, and so on. It is now clear that, if we transpose the coordinates and spins of two electrons, we must make a single additional transposition in each product to bring it back to the principal diagonal, and hence each product has the opposite sign to what it had in the original determinant. In other words, the determinantal function changes sign when the coordinates and spins of two electrons are interchanged, or it has the desired property of antisymmetry.

Another way to state this property is based on the theorem that, if we interchange two rows or two columns of a determinant, the determinant changes sign. This must be true, on account of the argument given in the preceding paragraph. But the interchange of the coordinates and spins of two electrons involves the interchange of the corresponding columns in the determinant. Hence it must change the sign of the function.

Another application of the same theorem provides the proof of Pauli's exclusion principle. Let us suppose that two of the spin-orbitals, such as u_1 and u_2, were identical. Then two rows of the determinant of Eq. (12-21) would be identical. But a determinant with two identical rows or columns must be zero. The reason is that interchange of these rows or columns must change the sign of the determinant, by the argument of the preceding paragraphs. But if the rows or columns are identical, the determinant cannot be changed by interchanging them. The only value which the determinant can have which simultaneously changes sign and remains unchanged in this process is zero. Hence, if we try to set up a determinantal function in which two electrons are in the same spin-orbital, violating Pauli's principle, the result is zero; no such antisymmetric function can be set up.

Still another application of this theorem shows that in general, in the N-electron case, we have the same result which we pointed out in the preceding section, namely, that the wave function goes to zero when two electrons of the same spin go to the same point of space. For if this were to happen, the coordinates and spins of two electrons would be identical, which would mean that two columns of the determinant would become identical and the determinant, or wave function, would go to zero. Thus we see quite generally that the Coulomb repulsive energy between two electrons will be decreased if the electrons have parallel spins, for then they must keep out of each other's way, in a manner not required if their spins are opposite. The explanation which we gave earlier of the way in which the electrostatic energy depends on spin orientation then carries through to the N-electron case.

We are now ready to state the general procedure which we shall use in the next few chapters, on the basis of determinantal wave functions, to get a general solution of a problem in atomic structure, following the method proposed by the author in the paper cited above. We set up, in principle, a complete set of one-electron spin-orbitals. Ordinarily these consist of a complete set of functions of coordinates, each one of which can be combined with either the spin function α or the spin function β. From this complete set, we can pick out N spin-orbitals in an infinite number of ways. From each choice of N spin-orbitals, we can construct a determinantal wave function according to Eq. (12-21). We find the matrix components of the Hamiltonian between these determinantal functions and find linear combinations of the determinantal functions which make the Hamiltonian diagonal, or which in the language of variation principle make the average value stationary. These combinations of determinantal functions will be the precise solutions of Schrödinger's equation satisfying the condition of antisymmetry. In practical cases, of course, we cannot use such infinite sets of functions, and we are often driven to use a relatively small number of determinantal functions, constructed out of a small number of spin-orbitals. Our effort is to choose these determinantal functions so that we get as good an approximation as possible in this way.

In the cases which we have discussed in the preceding chapter and which we shall be handling in the next few chapters, the determinantal functions which we use are those arising from a single configuration: we choose the spin-orbitals in such a way that in each case we have the desired number with each set of nl values, but we take all possible combinations of m_l and m_s consistent with this configuration. This is the simplest case which we can handle which gives anything like the correct wave functions. Later, however, we shall discuss configuration interaction: the process of making linear combinations of determinantal functions arising from different configurations, to get better approximate solutions of Schrödinger's equation. This is necessary to get really quantitative results, but an adequate description of multiplet theory can be secured without bothering with it, and consequently we put off the discussion of configuration interaction for the present.

12-5. Matrix Components of Operators with Respect to Determinantal Wave Functions. Since we shall be dealing from now on with determinantal functions, it is essential to know how to compute the matrix components of various operators with respect to them. There is a useful general theorem which we shall first prove. Let us take two determinantal functions of the form of Eq. (12-21), the first containing spin-orbitals $u_1, u_2, \ldots, u_N$, and the second $u_1', u_2', \ldots, u_N'$. Let us compute the matrix component of an operator $(F)_{op}$, which might be the Hamiltonian, angular momentum, or any of the other operators we are interested in. The matrix component is then equal to

$$(N!)^{-1}\int \begin{vmatrix} u_1^*(1) & \cdots & u_1^*(N) \\ \cdots & \cdots & \cdots \\ u_N^*(1) & \cdots & u_N^*(N) \end{vmatrix} (F)_{op} \begin{vmatrix} u_1'(1) & \cdots & u_1'(N) \\ \cdots & \cdots & \cdots \\ u_N'(1) & \cdots & u_N'(N) \end{vmatrix} dv_1 \cdots dv_N$$

$$(12\text{-}22)$$

where $\int \cdots dv_1 \cdots dv_N$ is understood to include summation over the spin variables as well as integration of the spatial coordinates.

Now let us consider that part of Eq. (12-22) in which we use only the factor arising from the product of principal diagonal terms in the determinant on the left. This term is

$$(N!)^{-1}\int u_1^*(1) \cdots u_N^*(N)(F)_{op} \begin{vmatrix} u_1'(1) & \cdots & u_1'(N) \\ \cdots & \cdots & \cdots \\ u_N'(1) & \cdots & u_N'(N) \end{vmatrix} dv_1 \cdots dv_N$$

$$(12\text{-}23)$$

This integral will have a particular value. But now consider another such term, in which we use another of the products on the left; we know that there are $N!$ such terms in all. For example, we may have the term

$$(N!)^{-1}\int - u_2^*(1)u_1^*(2)u_3^*(3) \cdots u_N^*(N)(F)_{op} \begin{vmatrix} u_1'(1) & \cdots & u_1'(N) \\ \cdots & \cdots & \cdots \\ u_N'(1) & \cdots & u_N'(N) \end{vmatrix}$$

$$dv_1 \cdots dv_N \quad (12\text{-}24)$$

in which we have interchanged the subscripts on the first two spin-orbitals. We can now show that this integral is identical with that of

Eq. (12-23).   The reason is that the variables of integration are purely
dummy indices, which can be given other names without changing the
value of the integral, since we are integrating over them.   Let us then
interchange the meaning of the variables 1 and 2.   The integral of Eq.
(12-24) is then identical with

$$(N!)^{-1}\int - u_2^*(2)u_1^*(1)u_3^*(3) \cdots u_N^*(N)(F)_{op} \begin{vmatrix} u_1'(2) & u_1'(1) & \cdots & u_1'(N) \\ \cdots & \cdots & \cdots & \cdots \\ u_N'(2) & u_N'(1) & \cdots & u_N'(N) \end{vmatrix}$$
$$dv_1 \cdots dv_N \quad (12\text{-}25)$$

In making this change, we must notice that, on account of the fact that
all electrons are identical, $(F)_{op}$ must involve the coordinates of the electrons in a symmetric fashion, so that interchanging the names of electrons 1 and 2 makes no change in $(F)_{op}$.

We now notice, however, that, if we take the integral of Eq. (12-25)
and interchange the first two columns in the determinant, we bring the
determinant into the same form as that of Eq. (12-23).   We change its
sign, and this cancels the minus sign present in Eq. (12-25).   The first
factor of Eq. (12-25) is already identical with that of Eq. (12-23), except
that the factors are written in a different order.   Hence we have shown
that the quantity of Eq. (12-25), and hence of (12-24), is identical with
that of Eq. (12-23).   An analogous proof holds for each of the $N!$ terms
in the expansion of Eq. (12-22).   Hence the integral of Eq. (12-22) consists of $N!$ identical terms, each like Eq. (12-23).   This cancels the factor
$(N!)^{-1}$, and the result is that the matrix component of $(F)_{op}$ between our
two determinantal functions is

$$\int u_1^*(1) \cdots u_N^*(N)(F)_{op} \begin{vmatrix} u_1'(1) & \cdots & u_1'(N) \\ \cdots & \cdots & \cdots \\ u_N'(1) & \cdots & u_N'(N) \end{vmatrix} dv_1 \cdots dv_N \quad (12\text{-}26)$$

This formula is much more convenient to use than Eq. (12-22), since it
involves only a single summation over $N!$ terms, rather than a double
summation.

Now let us investigate the nature of the matrix components of various
sorts of operators.   The operators we deal with are usually constants
independent of the electron coordinates (as in computing the normalization integral), operators which are sums of one-electron operators like
the f's of Eq. (12-2), or like angular-momentum operators, or operators
which are sums of two-electron operators like the g's of Eq. (12-2).   The
calculation of the matrix component is greatly simplified if we assume,
as we shall do, that all the spin-orbitals $u_1, u_2, \ldots, u_N, u_1', u_2', \ldots,$
u_N' are orthogonal to each other, as well as being normalized.   The relations can be set up for nonorthogonal orbitals, but they are much more

complicated, and we shall not need them for work with atomic wave functions. We then first notice that, if $(F)_{op}$ is a constant, the orthogonality of the spin-orbitals will cancel most of the terms in the integral of Eq. (12-26). We shall get nothing, in fact, unless one of the permutations of $u_1'(1)u_2'(2) \cdots u_N'(N)$ is identical with $u_1(1)u_2(2) \cdots u_N(N)$, since if even one spin-orbital were different, the integral would be zero. In other words, any two determinantal functions formed from different spin-orbitals are orthogonal to each other. If the determinants are identical, so that $u_1' = u_1$, etc., then only the product of principal diagonal terms in the determinant of Eq. (12-26) will give anything, and it will give unity, showing that our determinantal function of Eq. (12-21) is normalized.

Next let us consider an operator $\Sigma(i)f_i$, where f_i is a one-electron operator operating on the ith electron. Then the matrix component will be nonvanishing only if the function formed from the u''s has one of its permutations in which it is identical with that formed from the u's or if it differs by only one spin-orbital. The first case is that of the diagonal matrix component, the two determinantal functions being formed from the same spin-orbitals. In the second case, we shall assume that the second determinant is formed from the first by replacing u_i by u_i', all other u's remaining unchanged and in the same order. The question of the order of the one-electron functions in the determinant is important, because a change of order in the spin-orbitals can change the sign of the determinant, and hence the sign of nondiagonal matrix components. We then have the following results:

$$\text{Diagonal matrix component of } \Sigma(i)f_i = \Sigma(i)(i/f/i) \qquad (12\text{-}27)$$

where
$$(i/f/i) = \int u_i^*(1)f_1 u_i(1) \, dv_1 \qquad (12\text{-}28)$$

and

Nondiagonal matrix component of $\Sigma(i)f_i$ between determinant formed from u's and determinant in which u_i is replaced by u_i', all other u's remaining
$$\text{unchanged and in the same order} = (i/f/i') \qquad (12\text{-}29)$$

where
$$(i/f/i') = \int u_i^*(1)f_1 u_i'(1) \, dv_1 \qquad (12\text{-}30)$$

In the definitions of Eqs. (12-28) and (12-30), we are summing over spins as well as integrating over the coordinates. We have indicated the variable of integration as being 1, the coordinates and spin of electron 1; this is only a dummy index of integration, and the integral depends on the orbitals u_i and u_i', not on the variable associated with the electron.

We shall also have operators of the form $\Sigma(\text{pairs } i,j)g_{ij}$, where g_{ij} is $2/r_{ij}$, as in Eq. (12-2), r_{ij} being the distance between the ith and jth electrons, so that this represents the Coulomb repulsion between pairs of electrons. In this case there will be nonvanishing components if the set of u'''s is identical with the set of u's, or if it differs by not more than two spin-orbitals. Here, as before, we assume that the u'''s which are identical with the u's are arranged in the same order. Then we find

Diagonal matrix component of $\Sigma(\text{pairs } i,j)g_{ij}$
$$= \Sigma(\text{pairs } i,j)[(ij/g/ij) - (ij/g/ji)] \quad (12\text{-}31)$$
where in general

$$(ij/g/rt) = \int u_i^*(1)u_j^*(2)g_{12}u_r(1)u_t(2) \, dv_1 \, dv_2 \quad (12\text{-}32)$$

where as before the integration includes summation over spins, and where the coordinates 1 and 2 are again dummy indices of integration. We have furthermore

> Nondiagonal matrix component of $\Sigma(\text{pairs } i,j)g_{ij}$ between determinant formed from u's and determinant in which u_i is replaced by u_i', all other u's remaining unchanged and in the same order $= \Sigma(j \neq i)[(ij/g/i'j) - (ij/g/ji')]$ (12-33)

and finally

> Nondiagonal matrix component of $\Sigma(\text{pairs } i,j)g_{ij}$ between determinant formed from the u's and determinant in which u_i is replaced by u_i', u_j replaced by u_j', all other u's remaining unchanged and in the same order $= (ij/g/i'j') - (ij/g/j'i')$ (12-34)

These rules of operation[1] tell us how to find the matrix components of the operators we are interested in, between determinantal wave functions of the type we meet in the atomic problem. In the next chapter we shall take up the detailed methods of calculating the matrix components of the Hamiltonian and shall apply these to a discussion of the problem of solving the secular equation and approximating to the solutions of Schrödinger's equation for atoms, using the determinantal method.

There is one very important point to notice regarding the matrix components of operators $\Sigma(i)f_i$: these matrix components are identical with what we should have if we used simple product functions, rather than determinants. It is only the product forming the principal diagonal in Eq. (12-26) which enters into these formulas (12-27), (12-29). The reason why this is important is that the angular momentum is such an operator, and all our arguments in Chap. 11 were based on product functions, which we now see are inadequate, since they are not antisymmetric. Fortunately, however, the matrix components of the angular momentum with respect to the determinantal functions have the same

[1] The rules for the diagonal matrix components were first set up by the author in the paper cited above; for the nondiagonal matrix components, by E. U. Condon, *Phys. Rev.*, **36**:1121 (1930).

values assumed in Chap. 11, so that the conclusions reached in that chapter are valid, even using determinantal functions.

PROBLEMS

1. In Prob. 1, Chap. 9, the ground state of the helium atom is discussed, with neglect of electron spin and of the antisymmetry of the wave function. Show that that discussion is nevertheless justified.

2. Consider the states ^1S, ^3S of the helium atom in the configuration $1s2s$. Write down the determinantal form of the wave function, in each case, and the expression for the energy, in terms of the various integrals concerned.

3. Consider a lithium atom in its ground state, $1s^2 2s\ ^2S$. Write out the determinantal wave function for this state, with $M_S = \frac{1}{2}$. Write out the expression for the energy of this state in terms of the various integrals concerned.

4. The configuration $1s2s3s$ of lithium would lead to one ^1S state, and two ^2S's. Set up the determinantal functions corresponding to the various combinations of m_s's, and derive the matrix components of the energy. Find the energy of the ^4S state and the sum of the energies of the two ^2S's, using the sum rule for the latter case.

5. Consider the problem of the states ^1S, ^3S of the helium atom, in the configuration $1s2s$, in case the $1s$ and $2s$ orbitals are not orthogonal to each other. Find the expression for the energies of the two states, in terms of appropriate integrals.

6. Discuss the same problem considered in Prob. 4, but for the case where the $1s$, $2s$, and $3s$ orbitals are not orthogonal to each other, so that you cannot apply the rules of Sec. 12-5.

13

The Elementary Theory of Multiplets

13-1. The Secular Problem in Russell-Saunders Coupling. In the preceding three chapters we have been laying the foundations for the study of multiplet structure, but we have not really faced the problem of how to set up and solve the secular problem for a general configuration. In the present chapter we shall give such general methods and illustrate them by examples. We shall find that we can go a long way by rather simple means, and for the benefit of the reader who may wish to understand only the simpler approaches, we shall now recapitulate the important results of the preceding chapters and shall endeavor to give a fairly complete account of these simple procedures in this chapter and the next, postponing the more complicated and advanced treatment for further chapters, to be found in the second volume.

The case which can be handled simply is that in which we are dealing with only a single configuration; where we are treating the extreme case of Russell-Saunders coupling, in which the magnetic spin-orbit interaction can be entirely neglected in comparison with the electrostatic terms; and in which there is no more than one multiplet of a given L and S value in the resulting spectrum. In this case there is a straightforward procedure for analyzing the problem, setting up secular equations for the determination of the energy; and we can get all the energy values, or eigenvalues, by application of the diagonal sum rule, without the necessity of solving any secular equations at all. This simple scheme is in fact sufficient to get the energies of multiplets in many important cases, and it is necessary to understand it before going on to the more complicated cases where more advanced methods are required.

The first step in the process is to consider how many unperturbed wave functions we are dealing with and to get some systematic way of describing and tabulating them. Let us suppose that our configuration includes a shell capable of holding N_0 electrons [equal to $2(2l + 1)$, where l is the azimuthal quantum number], but containing in fact only N_1 electrons, where $N_1 < N_0$. We then have $N_0!/[N_1!(N_0 - N_1)!]$ different ways of picking out N_1 spin-orbitals to be occupied by the N_1 electrons, leaving the remaining $N_0 - N_1$ spin-orbitals empty [in which we disregard the $N_1!$ ways of arranging the N_1 occupied spin-orbitals, and the $(N_0 - N_1)!$ ways of arranging the $N_0 - N_1$ empty spin-orbitals]. Each of these assignments of electrons to spin-orbitals will lead to a different unperturbed wave function. If the configuration includes more than one incompleted shell, the total number of unperturbed wave functions will be the product of the quantities $N_0!/[N_1!(N_0 - N_1)!]$ for each of these incompleted shells, since each assignment of electrons to spin-orbitals of one shell can be combined with each assignment of another shell. We note that the factors associated with a filled shell are unity, since there is just one possible way of picking out the spin-orbitals when $N_0 = N_1$. In other words, a filled shell does not affect the number of unperturbed wave functions; it is only the incompleted shells which we need to consider in counting them.

Each choice of occupied spin-orbitals leads to an unperturbed wave function in the form of a determinant, as given in Eq. (12-21), as a result of the Heisenberg-Dirac interpretation of the Pauli exclusion principle. Each of the u's appearing in that determinant is a spin-orbital; a product of a function $u_{nlm_l}(r\theta\phi)$ of the coordinates of the electron, of the form given in Eq. (7-31), only with the radial function $R_{nl}(r)$ determined by a self-consistent-field method, as described in Chaps. 8 and 9; and a function $v_{m_s}(s)$, a function of the spin, of the type defined in Eqs. (11-33), (11-34), where m_s, the spin magnetic quantum number, can take on only the values $\pm\frac{1}{2}$, and where $v_{\frac{1}{2}}(s)$ is often called $\alpha(s)$, $v_{-\frac{1}{2}}(s)$ is called $\beta(s)$. Here s is the spin variable, which can take on the values $\pm\frac{1}{2}$. We shall assume the $R_{nl}(r)$'s to be orthogonal to each other, as remarked in Sec. 9-4; then all spin-orbitals will be orthogonal to each other and normalized. In Sec. 12-5, we have seen in a general way how to find matrix components of various operators between determinantal functions of the type we are considering here. We shall work out these general rules later in much more detail, so that we shall know precisely how to find matrix components of the Hamiltonian, angular momentum, and so on, between determinantal functions.

The $2(2l + 1)$ spin-orbitals associated with a given (nl) value arise from combining the two values of m_s, and the $2l + 1$ values of m_l, which can take on the values $l, l - 1, \ldots, -l$. We can describe one of the determinantal functions by listing the values of the m_l's and m_s's of the spin-orbitals which are occupied in this particular determinantal function, as in Tables 11-2, 11-3. We note that on account of the nature of the determinantal function, as given in Eq. (12-21), it makes no sense to say that one particular electron occupies one particular spin-orbital. The wave function depends in an antisymmetric way on the coordinates and spins of all electrons, so that the interchange of two electrons has no effect on the wave function beyond a change of sign.

As an example of this listing of the unperturbed wave functions, we gave in Table 11-3 the unperturbed states for a configuration consisting of one s and one p electron outside closed shells. It is not necessary to list the occupied spin-orbitals for closed shells, for this is obvious: all spin-orbitals associated with the (nl) value characterizing the shell are occupied. Hence a table like Table 11-3 will hold for any configuration so long as it has only an s and a p electron outside closed shells: it might, for instance, be calcium in the configuration $(1s)^2(2s)^2(2p)^6(3s)^2(3p)^64s4p$, as well as the case $1s2p$ mentioned in Table 11-3. The magnetic quantum numbers of the s electron are denoted by m_{l1} and m_{s1}; since m_{l1} must be zero for an s electron, we do not have to list it. For the p electron, we have m_{l2} and m_{s2}. The quantum number m_{s1} can take on two values, m_{l1} can take on three, and m_{s2} can take on two, so that the total number of unperturbed wave functions is the product of these numbers, or 12, each of which is listed in Table 11-3.

In Table 11-3 we also list M_L and M_S, the sums, respectively, of the m_l's and m_s's of the two electrons. These represent the components, along the z axis, of the orbital and spin angular momentum of the whole atom. In the case we are considering, in which spin-orbit interaction is entirely disregarded, each of these quantities is constant and is quantized, and M_L and M_S are the corresponding quantum numbers. The constancy means that the operators representing the z component of orbital or of spin angular momentum commute with the Hamiltonian, which is the case when no torques act between orbital and spin angular momentum. We can then prove that the Hamiltonian has no matrix components, with respect to our unperturbed wave functions, between two functions unless they have the same M_L and M_S. This proof is similar to the one which we gave in a slightly different connection in Eq. (11-29). It is so important for our present purposes that we shall repeat the proof here.

Let us write down the commutation relation between the z component of orbital angular momentum, $(L_z)_{op}$, and the Hamiltonian, and let us take the matrix component of this commutation relation between two states out of such a set as is given in Table 11-3. The operator $(L_z)_{op}$ is diagonal for the unperturbed wave functions, its diagonal matrix component being M_L, but the Hamiltonian is not in general diagonal, since we are dealing with unperturbed functions. Thus we have

$$(M_L - M_L')H^0_{M_L,M_S;M_L',M_S'} = 0 \qquad (13\text{-}1)$$

where M_L, M_L' are values of M_L in the two states and $H^0_{M_L,M_S;M_L',M_S'}$ is the matrix component of the Hamiltonian between one of the unperturbed wave functions with quantum numbers M_L, M_S and one with quantum numbers M'_L, M'_S. We see from Eq. (13-1) that the matrix component must be zero unless $M'_L = M_L$. Similarly from the commutation relation between $(S_z)_{op}$ and the Hamiltonian, where $(S_z)_{op}$ is the operator representing the z component of the spin angular momentum, we see that there will be no matrix component of the Hamiltonian except between two unperturbed functions for which $M'_S = M_S$. We shall then have a separate secular problem for each combination of M_L and M_S values, greatly simplifying the solution of the secular equation. In the case of Table 11-3, instead of having a secular equation with 12 rows and

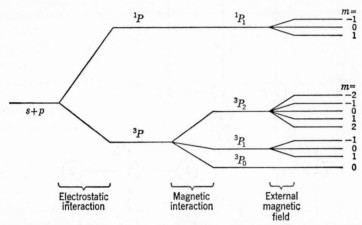

FIG. 13-1. Splitting of energy levels of multiplets arising from an s and a p electron, from electrostatic interaction, magnetic spin-orbit interaction, and a weak external magnetic field (schematic).

columns, between all 12 unperturbed functions, we have nine separate secular problems, of which the six characterized by $M_L = 1, 0, -1$ and $M_S = 1, -1$ have only one function each, while the three characterized by $M_L = 1, 0, -1$ and $M_S = 0$ have two functions each.

Let us next inquire regarding the significance of these various secular problems. According to the vector model, as outlined in Chap. 10, the s and p electrons should result in two multiplets, ^1P and ^3P, since the spin vectors of the two can lead to $S = 0$ or 1, and the orbital angular momentum vectors must give $L = 1$, since the s electron has no orbital angular momentum. When we take electrostatic interaction into account, these multiplets will be separated from each other, as shown schematically in Fig. 13-1. If we go further and include the magnetic spin-orbit interaction, the ^3P multiplet will be split into three components, with $J = 2$, 1, 0, respectively, and finally in a magnetic field each level will be split into $2J + 1$ separate states. We are considering the approximation in which all magnetic effects are disregarded. Hence we expect to find only the electrostatic splitting between the ^1P and the ^3P multiplets.

The L and S vectors of each of these multiplets will be separately space-quantized in this approximation; it is only when we consider the spin-orbit interaction that we must consider that the resultant J of L and S is quantized, and that its component M is quantized. It is much more convenient, in the simple methods we are now using, to use the

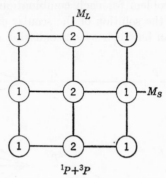

$^1P+^3P$

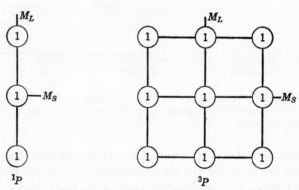

^1P ^3P

Fig. 13-2. M_L versus M_S, for an s and a p electron combining to give ^1P and ^3P.

space quantization of L and S separately. Then for the ^1P, where $L = 1$, $S = 0$, we shall have three states, for $M_L = 1, 0, -1$, $M_S = 0$; and for the ^3P, where $L = 1$, $S = 1$, we shall have nine states, with the various combinations arising from $M_L = 1, 0, -1$ and $M_S = 1, 0, -1$. These amount to just the states which are found in Table 11-3. We can show this more clearly in Fig. 13-2, where we show diagrams of M_L against M_S. The first diagram shows the nine possible combinations of M_L and M_S, and the numbers inside each circle give the number of states, from Table 11-3, having the indicated values of M_L and M_S. The second and third diagrams show the corresponding states for ^1P and ^3P, and it is obvious that the two superpose to give the states found from the first diagram.

To the approximation to which we are working in the present chapter, all terms of a multiplet will have the same energy. Hence, if we solve the nine secular equations arising from our case of an s and a p electron, we must find the energy of the ^3P multiplet from the six cases $M_L = 1$, $0, -1, M_S = 1, -1$, for as we see from Fig. 13-2, these all lead to terms of the ^3P. The three secular equations corresponding to $M_L = 1, 0, -1$, $M_S = 0$, each of which has two unperturbed functions, will have two eigenvalues, one agreeing with the same ^3P energy already found, and the other giving the ^1P energy. But now we see how we can get these energies by use of the diagonal sum rule, without solving even the quadratic secular equation corresponding to one of these cases $M_L = 1, 0, -1$, $M_S = 0$. For we recall that, according to Eq. (5-39), the sum of the diagonal matrix components of the Hamiltonian with respect to the unperturbed wave functions must equal the sum of the eigenvalues. In the present case, for instance for $M_L = 0$, $M_S = 0$, we know that one of the eigenvalues will be the ^3P energy, which has already been determined as, for instance, the diagonal matrix component of the Hamiltonian for the unperturbed function with $M_L = 1$, $M_S = 1$. The sum of the two diagonal matrix components for the case $M_L = 0$, $M_S = 0$ can be easily found; then by subtraction we can find the unknown energy of the multiplet ^1P. This is a very simple example of the application of the sum rule to the determination of the multiplet energies. Before we can make quantitative use of it, of course we must actually compute the matrix components of the Hamiltonian, which we shall do later, in Sec. 13-3.

13-2. Further Examples of the Secular Problem. In the preceding section we have given a general sketch of the procedure used in solving a problem of multiplets by use of the diagonal sum rule. Next we shall take another problem which introduces some new features, that of two p electrons. The vector model indicates that the two orbital angular-momentum vectors can combine to give $L = 2, 1, 0$, and the two spins to give $S = 1, 0$. Hence the multiplets should be ^3D, ^3P, ^3S, ^1D, ^1P, ^1S. In Table 13-1 we give part of the table, similar to Table 11-3, illustrating the states. Similarly, in Fig. 13-3, we give tabulations of all the states, according to their values of M_L and M_S, and of the multiplets arising from these two p electrons. Let us see how far we can go with the diagonal sum rule in evaluating the energies of these multiplets. The state $M_L = 2$, $M_S = 1$ corresponds obviously to the ^3D; thus we can find its energy from the unperturbed wave functions. The two states with $M_L = 2$, $M_S = 0$ correspond to ^3D and ^1D; hence the energy of ^1D can be found by subtraction. The two states with $M_L = 1$, $M_S = 1$ correspond to ^3D and ^3P, so that ^3P can be found by subtraction, and similarly from $M_L = 0$, $M_S = 1$, we can find ^3S. The four states $M_L = 1$, $M_S = 0$

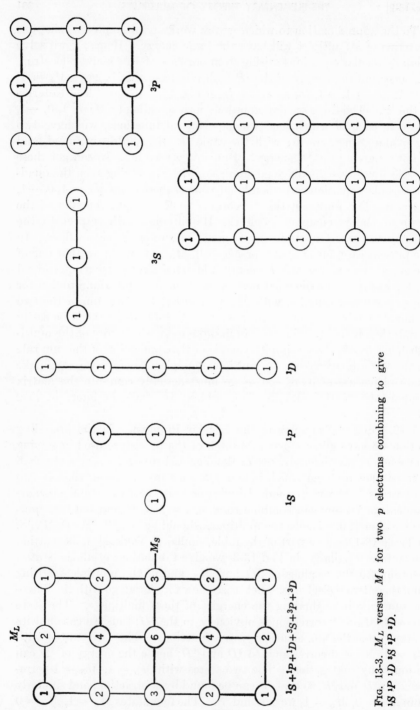

FIG. 13-3. M_L versus M_S for two p electrons combining to give ^1S ^1P ^1D ^3S ^3P ^3D.

Table 13-1. Unperturbed States for Two p Electrons

M_L	M_S	m_{l1}	m_{l2}	m_{s1}	m_{s2}
2	1	1	1	$\frac{1}{2}$	$\frac{1}{2}$
2	0	1	1	$\frac{1}{2}$	$-\frac{1}{2}$
2	0	1	1	$-\frac{1}{2}$	$\frac{1}{2}$
2	-1	1	1	$-\frac{1}{2}$	$-\frac{1}{2}$
1	1	1	0	$\frac{1}{2}$	$\frac{1}{2}$
1	1	0	1	$\frac{1}{2}$	$\frac{1}{2}$
1	0	1	0	$\frac{1}{2}$	$-\frac{1}{2}$
1	0	1	0	$-\frac{1}{2}$	$\frac{1}{2}$
1	0	0	1	$\frac{1}{2}$	$-\frac{1}{2}$
1	0	0	1	$-\frac{1}{2}$	$\frac{1}{2}$
1	-1	1	0	$-\frac{1}{2}$	$-\frac{1}{2}$
1	-1	0	1	$-\frac{1}{2}$	$-\frac{1}{2}$
0	1	1	-1	$\frac{1}{2}$	$\frac{1}{2}$
0	1	0	0	$\frac{1}{2}$	$\frac{1}{2}$
0	1	-1	1	$\frac{1}{2}$	$\frac{1}{2}$
.	.	.	.	.	.
.	.	.	.	.	.

correspond to ^3D, ^3P, ^1D, ^1P; we can then get ^1P by subtraction. Finally the six states $M_L = 0$, $M_S = 0$ allow us to get ^1S. Thus the whole problem can be solved by means of the sum rule, as in the preceding case.

If our two p electrons are equivalent, meaning that their n's, or principal quantum numbers, are equal, many of the states are forbidden by the exclusion principle and many other pairs of states become identical. Thus, of those shown in Table 13-1, the first and fourth are forbidden, and the second and third, the fifth and sixth, and many other pairs, become identical. When we take account of these forbidden or identical states, we find that the remaining number of states is as given in Fig. 13-4. We may then compare these with the patterns of the various multiplets shown in Fig. 13-3, and we see at once that we have enough states to correspond to the multiplets ^3P, ^1S, ^1D and that the other three, ^3S, ^3D, ^1P, are forbidden by the exclusion principle. We can also proceed by the sum rule to get the energies of the three allowed multiplets.

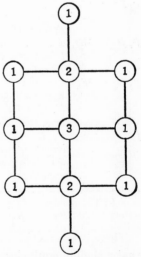

Fig. 13-4. M_L versus M_S for two equivalent p electrons combining to give ^1S ^1D ^3P.

This example shows us that the exclusion principle can operate in very complicated ways to exclude certain multiplets and to allow others. We can proceed by application of analogous methods to more complicated cases involving equivalent electrons, and we find that the allowed multiplets for various numbers of equivalent p, d, and f electrons are as given in Table 13-2. The type of analysis carried out in the present section, as far as it leads to the exclusion of certain multiplets, is due to Hund,[1] who was very active in the interpretation of the spectra of complex atoms.

Table 13-2. Multiplets for Equivalent p, d, and f Electrons

p^1, p^5	$^2P^o$
p^2, p^4	^3P, ^1D, ^1S
p^3	$^4S^o$, $^2D^o$, $^2P^o$

d^1, d^9	^2D
d^2, d^8	^3F, ^3P, ^1G, ^1D, ^1S
d^3, d^7	^4F, ^4P, ^2H, ^2G, ^2F, two ^2D's, ^2P
d^4, d^6	^5D, ^3H, ^3G, two ^3F's, ^3D, two ^3P's, ^1I, two ^1G's, ^1F, two ^1D's, two ^1S's
d^5	^6S, ^4G, ^4F, ^4D, ^4P, ^2I, ^2H, two ^2G's, two ^2F's, three ^2D's, ^2P, ^2S

f^1, f^{13}	$^2F^o$
f^2, f^{12}	^3H, ^3F, ^3P, ^1I, ^1G, ^1D, ^1S
f^3, f^{11}	$^4I^o$, $^4G^o$, $^4F^o$, $^4D^o$, $^4S^o$, $^2L^o$, $^2K^o$, $^2I^o$, two $^2H^o$'s, two $^2G^o$'s, two $^2F^o$'s, two $^2D^o$'s, $^2P^o$
f^4, f^{10}	^5I, ^5G, ^5F, ^5D, ^5S, ^3M, ^3L, two ^3K's, two ^3I's, four ^3H's, three ^3G's, four ^3F's, two ^3D's, three ^3P's, ^1N, two ^1L's, ^1K, three ^1I's, two ^1H's, four ^1G's, ^1F, four ^1D's, two ^1S's
f^5, f^9	$^6H^o$, $^6F^o$, $^6P^o$, $^4M^o$, $^4L^o$, two $^4K^o$'s, three $^4I^o$'s, three $^4H^o$'s, four $^4G^o$'s, four $^4F^o$'s, three $^4D^o$'s, two $^4P^o$'s, $^4S^o$, ^2O, ^2N, two $^2M^o$'s, three $^2L^o$'s, five $^2K^o$'s, five $^2I^o$'s, seven $^2H^o$'s, six $^2G^o$'s, seven $^2F^o$'s, five $^2D^o$'s, four $^2P^o$'s
f^6, f^8	^7F, ^5L, ^5K, two ^5I's, two ^5H's, three ^5G's, two ^5F's, three ^5D's, ^5P, ^5S, ^3O, ^3N, three ^3M's, three ^3L's, six ^3K's, six ^3I's, nine ^3H's, seven ^3G's, nine ^3F's, five ^3D's, six ^3P's, ^1Q, two ^1N's, two ^1M's, four ^1L's, three ^1K's, seven ^1I's, four ^1H's, eight ^1G's, four ^1F's, six ^1D's, ^1P, four ^1S's
f^7	$^8S^o$, $^6I^o$, $^6H^o$, $^6G^o$, $^6F^o$, $^6D^o$, $^6P^o$, $^4N^o$, $^4M^o$, three $^4L^o$'s, three $^4K^o$'s, five $^4I^o$'s, five $^4H^o$'s, seven $^4G^o$'s, five $^4F^o$'s, six $^4D^o$'s, two $^4P^o$'s, two $^4S^o$'s, $^2Q^o$, $^2O^o$, two $^2N^o$'s, four $^2M^o$'s, five $^2L^o$'s, seven $^2K^o$'s, nine $^2I^o$'s, nine $^2H^o$'s, ten $^2G^o$'s, ten $^2F^o$'s, seven $^2D^o$'s, five $^2P^o$'s, two $^2S^o$'s

Note: The sequence of L values, corresponding to $L = 0, 1, \ldots$, is denoted by the letters $SPDFGHIKLMNOPQ \ldots$, omitting J.

There is one feature of multiplet theory which is rather simple: we find that a shell of equivalent electrons, containing N_1 electrons, has the same multiplet structure as a shell containing $N_0 - N_1$ electrons, where N_0 is the number in a completed shell. For instance, a shell of five equivalent

[1] F. Hund, *Z. Physik*, **33**:345 (1925); **34**:296 (1925); "Linienspektren und periodisches System der Elemente," Springer-Verlag OHG, Berlin, 1927.

p electrons has the same type of spectrum as a single p electron, and nine d's have a spectrum like a single d. This symmetry is shown in Table 13-2.   It follows in a very simple way from our general procedure. If we are dealing with a shell containing $N_0 - N_1$ electrons, we can list the m_l's and m_s's of the occupied orbitals, but we can equally well describe the unperturbed functions by listing the unoccupied orbitals, and in that case the resulting table, similar to Table 11-3 or 13-1, will be like that of the shell containing N_1 electrons.   The only difference is that the M_L and M_S of a given state are the negative of the sums of the m_l's and m_s's of the unoccupied orbitals.   This does not change the appearance of the figures such as Fig. 13-2, 13-3, and 13-4, which therefore lead to the same set of multiplets as for the shell containing N_1 electrons.

An important example of this situation is found in the X-ray spectra, mentioned in Sec. 8-4.   Here we have removed an electron from an inner, complete shell.   We must find, then, that the stationary state of the shell with one electron removed is like that of a single electron and hence is a spectrum of doublets, the electron spin being oriented either parallel or opposite to the orbital angular momentum.   The relative orientation of L and S affects the energy through spin-orbit interaction.   This interaction is quite large for the inner, X-ray electrons; for it turns out to be proportional to the mean inverse third power of the radius of the orbit. Thus it comes about that the X-ray levels are split by quite appreciable amounts by magnetic interaction.   This doubling of the levels is a quite conspicuous feature of the observed X-ray spectra.

Another important result of the symmetry between the multiplets found for N_1 and $N_0 - N_1$ electrons is that a closed shell has only a ^1S term in its spectrum.   Since each value of m_l and m_s is occupied, we must have M_L and M_S each equal to zero.   The importance of this fact is that a closed shell behaves as if it had no orbital or spin angular momentum; in other words, it acts like a spherically symmetrical system and does not take part in the multiplet structure of any electrons which may lie outside it.   This is the feature which simplifies the problem of atomic spectra so greatly, in that only those electrons outside closed shells need to be considered in the vector model.

Let us now give a final example, in order to show the reader that we cannot always get our answers by use of the diagonal sum rule alone; the success of this method in the cases we have so far taken up might lead him to think it was always applicable.   Let us take the simple case of three nonequivalent s electrons, which we have already taken up in Prob. 4, Chap. 12.   Two s electrons will give us the multiplets ^3S and ^1S, and when we add a third, we should have a ^4S and ^2S arising from the ^3S as a parent and ^2S arising from the ^1S as a parent.   That this is the case follows from Table 13-3.   The state with $M_S = \frac{3}{2}$ will correspond to

Table 13-3. Unperturbed States for Three s Electrons

M_S	m_{s1}	m_{s2}	m_{s3}
$\frac{3}{2}$	$\frac{1}{2}$	$\frac{1}{2}$	$\frac{1}{2}$
$\frac{1}{2}$	$\frac{1}{2}$	$\frac{1}{2}$	$-\frac{1}{2}$
$\frac{1}{2}$	$\frac{1}{2}$	$-\frac{1}{2}$	$\frac{1}{2}$
$\frac{1}{2}$	$-\frac{1}{2}$	$\frac{1}{2}$	$\frac{1}{2}$
.	.	.	.
.	.	.	.
.	.	.	.

the ^4S, so that its energy will be found from the unperturbed function. Of the three states with $M_S = \frac{1}{2}$, we shall have states from the ^4S and from each ^2S. Subtraction of the ^4S energy from the sum of the diagonal matrix components of the three unperturbed states will then give the sum of the energies of the two ^2S's, but the diagonal sum rule cannot give their separate energies. We must instead set up nondiagonal matrix components of energy and solve the secular equation. This will be a cubic equation, for the states $M_S = \frac{1}{2}$, but since we know one of its roots, the energy of the ^4S state, we can reduce it to a quadratic equation for the two ^2S's. This problem is one of the simplest in which the diagonal sum rule does not suffice, but there are many others. In fact, we can see very simply that, whenever by the vector model we find that there are several multiplets of the same L and S, we shall not be able to get their separate energies by the diagonal sum rule but must solve a secular equation of degree equal to the number of such multiplets. We shall later give examples of how this procedure is actually carried out.

13-3. Matrix Components of the Hamiltonian for the Central-field Problem. To go further with our problem, we must be able to compute the matrix components of the Hamiltonian with respect to our unperturbed wave functions. In Sec. 12-5, we have seen how to write these matrix components in terms of certain integrals over the wave functions of one or of two electrons. In the present section we shall go over the methods of computing these integrals when the one-electron functions have the form given in Eq. (7-31). We continue to disregard spin-orbit interaction and magnetic effects, so that we shall be using the Hamiltonian of Eq. (9-6). This is

$$(H)_{op} = \Sigma(i)f_i + \Sigma(\text{pairs } i,j)g_{ij}$$

where
$$f_i = -\nabla_i^2 - \frac{2Z}{r_i} \qquad g_{ij} = \frac{2}{r_{ij}} \qquad (13\text{-}2)$$

We shall find that we can evaluate the various integrals met in Sec. 12-5 rather completely, reducing them to radial integrals which must be computed in terms of the radial functions R_{nl}. Let us first consider the one-electron integrals. We take the integral $(i/f/i')$ of Eq. (12-30) and later can get $(i/f/i)$ from it by letting $u_i' = u_i$.

We proceed as in Eq. (9-11) and find

$$-\nabla^2 u_i' = \frac{(-1)^{(m_{li'}+|m_{li}'|)/2}}{\sqrt{4\pi}} \sqrt{\frac{(2l_i'+1)(l_i'-|m_{li}'|)!}{(l_i'+|m_{li}'|)!}} \, P_{l_i'}^{|m_{li'}'|}(\cos\theta)$$

$$\times \exp{(im_{li}'\phi)} v_{m_{si}'}(s) \frac{1}{r}\left[-\frac{d^2}{dr^2} + \frac{l_i'(l_i'+1)}{r^2}\right] P_{n_i'l_i'} \quad (13\text{-}3)$$

We multiply by u_i^* and integrate and sum over the coordinates and spins. On account of the orthogonality of the associated Legendre functions, the exponential, and the spin functions, the result is zero unless $l_i = l_i'$, $m_{li} = m_{li}'$, and $m_{si} = m_{si}'$. We find

$$\int u_i^*(-\nabla^2)u_i' \, dv = \delta(l_1,l_1') \, \delta(m_{li},m_{li}') \, \delta(m_{si},m_{si}')$$

$$\times \int_0^\infty P_{n_i l_i}^*(r)\left[-\frac{d^2}{dr^2} + \frac{l_i(l_i+1)}{r^2}\right] P_{n_i'l_i}(r) \, dr \quad (13\text{-}4)$$

By integration by parts we can put this integral into a more symmetrical form, exhibiting the Hermitian nature of the matrix of kinetic energy, and expressing the kinetic energy in terms of the product of first derivatives rather than in terms of a second derivative. This form, which is sometimes more convenient for the calculation than Eq. (13-4), can be written alternatively in two ways, as

$$\int u_i^*(-\nabla^2)u_i' \, dv = \delta(l_i,l_i') \, \delta(m_{li},m_{li}') \, \delta(m_{si},m_{si}')$$

$$\times \int_0^\infty \left[r^2\frac{dR_{n_i l_i}^*}{dr}\frac{dR_{n_i'l_i}}{dr} + l_i(l_i+1)R_{n_i l_i}^* R_{n_i'l_i}\right] dr$$

$$= \delta(l_i,l_i') \, \delta(m_{li},m_{li}') \, \delta(m_{si},m_{si}')$$

$$\times \int_0^\infty r^{2l_i+2}\frac{d}{dr}\left(\frac{R_{n_i l_i}^*}{r^{l_i}}\right)\frac{d}{dr}\left(\frac{R_{n_i'l_i}}{r^{l_i}}\right) dr \quad (13\text{-}5)$$

The second of these forms, which is not commonly found in the literature, is due to Freeman and Löwdin[1] and is very convenient for numerical calculation. The special case where $i = i'$, $n_i = n_i'$, given in Eq. (9-13), follows in an obvious manner from Eq. (13-4) or Eq. (13-5).

The matrix components of the potential energy in the field of the nucleus are very simple. As in the preceding case, the matrix component is zero unless $l_i = l_i'$, $m_{li} = m_{li}'$, $m_{si} = m_{si}'$. Then we have

$$\int u_i^*\left(-\frac{2Z}{r}\right)u_i' \, dv = \delta(l_i,l_i') \, \delta(m_{li},m_{li}') \, \delta(m_{si},m_{si}')$$

$$\times \left(-2Z\int_0^\infty rR_{n_i l_i}^* R_{n_i'l_i} \, dr\right) \quad (13\text{-}6)$$

[1] A. J. Freeman and P. O. Löwdin, *Phys. Rev.*, **111**:1212 (1958).

We shall find it convenient to have an abbreviation for the sum of the two one-electron integrals, when we are dealing with diagonal matrix components: we shall let

$$I(nl) = \int u_i^* \left(-\nabla^2 - \frac{2Z}{r} \right) u_i \, dv$$

$$= \int_0^\infty \left[r^{2l+2} \frac{d}{dr} \left(\frac{R_{nl}^*}{r^l} \right) \frac{d}{dr} \left(\frac{R_{nl}}{r^l} \right) - 2Zr R_{nl}^* R_{nl} \right] dr \quad (13\text{-}7)$$

as in Eq. (9-14).

The two-electron operators $g_{ij} = 2/r_{ij}$ are more complicated to handle. We shall discuss the general case of the integral $(ij/g/rt)$ of Eq. (12-32). We need to be able to express the quantity $1/r_{12}$ in terms of the coordinates in a convenient way.   To do this, we use the familiar expansion

$$\frac{1}{r_{12}} = \sum_{k=0}^\infty \sum_{m=-k}^k \frac{(k - |m|)!}{(k + |m|)!} \frac{r(a)^k}{r(b)^{k+1}} P_k^{|m|}(\cos \theta_1) P_k^{|m|}(\cos \theta_2)$$

$$\times \exp[im(\phi_1 - \phi_2)] \quad (13\text{-}8)$$

Here r_{12} is the distance between the points given by the coordinates r_1, θ_1, ϕ_1 and r_2, θ_2, ϕ_2 and $r(a)$ is the smaller, $r(b)$ the larger of r_1 and r_2. In terms of this expansion, we can then write the integral $(ij/g/rt)$ in the following form:

$$(ij/g/rt) = \sum_{k=0}^\infty \sum_{m=-k}^k \frac{(k - |m|)!}{(k + |m|)!} \delta(m_{si}, m_{sr}) \, \delta(m_{sj}, m_{st})$$

$$\times (-1)^{(m_{li} + |m_{li}| + m_{lj} + |m_{lj}| + m_{lr} + |m_{lr}| + m_{lt} + |m_{lt}|)/2}$$

$$\times \sqrt{\frac{(2l_i + 1)(l_i - |m_{li}|)!}{(l_i + |m_{li}|)!}} \sqrt{\frac{(2l_j + 1)(l_j - |m_{lj}|)!}{(l_j + |m_{lj}|)!}}$$

$$\times \sqrt{\frac{(2l_r + 1)(l_r - |m_{lr}|)!}{(l_r + |m_{lr}|)!}} \sqrt{\frac{(2l_t + 1)(l_t - |m_{lt}|)!}{(l_t + |m_{lt}|)!}}$$

$$\times \int_0^\infty \int_0^\infty R_{n_i l_i}^*(r_1) R_{n_j l_j}^*(r_2) R_{n_r l_r}(r_1) R_{n_t l_t}(r_2) \frac{2r(a)^k}{r(b)^{k+1}} r_1^2 r_2^2 \, dr_1 \, dr_2$$

$$\times \int_0^\pi P_{l_i}^{|m_{li}|}(\cos \theta_1) P_{l_r}^{|m_{lr}|}(\cos \theta_1) P_k^{|m|}(\cos \theta_1) \frac{\sin \theta_1}{2} \, d\theta_1$$

$$\times \int_0^\pi P_{l_j}^{|m_{lj}|}(\cos \theta_2) P_{l_t}^{|m_{lt}|}(\cos \theta_2) P_k^{|m|}(\cos \theta_2) \frac{\sin \theta_2}{2} \, d\theta_2$$

$$\times \int_0^{2\pi} \exp[i(-m_{li} + m_{lr} + m)\phi_1] \frac{d\phi_1}{2\pi}$$

$$\times \int_0^{2\pi} \exp[i(-m_{lj} + m_{lt} - m)\phi_2] \frac{d\phi_2}{2\pi} \quad (13\text{-}9)$$

The rather formidable expression of Eq. (13-9) simplifies on account of the integrals over the ϕ's.   Each such integral is zero unless the exponent is zero, in which case it is unity.   Hence, in order to have a nonvanishing integral, we must have

$$m = m_{li} - m_{lr} = -m_{lj} + m_{lt} \tag{13-10}$$

from which $m_{li} + m_{lj} = m_{lr} + m_{lt}$ (13-11)

That is, there is a nonvanishing matrix component of the Coulomb energy only between two states for which the sum of the m_l's is the same in both initial and final states.   Furthermore, since m must be fixed by Eq. (13-10), we do not really have a summation over m in Eq. (13-9) but have only one term out of this summation.

The integral over θ in Eq. (13-9) involves the integral of a product of three associated Legendre functions.   Any such integral can be worked out by elementary methods, since the associated Legendre functions are known in terms of powers of sines and cosines.   However, a general formula has been given by Gaunt[1] and later in another form by Racah.[2] Gaunt's formula is as follows:

$$\frac{1}{2} \int_{-1}^{1} P_l^u(\mu) P_m^v(\mu) P_n^w(\mu) \, d\mu$$

$$= (-1)^{s-m-w} \frac{(m+v)!(n+w)!(2s-2n)!s!}{(m-v)!(s-l)!(s-m)!(s-n)!(2s+1)!}$$

$$\times \sum (t)(-1)^t \frac{(l+u+t)!(m+n-u-t)!}{t!(l-u-t)!(m-n+u+t)!(n-w-t)!} \tag{13-12}$$

In this formula in the first place it is assumed that u, v, and w are zero or positive and that

$$u = v + w \tag{13-13}$$

Thus we shall make different choices of u in the integrals of Eq. (13-9), depending on the signs of the m_i's.   The quantity s in Eq. (13-12) is defined as

$$l + m + n = 2s \tag{13-14}$$

where s is an integer; the integral is zero unless $l + m + n$ is an even integer.   The integral is also zero unless

$$m + n \geq l \geq m - n \tag{13-15}$$

the so-called triangular condition, according to which l, m, n can be chosen to be the sides of a triangle.   It is assumed that

$$m \geq n \tag{13-16}$$

[1] J. A. Gaunt, *Phil. Trans. Roy. Soc. (London)*, **A228**:151 (1929).
[2] G. Racah, *Phys. Rev.*, **61**:186 (1942).

In the summation over t, we are to go over just those values for which all the factorials have a meaning; that is, t goes from the greater of 0, $-m + n - u$, to the smaller of $m + n - u$, $l - u$, and $n - w$.

In order to have the final formulas in as simple a form as possible, it is now conventional, as first suggested by Inglis and Shortley,[1] to define certain coefficients which incorporate the integrals over θ in Eq. (13-9), and the square roots and powers of -1 which naturally go with them. The definition is

$$c^k(lm;l'm') = (-1)^{[m+|m|+m'+|m'|+(m-m')+|m-m'|]/2}$$

$$\times \sqrt{\frac{(k - |m - m'|)!}{(k + |m - m'|)!}} \sqrt{\frac{(2l + 1)(l - |m|)!}{(l + |m|)!}} \sqrt{\frac{(2l' + 1)(l' - |m'|)!}{(l' + |m'|)!}}$$

$$\times \frac{1}{2} \int_{-1}^{1} P_l^{|m|}(\mu) P_{l'}^{|m'|}(\mu) P_k^{|m-m'|}(\mu) \, d\mu \quad (13\text{-}17)$$

These c's can be computed from Eq. (13-12). They are tabulated, for all combinations of electrons up to $l = 2$, or d electrons, in Appendix 20a. In the more complete Appendix 20, contained in Vol. II, we also include the case of $l = 3$, f electrons.

In terms of these coefficients, the expression of Eq. (13-9) can be rewritten in the form

$$(ij/g/rt) = \delta(m_{si}, m_{sr}) \, \delta(m_{sj}, m_{st}) \, \delta(m_{li} + m_{lj}, m_{lr} + m_{lt})$$

$$\times \sum_{k=0}^{\infty} c^k(l_i m_{li}; l_r m_{lr}) c^k(l_t m_{lt}; l_j m_{lj}) R^k(ij;rt) \quad (13\text{-}18)$$

where

$$R^k(ij;rt)$$

$$= \int_0^{\infty} \int_0^{\infty} R_{n_i l_i}^*(r_1) R_{n_j l_j}^*(r_2) R_{n_r l_r}(r_1) R_{n_t l_t}(r_2) \frac{2r(a)^k}{r(b)^{k+1}} r_1^2 r_2^2 \, dr_1 \, dr_2 \quad (13\text{-}19)$$

We have defined the various quantities in this expression to agree with the notation in the well-known book of Condon and Shortley,[2] except that we are using the Rydberg as the unit of energy, rather than Hartree's atomic unit of 2 Rydbergs. One should note particularly the reversed order of subscripts in the second factor $c^k(l_t m_{lt}; l_j m_{lj})$ in Eq. (13-18). One notices also from the table of the c^k's in Appendix 20a that the highest value of k for which c^k is nonvanishing is $l + l'$; this follows from the triangular condition of Eq. (13-15), written in the alternative form $l + m \geq n \geq l - m$. Hence the summation in Eq. (13-18) is not really

[1] D. R. Inglis, *Phys. Rev.*, **38**:862 (1931); G. H. Shortley, *Phys. Rev.*, **40**:185 (1932); C. W. Ufford and G. H. Shortley, *Phys. Rev.*, **42**:167 (1932).

[2] E. U. Condon and G. H. Shortley, "Theory of Atomic Spectra," Cambridge University Press, New York, 1935.

from zero to infinity, but only to a finite upper limit which is the smaller of the two quantities $l_i + l_r$ or $l_j + l_t$. This means that the calculation of the matrix components of the Coulomb energy is not at all an unmanageable problem.

The special case of diagonal matrix components comes up so frequently that it is worth while stating the form which Eqs. (13-18) and (13-19) take in that case. From Eq. (12-31) we see that we need two types of terms: the so-called Coulomb integral $(ij/g/ij)$, and the exchange integral $(ij/g/ji)$. For the Coulomb integral, it is customary, following the notation of the author, to write

$$(ij/g/ij) = \sum_{k=0}^{\infty} a^k(l_i m_{li}; l_j m_{lj}) F^k(n_i l_i; n_j l_j) \qquad (13\text{-}20)$$

where $\qquad a^k(l_i m_{li}; l_j m_{lj}) = c^k(l_i m_{li}; l_i m_{li}) c^k(l_j m_{lj}; l_j m_{lj}) \qquad (13\text{-}21)$

and

$$F^k(n_i l_i; n_j l_j) = R^k(ij; ij)$$
$$= \int_0^\infty \int_0^\infty R_{n_i l_i}^*(r_1) R_{n_j l_j}^*(r_2) R_{n_i l_i}(r_1) R_{n_j l_j}(r_2) \frac{2r(a)^k}{r(b)^{k+1}} r_1^2 r_2^2 \, dr_1 \, dr_2 \qquad (13\text{-}22)$$

The special case of $k = 0$, given in Eq. (9-21), agrees with Eq. (13-22). Though the a^k's can be easily calculated from the c^k's, it is convenient to have them tabulated directly, and they are given in Appendix 20a and in Appendix 20 (Vol. II). As for the exchange integrals, one writes

$$(ij/g/ji) = \delta(m_{si}, m_{sj}) \sum_{k=0}^{\infty} b^k(l_i m_{li}; l_j m_{lj}) G^k(n_i l_i; n_j l_j) \qquad (13\text{-}23)$$

where $\qquad b^k(l_i m_{li}; l_j m_{lj}) = [c^k(l_i m_{li}; l_j m_{lj})]^2 \qquad (13\text{-}24)$

and

$$G^k(n_i l_i; n_j l_j) = R^k(ij; ji)$$
$$= \int_0^\infty \int_0^\infty R_{n_i l_i}^*(r_1) R_{n_j l_j}^*(r_2) R_{n_j l_j}(r_1) R_{n_i l_i}(r_2) \frac{2r(a)^k}{r(b)^{k+1}} r_1^2 r_2^2 \, dr_1 \, dr_2 \qquad (13\text{-}25)$$

It is so simple to get the b^k's from the c^k's that a separate table is not required. Following Condon and Shortley,[1] one frequently introduces integrals F_k and G_k, equal to F^k/D_k and G^k/D_k, respectively, where the D_k's are the denominators occurring in the table of the a_k's and b_k's. We shall not use this notation in the present volume.

[1] E. U. Condon and G. H. Shortley, *Phys. Rev.*, **37**:1025 (1931).

13-4. Energy Values for Simple Multiplets. Now that we have found how to compute the matrix elements of the Hamiltonian, we can go back to the simple cases which we have discussed earlier in this chapter and find the energy values of the various multiplets. Let us start with the s and p electrons, which we illustrated in Table 11-3 and Fig. 13-2. We shall assume that there are no inner shells in the atom, but only the s and p electrons, as if we were dealing with a configuration $1s2p$ of helium; in the next chapter we shall take up the general question of the effect of inner shells and shall show that they result only in an additive constant added to all the multiplet energies of the configuration. Our first step is to compute the matrix components of the Hamiltonian with respect to the original determinantal functions. We find, as we expected from general principles, that there is no matrix component of the Hamiltonian between two states of different M_L or M_S values. Thus the six determinantal functions corresponding to $M_L = 1, 0, -1, M_S = \pm 1$ are eigenfunctions as they stand. When we compute the diagonal matrix components of the Hamiltonian for these states, using the rules of the preceding section, we find

$$\text{Energy} = I(1s) + I(2p) + F^0(1s,2p) - \tfrac{1}{3}G^1(1s,2p) \quad (13\text{-}26)$$

These single determinants are all eigenfunctions corresponding to the ^3P, so that the energy of that state is given by Eq. (13-26).

Next we consider the cases in which there are two determinantal functions with the same M_L, M_S values, namely, the cases $M_L = 1, 0, -1$, $M_S = 0$. We find in each case that the diagonal matrix component for each of the two states is $I(1s) + I(2p) + F^0(1s,2p)$ and the nondiagonal matrix component between them is $-(\tfrac{1}{3})G^1(1s,2p)$. Since the two states are degenerate, the solutions of the secular problem will be the diagonal energy plus or minus the nondiagonal matrix component, the first case leading to the energy of the ^3P state given in Eq. (13-26), and the second leading to the energy of the ^1P state,

$$\text{Energy of } {}^1P = I(1s) + I(2p) + F^0(1s,2p) + \tfrac{1}{3}G^1(1s,2p) \quad (13\text{-}27)$$

It is obvious that the energy of the ^1P could have been found by the sum rule, but this secular problem is so simple to solve that it is immaterial whether we use the sum rule or not.

As a next example, we take the case of two nonequivalent p electrons, as given in Table 13-1 and Fig. 13-3. We consider first the single determinantal function corresponding to $M_L = 2$, $M_S = 1$, which is a state of ^3D. We find that its diagonal energy is

$$\begin{aligned}
\text{Energy of } {}^3D = I(2p) + I(3p) + F^0(2p,3p) + \tfrac{1}{25}F^2(2p,3p) \\
- G^0(2p,3p) - \tfrac{1}{25}G^2(2p,3p) \quad (13\text{-}28)
\end{aligned}$$

Next we consider the two states with $M_L = 1$, $M_S = 1$.   Here we must have ^3D and ^3P as the eigenfunctions, so that the sum of the two diagonal matrix components of the unperturbed functions must equal the sum of the eigenvalues of ^3D and ^3P.   Since we have already determined the energy of ^3D, we can subtract and find the energy of ^3P.   We find that it is

$$\text{Energy of } ^3P = I(2p) + I(3p) + F^0(2p,3p) - \tfrac{5}{25}F^2(2p,3p)$$
$$+ G^0(2p,3p) - \tfrac{5}{25}G^2(2p,3p) \quad (13\text{-}29)$$

In similar ways, we can use the sum rule as we have already described it in Sec. 13-2.   We find for the energies of the remaining multiplets the following values:

Energy of ^3S:
$$I(2p) + I(3p) + F^0(2p,3p) + \tfrac{10}{25}F^2(2p,3p)$$
$$- G^0(2p,3p) - \tfrac{10}{25}G^2(2p,3p)$$

Energy of ^1D:
$$I(2p) + I(3p) + F^0(2p,3p) + \tfrac{1}{25}F^2(2p,3p)$$
$$+ G^0(2p,3p) + \tfrac{1}{25}G^2(2p,3p) \quad (13\text{-}30)$$

Energy of ^1P:
$$I(2p) + I(3p) + F^0(2p,3p) - \tfrac{5}{25}F^2(2p,3p)$$
$$- G^0(2p,3p) + \tfrac{5}{25}G^2(2p,3p)$$

Energy of ^1S:
$$I(2p) + I(3p) + F^0(2p,3p) + \tfrac{10}{25}F^2(2p,3p)$$
$$+ G^0(2p,3p) + \tfrac{10}{25}G^2(2p,3p)$$

In a similar way we can proceed with the case of two equivalent p electrons, which we have also discussed in Sec. 13-2 by means of the sum rule. We find without trouble that

$$\text{Energy of } ^3P = 2I(2p) + F^0(2p,2p) - \tfrac{5}{25}F^2(2p,2p)$$
$$\text{Energy of } ^1D = 2I(2p) + F^0(2p,2p) + \tfrac{1}{25}F^2(2p,2p) \quad (13\text{-}31)$$
$$\text{Energy of } ^1S = 2I(2p) + F^0(2p,2p) + \tfrac{10}{25}F^2(2p,2p)$$

These simple examples show the power of the diagonal sum method: in the case of the nonequivalent p electrons, the only secular problem in which the ^1S appears is that corresponding to $M_L = 0$, $M_S = 0$, which involves a 6×6 secular equation, which would be very difficult to solve if we did not have this feature simplifying the problem.   The general procedure we have been using in this section has been applied in a great many cases of multiplets.   In Appendix 21a we tabulate the resulting formulas for the energies, in a number of simple cases.   There is one point concerning these formulas for which the reader will wish to consult the following chapter: we give in that chapter a number of theorems relating to the effect of closed shells on multiplet energies, the average energy of all the terms in a multiplet, and closely related theorems, which help in interpreting the results. The energy values of Appendix 21a are set up in terms of the average energies of the multiplets, as explained in the following chapter, and for that reason differ by additive constants from the examples which we have already given.

In Appendix 21, which is given in Vol. II, we give a greatly expanded version of Appendix 21a, including many further cases, not only the simple cases which can be handled by the sum rule, but also many other cases which have been discussed in the literature by methods to be given in Vol. II. In cases where we have more than one multiplet with the same L and S value, there are nondiagonal matrix components of the Hamiltonian between these multiplets. These nondiagonal components, as well as the diagonal components, are given in Appendix 21, and of course we must solve a secular equation to determine the eigenvalues. The methods of setting up these nondiagonal matrix components will be given in later chapters, particularly Chaps. 21 and 22 (Vol. II), but the reader who does not wish to go into those more elaborate methods will still be able to make use of the results of Appendix 21. In addition to this material included in Appendix 21, we also give there a bibliography of some of the important papers in the development of multiplet theory.

The reader will realize that in this chapter we have made practically no use of the properties of the angular-momentum operators. For simple cases which can be handled by the diagonal sum rule, we can avoid discussing the angular momentum, and for several chapters we shall be treating the problem without much use of the angular momentum. But for a deeper understanding of the problem, and for a discussion of cases too complicated to handle by the diagonal sum rule, a study of the angular-momentum operators is essential and we shall come back to them in Chap. 20 (Vol. II), where we shall take up the general question of finding the eigenfunctions, as well as the eigenvalues, of our secular problem and shall investigate the matrix components of the angular-momentum operators. After we have done that, we shall be prepared to go ahead with more advanced discussion of multiplet theory, and with a study of spin-orbit interaction, which we are also disregarding entirely in this chapter and in a number of the following chapters.

PROBLEMS

1. Find the average energy of the multiplets in the configuration $(2p)^2$, as given in Eq. (13-31). This average is to be a weighted mean, in which a multiplet of a given L, S value is weighted by the number $(2L + 1)(2S + 1)$ of states involved in it. Find the energy of each of the multiplets in this configuration, with respect to the average. Compare with the values given for this configuration in Table 15-3 and Appendix 21a, both of which are computed in terms of the average.

2. Find the energies of the various multiplets of the configuration $1s2p^2$, referred to the average energy, and compare with the values in Table 15-3 and Appendix 21a.

3. Show that the energies of the multiplets of the configuration $1s2p^4$, when referred to the average energy, have the same formula as those of $1s2p^2$.

4. Find the energies of the various multiplets of the configurations $2p^3$ and $1s2p^3$ referred to their average energies, and compare with the values in Table 15-3 and Appendix 21a.

5. Find the energies of the various multiplets of the configuration $3d^2$, referred to the average energy, and compare with the values in Appendix 21a.

6. Assume that the $1s$ orbital is given by a normalizing factor times $\exp(-ar)$ and the $2p$ orbital by a normalizing factor times a function of angle times $r \exp(-cr)$, according to the assumptions of Eq. (15-6) (setting the factor μ which appears in that equation equal to unity). Compute the one-electron integrals $I(1s)$ and $I(2p)$ for these orbitals, and show that they check the values given in Table 15-6.

7. Use the $1s$ and $2p$ orbitals described in Prob. 6, and compute the integrals $F^0(1s,1s)$, $F^0(1s,2p)$, $F^0(2p,2p)$, $G^1(1s,2p)$, and $F^2(2p,2p)$, showing that they agree with the values given in Table 15-6.

14

Further Results of Multiplet Theory: Closed Shells and Average Energies

14-1. Closed and Almost Closed Shells. In the preceding chapter we have explored the general methods of handling multiplets, and in the present chapter we shall extend these results in a number of respects, without using more advanced methods. The first theorems which we shall prove will concern the effect of closed shells of electrons. Briefly, we shall show that the only effect of a closed shell on the calculation of the multiplets arising from certain electrons in configurations outside the closed shell is to contribute an additive constant to the energy.

This is what is to be expected intuitively on general grounds. From the result of Eq. (7-36), that any closed shell corresponds to a spherically symmetrical distribution of charge, we expect that the electrostatic interaction between these closed shells and the outer electrons will behave just like a central field acting on these outer electrons. But we have seen in Eq. (13-6) that such a central field (as, for instance, the Coulomb attraction of the nucleus) will give identical contributions to the diagonal energy of all electronic wave functions of a given (nl) value, irrespective of their m_l value (for that really determines only the orientation of the orbit in space), and furthermore the central field will give no nondiagonal matrix components between different determinantal functions associated with the same configuration, but only between determinantal functions in which an orbital u_i in one determinant is replaced by an orbital u_i' of the same l, m_l, m_s but different n value in the other determinant. It is only the electronic interactions, or the two-electron operators, which can give nondiagonal matrix components between functions in the same configuration. In the present section, we shall show by methods due to Shortley[1] that closed shells act like spherical potentials, as far as the multiplet structure is concerned.

[1] G. H. Shortley, *Phys. Rev.*, **40**:185 (1932).

We shall first show that in the summation $\Sigma(j)(ij/g/ij)$ involved in the diagonal matrix component of energy, where j goes over a closed shell and i refers to an electron outside this shell, the result is independent of the m_l of the ith electron. From Eq. (7-31) for the wave functions and Eq. (7-36), we find that

$$\sum (j)u_j^*(x_2)u_j(x_2) = \frac{2l_j + 1}{4\pi}[R_{n_jl_j}(r_2)]^2 \qquad (14\text{-}1)$$

where x_2 symbolizes the coordinates r_2, θ_2, ϕ_2, and spin s_2 of the second electron and where we have omitted the asterisk from R, since the R's are real. The summation over j in Eq. (14-1) is over the various values of m_{lj} but not over m_{sj}. If in addition we sum over m_{sj}, the effect is to multiply the right side of Eq. (14-1) by 2.

We now multiply by $u_i^*(x_1)u_i(x_1)(2/r_{12})$, express $2/r_{12}$ in the form of Eq. (13-8), and integrate over dv_1 and dv_2, including summation over the spins. We find that

$$\Sigma(j)(ij/g/ij) = 2(2l_j + 1)F^0(ij) \qquad (14\text{-}2)$$

where we now extend the summation over j to both m_{lj} and m_{sj}, or over the $2(2l_j + 1)$ states in the complete shell. The result, as we wished to show, is independent of the m_l of the ith electron.

Next we wish to show that the same situation holds with the sum of the exchange integrals, $\Sigma(j)(ij/g/ji)$. This is a more difficult thing to do. The quantity which we wish to compute is

$$\Sigma(j)\int u_i^*(x_1)u_j^*(x_2)(2/r_{12})u_j(x_1)u_i(x_2)\, dv_1\, dv_2 \qquad (14\text{-}3)$$

We remember that exchange integrals are zero unless $m_{si} = m_{sj}$. Hence we may assume from the outset that this is the case and may interpret the integration in Eq. (14-3) as being only over spatial coordinates, without summation over spins, the u_i and u_j being interpreted as orbital functions of coordinates. In this case $\Sigma(j)$ includes only a summation over values of m_{lj}, m_{sj} taking on only the value equal to m_{si}. As a first step, we now consider the quantity $\Sigma(j)u_j^*(x_2)u_j(x_1)$. We again use Eq. (7-31) for the wave functions and Eq. (7-34) and now find that

$$\sum (j)u_j^*(x_2)u_j(x_1) = \frac{2l_j + 1}{4\pi} R_{n_jl_j}(r_1)R_{n_jl_j}(r_2)P_{l_j}(\cos \gamma) \qquad (14\text{-}4)$$

where γ is the angle between the radius vectors to the two electrons. The quantity $1/r_{12}$ in Eq. (14-3) can be expanded in the form

$$\frac{1}{r_{12}} = \sum (k)\frac{r(a)^k}{r(b)^{k+1}}P_k(\cos \gamma) \qquad (14\text{-}5)$$

where as before $r(a)$ is the smaller, $r(b)$ the greater of the two quantities r_1, r_2 and γ has the same meaning as above. This equation is one which, by use of Eq. (7-34), results in the expression of Eq. (13-8), which we have used earlier. Then we have

$$\sum (j) u_j^*(x_2) u_j(x_1) \frac{1}{r_{12}} = \sum (k) \frac{2l_j + 1}{4\pi} R_{n_j l_j}(r_1) R_{n_j l_j}(r_2)$$
$$\times \frac{r(a)^k}{r(b)^{k+1}} P_k(\cos \gamma) P_{l_j}(\cos \gamma) \quad (14\text{-}6)$$

But now the product $P_k(\cos \gamma) P_{l_j}(\cos \gamma)$ can be expanded in Legendre functions of the angle γ, for any function of γ can be so expanded. That is, we can write

$$P_k(\cos \gamma) P_{l_j}(\cos \gamma) = \Sigma(l) A(k, l_j, l) P_l(\cos \gamma) \quad (14\text{-}7)$$

We shall shortly evaluate the coefficients $A(k, l_j, l)$, but first let us proceed and see how the expansion of Eq. (14-7) allows us to prove our theorem.

We substitute Eq. (14-7) into Eq. (14-6) and substitute that in turn in Eq. (14-3). We write $u_i^*(x_1) u_i(x_2)$ from Eq. (7-31). We take $P_l(\cos \gamma)$ from Eq. (14-7) and expand it according to Eq. (7-34). Then we have

$$\sum (j)(ij/g/ji) = \sum (k) \sum (l) \sum_{m=-l}^{l} A(k, l_j, l) \frac{(2l_i + 1)(l_i - |m_{li}|)!}{(l_i + |m_{li}|)!}$$
$$\times \frac{(2l_j + 1)(l - |m|)!}{(l + |m|)!}$$
$$\times \int_0^\infty \int_0^\infty R_{n_i l_i}(r_1) R_{n_j l_j}(r_2) R_{n_j l_j}(r_1) R_{n_i l_i}(r_2) \frac{2r(a)^k}{r(b)^{k+1}} r_1^2 r_2^2 \, dr_1 \, dr_2$$
$$\times \int_0^\pi P_{l_i}^{|m_{li}|}(\cos \theta_1) P_l^{|m|}(\cos \theta_1) \frac{\sin \theta_1}{2} \, d\theta_1$$
$$\times \int_0^\pi P_{l_i}^{|m_{li}|}(\cos \theta_2) P_l^{|m|}(\cos \theta_2) \frac{\sin \theta_2}{2} \, d\theta_2$$
$$\times \int_0^{2\pi} \exp[i(m - m_{li})\phi_1] \frac{d\phi_1}{2\pi} \int_0^{2\pi} \exp[-i(m - m_{li})\phi_2] \frac{d\phi_2}{2\pi} \quad (14\text{-}8)$$

In the integrals over ϕ_1 and ϕ_2 we have zero unless $m = m_{li}$, in which case each integral equals unity. Then, using Eq. (7-11), we see that each of the integrals over θ_1 or θ_2 is zero unless $l = l_i$, in which case each one equals

$$\frac{1}{2l_i + 1} \frac{(l_i + |m_{li}|)!}{(l_i - |m_{li}|)!} \quad (14\text{-}9)$$

Furthermore, the integral over the r's in Eq. (14-8) equals $G^k(n_i l_i; n_j l_j)$. Then Eq. (14-8) can be rewritten

$$\sum (j)(ij/g/ji) = \sum (k) \frac{2l_j + 1}{2l_i + 1} A(k, l_j, l_i) G^k(n_i l_i; n_j l_j) \quad (14\text{-}10)$$

In Eq. (14-10), the magnetic quantum number m_{l_i} no longer appears, so that we have proved our point that the summation is independent of the m_l of the ith electron. We remember that the orbitals over which we were summing had the same spin as the ith orbital; otherwise the terms are zero.

We can now go further and evaluate the constant $A(k,l_j,l_i)$ in Eq. (14-10), and hence get a closed formula for the summation we desire. We multiply Eq. (14-7) by $P_{l_i}(\cos \gamma) \sin \gamma$ and integrate from 0 to π with respect to γ. We then use Eq. (7-11) in the special case where $m = 0$ and have

$$\int_0^\pi P_{l_i}(\cos \gamma) P_{l_i}(\cos \gamma) P_k(\cos \gamma) \sin \gamma \, d\gamma = \frac{2A(k,l_j,l_i)}{2l_i + 1} \quad (14\text{-}11)$$

Thus we have expressed $A(k,l_j,l_i)$ in terms of an integral of a product of three Legendre functions, for which we have given a formula in Eq. (13-12). It is convenient to express this quantity in terms of the c's, which are defined in terms of these integrals in Eq. (13-17). That equation takes a very simple form in the present case, where the m's are zero, and we have

$$A(k,l_j,l_i) = \sqrt{\frac{2l_i + 1}{2l_j + 1}} \, c^k(l_i 0; l_j 0) \quad (14\text{-}12)$$

Thus finally, substituting in Eq. (14-10), we have

$$\sum (j)(ij/g/ji) = \sqrt{\frac{2l_j + 1}{2l_i + 1}} \sum (k) c^k(l_i 0; l_j 0) G^k(n_i l_i; n_j l_j) \quad (14\text{-}13)$$

In Eq. (14-13) we have a simple formula for the sum of the exchange interactions of an electron i outside a closed shell of electrons j having the same spin as the ith. As we have pointed out before, this is independent of the m_l of the ith electron.

We have thus discussed the diagonal matrix components of energy for an atom containing a closed shell and electrons outside the closed shell and have shown that these matrix components involving interaction between one of the outer electrons and the closed shell are independent of the m_l of the outer electron. This leaves the contributions to the diagonal energy arising from Coulomb interactions between electrons outside closed shells as the only ones for which there can be a dependence on the m_l's of the outer electrons, which is what we wished to prove.

To complete our discussion, we must show that there are no non-diagonal matrix components of energy arising from interactions with the electrons in the closed shells. This can be proved easily in ways analogous to those used for the diagonal components. First we have the terms $\Sigma(j)[(ij/g/i'j) - (ij/g/ji')]$. We find easily that terms of this sort arise only for the case where $l_i = l'_i$, $m_{li} = m'_{li}$. Hence we find nondiagonal matrix components arising from these terms only in case the orbital u_i is changed to another orbital u'_i with the same azimuthal and magnetic quantum numbers. It can then differ only in principal quantum number n. Such nondiagonal matrix components do not occur in the case of a single configuration, such as we are discussing in the present chapter, though they could occur in case we were considering the interaction between different configurations. In that case, they would be of just the same sort as nondiagonal matrix components which would be produced by a central field, as we see from Eq. (13-6), where a central field, in this case the Coulomb potential $-2Z/r$, produces nondiagonal matrix components only between two determinantal functions differing by a single orbital whose principal quantum number is different but whose other quantum numbers are the same in u_i and u'_i.

Finally we have the nondiagonal matrix components involving the change of two orbitals between the initial and final determinantal functions. We see from Eq. (12-34) that these matrix components involve only the two electronic orbitals concerned in the transition. Since these must both refer to the electrons outside closed shells, it is obvious that the presence of the closed shells will have no effect on them. Thus we complete our proof that the effect of the closed shell on the multiplet structure is of the sort which would be produced by a spherically symmetrical field.

Next we shall consider the case of an almost closed shell. In Sec. 13-2 we pointed out that a shell containing $N_0 - N_1$ electrons has the same multiplets as one containing N_1 electrons, where N_0 is the number in the completed shell. Going further than this, Heisenberg[1] showed in a simple case that the multiplet separations as well will be the same for a shell lacking N_1 electrons as they will be for the shell with N_1 electrons present. We shall now take up the general proof of this result.

First we consider the diagonal energy. From the discussion just given, we see that we do not need to consider any closed shells, and we confine ourselves to the shell lacking N_1 electrons. The contribution of this shell to the diagonal energy is $\Sigma(\text{pairs } i,j)[(ij/g/ij) - (ij/g/ji)]$, where the summation is over the occupied orbitals in the shell. For convenience in the present calculation, let us number all the orbitals in a complete shell, the numbers from 1 to $N_0 - N_1$ being occupied, those from $N_0 - N_1 + 1$ to N_0 being empty. We note in the first place that our summation can be written as $\frac{1}{2}$ times the sum over i and j separately, each running from 1 to $N_0 - N_1$. This double sum includes the terms for which $i = j$, which are zero anyway, so that it is immaterial whether they are included or not.

[1] W. Heisenberg, *Ann. Physik*, **10**:888 (1931).

We then have

$$\text{Energy} = \frac{1}{2} \sum_{i=1}^{N_0} \sum_{j=1}^{N_0} [(ij/g/ij) - (ij/g/ji)]$$

$$- \frac{1}{2} \sum_{i=N_0-N_1+1}^{N_0} \sum_{j=1}^{N_0} [(ij/g/ij) - (ij/g/ji)]$$

$$- \frac{1}{2} \sum_{j=N_0-N_1+1}^{N_0} \sum_{i=1}^{N_0} [(ij/g/ij) - (ij/g/ji)]$$

$$+ \frac{1}{2} \sum_{i=N_0-N_1+1}^{N_0} \sum_{j=N_0-N_1+1}^{N_0} [(ij/g/ij) - (ij/g/ji)] \quad (14\text{-}14)$$

In Eq. (14-14), the first summation is over the complete shell and hence gives a constant. The second term, for each value of i, involves a summation over all j's in the complete shell and hence, by the results given earlier in this section, gives a result independent of the magnetic quantum number m_{li} of the missing electron. Similarly the third summation gives a result independent of the magnetic quantum number m_{lj} of the missing electron. These first three terms, then, are the same for any one of the determinantal functions involved in the configuration. They merely contribute to the average energy of the configuration.

The last term is the one differing from one determinantal function of the configuration to another, and it is just the same term which we should have for a configuration in which the orbitals from 1 to $N_0 - N_1$ were empty, those from $N_0 - N_1 + 1$ to N_0 being filled. Hence we have proved our result, that as far as the diagonal matrix components of energy are concerned, a shell lacking N_1 electrons has the same matrix components (aside from constant terms, which of course arise from the interaction of the electrons with the spherically symmetrical charge distribution of the complete shell) as a shell containing just N_1 electrons.

To complete our discussion, we must consider nondiagonal matrix components. If a hole shifts from orbital u_i' to u_i, and one from u_j' to u_j, this is the same as an electron shifting from u_i to u_i', and one from u_j to u_j'. From Eq. (12-34), the matrix component of energy will be the same in either case. Thus the secular equation for the multiplets in the complete shell lacking N_1 electrons is precisely the same, except for the constant correction to the energy, as in the shell containing N_1 electrons. Our result is then proved, that a closed shell lacking N_1 electrons has the same multiplet structure as a shell containing N_1 electrons.

If we have a configuration with several partially filled shells, such as a shell capable of holding N_0 electrons which has only N_1, and a shell capable of holding N_0' electrons which has only N_1', and so on, then we can prove in the same way that the multiplet separations are the same as if the first shell had $N_0 - N_1$ electrons, the second $N_0' - N_1'$, and so on. On the other hand, the situation if the first has $N_0 - N_1$ electrons but the second has N_1' is entirely different. Thus, for example, the multiplet separations arising from the configuration $(np)^5(n'p)^5$ are the same as theos arising from $(np)(n'p)$, where n and n' are two principal quantum numbers, but the separations arising from $(np)^5n'p$ are quite different, though we shall have multiplets of the same L, S values as for the case $(np)^5(n'p)^5$. The s shell, which can contain only two electrons, forms a special case, since the s shell lacking one electron is identical with that containing one electron. For this reason the multiplet separations arising, for instance, from $(np)^5(n's)$ are identical with those arising from $(np)(n's)$, or more generally an s electron outside a shell of electrons capable of containing N_0 electrons, but containing only N_1, has multiplets identical with an s electron outside the corresponding shell containing $N_0 - N_1$ electrons.

14-2. The Average Energy of a Configuration. In Sec. 13-4, we have seen that there are several terms in the energy of a multiplet which are common to all multiplets of a configuration, such as the quantities $I(2p) + I(3p) + F^0(2p,3p)$ for the configuration $2p3p$, whereas there are other terms by which one multiplet differs from another. These common terms appear in each diagonal matrix component. In a configuration containing a number of closed shells, the number of such common terms is very large. In most calculations of multiplet separations in the literature, these common terms are disregarded, since the interest is generally only in finding the separations between multiplets. However, these common terms are needed if one is interested in the average energy of the multiplets. We have pointed out in Sec. 8-6 that these average energies are important if we are comparing a simple central-field model with experimental energy levels. We shall show in the present section, following Shortley,[1] that simple and general formulas can be set up for the average energies of all the multiplets in a configuration and that this formula for the average energy can be used as the starting point in computing the common terms in the energies of the various multiplets.

By average we refer to a weighted mean, in which each multiplet, in L-S coupling, is given a weight $(2L + 1)(2S + 1)$, equal to the number of separate wave functions comprising this multiplet. When we use this weighted mean, we can use the diagonal sum rule, which tells us that the sum of diagonal matrix components for the determinantal functions equals the sum of the eigenvalues for all wave functions. Since the

[1] G. H. Shortley, *Phys. Rev.*, **50**:1072 (1936).

mean energy equals this sum divided by the number of determinantal functions, this shows that we can get the same answer by computing the mean energy for all the determinantal functions as by computing the weighted mean of the multiplets in L-S coupling. It is for this reason that we find a simple result. We shall start by considering the case where all electrons are in a single partially filled shell and shall later proceed to the case where there are any number of filled or partially filled shells.

Let us consider a shell which when filled would contain N_0 electrons but which actually contains N_1 electrons. There will then be $N_0!/[N_1!(N_0 - N_1)!]$ determinantal functions. The diagonal matrix component of the term $\Sigma(\text{pairs } i,j)g_{ij}$ in the Hamiltonian, which is the only part of the Hamiltonian about which there is any trouble, is the sum over all pairs i, j of the quantity $(ij/g/ij) - (ij/g/ji)$. We note as in the preceding section that this quantity vanishes if $i = j$, so that it is immaterial whether we include the case $i = j$ in the sum over pairs or not.

Let us now consider a particular pair of spin-orbitals, denoted by i, j. Out of all our determinantal functions, this pair will occur in $(N_0 - 2)!/[(N_1 - 2)!(N_0 - N_1)!]$ determinants, for this is the number of ways of choosing $N_1 - 2$ additional spin-orbitals to supplement the ith and jth. When we average over all determinants, the term $(ij/g/ij) - (ij/g/ji)$ connected with this pair of determinants will then occur with the coefficient

$$\frac{(N_0 - 2)!}{(N_1 - 2)!(N_0 - N_1)!} \frac{N_1!(N_0 - N_1)!}{N_0!} = \frac{N_1(N_1 - 1)}{N_0(N_0 - 1)} \quad (14\text{-}15)$$

This coefficient is the same for each pair of spin-orbitals. If we denote the average value of the expression $(ij/g/ij) - (ij/g/ji)$, averaged over pairs i, j, where $i \neq j$, by $[(ij/g/ij) - (ij/g/ji)]_{\text{av}}$, and if we remember that there are $N_0(N_0 - 1)/2$ pairs of spin-orbitals, we see that the contribution of these two-electron operators to the sum of the energies of the configuration containing N_1 electrons in a shell capable of holding N_0 electrons will be the product of $N_0(N_0 - 1)/2$ times the average times the expression of Eq. (14-15), or will be

$$\frac{N_1(N_1 - 1)}{2} [(ij/g/ij) - (ij/g/ji)]_{\text{av}} \quad (14\text{-}16)$$

Since $N_1(N_1 - 1)/2$ is the number of pairs of electrons in the shell, this means that we can compute the average energy just as if each electron acted on each other electron with an interaction energy equal to $[(ij/g/ij) - (ij/g/ji)]_{\text{av}}$. Let us then compute this average.

For the first term $(ij/g/ij)$, we can use Eq. (14-2), where we showed that $\Sigma(j)(ij/g/ij) = (2l_j + 1)F^0(ij)$. Here we were summing over the

$2l_j + 1$ orbitals of a given spin in a shell with azimuthal quantum number l_j. For the second term $(ij/g/ji)$, we can use Eq. (14-13), which becomes

$$\Sigma(j)(ij/g/ji) = \Sigma(k)c^k(l0,l0)F^k(l,l) \qquad (14\text{-}17)$$

for the case where both orbitals are in the same shell; an examination of the derivation of Eq. (14-13) shows that, though it was intended for the case where the orbitals are in different shells, it applies to the present case as well. Now in finding our average, we can take one-half the double sum over i and j, which includes all pairs of spin-orbitals (including the cases $i = j$, which as we have seen do not contribute to the sum) and divide by $N_0(N_0 - 1)/2 = (4l + 2)(4l + 1)/2$, where l is the azimuthal quantum number, the number of pairs of spin-orbitals which make nonvanishing contributions to the average.

For the term $(ij/g/ij)$, it is clear that the contribution to half the double sum will be $[(4l + 2)^2/2]F^0(l,l)$. This includes the cases $i = j$. For the term $(ij/g/ji)$, each of the $4l + 2$ spin-orbitals will contribute a term given by Eq. (14-17) to the double sum (this takes account of the fact that only electrons of the same spin have nonvanishing terms of this type), so that in finding half the double sum we must multiply Eq. (14-17) by $(4l + 2)/2$. This again includes the case $i = j$. Thus we find for half the double sum

$$\tfrac{1}{2}(4l + 2)^2F^0(l,l) - \tfrac{1}{2}(4l + 2)\Sigma(k)c^k(l0,l0)F^k(l,l) \qquad (14\text{-}18)$$

We note from Appendix 20a that, for any l, $c^0(l0,l0) = 1$. Hence we may combine the term in $F^0(l,l)$ from the second term of Eq. (14-18) with the first term, which then becomes $\tfrac{1}{2}(4l + 2)(4l + 1)F^0(l,l)$, leaving the summation in the second term running only over the values $k = 2$, $4, \ldots$. Finally we have

$$[(ij/g/ij) - (ij/g/ji)]_{\text{av}} = F^0(l,l)$$
$$- \frac{1}{4l + 1}[c^2(l0,l0)F^2(l,l) + c^4(l0,l0)F^4(l,l) \cdots] \qquad (14\text{-}19)$$

This quantity then indicates the average interaction energy of a pair of electrons in the shell with azimuthal quantum number l.

When we use the values of Appendix 20a, we find

Interaction energy of pair of equivalent s electrons $= F^0(s,s)$
p electrons: $F^0(p,p) - \tfrac{2}{25}F^2(p,p)$
d electrons: $F^0(d,d) - \tfrac{2}{63}F^2(d,d) - \tfrac{2}{63}F^4(d,d)$
f electrons: $F^0(f,f) - \dfrac{4}{195}F^2(f,f) - \dfrac{2}{143}F^4(f,f) - \dfrac{100}{5,577}F^6(f,f)$
$\qquad\qquad\qquad\qquad\qquad\qquad\qquad\qquad\qquad\qquad\qquad (14\text{-}20)$

We see an example in the case of two equivalent p electrons, which we examined in Eq. (13-31). The weighted mean of the energies of the ^3P,

^1D, and ^1S multiplets is there $2I(2p) + F^0(2p,2p) - \frac{2}{25}F^2(2p,2p)$, in agreement with Eq. (14-20).

Next we must consider the interaction terms between an electron in one shell and another electron in another. Let us consider one shell containing N_1 electrons, the second containing N'_1, where the corresponding filled shells would contain N_0 and N'_0, respectively. We shall assume for the moment that we have just these two shells present. By a discussion similar to that already given, we can show again that all pairs of orbitals of which one is in one shell, the other in the other, will appear in the weighted mean with the same weights, so that if we find the average value of the energy term $(ij/g/ij) - (ij/g/ji)$, we can simply multiply this by $N_1N'_1$, the number of pairs in which one orbital is in each shell, to find the contribution of these terms to the average energy. In finding the average of $(ij/g/ij) - (ij/g/ji)$, we can sum over the N_1 spin-orbitals in the first shell and the N'_1 in the second and divide by $N_1N'_1$, the number of pairs of spin-orbitals. We use Eqs. (14-2) and (14-13) as before and find

$$[(ij/g/ij) - (ij/g/ji)]_{av} = F^0(l_1,l_2)$$
$$- \frac{1}{2}[(2l_1 + 1)(2l_2 + 1)]^{-\frac{1}{2}}\Sigma(k)c^k(l_10;l_20)G^k(l_1,l_2) \quad (14-21)$$

From this we find

Interaction of pair of nonequivalent electrons

$$(ss'): F^0(ss') - \frac{1}{2}G^0(ss')$$
$$(sp): F^0(sp) - \frac{1}{6}G^1(sp)$$
$$(sd): F^0(sd) - \frac{1}{10}G^2(sd)$$
$$(sf): F^0(sf) - \frac{1}{14}G^3(sf)$$
$$(pp'): F^0(pp') - \frac{1}{6}G^0(pp') - \frac{1}{15}G^2(pp')$$
$$(pd): F^0(pd) - \frac{1}{15}G^1(pd) - \frac{3}{70}G^3(pd) \quad (14-22)$$
$$(pf): F^0(pf) - \frac{3}{70}G^2(pf) - \frac{2}{63}G^4(pf)$$
$$(dd'): F^0(dd') - \frac{1}{10}G^0(dd') - \frac{1}{35}G^2(dd') - \frac{1}{35}G^4(dd')$$
$$(df): F^0(df) - \frac{3}{70}G^1(df) - \frac{2}{105}G^3(df) - \frac{5}{231}G^5(df)$$
$$(ff'): F^0(ff') - \frac{2}{105}G^2(ff') - \frac{1}{77}G^4(ff') - \frac{50}{3,003}G^6(ff')$$

Now that we have found these formulas for interaction energies, we can generalize at once for the case where we have many shells of electrons. The rule is very simple: the average energy of a configuration is given by

$$\Sigma I(nl) + \Sigma(\text{pairs}) \text{ interaction energy} \quad (14-23)$$

where $I(nl)$ is the one-electron integral given in Eq. (13-7), these terms are to be summed over all electrons in the atom, and the interaction energies are given for equivalent electrons in Eq. (14-20) and for nonequivalent electrons in Eq. (14-22). This rule is very simple to apply, and it shows us that the weighted average energy of a configuration has a fundamental meaning, since it is determined by such a simple rule. The reader can give these results a simple test, by computing the weighted mean of the levels of the configuration $2p3p$, computed in Sec. 13-4. He will find that the result agrees with Eq. (14-22).

For many purposes it is more convenient to state the formulas for the various multiplets arising from a configuration in terms of the average energy of this configuration. Thus, for the configuration $2p3p$, or pp', which we have just mentioned, we can rewrite Eqs. (13-28), (13-29), and (13-30) in the form

$$
\begin{aligned}
{}^3D &= E_{av} + \tfrac{1}{25}F^2(pp') - \tfrac{5}{6}G^0(pp') + \tfrac{2}{75}G^2(pp') \\
{}^3P &= E_{av} - \tfrac{5}{25}F^2(pp') + \tfrac{7}{6}G^0(pp') - \tfrac{10}{75}G^2(pp') \\
{}^3S &= E_{av} + \tfrac{10}{25}F^2(pp') - \tfrac{5}{6}G^0(pp') - \tfrac{25}{75}G^0(pp') \\
{}^1D &= E_{av} + \tfrac{1}{25}F^2(pp') + \tfrac{7}{6}G^0(pp') + \tfrac{8}{75}G^2(pp') \\
{}^1P &= E_{av} - \tfrac{5}{25}F^2(pp') - \tfrac{5}{6}G^0(pp') + \tfrac{20}{75}G^2(pp') \\
{}^1S &= E_{av} + \tfrac{10}{25}F^2(pp') + \tfrac{7}{6}G^0(pp') + \tfrac{35}{75}G^2(pp')
\end{aligned}
\tag{14-24}
$$

The reader will readily verify that the weighted average of these values equals E_{av} and that their separations are as given in Eqs. (13-28), (13-29), and (13-30). The advantage of this method of writing the energy formulas arises because we can calculate E_{av} so easily from Eq. (14-23), thereby getting the complete expressions for the energy of each multiplet, including all the integrals between all shells in the atom. The tabulation of the results of calculations of the energies of multiplets, given in Appendix 21a and in Appendix 21 (Vol. II), is in this form, involving E_{av}. The reader has obtained practice in writing formulas for multiplet energies in this way in the problems of Chap. 13. It should be mentioned, however, that this method is not commonly used, so that our formulas will appear different from those found in the literature. As a result of a rather general lack of understanding of the average energy, the reader will find in the literature many misconceptions regarding the meaning of the additive constant in multiplet energies, and he is warned to be on his guard against incorrect interpretations of these additive constants.

14-3. Formulation of Multiplet Calculations in Terms of Average Energy. In Chap. 13 we have proceeded with our multiplet theory in the conventional manner, as it appears in the literature. However, we have just seen that it is simpler for many purposes to express multiplet energies in terms of the average energy. If we wish to do this, it is convenient to introduce the average energy from the beginning. In place of the formulas of Sec. 13-3 for the diagonal matrix components of the two-electron operator g_{ij} between two one-electron functions, we may conveniently substitute formulas in which we give the deviation of the energy

Table 14-1

Deviation of interaction energy $(ij/g/ij) - (ij/g/ji)$ of Sec. 13-3 from average interaction energies. Interaction energies symbolized by $E(m_l, m_l')$, where m_l, m_l' are quantum numbers of the two orbitals. The integral is unchanged if the signs of both m_l and m_l' are simultaneously changed. Cases where the two orbitals have the same spin and opposite spin are handled separately. Note that, for equivalent electrons, no entry appears for the case where $m_l = m_l'$ and the spins are the same, since this case is forbidden by the exclusion principle. The entries in the table are to be multiplied by the quantities, such as $F^2(pp)/25$, appearing at the head of the columns. Results are obtained from Appendix 20a, from Appendix 20 (Vol. II), and from Eqs. (14-20) and (14-22).

Equivalent electrons		
(pp)	$F^2(pp)/25$	
Same spin		
$E(1,0)$	-3	
$E(1,-1)$	-3	
Opposite spin		
$E(1,1)$	3	
$E(1,0)$	0	
$E(1,-1)$	3	
$E(0,0)$	6	
(dd)	$F^2(dd)/441$	$F^4(dd)/441$
Same spin		
$E(2,1)$	-58	5
$E(2,0)$	-58	5
$E(2,-1)$	-4	-25
$E(2,-2)$	50	-55
$E(1,0)$	23	-40
$E(1,-1)$	-31	-10
Opposite spin		
$E(2,2)$	50	15
$E(2,1)$	-4	10
$E(2,0)$	-22	20
$E(2,-1)$	-4	10
$E(2,-2)$	50	15
$E(1,1)$	23	30
$E(1,0)$	32	-10
$E(1,-1)$	23	30
$E(0,0)$	50	50

Table 14-1 (Continued)

Nonequivalent electrons	
(ss')	$G^0(ss')/2$

Same spin	
$E(0,0)$	-1

Opposite spin	
$E(0,0)$	1

(sp)	$G^1(sp)/6$

Same spin	
$E(0,1)$	-1
$E(0,0)$	-1

Opposite spin	
$E(0,1)$	1
$E(0,0)$	1

(sd)	$G^2(sd)/10$

Same spin	
$E(0,2)$	-1
$E(0,1)$	-1
$E(0,0)$	-1

Opposite spin	
$E(0,2)$	1
$E(0,1)$	1
$E(0,0)$	1

(pp')	$F^2(pp')/25$	$G^0(pp')/6$	$G^2(pp')/75$
Same spin			
$E(1,1)$	1	-5	2
$E(1,0)$	-2	1	-4
$E(1,-1)$	1	1	-13
$E(0,0)$	4	-5	-7

Table 14-1 (Continued)

(pp')	$F^2(pp')/25$	$G^0(pp')/6$	$G^2(pp')/75$
	Opposite spin		
$E(1,1)$	1	1	5
$E(1,0)$	-2	1	5
$E(1,-1)$	1	1	5
$E(0,0)$	4	1	5

(pd)	$F^2(pd)/35$	$G^1(pd)/15$	$G^3(pd)/490$
	Same spin		
$E(1,2)$	2	-5	15
$E(1,1)$	-1	-2	3
$E(1,0)$	-2	0	-15
$E(1,-1)$	-1	1	-39
$E(1,-2)$	2	1	-69
$E(0,2)$	-4	1	-9
$E(0,1)$	2	-2	-27
$E(0,0)$	4	-3	-33
	Opposite spin		
$E(1,2)$	2	1	21
$E(1,1)$	-1	1	21
$E(1,0)$	-2	1	21
$E(1,-1)$	-1	1	21
$E(1,-2)$	2	1	21
$E(0,2)$	-4	1	21
$E(0,1)$	2	1	21
$E(0,0)$	4	1	21

(dd')	$F^2(dd')/49$	$F^4(dd')/441$	$G^0(dd')/10$	$G^2(dd')/245$	$G^4(dd')/2,205$
	Same spin				
$E(2,2)$	4	1	-9	-13	58
$E(2,1)$	-2	-4	1	-23	38
$E(2,0)$	-4	6	1	-13	-12
$E(2,-1)$	-2	-4	1	7	-112
$E(2,-2)$	4	1	1	7	-287
$E(1,1)$	1	16	-9	2	-17
$E(1,0)$	2	-24	1	2	-87
$E(1,-1)$	1	16	1	-23	-137
$E(0,0)$	4	36	-9	-13	-117

Table 14-1 (Continued)

(dd')	$F^2(dd')/49$	$F^4(dd')/441$	$G^0(dd')/10$	$G^2(dd')/245$	$G^4(dd')/2,205$
		Opposite spin			
$E(2,2)$	4	1	1	7	63
$E(2,1)$	-2	-4	1	7	63
$E(2,0)$	-4	6	1	7	63
$E(2,-1)$	-2	-4	1	7	63
$E(2,-2)$	4	1	1	7	63
$E(1,1)$	1	16	1	7	63
$E(1,0)$	2	-24	1	7	63
$E(1,-1)$	1	16	1	7	63
$E(0,0)$	4	36	1	7	63

from the average value; then the final formulas for energies come out very simply in terms of the average energies. The necessary formulas, for s, p, and d electrons, are given in Table 14-1. The diagonal energy of a determinantal function, using this table, is E_{av} plus the sum of interaction terms, as given in the table, for all pairs of electrons in the atom, where E_{av} is the average for the configurations, as computed in Sec. 14-2.

We may illustrate the application of this table by working out the configuration pp', which we handled in Sec. 13-4. We shall find some of these energy levels by the method of diagonal sums. The determinantal function corresponding to $m_l = 1$, $m_l' = 1$, with both spins $+$, corresponds to the multiplet ^3D. Its diagonal energy, from Table 14-1, is $E_{av} + F^2(pp')/25 - \frac{5}{6}G^0(pp') + \frac{2}{75}G^2(pp')$, which then must be the energy of the ^3D multiplet; this agrees with Eq. (14-24). Again, the two determinantal functions corresponding to $m_l = 1$, $m_l' = 0$ and $m_l = 0$, $m_l' = 1$, with both spins $+$, correspond to ^3D and ^3P. They both have the same diagonal energy, $E_{av} - \frac{2}{25}F^2(pp') + \frac{1}{6}G^0(pp') - \frac{4}{75}G^2(pp')$. Since this must be the sum of the energy of ^3D, which we have found above, and ^3P, we see that the energy of ^3P is $E_{av} - \frac{5}{25}F^2(pp') + \frac{1}{6}G^0(pp') - \frac{10}{75}G^2(pp')$, again in agreement with Eq. (14-24). When we handle a configuration with more than two electrons, the method of procedure is similar: we use expressions from Table 14-1 for the diagonal energies, and when we are finished with the calculation, we have an average E_{av} in the final formula for the energies of the multiplets, which is now computed from the interactions of all pairs of electrons according to the method of Sec. 14-2.

There is one advantage to be noted in this method of calculating multiplets in terms of the average energies. We have already seen that the separations of the multiplets arising from a shell containing N_1 electrons and a shell containing $N_0 - N_1$ electrons, where N_0 is the number in the

completed shell, are identical.   Hence the formulas for the various multiplets of both configurations, expressed in terms of their average energies,
are identical.   We have taken advantage of this fact in Appendix 21a
and in Appendix 21 (Vol. II).   It is only the average energy E_{av} which is
different in the two cases, but this is so simple to compute that it is no
bother.

PROBLEMS

1. Compute the average energies of the configurations $1s2p^2$, $1s2p^4$, $2p^3$, $1s2p^3$, $3d^2$,
by the method of Sec. 14-2.   Compare with the values found directly in Probs. 2, 3,
4, and 5, Chap. 13.

2. Use the method of Table 14-1 to derive the energies of the multiplets in the configurations $1s2p^2$, $2p^3$, $1s2p^3$, $3d^2$, and compare with the values given in Table 15-3
and Appendix 20a.

3. Use the method of Table 14-1 to derive the energies of the multiplets in the configuration $3d^3$.   Note that by the diagonal sum method you will be able to get only
the average energy of the two ^2D's indicated for this case in Table 13-2.   Compare
your results with those of Appendix 20a.

4. Take the values given in Appendix 20a for the multiplets of the configuration
$3d^4$.   Compute the weighted mean of the energies of the various multiplets, and
verify that it is equal to E_{av} as given in the formulas.

15

Multiplet Calculations for Light Atoms

15-1. Introduction. In the two preceding chapters, in Appendix 21*a*, and in Appendix 21 (Vol. II), we have given the main theoretical results concerning the energies of atomic multiplets, in the approximation in which we can completely disregard spin-orbit interaction, treating all levels of a multiplet, with given L and S values, as being degenerate with each other. For the lighter atoms this is not a bad approximation, though for the heavier atoms, for which spin-orbit interaction is more important, it is not adequate. We have not yet treated the theory nearly completely; we have made very little use of angular-momentum methods, and we have not presented any method for handling the cases where we have more than one multiplet of a given L, S value, though the answers for these cases are tabulated in Appendix 21*a* and in Appendix 21 (Vol. II). These deficiencies will be filled in in Chaps. 20, 21, and 22 (Vol. II), after which we shall go on to handle spin-orbit interaction and multiplet separations more completely than we have done so far. In spite of these shortcomings, still we have got far enough so that it will pay to stop, survey the results of the theory, and ask how far they agree with experiment. We shall do this in the present and the next chapters. In the present chapter we shall treat the elements from lithium to neon, which have been worked on very extensively. This will give us an idea of how the theory works out for shells of eight electrons. In the next chapter we shall take up the transition group in which the $3d$ electrons are being added. These two detailed studies will give us a very good idea of how the theory works out for different types of atoms.

There are, broadly speaking, three different types of comparisons between spectrum theory and experiment which have been made. The first, and simplest, is suggested by the form of the multiplet energies, as indicated in Appendix 21*a* and in Appendix 21 (Vol. II). The separations between the various multiplets associated with a configuration are given, as we see there, in terms of certain integrals. In the simplest case, such as, for instance, the configuration $2p^2$, only one such integral is concerned, in that case $F^2(2p,2p)$; in other cases several more integrals are concerned. In practically every case, however, there are more energy-level separations than integrals. Thus a first test is: Can values for these integrals be found empirically, which will reproduce the observed multiplet energies? For instance, in $2p^2$, the energy separations between ^2P, ^1D, and ^1S are all written in terms of the one integral $F^2(2p,2p)$, so that the test is a simple one: Are the observed separations in the ratios predicted by theory? By the time we get to the iron group, there are a number of such energy integrals. We may try to determine by least squares a set of values for these integrals and ask how accurately they will reproduce the observed multiplets. There is a large body of literature devoted to exploring this question. Briefly, the agreement is qualitatively fairly good, in that the observed multiplets fall approximately in the order predicted by theory, with separations similar to those predicted; but quantitatively the agreement is far from perfect, the ratios between multiplets as observed differing quite markedly from the theory. The discrepancies are ascribed, as we shall explain later, to the poor approximation involved in considering only a single configuration.

The second type of comparison between theory and experiment involves the calculation of these energy integrals from the theoretical wave functions. We have found the equations for doing this. Suppose we use self-consistent-field orbitals and compute the integrals; will they agree with the ones deduced, by least squares, from the spectrum? If not, and if we use the integrals calculated from the wave function as a starting point, how bad are the discrepancies between theory and experiment? Here again there has been a good deal of work carried out. The general conclusion from this is that the agreement is only moderately good between the integrals as computed from the wave functions and those deduced by least squares from experiment. In general, the integrals computed from the wave functions lead to spacings between the multiplets which are considerably larger than observed experimentally. Again we ascribe the errors to the approximations made in our method.

Finally, we may be concerned, not with the energy separation between multiplets, but with the average energy of a multiplet. We may use wave functions determined by self-consistent-field methods and calculate all the integrals required to find the total energy of the atom—the negative of the energy required to remove all electrons from the atom. This can be checked directly, for the lighter atoms, where we know the experimental ionization potentials in all stages of ionization. Or we may calculate the energy difference between the atom and its ion and compare this with an observed ionization potential. We have seen in Sec. 9-5 that these ionization potentials should agree closely with the one-electron energies met in the Hartree method. Calculations of this type really test the accuracy of the wave functions, and they have been made in a considerable number of cases. They indicate rather good agreement between theory and experiment.

For the second and third types of comparison just described, we need one-electron wave functions or orbitals. In some cases the functions used have been determined by the self-consistent-field method, and the calculation has been carried out numerically, since these functions are given as tables of values. In other cases, particularly for the light atoms, and more recently for the transition elements, a great deal of use has been made of analytic functions which form good approximations to the self-consistent-field functions and which have the advantage that the calculations can be made analytically. We shall describe this analytic approach in detail in the present chapter. In connection with both these methods, we need to understand how the self-consistent-field method is to be applied to cases more complicated than the alkali atoms. We have so far discussed only the Hartree method, in Chaps. 8 and 9, and not the Hartree-Fock method, which we put off until Chap. 17 (Vol. II). It is important, however, for the understanding of the comparisons of theory and experiment, to understand what the Hartree-Fock method is, even though its detailed analytic treatment will be postponed until later.

The general idea behind the Hartree-Fock method can be described very simply. In Sec. 9-4, we showed that the Hartree method can be formulated in terms of a variation method: we write the wave function as a product of one-electron orbitals and vary these orbitals so as to minimize the energy of the whole atom. The resulting orbitals are the Hartree wave functions (except for Hartree's assumption that the potential acting on a given orbital is a spherical average of that really given by the self-consistent-field method). But now we have seen, in Chap. 12, that a product of one-electron orbitals is not the proper form for the wave function: we must have an antisymmetric function. Thus we should set up such an antisymmetric function in terms of one-electron orbitals, compute the energy by using such a function, and vary the one-electron orbitals so as to minimize the energy. This is the essential procedure leading to the Hartree-Fock equation.

As we have seen, the expression for energy now involves certain exchange integrals, and these appear in the Hartree-Fock method as certain terms in the Schrödinger equation of different form from those met in the Hartree method. When actual calculations are made, the one-electron orbitals found by the two methods are appreciably different from each other, though they are not strikingly different. We may expect the Hartree-Fock wave functions to be somewhat more accurate and therefore may expect calculations of multiplet structure and total energy made with the Hartree-Fock orbitals to be better than those made with Hartree orbitals. We can, however, use either type of orbitals to carry through the complete calculation of energy, multiplet structure, and so on; the only difference is that the Hartree-Fock orbitals are chosen to minimize the energy as computed properly from multiplet theory, whereas we saw in Chap. 9 that the Hartree orbitals minimize the energy as computed from the one-electron integrals $I(nl)$, the integrals $F^0(nl,n'l')$, but disregarding all other energy integrals. Thus the Hartree orbitals do not quite minimize the correct energy expression; but on account of the fact that we are dealing with a variation problem, they will not lead to a very much poorer value of total energy than the Hartree-Fock orbitals. It is fortunate that this is true, for calculations by the Hartree method have been made in a good many cases in which the more difficult Hartree-Fock calculations have not been carried through, so that we are forced to use orbitals of both types in comparing theory and experiment.

The simplest case of the Hartree-Fock problem is that in which we are dealing with an atom or ion containing only closed shells. Then the atom is in a ^1S state, and the wave function consists of a single determinant. Hence often the Hartree-Fock method is described as that in which we vary the orbitals in a single determinant to minimize its energy. However, it is not hard, as Hartree[1] has shown, to extend the method to other cases, in which the wave function must be written as a linear combination of determinants. The general procedure which Hartree has adopted still follows the same lines: we write the energy of the atom, in the multiplet in which we are interested, in the form given in Appendix 21a or in Appendix 21 (Vol. II), in terms of various one-electron and two-electron integrals over the one-electron orbitals. Then we vary the radial parts of these orbitals so as to minimize the energy. In Chap. 17 (Vol. II) we shall show that this leads to differential equations for the orbitals which can be handled in a practical way and which have been calculated in a good many cases.

It is clear that in this way we could carry out a separate variation process for each multiplet, obtaining slightly different orbitals in each case. Or we could use a simpler method, varying the energy of only one multiplet, for instance that of lowest energy, finding orbitals from this, and using them to calculate the energies of the various multiplets. This procedure is much simpler to carry out, for it gives orthogonal orbitals, which we have presupposed in our multiplet calculations; on the other hand, the slightly different orbitals which we should get by varying each multiplet separately will not be orthogonal to each other. Later in this chapter we shall give some examples of cases in which each multiplet

[1] D. R. Hartree and W. Hartree, *Proc. Roy. Soc. (London)*, **A150**:9 (1935); **A154**:588 (1936); D. R. Hartree, "The Calculation of Atomic Structures," John Wiley & Sons, Inc., New York, 1957; G. W. Shortley, *Phys. Rev.*, **50**:1072 (1936).

has been varied separately and shall estimate the errors made if we do not carry through this separate variation. Rather than varying the energy of the multiplet of lowest energy, Shortley has suggested the alternative scheme of varying the average energy of a configuration, as we have computed it in Sec. 14-2, and determining the one-electron orbitals from this variation process. If we are interested in applying the present multiplet methods, this is probably the best procedure to use.

In the present chapter, we shall discuss a number of calculations which have been made for the light atoms, using analytic functions, as we mentioned earlier. Exactly the same considerations come up here as with the Hartree-Fock method, in the matter of variation of the parameters of these analytic functions. We compute from the analytic orbitals the total energy of the atom, either for a single multiplet or for the average of a configuration, then vary the parameters involved in the analytic functions to minimize the energy. If we had enough parameters so that the function could approach the Hartree-Fock orbitals as closely as we please, the result would be the same as the Hartree-Fock method. We shall describe examples of such calculations, for the iron group, in the next chapter. Actually, however, many fewer parameters have been used in most of the calculations for light atoms, so that the orbitals cannot approach the Hartree-Fock orbitals very closely. The final energy of the atom will then necessarily lie higher, as computed with these orbitals, than with the Hartree-Fock orbitals; the discrepancy between the two and the comparison with experiment give us an interesting check on the accuracy of the analytic orbitals.

As we have mentioned, the final results of our calculation, even using Hartree-Fock orbitals, are far from perfect: the total energies of the atom are in error by something of the order of magnitude of a per cent, and the multiplet separations, being differences of quantities each of which is in error by such an amount, are wrong by larger magnitudes. We ask ourselves: Why do we have these errors? Is wave mechanics wrong, or are the errors a result of our method of approximation? We shall answer this question in Chap. 18 (Vol. II), where we discuss the atom with two electrons, helium, or a two-electron ion. Here the calculation of Hylleraas, which we mentioned in Sec. 8-1, and later, more elaborate calculations of Kinoshita[1] and Pekeris[2] give results which agree with experiment with great precision. Hence we conclude that the trouble is, not with wave mechanics, but with the approximations based on the self-consistent field. In that chapter, we shall be able to follow through in detail the methods necessary to correct for these approximations. We shall find that, if we set up all possible configurations, built up from a complete set of orthonormal orbitals, and write the wave function as a

[1] T. Kinoshita, *Phys. Rev.*, **105**:1490 (1957).
[2] C. L. Pekeris, *Phys. Rev.*, **112**:1649 (1958).

linear combination of those derived from all possible configurations, the result is exactly correct; it is possible in helium to carry this process of configuration interaction, or configuration mixing as it is called, far enough with a practicable amount of effort to remove all but a very small part of the error.   This process of configuration interaction is then what has to be added to the Hartree-Fock method, and to our methods of handling multiplets, in order to get improved accuracy.   Unfortunately it is too complicated and elaborate a process to carry very far, except in such a simple atom as helium.   But it shows us where the errors arise, in the type of theory we shall be discussing in the present chapter.

15-2. Experimental Energy Levels of Light Elements.   The first step in comparing theory and experiment in the multiplets of light elements from lithium to neon is to look at the experimental facts.   Most of the lower energy levels of the light atoms, in many stages of ionization, have been observed by the spectroscopists, and the experimental data are collected in the volumes entitled "Atomic Energy Levels as Derived from Analyses of Optical Spectra."[1]   Every student of atomic structure should become thoroughly familiar with this invaluable tabulation.   To describe the nature of these tables, let us consider the case of beryllium, $Z = 4$.   In its ground state this atom has the configuration $1s^2 2s^2$, with the multiplet ^1S.   There are also low-lying configurations $1s^2 2s 2p$, leading to multiplets $^3P^o$ and $^1P^o$, and $1s^2 2p^2$, leading to ^3P, ^1D, and ^1S.   We shall consider these configurations, in which all electrons have principal quantum numbers of 1 or 2, but shall not go into the higher levels, in which one of the electrons is excited into a state ns, np, nd, etc., where $n > 2$.   Now, in the tables, we find that the wave numbers of the various levels of the multiplets we have enumerated are all tabulated, in units of cm^{-1}; the wave number, so called, in cm^{-1}, is the reciprocal of the wavelength in centimeters.   In very recent work, this unit cm^{-1} is referred to as the Kayser, abbreviated K.   These numbers can be converted at once into Rydbergs, by using the value of the Rydberg in cm^{-1}.   This, on account of the finite mass of the nucleus, is slightly different for each element, as indicated in Eqs. (7-1) and (7-4).   For beryllium, the value of the Rydberg, in cm^{-1}, is 109,730.623 cm^{-1}.

We then find entries in the tables as given in Table 15-1, for the terms we are considering in Be I (that is, neutral beryllium).   The subscripts, as in $^3P^o_1$, give the total angular momentum, or inner quantum number, and we note that the three components of a triplet, for instance, are separately tabulated.   The lowest level is arbitrarily taken as a zero of energy, and the series limit indicates the energy of the ion in which the most easily removed electron, in this case a $2s$, has been removed.   We have a similar table for Be II (that is, singly ionized beryllium, or Be$^+$), for Be III (doubly ionized, or Be^{++}), and Be IV (triply ionized, or Be^{3+}).

[1] *Natl. Bur. Standards Circ.* 467, 1949.

In each case the lowest level is taken as zero in the tabulations. However, by combining the series limits we can find the energy required to remove all electrons from the atom. Thus, we have seen that the energy required to remove a $2s$ electron from neutral beryllium is 75,192.29 cm^{-1},

Table 15-1. Energies of Low States of Be I, in Cm^{-1}

Be I	$1s^22s^2$	$^1S_0$	0
	$1s^22s2p$	$^3P^o_0$	21,979.43
		$^3P^o_1$	21,980.11
		$^3P^o_2$	21,982.46
		$^1P^o_1$	42,565.3
	$1s^22p^2$	$^1D_2$	56,432.5
		$^3P_0$	59,694.61
		$^3P_1$	59,696.01
		$^3P_2$	59,698.04
		$^1S_0$	71,498.9
Series limit		$\ldots$	75,192.29

the series limit. Similarly we find that to remove the second $2s$ electron from the Be$^+$ ion requires 146,881.7 cm^{-1} (the series limit for Be II), to remove one of the $1s$ electrons from Be^{++} requires 1,241,225 cm^{-1},[†] and to remove the final $1s$ electron from Be^{3+} requires 1,756,004 cm^{-1}. Thus the energy required to remove all four electrons is the sum of these quantities (we use Pekeris's value for the ionization potential of Be^{++}), which transformed to Rydbergs gives 29.33854 Rydbergs. If we wish to use the state with all electrons removed as a zero of energy, we should then say that the ground state has an energy of -29.33854 Rydbergs.

In the present chapter we are not considering the spin-orbit interaction. We thus do not wish to be troubled with the small energy separations between the various terms of the same multiplet. As the simplest way of eliminating these separations, we take the weighted mean of the terms of a multiplet, weighted according to the number of separate wave functions with each J value, or $2J + 1$. That is, for the multiplet Be I $1s^22s2p$ $^3P^o$, we give a weight 1 to $^3P^o_0$, 3 to $^3P^o_1$, and 5 to $^3P^o_2$, finding a weighted energy of 21,981.34 cm^{-1} for this multiplet. In the same way, we can find averaged energies for each multiplet of each stage of ionization. When we refer these to the state of the atom with all electrons removed as the zero of energy, the energies of the various multiplets, in Rydbergs, are as given in Table 15-2, where we also give similar information for all the elements from lithium to oxygen, for all of which we have experimental data for all stages of ionization.

† The last two figures of this quantity 1,241,225 cm^{-1} are experimentally uncertain. A more accurate value is probably the computed value given by Pekeris, *op. cit.*, namely, 1,241,259.4 cm^{-1}.

Table 15-2. Energies of Low States of Atoms and Ions from Lithium to Oxygen in All Stages of Ionization, in Rydbergs

Zero of energy in each case is the nucleus with all electrons removed. The energies of the one-electron ions differ from the hydrogenic value $-Z^2$ on account of the relativistic correction, which will be discussed later, in Appendix 29 (Vol. II); these values are theoretical, derived from Eq. (A29-31) appearing in Vol. II. The ionization potentials of the two-electron ions are taken from the theoretical calculations of C. L. Pekeris, *Phys. Rev.*, **112**:1649 (1958), which are probably more accurate than the experimental values. Other ionization potentials are taken from experiment. Note that the Rydberg is different for each atom, on account of the finite mass of the nucleus; the value of the Rydberg in each case is tabulated. We also give average energies of configurations, and quantities $F^2(2p,2p)$ and $G^1(2s,2p)$, computed from observed energies by use of Table 15-3, also in Rydbergs.

Atom	State		Energy	E_{av}	$F^2(2p,2p)$	$G^1(2s,2p)$
	Lithium: Rydberg = 109,727.295 cm^{-1}					
Li	$1s^2 2s$	^2S	-14.95730			
	$1s^2 2p$	$^2P^o$	-14.82147			
Li$^+$	$1s^2$	^1S	-14.56098			
Li^{++}	$1s$	^2S	-9.00102			
	Beryllium: Rydberg = 109,730.623 cm^{-1}					
Be	$1s^2 2s^2$	^1S	-29.33854			
	$1s^2 2s 2p$	$\begin{cases}{}^3P^o \\ {}^1P^o\end{cases}$	$\left.\begin{array}{l}-29.13823 \\ -28.95064\end{array}\right\}$	-29.09133		0.28140
	$1s^2 2p^2$	$\begin{cases}{}^3P \\ {}^1D \\ {}^1S\end{cases}$	$\left.\begin{array}{l}-28.79452 \\ -28.82427 \\ -28.68696\end{array}\right\}$	$-28.77302\dagger$	$0.17925\dagger$	
Be$^+$	$1s^2 2s$	^2S	-28.65331			
	$1s^2 2p$	$^2P^o$	-28.36230			
Be^{++}	$1s^2$	^1S	-27.31474			
Be^{3+}	$1s$	^2S	-16.00286			
	Boron: Rydberg = 109,731.835 cm^{-1}					
B	$1s^2 2s^2 2p$	$^2P^o$	-49.31852			
	$1s^2 2s 2p^2$	$\begin{cases}{}^4P \\ {}^2D \\ {}^2S \\ {}^2P\end{cases}$	$\left.\begin{array}{l}-49.05605 \\ -48.88249 \\ -48.73938 \\ -48.65753\end{array}\right\}$	-48.89738	0.26082	0.39853
	$1s^2 2p^3$	$\begin{cases}{}^4S^o \\ \;\dots\dots\end{cases}$	$\left.\begin{array}{l}-48.44431 \\ \dots\dots\dots\end{array}\right\}$	$-48.27779\ddagger$		

† These values are computed from the multiplets ^3P and ^1S alone, using the methods of Table 15-3, and disregarding the multiplet ^1D, which is strongly perturbed on account of other nearby ^1D multiplets in the spectrum.

‡ This value is computed from the only observed multiplet of this configuration, $^4S^o$, using the methods of Table 15-3, and assuming the same value of $F^2(2p,2p)$ found for the configuration $1s^2 2s 2p^2$.

Table 15-2. Energies of Low States of Atoms and Ions from Lithium to
Oxygen in All Stages of Ionization, in Rydbergs (Continued)

Atom	State		Energy	E_{av}	$F^2(2p,2p)$	$G^1(2s,2p)$
B$^+$	$1s^22s^2$	^1S	-48.70868			
	$1s^22s2p$	$\begin{cases}^3P^o\\^1P^o\end{cases}$	$\left.\begin{matrix}-48.36832\\-48.03980\end{matrix}\right\}$	-48.28619		0.41061
	$1s^22p^2$	$\begin{cases}^3P\\^1D\\^1S\end{cases}$	$\left.\begin{matrix}-47.80715\\-47.77584\\-47.54528\end{matrix}\right\}$	-47.77926	0.33445	
B^{++}	$1s^22s$	^2S	-46.85967			
	$1s^22p$	$^2P^o$	-46.41877			
B^{3+}	$1s^2$	^1S	-44.07168			
B^{4+}	$1s$	^2S	-25.00699			

Carbon: Rydberg $= 109{,}732.286$ cm^{-1}

Atom	State		Energy	E_{av}	$F^2(2p,2p)$	$G^1(2s,2p)$
C	$1s^22s^22p^2$	$\begin{cases}^3P\\^1D\\^1S\end{cases}$	$\left.\begin{matrix}-75.71369\\-75.62106\\-75.51668\end{matrix}\right\}$	-75.66968	0.34744	
	$1s^22s2p^3$	$\begin{cases}^5S^o\\^3D^o\\^3P^o\end{cases}$	$\left.\begin{matrix}-75.40653\\-75.12989\\-75.02814\end{matrix}\right\}$	-75.06790†	0.42399†	0.37201†
C$^+$	$1s^22s^22p$	$^2P^o$	-74.88559			
	$1s^22s2p^2$	$\begin{cases}^4P\\^2D\\^2S\\^2P\end{cases}$	$\left.\begin{matrix}-74.49362\\-74.20292\\-74.00642\\-73.79740\end{matrix}\right\}$	-74.24099	0.43150	0.61623
	$1s^22p^3$	$\begin{cases}^4S^o\\^2D^o\\^2P^o\end{cases}$	$\left.\begin{matrix}-73.59150\\-73.51458\\-73.34800\end{matrix}\right\}$	-73.47999	0.40576	
C^{++}	$1s^22s^2$	^1S	-73.09361			
	$1s^22s2p$	$\begin{cases}^3P^o\\^1P^o\end{cases}$	$\left.\begin{matrix}-72.61638\\-72.16087\end{matrix}\right\}$	-72.50251		0.68326
	$1s^22p^2$	$\begin{cases}^3P\\^1D\\^1S\end{cases}$	$\left.\begin{matrix}-71.84123\\-71.76424\\-71.43029\end{matrix}\right\}$	-71.78808	0.56342	
C^{3+}	$1s^22s$	^2S	-69.57450			
	$1s^22p$	$^2P^o$	-68.98620			
C^{4+}	$1s^2$	^1S	-64.83407			
C^{5+}	$1s$	^2S	-36.01447			

† These values are determined from the formulas of Table 15-3, using the three
multiplets of this configuration which have been observed.

Table 15-2. Energies of Low States of Atoms and Ions from Lithium to Oxygen in All Stages of Ionization, in Rydbergs (Continued)

Atom	State		Energy	E_{av}	$F^2(2p,2p)$	$G^1(2s,2p)$
	*Nitrogen:* Rydberg = 109,733.004 cm^{-1}

Atom	State		Energy	E_{av}	$F^2(2p,2p)$	$G^1(2s,2p)$
N	$1s^22s^22p^3$	$^4S^o$	-109.22713			
		$^2D^o$	-109.05192	-109.06068	0.43811	
		$^2P^o$	-108.96431			
	$1s^22s2p^4$	^4P	-108.42395	-108.11239†		
		.....	....			
N$^+$	$1s^22s^22p^2$	^3P	-108.15695			
		^1D	-108.01819	-108.09089	0.52286	
		^1S	-107.85988			
	$1s^22s2p^3$	$^5S^o$	-107.72792			
		$^3D^o$	-107.31719			
		$^3P^o$	-107.16244	-107.18059	0.54610	0.73810
		$^1D^o$	-106.84376			
		$^3S^o$	-106.74406			
		$^1P^o$	-106.63802			
N^{++}	$1s^22s^22p$	$^2P^o$	-105.98008			
	$1s^22s2p^2$	^4P	-105.45912			
		^2D	-105.06048	-105.11985	0.62678	0.82804
		^2S	-104.78730			
		^2P	-104.65100			
	$1s^22p^3$	$^4S^o$	-104.27881			
		$^2D^o$	-104.13048	-104.08543	0.66229	
		$^2P^o$	-103.88143			
N^{3+}	$1s^22s^2$	^1S	-102.49426			
	$1s^22s2p$	$^3P^o$	-101.88120	-101.64558		0.86695
		$^1P^o$	-101.30323			
	$1s^22p^2$	^3P	-100.89403			
		^1D	-100.77295	-100.81735	0.77340	
		^1S	-100.34933			
N^{4+}	$1s^22s$	^2S	-96.79997			
	$1s^22p$	$^2P^o$	-96.06512			
N^{5+}	$1s^2$	^1S	-89.60493			
N^{6+}	$1s$	^2S	-49.02682			
	*Oxygen:* Rydberg = 109,733.539 cm^{-1}
O	$1s^22s^22p^4$	^3P	-150.22487			
		^1D	-150.08098	-150.15642	0.54123	
		^1S	-149.91763			
	$1s^22s2p^5$	$^3P^o$	-149.07457	-148.92983		0.86846
		$^1P^o$	-148.49560			

† This value is computed from the only observed multiplet of this configuration, ^4P, using the methods of Table 15-3, and assuming the same values of $F^2(2p,2p)$ and $G^1(2s,2p)$ as in the configuration $1s^22s2p^3$ of N$^+$.

Table 15-2. Energies of Low States of Atoms and Ions from Lithium to Oxygen in All Stages of Ionization, in Rydbergs (Continued)

Atom	State		Energy	E_{av}	$F^2(2p,2p)$	$G^1(2s,2p)$
O^+	$1s^22s^22p^3$	$^4S^o$ $^2D^o$ $^2P^o$	-149.22464 -148.98026 -148.85586	-148.99182	0.61463	
	$1s^22s2p^4$	^4P ^2D ^2S ^2P	-148.13169 -147.71197 -147.44113 -147.28677	-147.77676	0.64613	0.84492
O^{++}	$1s^22s^22p^2$	^3P ^1D ^1S	-146.63875 -146.45592 -146.24712	-146.55170	0.68908	
	$1s^22s2p^3$	$^5S^o$ $^3D^o$ $^3P^o$ $^1D^o$ $^3S^o$ $^1P^o$	-146.09103 -145.54672 -145.34311 -144.93607 -144.84460 -144.72275	-145.37816	0.72600	0.92887
	$1s^22p^4$	^3P ^1D ^1S	-144.05378 -143.92234 -143.51214	-143.97386	0.78438	
O^{3+}	$1s^22s^22p$	$^2P^o$	-142.59948			
	$1s^22s2p^2$	^4P ^2D ^2S ^2P	-141.95136 -141.44501 -141.10396 -140.95563	-141.52694	0.81504	0.99573
	$1s^22p^3$	$^4S^o$ $^2D^o$ $^2P^o$	-140.49422 -140.27648 -139.96798	-140.22748	0.87707	
O^{4+}	$1s^22s^2$	^1S	-136.91171			
	$1s^22s2p$	$^3P^o$ $^1P^o$	-136.16068 -135.46659	-135.98666		1.04414
	$1s^22p^2$	^3P ^1D ^1S	-134.96217 -134.80003 -134.28800	-134.86318	0.97427	
O^{5+}	$1s^22s$ $1s^22p$	^2S $^2P^o$	-128.53959 -127.65809			
O^{6+}	$1s^2$	^1S	-118.38773			
O^{7+}	$1s$	^2S	$-\ 64.04578$			

15-3. Determination of E_{av}, $F^2(2p,2p)$, and $G^1(2s,2p)$ from Experiment, Using Least Squares. Now we ask how we can compare these experimental values with theory. In the first place, we have seen that there are certain broad types of information which we can find from the experimental values. These are of two sorts: we can study the separations of the various multiplets in a configuration, and we can consider the weighted means of the multiplets in each configuration. We have seen in Sec. 14-2 that these weighted means have simple properties. Let us first go as far as we can in finding these quantities from experiment, before asking whether the experimental values can be computed accurately from theoretical wave functions.

It is in the first place convenient to collect together the formulas for the energies of all multiplets which we meet with these atoms and ions, which we can do from Appendix 21a and from Appendix 21 (Vol. II). In Table 15-3 we give the values of the energy for the required multiplets.

Table 15-3

Energies of multiplets arising from configurations of s and p electrons. In each case E_{av} is the average energy, computed by the methods of Sec. 14-2.

sp or sp^5	$^3P^o$: $E_{av} - \frac{1}{6}G^1(sp)$
	$^1P^o$: $E_{av} + \frac{3}{6}G^1(sp)$
p^2 or s^2p^2 or p^4 or s^2p^4	^3P: $E_{av} - \frac{3}{25}F^2(pp)$
	^1D: $E_{av} + \frac{3}{25}F^2(pp)$
	^1S: $E_{av} + \frac{12}{25}F^2(pp)$
sp^2 or sp^4	^4P: $E_{av} - \frac{3}{25}F^2(pp) - \frac{1}{3}G^1(sp)$
	^2P: $E_{av} - \frac{3}{25}F^2(pp) + \frac{2}{3}G^1(sp)$
	^2D: $E_{av} + \frac{3}{25}F^2(pp)$
	^2S: $E_{av} + \frac{12}{25}F^2(pp)$
p^3 or s^2p^3	$^4S^o$: $E_{av} - \frac{9}{25}F^2(pp)$
	$^2D^o$: E_{av}
	$^2P^o$: $E_{av} + \frac{6}{25}F^2(pp)$
sp^3	$^5S^o$: $E_{av} - \frac{9}{25}F^2(pp) - \frac{1}{2}G^1(sp)$
	$^3S^o$: $E_{av} - \frac{9}{25}F^2(pp) + \frac{5}{6}G^1(sp)$
	$^3D^o$: $E_{av} - \frac{1}{6}G^1(sp)$
	$^1D^o$: $E_{av} + \frac{1}{2}G^1(sp)$
	$^3P^o$: $E_{av} + \frac{6}{25}F^2(pp) - \frac{1}{6}G^1(sp)$
	$^1P^o$: $E_{av} + \frac{6}{25}F^2(pp) + \frac{1}{2}G^1(sp)$

It is to be noted that the average energy E_{av} is different for each configuration but has a fixed value for the various multiplets of a single configuration. The averages are, of course, weighted averages; this explains the fact, which at first sight might be paradoxical, that in the first entry in the table, the energy of $^3P^o$ is $E_{av} - \frac{1}{6}G^1(sp)$, while that of sp $^1P^o$ is $E_{av} + \frac{3}{6}G^1(sp)$; in computing the average, the weight of the triplet is three times as great as that of the singlet. Similar remarks apply to the other cases.

When we examine the results of Table 15-3, we note that, in most cases, the separations of the various multiplets in a configuration are determined by fewer constants than the number of separations. Thus, in the case of p^2, the two separations between the three terms are given in terms of one quantity $F^2(pp)$. The same situation holds for p^3. For sp^2 the three separations are determined by two constants, and for sp^3 the five separations are determined by two constants. Thus an immediate form of check with experiment is provided by asking whether or not the separations have the proper relations to each other to be given by this smaller number of constants. Even a superficial check of the experimental values shows that these relations are not well satisfied. For instance, in nitrogen, we see an example of the configuration s^2p^3 in neutral N; the separations between $^4S^o$ and $^2D^o$ and between $^2D^o$ and $^2P^o$ should be in the ratio of 3:2 according to Table 15-3. On the other hand, from the experimental values of Table 15-2, the ratio is very close to 2:1. In N$^+$, we have the configuration $2s^22p^2$, in which the ratio of the separation of ^1D from ^1S to the separation of ^3P from ^1D should again be 3:2 from the theory; it is experimentally 1.14. In each case the discrepancy is in the direction which could be described by saying that the topmost multiplet arising from the configuration seems to be pushed down with respect to the others: the $^2P^o$ arising from N $2s^22p^3$ is the topmost multiplet, and it lies too low to fit in with the theory, and in a similar way the ^1S of N$^+$ $2s^22p^2$ is too low. Such discrepancies are found in almost every case, both in these light elements and in the transition-group elements which we shall take up in the next chapter, and they obviously cannot be explained in terms of the simple theory we have been considering so far. When we consider the mixing of configurations, we can understand such results: the multiplets are pushed downward by perturbative interaction with higher configurations, and this affects the higher multiplets, which have closer neighbors, more than the lower ones.

Under these circumstances, we cannot use the experimental values to determine the constants $F^2(2p,2p)$ and $G^1(2s,2p)$, which occur in Table 15-3, in an unambiguous way. However, it is interesting to do as well as possible in finding these quantities from experiment, and a natural thing is to use the method of least squares. This can be done as follows: We are trying to find a set of parameters [in this case E_{av}, $F^2(pp)$, and $G^1(sp)$], which in case the theory worked perfectly would be given by equations such as

$$
\begin{aligned}
a_{11}x_1 + a_{12}x_2 + \cdots + a_{1n}x_n &= c_1 \\
a_{21}x_1 + a_{22}x_2 + \cdots + a_{2n}x_n &= c_2 \\
&\cdots\cdots\cdots\cdots\cdots \\
a_{m1}x_1 + a_{m2}x_2 + \cdots + a_{mn}x_n &= c_m
\end{aligned} \tag{15-1}
$$

Here the x's stand for the parameters, the a's are the numerical coefficients arising from Table 15-3, and the c's are the values of the energies of the various multiplets. Thus, if we were dealing with the case p^2, there would be two x's, namely, E_{av} and $F^2(pp)$, so that n would be 2; there would be three c's, so that the equations would be

$$E_{av} - \tfrac{3}{25}F^2(pp) = {}^3P$$
$$E_{av} + \tfrac{3}{25}F^2(pp) = {}^1D \qquad\qquad (15\text{-}2)$$
$$E_{av} + \tfrac{12}{25}F^2(pp) = {}^1S$$

and in this case m would be 3, and we should have $a_{11} = 1$, $a_{12} = -\tfrac{3}{25}$, $a_{21} = 1$, $a_{22} = \tfrac{3}{25}$, $a_{31} = 1$, $a_{32} = \tfrac{12}{25}$.

The theory, however, is not perfect, and Eqs. (15-1) are not satisfied. The error in the kth multiplet is $\Sigma(s)a_{ks}x_s - c_k$. Let us ask for those values of the parameters x_i which will minimize the mean-square error, weighted proportionally to the weight $(2L + 1)(2S + 1)$ which we are assigning to the multiplet. Let this weight, for the kth multiplet, be called α_k, so that in the case of Eq. (15-2) we should have $\alpha_1 = \tfrac{9}{15}$, $\alpha_2 = \tfrac{5}{15}$, $\alpha_3 = \tfrac{1}{15}$. We then wish to find values of the x's which will minimize the quantity

$$\Sigma(k)\alpha_k[\Sigma(s)a_{ks}x_s - c_k]^2 \qquad\qquad (15\text{-}3)$$

We differentiate the expression of Eq. (15-3) with respect to one of the x's, say x_i, set the derivative equal to zero, and find the equations

$$\Sigma(s)[\Sigma(k)\alpha_k a_{ks}a_{ki}]x_s = \Sigma(k)\alpha_k a_{ki}c_k \qquad i = 1, 2, \ldots, n \qquad (15\text{-}4)$$

Here we have n simultaneous linear equations for the n unknowns x_s, rather than having the m simultaneous equations (in general $m > n$) of Eq. (15-1), which cannot be solved unless the c's are properly related. In our case, where n is 2 or 3, it is easy to solve these equations and to find the expressions for the best values of the quantities E_{av}, $F^2(pp)$, and $G^1(sp)$, in terms of the experimentally determined multiplet energies.

We note in the first place that the value of E_{av} found by this procedure will be just the correctly determined weighted mean of the experimental energies. To prove this, we note that, on account of the structure of the formulas of Table 15-3, the unknown quantity E_{av} enters with a unit coefficient in each case; that is, $a_{k1} = 1$, independent of k. Let us then set $i = 1$ in Eq. (15-4). We find

$$\Sigma(s)[\Sigma(k)\alpha_k a_{ks}]x_s = \Sigma(k)\alpha_k c_k \qquad\qquad (15\text{-}5)$$

Now $\Sigma(s)a_{ks}x_s$, as we see from Eq. (15-1), is the computed value of the energy of the kth multiplet, using the values of the parameters x_s which we have determined from Eq. (15-4), or from the least-squares method. The quantity $\Sigma(k)\alpha_k\Sigma(s)a_{ks}x_s$ is then the weighted mean of these computed energies, which must be E_{av}, on account of the nature of the formulas of Table 15-3. On the other hand, the quantity $\Sigma(k)\alpha_k c_k$ is the weighted mean of the observed energies. Equation (15-5) then tells us that the value of E_{av} determined from Eq. (15-4) equals the weighted mean of the experimental energies.

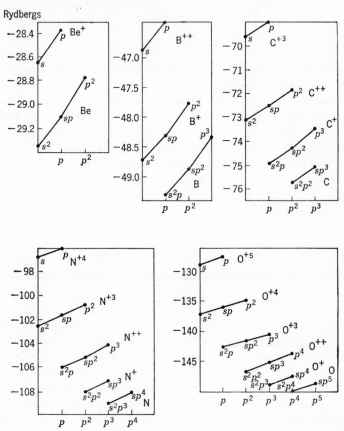

FIG. 15-1. Average energies of light atoms and ions, as function of number of p electrons.

As for the other two constants $F^2(pp)$ and $G^1(sp)$, we can easily solve Eq. (15-4) in the cases discussed in Table 15-3 and find the explicit formulas for the least-squares approximation to these quantities in terms of the experimental energies. These formulas are given in Table 15-4. They allow us at once to write down the best approximation to these quantities in terms of the observed energies.

We have given in Table 15-2 the values of E_{av}, $F^2(2p,2p)$, and $G^1(2s,2p)$, determined by this method, for those configurations of the light elements for which we have sufficient information. In Table 15-5, we give computed values of a number of multiplets, found from the constants of Table 15-2 by the formulas of Table 15-3. We see that the agreement with observation is not very good; this of course is inevitable when we remember that the observed separations are not in the correct ratios. Nevertheless the agreement is far from a failure. The observed levels come in the correct order, with spacings not impossibly far from the correct ratios, and the parameters $F^2(2p,2p)$ and $G^1(2s,2p)$ vary fairly smoothly from atom to atom and from one state of ionization to another. The average energies in particular vary quite smoothly; in Fig. 15-1 we plot these average energies, as a function of the number of p electrons in the atom. We clearly have very nearly a family of parallel straight lines,

Table 15-4
Best approximations to $F^2(pp)$ and $G^1(sp)$, using least-squares methods applied to experimental multiplet energies.

sp or sp^5: $G^1(sp) = \frac{3}{2}(^1P^o - {}^3P^o)$

p^2 or s^2p^2 or
$\quad p^4$ or s^2p^4: $F^2(pp) = \frac{5}{18}(-9\ ^3P + 5\ ^1D + 4\ ^1S)$

sp^2 or sp^4: $F^2(pp) = \frac{5}{18}(-6\ ^4P + 5\ ^2D + 4\ ^2S - 3\ ^2P)$
$\qquad\qquad\ \ G^1(sp) = (^2P - {}^4P)$

p^3 or s^2p^3: $F^2(pp) = \frac{5}{6}(^2P^o - {}^4S^o)$

sp^3: $F^2(pp) = \frac{5}{24}(-5\ ^5S^o - 3\ ^3S^o + 6\ ^3P^o + 2\ ^1P^o)$
$\qquad\qquad G^1(sp) = (12)^{-1}(-5\ ^5S^o + 5\ ^3S^o - 5\ ^3D^o + 5\ ^1D^o - 3\ ^3P^o + 3\ ^1P^o)$

Table 15-5
Comparison of observed multiplet energies for several configurations of N^+ and N^{++}, together with multiplet energies calculated by formulas of Table 15-3 from empirically determined parameters tabulated in Table 15-2.

			Experimental	Calculated
N^+	$1s^22s^22p^2$	^3P	-108.15695	-108.15363
		^1D	-108.01819	-108.02815
		^1S	-107.85988	-107.83992
	$1s^22s^22p^3$	$^5S^o$	-107.72792	-107.74624
		$^3D^o$	-107.31719	-107.30361
		$^3P^o$	-107.16244	-107.17255
		$^1D^o$	-106.84376	-106.81154
		$^3S^o$	-106.74406	-106.76210
		$^1P^o$	-106.63802	-106.68048
N^{++}	$1s^22s2p^2$	^4P	-105.45912	-105.47107
		^2D	-105.06048	-105.04464
		^2S	-104.78730	-104.81900
		^2P	-104.65100	-104.64303
	$1s^22p^3$	$^4S^o$	-104.27881	-104.32385
		$^2D^o$	-104.13048	-104.08543
		$^2P^o$	-103.88143	-103.92648

indicating that it requires approximately the same amount of energy to raise an electron from a $2s$ to a $2p$ level in the atom or ion, irrespective of the number of $2s$ or $2p$ electrons already present. This is an interesting approximate generalization, which we shall consider in a later section.

15-4. Simple Analytic Models for Wave Functions and Energies. In all our work so far on atomic multiplets, we have been presupposing the existence of one-electron wave functions of the form given in Eq. (7-31), including radial functions $R_{nl}(r)$. The various integrals concerned in the energy are to be computed from these radial functions by the formulas of Sec. 13-3. We have now reached the point where, to carry our discussion of the experimental results further, we wish some specific radial functions, so that we can carry out calculation of the integrals and see how they agree with those given in Table 15-2. Many different sets of functions have been used, and we shall discuss a number of them later. We shall start with analytic functions of a type first used by Zener,[1] Eckart,[2] and others and developed particularly by Morse and his collaborators.[3] These are simple analytic functions, which give a moderately satisfactory approximation to the solutions of the self-consistent-field problem and are much simpler to handle; we shall discuss their accuracy in a later section.

The functions used by Morse and his collaborators are given by

$$R(1s) = (4\mu^3 a^3)^{1/2} \exp(-\mu a r)$$
$$R(2s) = (4\mu^5/3N)^{1/2}[r \exp(-\mu r) - (3A/\mu) \exp(-\mu b r)] \quad (15\text{-}6)$$
$$R(2p) = (4\mu^5 c^5/3)^{1/2} r \exp(-\mu c r)$$

where a, b, c, μ are parameters to be determined and

$$A = \frac{(a+b)^3}{(a+1)^4} \qquad N = 1 - \frac{48A}{(b+1)^4} + \frac{3A^2}{b^3} \quad (15\text{-}7)$$

The functions as defined in Eq. (15-6) are normalized in the sense of Eq. (7-25), $\int_0^\infty R^2 r^2 \, dr = 1$. The functions $R(1s)$ and $R(2s)$ are orthogonal to each other; Eq. (15-7), defining A and N, leads to the normalization of $R(2s)$ and its orthogonality to $R(1s)$. The reason for writing the four arbitrary exponents μa, μ, μb, and μc in this form in terms of a factor μ will be explained later in this section. These arbitrary exponents

[1] C. Zener, *Phys. Rev.*, **36**:51 (1930).

[2] C. Eckart, *Phys. Rev.*, **36**:878 (1930).

[3] P. M. Morse, L. A. Young, and E. Haurwitz, *Phys. Rev.*, **48**:948 (1935); A. Tubis, *Phys. Rev.*, **102**:1049 (1956); P. M. Morse and H. Yilmaz, "Tables for the Variational Determination of Atomic Wave Functions," Technology Press, M.I.T., Cambridge, Mass., 1956. [The reader should be warned against several typographical errors in the papers of Morse et al.; in particular, the formulas in Tubis's papers equivalent to Eqs. (15-6) and (15-7) contain several errors.]

have been determined, for each configuration of each of the atoms, by evaluating the energy of the atomic state and varying the exponents to minimize this energy, making use of the variation principle. We shall later tabulate the values of the exponents so obtained.

If we use the radial functions of Eq. (15-6), it is a straightforward procedure to use the formulas of Sec. 13-3 and to compute all the required one- and two-electron integrals. We find that they have the values given in Table 15-6.

We note that the integrals $I(1s)$, $I(2s)$, $I(2p)$ contain terms in μ^2 and terms in μ. Of these, the first are the kinetic-energy integrals, the second are the potential-energy. All the other integrals, which represent the two-electron contributions to the potential energy, are proportional to μ. Thus we see that the total kinetic energy is proportional to μ^2, the potential energy to μ:

$$\text{Energy} = C\mu^2 + D\mu \qquad (15\text{-}8)$$

The reason for this dependence is simple. When we examine the wave functions of Eq. (15-6), we see that μ is of the nature of a scale factor: if μ changes, but a, b, and c remain fixed, the linear dimensions of all three wave functions vary proportionally to $1/\mu$ but the shape of the functions is unchanged. Since all terms in the potential energy are proportional to the reciprocal of a linear dimension, it is clear that in this case the total potential energy will be inversely proportional to the linear dimensions of the wave function, or directly proportional to μ. As for the kinetic energy, we remember that the kinetic-energy operator is a second derivative with respect to a linear dimension, so that the kinetic energy must vary inversely as the square of the linear dimension, or proportionally to μ^2. The dependence on μ which we have found in Eq. (15-8) is then more general than our assumption of Eq. (15-6) regarding the wave functions. Quite generally, if we have a scale factor such that the linear dimensions of all wave functions are proportional to $1/\mu$, the kinetic energy will have the form $C\mu^2$, the potential energy the form $D\mu$.

We now see the advantage of including the factor μ in the way we have done, in Eq. (15-6): the minimization of the energy with respect to the variation of the parameter μ can be carried out analytically. If we differentiate the energy in Eq. (15-8) with respect to μ and set the derivative equal to zero, we find at once that

$$\mu_0 = -\frac{D}{2C} \qquad (15\text{-}9)$$

where the value μ_0 of Eq. (15-9) is the value which minimizes the energy. There are then only three parameters, in the present case, which must really be varied to minimize the energy: a, b, and c. There is no con-

Table 15-6

Values of energy integrals of light atoms, in terms of radial wave functions of Eq. (15-6). Energies are in Rydbergs.

$$I(1s) = \mu^2 a^2 - 2Z\mu a$$

$$I(2s) = \frac{\mu^2}{3N}\left[1 + \frac{48Ab(b-2)}{(b+1)^4} + \frac{9A^2}{b}\right] - \frac{Z\mu}{N}\left[1 - \frac{32A}{(b+1)^3} + \frac{6A^2}{b^2}\right]$$

$$I(2p) = \mu^2 c^2 - Z\mu c$$

$$F^0(1s,1s) = \tfrac{5}{8}\mu a$$

$$F^0(1s,2s) = \frac{2\mu a}{N}\left\{\frac{1}{2(a+1)^5}(a^4 + 5a^3 + 10a^2 + 10a + 2)\right.$$
$$- \frac{16A}{(2a+b+1)^4}\left[2\left(\frac{2a}{b+1}\right)^3 + 8\left(\frac{2a}{b+1}\right)^2 + 12\left(\frac{2a}{b+1}\right) + 3\right]$$
$$\left. + \frac{3A^2}{(a+b)^3}\left[\left(\frac{a}{b}\right)^2 + 3\left(\frac{a}{b}\right) + 1\right]\right\}$$

$$G^0(1s,2s) = \frac{2\mu a^3}{N}\left\{\frac{44}{(a+1)^7} - \frac{128A}{(a+b)^2(2a+b+1)^4}\left[\left(\frac{a+b}{a+1}\right)^3 + 4\left(\frac{a+b}{a+1}\right)^2\right.\right.$$
$$\left.\left. + 6\left(\frac{a+b}{a+1}\right) + \frac{3}{2}\right] + \frac{60A^2}{(a+b)^5}\right\}$$

$$F^0(1s,2p) = \frac{\mu a c^5}{(a+c)^5}\left[\left(\frac{a}{c}\right)^4 + 5\left(\frac{a}{c}\right)^3 + 10\left(\frac{a}{c}\right)^2 + 10\left(\frac{a}{c}\right) + 2\right]$$

$$G^1(1s,2p) = \frac{56\mu a^3 c^5}{(a+c)^7}$$

$$F^0(2s,2s) = \frac{2\mu}{N^2}\left\{\frac{93}{256} - \frac{128}{(b+3)^6}\left[\frac{16}{(b+1)^3} + \frac{48}{(b+1)^2} + \frac{60}{b+1} + \frac{45}{2} + \frac{9(b+1)}{2}\right.\right.$$
$$\left.+ \frac{3(b+1)^2}{8}\right] + \frac{528A^2}{(b+1)^7} + \frac{3A^2}{b^2(b+1)^5}(b^4 + 5b^3 + 10b^2 + 10b + 2)$$
$$\left. - \frac{192A^3}{b^2(3b+1)^4}\left[8\left(\frac{b}{b+1}\right)^3 + 16\left(\frac{b}{b+1}\right)^2 + 12\left(\frac{b}{b+1}\right) + \frac{3}{2}\right] + \frac{45A^4}{8b^5}\right\}$$

$$F^0(2s,2p) = \frac{2\mu}{N}\left\{\frac{c}{2(c+1)^7}(c^6 + 7c^5 + 21c^4 + 35c^3 + 21c^2 + 7c + 1)\right.$$
$$- \frac{96Ac^3}{(b+2c+1)^6}\left[\left(\frac{b+1}{2c}\right)^2 + 6\left(\frac{b+1}{2c}\right) + 15 + 20\left(\frac{2c}{b+1}\right) + 8\left(\frac{2c}{b+1}\right)^2\right.$$
$$\left.+ \frac{4}{3}\left(\frac{2c}{b+1}\right)^3\right] + \frac{3}{2}\frac{A^2 c^3}{(b+c)^5}\left[\left(\frac{b}{c}\right)^2 + 5\left(\frac{b}{c}\right) + 10 + 10\left(\frac{c}{b}\right) + 2\left(\frac{c}{b}\right)^2\right]\right\}$$

$$G^1(2s,2p) = \frac{2\mu c^5}{N}\left\{\frac{370}{3}\frac{1}{(c+1)^9} - \frac{512A}{(b+2c+1)^6(c+1)^2}\left[\frac{5}{2}\left(\frac{c+1}{b+c}\right)^2\right.\right.$$
$$\left.\left. + 15\left(\frac{c+1}{b+c}\right) + 6 + \left(\frac{b+c}{c+1}\right)\right] + \frac{84A^2}{(b+c)^7}\right\}$$

$$F^0(2p,2p) = \frac{93\mu c}{128}$$

$$F^2(2p,2p) = \frac{45\mu c}{128}$$

venient way to vary these parameters. In the work which we have quoted, the total energy was simply computed for a variety of values of these parameters, and those choices of parameters were made which gave the lowest energy. Since this is a tedious process, a digital computer was used to carry it out, in the work of Tubis which we have quoted.

The relation of Eq. (15-9) for μ has an interesting consequence, when we combine it with Eq. (15-8), in which we remember that the term $C\mu^2$ is the kinetic energy, $D\mu$ is the potential energy. We find

$$\text{Kinetic energy} = \frac{D^2}{4C} \qquad \text{Potential energy} = -\frac{D^2}{2C} \qquad (15\text{-}10)$$

from which
$$\begin{aligned}\text{Potential energy} &= -2(\text{kinetic energy})\\ \text{Total energy} &= -\text{kinetic energy}\end{aligned} \qquad (15\text{-}11)$$

These relations express what is called the virial theorem, in its application to the atomic problem. This is a general theorem, holding in either classical or quantum mechanics, relating the total potential energy to the total kinetic energy of a system. It has a much more general form than is given in Eq. (15-11), but the special case holding for inverse-square laws of force, which we are dealing with here, is what we find in Eq. (15-11), and since that is the only application of the theorem which we shall need in our problem of atomic structure, we shall not discuss the general theorem here. We note that the true wave function of an atom can be found by variation methods, since we have proved that they are equivalent to Schrödinger's equation. A wave function which is completely free to vary must, among other things, be able to change its scale, as we have accomplished with our parameter μ. Thus the same demonstration we have given applies rigorously to the true wave function, and not merely to the approximate function we are using, so that Eq. (15-11) holds rigorously for the true solution of Schrödinger's equation for an atom (in the approximation in which we are disregarding spin-orbit interaction).

Now we are ready to consider the results of Morse et al. In Table 15-7, we give some of these results, taken from the work of Tubis. We first give the atom, configuration, and multiplet. Next we give the values of the exponents, in the form μa, μb, 2μ, and $2\mu c$; we shall explain later why we have chosen these particular combinations. Next is E_{calc}, the calculated energy of the multiplet under discussion. The values of μa, μb, 2μ, and $2\mu c$ are determined by minimizing this calculated energy. In the next column we give the observed energy of the corresponding multiplet, from Table 15-2, and in the final column the error of the calculated energy. We observe several things about these errors. First, in every case the calculated energy lies above the observed value, as would be expected from the variation principle. Second, the errors are small, of the order of magnitude of $\frac{1}{2}$ to 1 per cent of the total energy, showing that we can get quite satisfactory energies by this method. Third, the errors within a single configuration tend to be greatest for the highest multiplet of the configuration, which means that the observed energies of the highest multiplets tend to be pushed down in comparison with the

Table 15-7

Calculated energies of multiplets of light atoms, from work of A. Tubis, *Phys. Rev.*, **102**:1049 (1956). The wave functions are given in Eq. (15-6), the parameters are tabulated. Experimental values from Table 15-2, in Rydbergs.

Multiplet			μa	μb	2μ	$2\mu c$	E_{calc}	E_{obs}	Error
B	$1s^2 2s^2 2p$	$^2P^o$	4.70	4.30	2.60	2.42	-49.005	-49.31852	0.314
C	$1s^2 2s^2 2p^2$	^3P	5.69	5.12	3.31	3.06	-75.257	-75.71369	0.457
		^1D	5.69	5.12	3.31	3.12	-75.126	-75.62106	0.495
		^1S	5.69	5.31	3.28	2.94	-74.934	-75.51668	0.683
C$^+$	$1s^2 2s^2 2p$	$^2P^o$	5.69	4.93	3.55	3.52	-74.532	-74.88559	0.354
N	$1s^2 2s^2 2p^3$	$^4S^o$	6.69	6.09	3.93	3.83	-108.553	-109.22713	0.674
		$^2D^o$	6.68	6.02	3.97	3.75	-108.313	-109.05192	0.739
		$^2P^o$	6.69	6.19	3.90	3.73	-108.153	-108.96431	0.812
N$^+$	$1s^2 2s^2 2p^2$	^3P	6.69	5.86	4.18	4.21	-107.657	-108.15695	0.500
		^1D	6.69	5.86	4.19	4.15	-107.481	-108.01819	0.538
		^1S	6.69	5.87	4.19	4.07	-107.220	-107.85988	0.640
N^{++}	$1s^2 2s^2 2p$	$^2P^o$	6.69	5.60	4.51	4.58	-105.579	-105.98008	0.401
O	$1s^2 2s^2 2p^4$	^3P	7.67	7.01	4.62	4.44	-149.101	-150.22487	1.124
		^1D	7.68	6.95	4.62	4.44	-148.914	-150.08098	1.167
		^1S	7.68	6.96	4.64	4.37	-148.633	-149.91763	1.284
O$^+$	$1s^2 2s^2 2p^3$	$^4S^o$	7.68	6.77	4.83	4.89	-148.501	-149.22464	0.724
		$^2D^o$	7.68	6.77	4.83	4.84	-148.193	-148.98026	0.787
		$^2P^o$	7.68	6.77	4.84	4.79	-147.990	-148.85586	0.866
O^{++}	$1s^2 2s^2 2p^2$	^3P	7.68	6.49	5.13	5.25	-146.081	-146.63875	0.558
		^1D	7.68	6.56	5.13	5.21	-145.860	-146.45592	0.596
		^1S	7.68	6.61	5.11	5.12	-145.532	-146.24712	0.715
O^{3+}	$1s^2 2s^2 2p$	$^2P^o$	7.69	6.26	5.44	5.63	-142.136	-142.59948	0.463

theory more than those of the lower multiplets, as we have pointed out earlier. Finally, the errors tend to increase as the number of electrons in the atom increases.

We can go further in discussing these results of Tubis, computing individual integrals, and so on, but before doing so we shall discuss a very similar but independent calculation made by Roothaan.[1] This calculation is essentially identical with that of Morse and his collaborators, except that Roothaan uses one less arbitrary parameter. The difference comes in the treatment of the $2s$ wave function. If we consider Eq. (15-6), we see that this function is given in the treatment of Morse and collaborators by a function $r \exp(-\mu r) - (3A/\mu) \exp(-\mu b r)$, times a normalizing factor. For orientation, let us consider a specific case, say O $1s^2 2s^2 2p^4$, where $\mu = 2.31$, $\mu b = 7.01$, from Table 15-7. We see, then, that the term $r \exp(-\mu r) = r \exp(-2.31r)$ falls off slowly

[1] C. J. Roothaan, unpublished.

with distance, both on account of the factor r and the small exponent, as compared with the term $\exp(-\mu br) = \exp(-7.01r)$. The former term is the important one for large r's, or in the outer loop of the $2s$ function, while the latter is the important one for small r's, or in the inner loop, since it does not contain the factor r which makes the other term go to zero as r approaches zero. Now, when we plot the function, we find that the inner loop of the true wave function is quite small. It looks almost like a miniature version of the $1s$ wave function; and this fact is correlated with the observation, which we can make from Table 15-7, that the exponent μb occurring in the exponential $\exp(-\mu br)$ is not far different from the exponent μa occurring in the $1s$ function $\exp(-\mu ar)$. It therefore seems plausible that we should not make a great error if we arbitrarily set $b = a$, that is, if we used the same exponential for the inner loop of the $2s$ function as for the $1s$ function. This is an approximation which had already been made before Roothaan's work, as we shall discuss in Sec. 15-7; and it is the assumption made by Roothaan. Roothaan thus used the same wave functions given in Eq. (15-6), but with the restriction $a = b$, and he varied the two parameters a and c, and μ, to minimize the energy, though he expressed his results in quite different notation from that of Morse and Tubis.

Roothaan has carried out this process for more configurations than Tubis has, but we shall not reproduce all his results. We shall choose the various stages of ionization of oxygen as an example to carry through, and in Table 15-8 we give Roothaan's calculated values, expressed in the same notation as in Table 15-7. We note by comparison with Table 15-7 that the parameters resulting from Roothaan's minimization procedure are appreciably different, even for the case of the $1s$ and $2p$ functions, from those of Tubis; whether this is significant or merely an indication of the difficulty of choosing those parameters which actually minimize the energy is hard to say. Both writers find that one can make considerable variations in the parameters with almost negligible change in the energy, a result of the variation principle, which makes it hard to determine the exact values of the parameters which really minimize the energy.

The interesting point of the comparison of the two tables, however, is not the small changes in parameters but the fact that, as we should expect from the variation principle, Tubis's calculation in each case gives a slightly lower energy than Roothaan's; the extra parameter which Tubis has varied to minimize the energy has resulted in a slight lowering, as compared with the arbitrary value $a = b$ assumed by Roothaan. The improvement is very small, however. Thus, in Table 15-9, we give the lowering of energy in Tubis's calculation as compared with Roothaan's, for the cases in which both have made calculations. We see that it is a

Table 15-8

Calculated energies of multiplets of oxygen, from work of C. J. Roothaan (unpublished). The wave functions are given in Eq. (15-6), specialized by letting $a = b$. Experimental values from Table 15-2, in Rydbergs.

	Multiplet		μa	2μ	$2\mu c$	E_{calc}	E_{obs}	Error
O	$1s^2 2s^2 2p^4$	^3P	7.6580	4.4922	4.4525	-149.08072	-150.22487	1.14415
		^1D	7.6581	4.4999	4.4247	-148.89344	-150.08098	1.18754
		^1S	7.6585	4.5108	4.3824	-148.61478	-149.91763	1.30285
	$1s^2 2s 2p^5$	$^3P^o$	7.6531	4.5674	4.4070	-147.68848	-149.07457	1.38609
		$^1P^o$	7.6527	4.4324	4.3915	-147.00138	-148.49560	1.49422
O^+	$1s^2 2s^2 2p^3$	$^4S^o$	7.6511	4.6702	4.9049	-148.46418	-149.22464	0.76046
		$^2D^o$	7.6513	4.6811	4.8498	-148.15556	-148.98026	0.82470
		$^2P^o$	7.6517	4.6874	4.8132	-147.95174	-148.85586	0.90412
	$1s^2 2s 2p^4$	^4P	7.6487	4.7713	4.8146	-147.26684	-148.13169	0.86485
		^2D	7.6484	4.7084	4.7832	-146.70178	-147.71197	1.01019
		^2S	7.6490	4.7179	4.7456	-146.40028	-147.44113	1.04085
		^2P	7.6474	4.5242	4.8078	-146.18902	-147.28677	1.09775
O^{++}	$1s^2 2s^2 2p^2$	^3P	7.6461	4.8904	5.2788	-146.01942	-146.63875	0.61933
		^1D	7.6465	4.8968	5.2242	-145.79788	-146.45592	0.65804
		^1S	7.6470	4.9048	5.1452	-145.46978	-146.24712	0.77734
	$1s^2 2s 2p^3$	$^5S^o$	7.6464	5.0099	5.2388	-145.61612	-146.09103	0.47491
		$^3D^o$	7.6461	4.9424	5.1869	-144.90714	-145.54672	0.63958
		$^3P^o$	7.6464	4.9472	5.1552	-144.68900	-145.34311	0.65411
		$^1D^o$	7.6446	4.7702	5.1896	-144.16034	-144.93607	0.77573
		$^3S^o$	7.6434	4.6395	5.2568	-144.12516	-144.84460	0.71944
		$^1P^o$	7.6451	4.7797	5.1546	-143.94214	-144.72275	0.78061
	$1s^2 2p^4$	^3P	7.6446		5.1418	-143.31860	-144.05378	0.73518
		^1D	7.6451		5.1192	-143.20218	-143.92234	0.72016
		^1S	7.6482		5.0861	-142.77934	-143.51214	0.73280
O^{3+}	$1s^2 2s^2 2p$	$^2P^o$	7.6425	5.1266	5.6478	-142.03894	-142.59948	0.56054
	$1s^2 2s 2p^2$	^4P	7.6472	5.1985	5.5961	-141.56910	-141.95136	0.38226
		^2D	7.6464	5.1246	5.5488	-140.94372	-141.44501	0.50129
		^2S	7.6472	5.1313	5.4762	-140.59488	-141.10396	0.50908
		^2P	7.6434	4.9300	5.6247	-140.41206	-140.95563	0.54357
	$1s^2 2p^3$	$^4S^o$	7.6473		5.5535	-140.09192	-140.49422	0.40230
		$^2D^o$	7.6481		5.5082	-139.74192	-140.27648	0.53456
		$^2P^o$	7.6487		5.4780	-139.51018	-139.96798	0.45780

relatively small fraction of the total error and that it is greater in the case of higher ionization. The reason for this latter fact is obvious from Table 15-7: the discrepancy between a and b, when both are allowed to vary, increases as we go to higher states of ionization. From the values of Table 15-9, we see that, if a careful calculation is needed, it pays to use the extra parameter b given by Tubis, but one still gets good calculations by using Roothaan's approximation.

Table 15-9. Differences between Roothaan's and Tubis's Energies, from Tables 15-7 and 15-8

O	$1s^2 2s^2 2p^4$	^3P	0.020
		^1D	0.021
		^1S	0.018
O$^+$	$1s^2 2s^2 2p^3$	$^4S^o$	0.037
		$^2D^o$	0.037
		$^2P^o$	0.038
O^{++}	$1s^2 2s^2 2p^2$	^3P	0.062
		^1D	0.062
		^1S	0.062
O^{3+}	$1s^2 2s^2 2p$	$^2P^o$	0.097

We note from Tables 15-7 and 15-8 that Tubis and Roothaan have both treated each multiplet as a separate problem, minimizing the parameters separately for each one. However, when we do this, the resulting one-electron orbitals will be slightly different for each multiplet in a configuration. This is contrary to the assumptions of the theory as we have been building it up in preceding chapters, in which we have assumed a fixed orthonormal set of orbitals, in terms of which we shall expand the wave functions of all multiplets. That is a restriction on the form of one-electron functions, which limits the free variation and hence will result in poorer agreement with experiment; on the other hand, it simplifies the calculations greatly. To test the additional error involved in that assumption, we have made the following calculation: For each stage of ionization of the oxygen atom, we have taken the parameters a, b, and c used by Tubis for the multiplet of lowest energy of the corresponding ion and have recalculated μ by Tubis's method to more significant figures than he uses. We have calculated all the integrals of Table 15-6 for each case, and in terms of these integrals we have calculated the energies of the various multiplets of this ion. This has involved a recalculation of Tubis's results for oxygen, which we have carried to more decimal places. The integrals are given in Table 15-10. In Table 15-11 we give the calculated energies of the multiplets. The multiplet of lowest energy for each ion should agree with the calculations of Tubis; the agreement is within an error of ± 2 in the last figure of Tubis's results, which is his stated accuracy. We see that as we go to higher multiplets of a given ion, including those in which $2s$ electrons are replaced by $2p$'s, the errors become greater, as judged by the comparison with Tubis's and Roothaan's calculations; but the errors do not become seriously greater. It seems from this that, for most purposes, it is an unnecessary refinement to use different orbital functions for the different multiplets or configurations of a given atom or ion. There are a few cases, however, where this refinement is probably worthwhile.

15-5. The Self-consistent-field Method for Light Atoms. When we examine the results of Tables 15-7, 15-8, and 15-11, we naturally ask how much of the error in the energies arises from the inadequacy of the specialized assumption of Eq. (15-6) for the one-electron orbitals and how much from the general nature of our method. We are surely not getting exact solutions of Schrödinger's equation when we build up determinantal combinations of one-electron 1s, 2s, and 2p orbitals and combine these to give wave functions diagonalizing $(L^2)_{op}$ and $(S^2)_{op}$ to give definite multiplets. What is the best approximation which we could get by this general method, but allowing indefinite freedom of variation in the 1s, 2s, and 2p orbitals, rather than confining them to the simple forms of Eq. (15-6)? This best approximation is formed by using Hartree's method of the self-consistent field, as we showed in Sec. 9-4. It is very interesting to compare the results of self-consistent calculations with those made by Tubis and Roothaan, which we have been discussing in the preceding section.

Calculations have been made[1] by the Hartree-Fock self-consistent-field method for the nitrogen atom and for oxygen in various stages of ionization. Hartree and his collaborators, who have made the calculations, have found wave functions which minimize the energy for the various multiplets, just as Tubis and Roothaan did using analytic functions; but they find, as we have already pointed out, that it makes comparatively little difference if we use different functions for the different multiplets or adopt the same ones for all multiplets of an atom or ion. Consequently, in Table 15-12 we give calculated values of the multiplets of N, O, and O+, computed from the integrals found from the one-electron functions which minimize the energy of the lowest multiplet for each atom or ion. The integrals are given in Table 15-10. This is analogous to the procedure which we have used in Table 15-11, and for comparison we give the results for oxygen from that table, and we give similar results for nitrogen, computed in the same way from the integrals of Table 15-10.

It is now very interesting to compare the errors in the calculations made by the self-consistent-field method (indicated by SCF in the table) with the calculations made by the method of Table 15-11, using approxi-

---

[1] D. R. Hartree and M. M. Black, *Proc. Roy. Soc. (London)*, **A139**:311 (1933); D. R. Hartree, W. Hartree, and B. Swirles, *Phil. Trans. Roy. Soc. (London)*, **A238**:229 (1939); D. R. Hartree and W. Hartree, *Proc. Roy. Soc. (London)*, **A193**:299 (1948). The author understands that C. C. J. Roothaan, in unpublished work, has carried out self-consistent-field calculations of the atoms up to neon, in various stages of ionization, using analytic functions with a number of parameters, somewhat similar to those used by Watson for the iron group in the calculations to be described in Chap. 16. When these results of Roothaan are available, they will result in improved and extensive self-consistent wave functions with which the approximate analytic functions which we have been describing can be compared.

Table 15-10. Energy Integrals for Nitrogen and Oxygen, Based on (a) Method of Morse and Collaborators, (b) Self-consistent Fields

Nitrogen: Constants for method of P. M. Morse et al., *Phys. Rev.*, **48**:948 (1935), $a = 3.4$, $b = 3.1$, $c = 0.976$, assumed from Tubis's tables, and $\mu = 1.964871$, determined by Eq. (15-9), by minimizing the energy of the multiplet $1s^2 2s^2 2p^3\ {}^4S^\circ$. Self-consistent-field integrals are taken from H. Kaplan, *J. Chem. Phys.*, **26**:1704 (1957), where they are computed from numerical self-consistent field functions of D. R. Hartree and W. Hartree, *Proc. Roy. Soc. (London)*, **A193**:299 (1948), in connection with a calculation of the ammonia molecule. *KE* stands for kinetic energy, *PE* for potential energy in field of nucleus. All integrals are given in Rydbergs.

	(a)	(b)
$KE(1s)$	44.62993	44.270
$PE(1s)$	-93.52788	-93.1214
$I(1s)$	-48.89795	-48.8514
$KE(2s)$	4.12960	4.458
$PE(2s)$	-14.72121	-15.0618
$I(2s)$	-10.59161	-10.6038
$KE(2p)$	3.67763	3.724
$PE(2p)$	-13.42400	-13.3650
$I(2p)$	-9.74637	-9.6410
$F^o(1s,1s)$	8.35070	8.2492
$F^o(1s,2s)$	1.91737	1.9380
$G^o(1s,2s)$	0.10685	0.1262
$F^o(1s,2p)$	1.90560	1.8890
$G^1(1s,2p)$	0.12464	0.1716
$F^o(2s,2s)$	1.37614	1.3666
$F^o(2s,2p)$	1.38285	1.3338
$G^1(2s,2p)$	0.89782	0.8220
$F^o(2p,2p)$	1.39334	1.3082
$F^2(2p,2p)$	0.67420	0.5884

Oxygen and O^+: Constants for method of Morse and collaborators, for oxygen, $a = 3.32$, $b = 3.08$, $c = 0.961$, from Tubis's tables; $\mu = 2.309303$, determined by minimizing energy of $1s^2 2s^2 2p^4\ {}^3P$. For O^+, $a = 3.18$, $b = 2.81$, $c = 1.013$, $\mu = 2.414427$. Self-consistent-field integrals were computed by A. J. Freeman (unpublished) from wave functions given by D. R. Hartree, W. Hartree, and B. Swirles, *Phil. Trans. Roy. Soc. (London)*, **A238**:229 (1939). The author is indebted to Dr. Freeman for these integrals.

	O (a)	O (b)	O^+ (a)	O^+ (b)
$KE(1s)$	58.78116	58.44	58.94981	58.50
$PE(1s)$	-122.67020	-122.2672	-122.84605	-122.3178
$I(1s)$	-63.88904	-63.8272	-63.89624	-63.8178
$KE(2s)$	5.91863	6.1896	6.32772	6.782
$PE(2s)$	-19.98562	-20.2110	-20.64970	-21.0878
$I(2s)$	-14.06699	-14.0214	-14.32198	-14.3058
$KE(2p)$	4.92503	5.0836	5.98201	6.075
$PE(2p)$	-17.75392	-17.7800	-19.56652	-19.6078
$I(2p)$	-12.82889	-12.6964	-13.58451	-13.5328

Table 15-10. Energy Integrals for Nitrogen and Oxygen, Based on (a) Method of Morse and Collaborators, (b) Self-consistent Fields (Continued)

	O (a)	O (b)	O⁺ (a)	O⁺ (b)
$F^0(1s,1s)$	9.58361	9.48424	9.59735	9.49158
$F^0(1s,2s)$	2.26025	2.26626	2.33187	2.35382
$G^0(1s,2s)$	0.13473	0.15336	0.14380	0.16572
$F^0(1s,2p)$	2.20486	2.19706	2.42484	2.41972
$G^1(1s,2p)$	0.14719	0.21106	0.20354	0.25956
$F^0(2s,2s)$	1.61692	1.59470	1.67429	1.66760
$F^0(2s,2p)$	1.61255	1.54708	1.71942	1.68002
$G^1(2s,2p)$	1.04516	0.94420	1.09992	1.03236
$F^0(2p,2p)$	1.61242	1.50956	1.77704	1.70548
$F^2(2p,2p)$	0.78020	0.67208	0.85986	0.78148

O^{++} and O^{3+}: Constants for method of Morse and collaborators, for O^{++}, $a = 2.99$, $b = 2.53$, $c = 1.023$, $\mu = 2.568965$. For O^{3+}, $a = 2.83$, $b = 2.30$, $c = 1.035$, $\mu = 2.718257$. Self-consistent-field integrals are from D. R. Hartree, W. Hartree, and B. Swirles, *Phil. Trans. Roy. Soc. (London)*, **A238**:229 (1939), and in each case are determined for multiplet of lowest energy.

	O^{++} (a)	O^{++} (b)	O^{3+} (a)	O^{3+} (b)
$KE(1s)$	59.00093		59.17714	
$PE(1s)$	−122.89930		−123.08268	
$I(1s)$	− 63.89837		− 63.90554	
$KE(2s)$	7.13278		7.93303	
$PE(2s)$	− 21.80863		− 22.89870	
$I(2s)$	− 14.67585		− 14.96567	
$KE(2p)$	6.90665		7.91520	
$PE(2p)$	− 21.02441		− 22.50717	
$I(2p)$	− 14.11776		− 14.59197	
$F^0(1s,1s)$	9.60151		9.61583	
$F^0(1s,2s)$	2.44594		2.55149	
$G^0(1s,2s)$	0.16247		0.18072	
$F^0(1s,2p)$	2.60041		2.77780	
$G^1(1s,2p)$	0.25707		0.31805	
$F^0(2s,2s)$	1.75930	1.752	1.83767	1.840
$F^0(2s,2p)$	1.82402	1.796	1.92468	1.908
$G^1(2s,2p)$	1.15107	1.096	1.19424	1.158
$F^0(2p,2p)$	1.90944	1.860	2.04411	2.008
$F^2(2p,2p)$	0.92392	0.868	0.98908	0.946

mate analytic functions. We see that the errors using the self-consistent-field method are markedly lower than by the other method, roughly two-thirds as great. In other words, a very significant improvement in accuracy is possible by giving complete freedom to the wave functions as compared with limiting them to the simple analytic forms of Eq. (15-6).

Table 15-11

Calculated energies of multiplets of oxygen, using parameters and integrals given in Table 15-10, based on a single set of analytic orbitals for each stage of ionization. Calculated values of A. Tubis and C. J. Roothaan are given for comparison, from Tables 15-7 and 15-8, and experimental values from Table 15-2, all in Rydbergs. Tabulated error is that of present calculation.

	Multiplet		E_{calc}	E (Tubis)	E (Roothaan)	E_{obs}	Error
O	$1s^2 2s^2 2p^4$	^3P	-149.09967	-149.101	-149.08072	-150.22487	1.12520
		^1D	-148.91243	-148.914	-148.89344	-150.08098	1.16855
		^1S	-148.63155	-148.633	-148.61478	-149.91763	1.28608
	$1s^2 2s 2p^5$	$^3P^o$	-147.69924		-147.68848	-149.07457	1.37533
		$^1P^o$	-147.00247		-147.00138	-148.49560	1.49313
	$1s^2 2p^6$	^1S	-145.75385				
O$^+$	$1s^2 2s^2 2p^3$	$^4S^o$	-148.50107	-148.501	-148.46418	-149.22464	0.72357
		$^2D^o$	-148.19162	-148.193	-148.15556	-148.98026	0.78864
		$^2P^o$	-147.98515	-147.990	-147.95174	-148.85586	0.87071
	$1s^2 2s 2p^4$	^4P	-147.28339		-147.26684	-148.13169	0.84830
		^2D	-146.71039		-146.70178	-147.71197	1.00158
		^2S	-146.40085		-146.40028	-147.44113	1.04028
		^2P	-146.18347		-146.18902	-147.28677	1.10330
	$1s^2 2p^5$	$^2P^o$	-145.12588				
O^{++}	$1s^2 2s^2 2p^2$	^3P	-146.08069	-146.081	-146.01942	-146.63875	0.55806
		^1D	-145.85895	-145.860	-145.79788	-146.45592	0.59697
		^1S	-145.52634	-145.532	-145.46978	-146.24712	0.72078
	$1s^2 2s 2p^3$	$^5S^o$	-145.66456		-145.61612	-146.09103	0.42647
		$^3D^o$	-144.93825		-144.90714	-145.54672	0.60847
		$^3P^o$	-144.71651		-144.68900	-145.34311	0.62660
		$^1D^o$	-144.17087		-144.16034	-144.93607	0.76520
		$^3S^o$	-144.11910		-144.12516	-144.84460	0.72550
		$^1P^o$	-143.94913		-143.94214	-144.72275	0.77362
	$1s^2 2p^4$	^3P	-143.30340		-143.31860	-144.05378	0.75038
		^1D	-143.08166		-143.20218	-143.92234	0.84068
		^1S	-142.74905		-142.77934	-143.51214	0.76309
O^{3+}	$1s^2 2s^2 2p$	$^2P^o$	-142.13551	-142.136	-142.03894	-142.59948	0.46397
	$1s^2 2s 2p^2$	^4P	-141.62395		-141.56910	-141.95136	0.32741
		^2D	-140.98849		-140.94372	-141.44501	0.45652
		^2S	-140.63242		-140.59488	-141.10396	0.47154
		^2P	-140.42971		-140.41206	-140.95563	0.52592
	$1s^2 2p^3$	$^4S^o$	-140.08355		-140.09192	-140.49422	0.41067
		$^2D^o$	-139.72748		-139.74192	-140.27648	0.54900
		$^2P^o$	-139.49010		-139.51018	-139.96798	0.47788

Table 15-12

Calculated energies of multiplets of N, O, and O⁺, using integrals from self-consistent-field method, compared with those calculated by method of Table 15-11 and experimental values from Table 15-2. Errors of both calculated values are given. All energies in Rydbergs. On account of one-electron integrals, absolute errors in $E(\text{SCF})$ can come in second decimal place, but relative accuracy of different multiplets is better than this.

	Multiplet		E (SCF)	E (Table 15-11)	E_{obs}	Error, SCF	Error, Table 15-11
N	$1s^2 2s^2 2p^3$	$^4S^o$	-108.8209	-108.55186	-109.22713	0.4062	0.67527
		$^2D^o$	-108.6091	-108.30915	-109.05192	0.4428	0.74277
		$^2P^o$	-108.4679	-108.14734	-108.96431	0.4964	0.81697
	$1s^2 2s 2p^4$	^4P	-107.9792	-107.62668	-108.42395	0.4447	0.79727
		^2D	-107.5640	-107.16561			
		^2S	-107.3522	-106.92289			
		^2P	-107.1572	-106.72856			
O	$1s^2 2s^2 2p^4$	^3P	-149.57800	-149.09967	-150.22487	0.64687	1.12520
		^1D	-149.41670	-148.91243	-150.08098	0.66428	1.16855
		^1S	-149.17475	-148.63155	-149.91763	0.74288	1.28608
	$1s^2 2s 2p^5$	$^3P^o$	-148.32582	-147.69924	-149.07457	0.74875	1.37533
		$^1P^o$	-147.69634	-147.00247	-148.49560	0.79926	1.49313
O⁺	$1s^2 2s^2 2p^3$	$^4S^o$	-148.65100	-148.50107	-149.22464	0.57364	0.72357
		$^2D^o$	-148.36966	-148.19162	-148.98026	0.61060	0.78864
		$^2P^o$	-148.18210	-147.98515	-148.85586	0.67376	0.87071
	$1s^2 2s 2p^4$	^4P	-147.57818	-147.28339	-148.13169	0.55351	0.84830
		^2D	-147.04652	-146.71039	-147.71197	0.66545	1.00158
		^2S	-146.76519	-146.40085	-147.44113	0.67594	1.04028
		^2P	-146.54584	-146.18347	-147.28677	0.74093	1.10330

Nevertheless, the remaining error is very considerable, of the order of magnitude of ½ per cent of the total energy. And now we see that this is the inescapable error made by using our determinantal method. In Chap. 18 (Vol. II) we shall examine in detail the source of this remaining error; for the present we are interested only in evaluating the accuracy of the various methods, and we see that even the quite crude method of Roothaan can still give results with errors only about twice as great as those arising with the self-consistent-field method.

We have gone as far as possible in the direction of improving the one-electron wave functions, and consequently of lowering the total calculated energy of the atom or ion, when we use the method of the self-consistent field. Thus we may consider the integrals determined in this way, given by the columns marked (b) for nitrogen and oxygen in Table 15-10, as the best values to use. Let us now return to the discussion of

Secs. 15-2 and 15-3, in which we found values of the average energy of configurations, and of the parameters $F^2(2p,2p)$ and $G^1(2s,2p)$, by application of least-squares methods to the observations, and let us see how closely these experimental values are reproduced by the theory.   This is a slightly different method of comparing theory and experiment from the one we have used in Table 15-12, where we compared the experimental and theoretical values for each multiplet.

First we consider the average energy of the configurations.   We use oxygen in its various stages of ionization as an example.   In Fig. 15-2

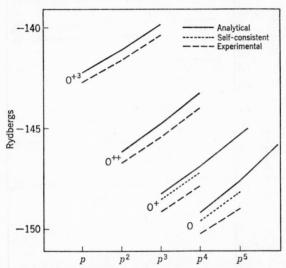

Fig. 15-2. Average energy of oxygen atom and ions, as function of number of p electrons, calculated from analytical wave functions, from self-consistent field, and experimental.

we give a diagram like that of Fig. 15-1, for oxygen, showing the average energy of a configuration, as a function of the number of p electrons in the atom or ion.   We give theoretical values computed by the method used in Table 15-11 (these values are merely the weighted means of the E_{calc} of Table 15-11) and also values computed from the self-consistent field [the weighted means of E (SCF) of Table 15-12].   It is clear that either set of theoretical values reproduces correctly the general trend of the experimental curves, though the self-consistent-field values of course lie closer to experiment.   When we ask why the energy increases when a $2s$ electron is shifted to a $2p$ orbit, the answer is given in terms of the integrals of Table 15-10.   The most important change is that the one-electron energy $I(2p)$ in every case lies higher than $I(2s)$.   But the numerous other integrals which enter into the energy difference have considerable effect, and we cannot give a simple qualitative explanation of why the lines of Fig. 15-2 are so nearly straight and parallel. As in most such cases of small changes in energy, the true explanation can be found only by carefully computing all the terms in the energy and seeing how they change from one state to the other. And similarly we cannot put our finger on a single integral which is responsible for the increased

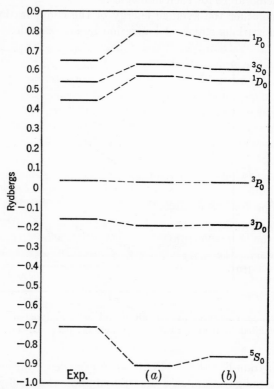

FIG. 15-3. Energy levels of multiplets of configuration $1s^2 2s 2p^3$ of O^{++}, as determined experimentally and by calculation from integrals (a) and (b) of Table 15-10, (a) being from analytic functions, (b) from self-consistent fields. Average energies adjusted to agree for each case.

accuracy of the self-consistent-field method as compared with the analytic functions. All the integrals change slightly from one method to the other, and a careful and accurate calculation of all these changes is required if we wish to investigate the difference between the different wave functions.

The multiplet separations are simpler to understand, for they depend on only two integrals, $F^2(2p,2p)$ and $G^1(2s,2p)$, rather than involving all the integrals as the average energy does. As we compare these integrals, as given in Table 15-10, with the experimental values of Table 15-2, we see that the theoretical integrals are too large to agree with experiment but that the integrals given by the self-consistent field are appreciably closer to experiment than those from the analytic wave functions. These integrals, as found from experiment, from the analytic wave functions [marked (a) in the table], and from self-consistent wave functions [marked (b)], are given in Table 15-13. We must interpret these facts along with the remark which we have made earlier, namely, that the interaction of higher configurations seems to push down the upper multiplets of a configuration more than the lower multiplets, thus changing the relative positions of the multiplets and squeezing them together. The parameters F^2 and G^1 found in Table 15-2 from experiment are influenced by this squeezing effect, and this is the probable reason why they are smaller than the calculated integrals. In most of the cases of Table 15-13, the experimental integrals average around 85 per cent of the self-consistent-field calculations. In every case the self-consistent calculation is closer to experiment than the analytic one.

It is interesting to plot the multiplet separations, as found experimentally, and as calculated by the two approximations we have used. This is done for the configuration $1s^2 2s 2p^3$ of O^{++} in Fig. 15-3. It is clear from this that the general arrangement of the levels is given correctly by the theory but that the levels are spread somewhat too widely by the theory. To make the diagrams clearer, they are drawn so that

Table 15-13

Values of parameters $F^2(2p,2p)$ and $G^1(2s,2p)$ for oxygen and nitrogen, as computed in Table 15-10, and as observed in Table 15-2.

	F^2 calculated (a)	F^2 calculated (b)	F^2 experimental
N	0.67420	0.5884	0.43811
O	0.78020	0.67208	0.54123
O^+	0.85986	0.78148	0.61463
			0.64613
O^{++}	0.92392	0.868	0.68908
			0.72600
			0.78438
O^{3+}	0.98908	0.946	0.81504
			0.87707

	G^1 calculated (a)	G^1 calculated (b)	G^1 experimental
O	1.04516	0.94420	0.86846
O^+	1.09992	1.03236	0.84492
O^{++}	1.15107	1.096	0.92887
O^{3+}	1.19424	1.158	0.99573

the average energies of the experimental and theoretical multiplets agree, though of course actually the theoretical energies will lie higher on the average than the experimental ones, as is shown in Fig. 15-2.

15-6. Ionization Potentials and X-ray Energy Levels. One of the features of the spectrum which we have not emphasized so far in this chapter is that of the ionization potentials of an atom: the energy required to remove an electron from the atom, leaving a positive ion. In our discussion of Table 15-1, the series limit gives the ionization potential. However, we have seen that this refers to the energy difference between the lowest state of the atom and the lowest state of the ion, and a more significant quantity is the energy difference between the weighted average of the lowest configuration of the atom and a similar weighted average of the ion. Thus, from Table 15-2, we find that experimentally the weighted mean energy of the configuration $1s^2 2s^2 2p^4$ of oxygen, its lowest configuration, is -150.15642 Rydbergs. Similarly the weighted mean of the configuration $1s^2 2s^2 2p^3$ of O^+ is -148.99182 Rydbergs, so that the energy difference is 1.16460 Rydbergs. We may very reasonably consider that this is the experimental value of the energy required to remove a $2p$ electron from the oxygen atom; it has more significance than the energy difference $150.22487 - 149.22464 = 1.00023$ Rydbergs between the lowest multiplets of the two configurations. In a similar way the energy required to remove a $2s$ electron from the oxygen atom may be taken to be the difference between the weighted mean of the lowest configuration of oxygen, which again is -150.15642 Rydbergs, and the weighted mean of the configuration $1s^2 2s 2p^4$ of O^+, which is -147.77676 Rydbergs. That is, this energy, the averaged ionization energy of the $2s$ electron, is 2.37966 Rydbergs, showing that it is much harder to remove a $2s$ electron than a $2p$ from the atom.

We can make a theoretical calculation of these ionization energies from the material tabulated in Tables 15-11 and 15-12. Thus, if we use the analytic functions of Table 15-11, we can average the energies given there and find that the average energy of O $1s^2 2s^2 2p^4$ is -149.00605 Rydbergs, that of O^+ $1s^2 2s^2 2p^3$ is -148.19152 Rydbergs, while that of O^+ $1s^2 2s 2p^4$ is -146.81357 Rydbergs. These give values of 0.81453 and 2.19248 Rydbergs, respectively, for the ionization potentials of $2p$ and $2s$ electrons, considerably below the experimental values of 1.16460 and 2.37966 Rydbergs. Or we can use the self-consistent-field energies of Table 15-10, from which we find that the average energy of O $1s^2 2s^2 2p^4$ is -149.49735 Rydbergs, that of O^+ $1s^2 2s^2 2p^3$ is -148.36966 Rydbergs, and that of O^+ $1s^2 2s 2p^4$ is -147.14029 Rydbergs. These give ionization potentials of 1.12769 and 2.35706 Rydbergs, respectively, much closer to the experimental values.

These calculations represent the proper way to find ionization potentials, and they show that the self-consistent-field method can be quite accurate. They have the drawback, however, that one must solve a separate self-consistent-field problem for the atom and the ion. We ask: Is there not any way in which we can get values of ionization potentials, even if not quite as accurate, from the wave functions of the neutral atom alone? There is a very obvious procedure which we can use, already discussed in Sec. 9-5. The energy of the ion should be calculated, by the methods discussed in the present chapter, from the wave functions and energy integrals appropriate for the ion. But the one-electron wave functions for the neutral atom are not very far from those for the ion, and the integrals are quite similar, as we see from Table 15-10. We know, from the variation principle, that, if we use slightly incorrect wave functions, we shall get an energy which is incorrect by only a small quantity of the second order. In other words, we can calculate the energy of the ion, but using the wave functions and integrals appropriate to the atom, with only a small error. As an illustration, we may use the integrals of type a from Table 15-10, determined from the analytic wave functions. When we use the proper integrals for O^+ and compute the average energies of the configurations $O^+ 1s^2 2s^2 2p^3$ and $1s^2 2s 2p^4$, respectively, we find the values -148.19152 and -146.81357 Rydbergs, respectively, quoted above. But if we use, not the integrals for O^+, but those for the neutral oxygen atom, we find for $1s^2 2s^2 2p^3$ and $1s^2 2s 2p^4$ the values -148.06454 and -146.69518 Rydbergs, respectively. These are higher than the values computed from the correct integrals by amounts 0.12698 and 0.11839 Rydbergs, respectively. In other words, if we had computed the ionization potentials by using these incorrect values for the ion, we should have found for the $2p$ electron

$$0.81453 + 0.12698 = 0.94151 \text{ Rydberg}$$

and for the $2s$ electron $2.19248 + 0.11839 = 2.31087$ Rydbergs. These, as a matter of fact, happen to be closer to the experimental values than those found above. It is clear from this that acceptable approximations to the ionization potentials can be found in this way.

There are very simple formulas for the ionization potentials, as computed by this approximation. For when we proceed in this way, the energy of the atom, as we see from Sec. 15-1, equals the sum of the one-electron integrals of all electrons, plus the sum of interaction energies of all pairs of electrons; the energy of the ion is the same thing for all electrons present in the ion, and in this approximation, the values of the integrals are the same for atom and ion. Thus the ionization potential, which is the energy of the ion minus the energy of the atom, is merely the negative of the one-electron integral of the removed electron, minus the sum of interaction energies between this electron and all others. For instance, in the cases we are considering, we have

Ionization potential of $2p$ electron from O $1s^2 2s^2 2p^4$
$$= -I(2p) - 2[F^0(1s,2p) - \tfrac{1}{6}G^1(1s,2p)]$$
$$- 2[F^0(2s,2p) - \tfrac{1}{6}G^1(2s,2p)] - 3[F^0(2p,2p) - \tfrac{2}{25}F^2(2p,2p)]$$
Ionization potential of $2s$ electron from O $1s^2 2s^2 2p^4$ (15-12)
$$= -I(2s) - 2[F^0(1s,2s) - \tfrac{1}{2}G^0(1s,2s)]$$
$$- F^0(2s,2s) - 4[F^0(2s,2p) - \tfrac{1}{6}G^1(2s,2p)]$$

The reader can easily verify, using the integrals of Table 15-10, that these formulas give the same results already quoted. As further examples of the use of this method, we may take the case of nitrogen, in which we have all the integrals for neutral nitrogen, computed both by the analytic and by the self-consistent-field method. If we use the analytic functions, we find for the ionization potential of the $2p$ electron the amount 0.83419 Rydberg; if we use the self-consistent field, we find 1.0044 Rydbergs; the experimental value is 0.96979 Rydberg. Again, the analytic method gives for the $2s$ electron the value 1.78794 Rydbergs, the self-consistent-field method gives 1.8970 Rydbergs, while the experimental value is 1.88009 Rydbergs. It is clear that the final results are in very good agreement with experiment, though this is partly a result of compensation of errors: the natural tendency of our calculation is to give too small theoretical values for ionization potential, since the calculated energy lies above the experimental by a larger amount, the more electrons there are in the system. But this is largely compensated by the error which we make in finding the energy of the ion by using the incorrect integrals, those appropriate for the atom.

We have used this procedure so far to give an alternative calculation of quantities already calculated by other methods, namely, the ionization potentials of the outer electrons of the atom. But we must remember that the ionization potential of the inner electrons is also a measurable quantity, through X-ray methods; in the present case, we may inquire what is the ionization potential of the $1s$ or K electron. We have not solved the problem of the ion lacking a $1s$ electron; as a matter of fact, no solutions, self-consistent or otherwise, have been worked out for this particular case. But if we make the same approximation as before, that we can describe the ion by using the same wave functions and integrals as for the neutral atom, we can immediately set up formulas for the X-ray ionization potentials. Thus, for oxygen, we have

Ionization potential of $1s$ electron from O $1s^2 2s^2 2p^4$
$$= -I(1s) - 2[F^0(1s,2s) - \tfrac{1}{2}G^0(1s,2s)] - F^0(1s,1s)$$
$$- 4[F^0(1s,2p) - \tfrac{1}{6}G^1(1s,2p)]   (15-13)$$

When we insert the integrals from Table 15-10, using the analytic values of the integrals, we find the value 41.19835 Rydbergs.   The approximate experimental value is 39.9 Rydbergs.   Again, for nitrogen, using the analytic integrals, we find 31.16483 Rydbergs, and using the self-consistent-field integrals, we have 31.2712 Rydbergs.   The experimental value is 30.0 Rydbergs.   Here again we have fairly good agreement, with errors of the order of 2 or 3 per cent.   Presumably the effect on the wave functions of removing a $1s$ electron is much more drastic than of removing a $2s$ or $2p$ electron, which means that the energy of the ion, computed by using the atomic integrals, is too high by a much larger amount than in the earlier case, explaining the larger absolute error, of something over 1 Rydberg.

From these examples we see that this simplified method of computing ionization potentials, by using the same one-electron orbitals for both atom and ion, is accurate enough to be very useful.   We can see from the discussion of Sec. 9-5 that it is closely related to the use of the one-electron energies ϵ_i in the Hartree method as the negatives of the ionization potentials.   We shall see later in Sec. 17-1 (Vol. II), where we discuss the Hartree-Fock method, that the ionization potentials as computed by the present method, as the difference between the average energy of a configuration of the atom and the ion, computed using the same one-electron orbitals for atom and ion, are just the negatives of the one-electron energies which we shall find in the particular version of the Hartree-Fock method in which we determine the orbitals by minimizing the average energy of a configuration.

We have been comparing these computed ionization potentials with those obtained from experiment, by finding the average energies of configurations in atom and ion and subtracting.   It is the experimental values obtained in this way which we have discussed in Sec. 8-6, tabulating them in Table 8-2, and plotting them in Fig. 8-4.   The reader will see that the values for oxygen given in Table 8-2 are the same ones which we have quoted in the present section.   There are points connected with the experimental values of Table 8-2 which we did not mention in Sec. 8-6. The tabulated energies for removal of inner, X-ray electrons are derived from X-ray spectra, and the experimental information is far less accurate than for the outer electrons.   The X-ray measurements are practically always made on solid targets, not on isolated atoms.   This means that the energy levels of the outer electrons of the atoms are greatly perturbed, on account of their binding in the solid.   What is ordinarily observed as the ionization potential is the energy required to remove an electron from an X-ray level to the energy bands of the solid.   This may differ by a very considerable amount from the ionization potential of the same electron in an isolated atom, which would be the energy required to remove

the electron to infinity.   The author[1] has attempted to correct for this
in deriving the values given in Table 8-2.

15-7. Simplified Treatment of Light Atoms.   Our effort in the preceding sections has been to outline the most accurate treatments which we
can give at present for the light elements.   However, the author[2] has
suggested a very much simplified treatment, based on the methods we
have been discussing, which has proved to be very useful in a practical
way.   At the time when this scheme was suggested, we did not have the
extensive calculations, of Morse and his collaborators and of Roothaan,
which we have discussed in earlier sections, but nevertheless there were
enough such calculations available[3] to suggest the scheme which we shall
discuss.   We shall describe the method by reference to the calculations
of Roothaan, though those calculations are really very recent.

Let us consider wave functions of the type given in Eq. (15-6).   The $1s$
function is $\exp(-\mu ar)$, which is like a hydrogenic $1s$ function $\exp(-Zr)$,
with an effective Z equal to μa.   If we look at Tables 15-7 and 15-8, we
see that in the work of Tubis and Roothaan this effective Z is approximately equal to the real Z minus a quantity between 0.30 and 0.35.
Similarly the $2p$ function is $r \exp(-\mu cr)$, which is like a hydrogenic $2p$
function $r \exp(-Zr/2)$, with an effective $\overset{\text{z}}{Z}$ equal to $2\mu c$.   The reason
why we have tabulated $2\mu c$ in Tables 15-7 and 15-8 is to make the comparison with an effective nuclear charge convenient.   The values of $2\mu c$
cannot be described as simply as those of μa, but we shall indicate rules
later for predicting them approximately.   As for the $2s$ function, its
outer part is given by the term $r \exp(-\mu r)$, which would be like the
corresponding term in a hydrogenic function with an effective Z equal to
2μ.   From Tables 15-7 and 15-8 we see that this quantity 2μ differs only
slightly from $2\mu c$, so that it is not a great error to use the same effective
Z for both $2s$ and $2p$ electrons.   The inner part of the $2s$ function, given
by the exponential $\exp(-\mu br)$, can be approximated as Roothaan has
shown by the corresponding exponential $\exp(-\mu ar)$ of the $1s$ function,
the coefficient being chosen to make the $2s$ function orthogonal to the $1s$.

With these facts in mind (though based on much less complete evidence than we have now), the author suggested that we describe the
outer part of each wave function by a function $r^{n-1} \exp(-Z_{\text{eff}}r/n)$, where
n is the principal quantum number, Z_{eff} an effective nuclear charge, and
he gave rules for determining these Z_{eff}'s, which will be stated in a
moment.   Once we have determined these outer parts of the function,
we can supplement them to give complete wave functions.   That is, with
the $2s$ function, we proceed as in the case of Roothaan, adding to the

[1] J. C. Slater, *Phys. Rev.*, **98**:1039 (1955).

[2] J. C. Slater, *Phys. Rev.*, **36**:57 (1930).

[3] V. Guillemin, Jr., and C. Zener, *Z. Physik*, **61**:199 (1930); Zener, *loc. cit.*

function $r \exp (-Z_{\text{eff}} r/2)$ enough of the $1s$ function to make the linear combination, as given in Eq. (15-6), orthogonal to the $1s$. With the $3s$ we add a linear combination of the $1s$ and $2s$ functions, to make the $3s$ orthogonal to both $1s$ and $2s$, and so on. This then prescribes the functions completely, once we have stated the rules for determining the Z_{eff}'s. The rules were stated, in the paper quoted above, for values of principal quantum number up to 6, but they really are rather questionable for n greater than 3, and for that reason we shall restrict the statement here to n's up to 3.

The rules are as follows: If we denote the effective Z for any shell of electrons by the expression $Z - s$, where s is a shielding constant, Z the true nuclear charge, then s is to be determined by dividing the electrons into the following groups, each having a different shielding constant: $1s$; $2s, 2p; 3s, 3p; 3d$. That is, the s and p of a given n are grouped together, but the d is separated. The shells are considered to be arranged from inside out in the order named. The shielding constant s is formed, for any group of electrons, from the following contributions:

1. Nothing from any shell outside the one considered
2. An amount 0.35 from each other electron in the group considered (except in the $1s$ group, where 0.30 is used instead)
3. If the shell considered is an s, p shell, an amount 0.85 from each electron with total quantum number less by 1, and an amount 1.00 from each electron still further in; but in a $3d$ shell, an amount 1.00 from every electron inside it

In Table 15-14 we give the effective nuclear charges computed by these rules for the cases tabulated in Tables 15-7 and 15-8, together with the values of μa, 2μ, $2\mu c$ from Table 15-7, which are to be compared with them. It is clear that the simple rules reproduce the values calculated

Table 15-14

Values of $Z_{\text{eff}}(1s)$ and $Z_{\text{eff}}(2s,2p)$ for light elements, computed from rules in the text, compared with values of μa, 2μ, and $2\mu c$ from Table 15-7.

	$Z_{\text{eff}}(1s)$	μa	$Z_{\text{eff}}(2s,2p)$	2μ	$2\mu c$
B	4.70	4.70	2.60	2.60	2.42
C	5.70	5.69	3.25	3.28–3.31	2.94–3.12
C+	5.70	5.69	3.60	3.55	3.52
N	6.70	6.68–6.69	3.90	3.90–3.97	3.73–3.83
N+	6.70	6.69	4.25	4.18–4.19	4.07–4.21
N++	6.70	6.69	4.60	4.51	4.58
O	7.70	7.67–7.68	4.55	4.62–4.64	4.37–4.44
O+	7.70	7.68	4.90	4.83–4.84	4.79–4.89
O++	7.70	7.68	5.25	5.11–5.13	5.12–5.25
O3+	7.70	7.69	5.60	5.44	5.63

by minimizing the energy about as well as we could hope. This means that we can use these rules to set up functions of the type of Eq. (15-6) without further trouble. We merely set $\mu a = Z_{\text{eff}}(1s)\mu b = \mu a$,

$$2\mu = 2\mu c = Z_{\text{eff}}(2s,2p)$$

using the rules above. We can then proceed to calculate the integrals and find the energy of the atoms or ions in any stages of ionization, just as we have done using the values of μ, a, b, and c given by Tubis or Roothaan. On account of the variation principle, the energies will lie higher than those found by Tubis or Roothaan, since they minimized the energy and our parameters are somewhat different; but also on account of the variation principle, the energies found in this way will not be very much higher than those given in Tables 15-7 and 15-8. Since the process of minimizing the energy to find the best values of the parameters is very laborious, and since the determination of the parameters by our rules makes this process unnecessary, it is a great timesaver and this is the reason why it has been so popular for a great many calculations involving light atoms. We must remember, however, that the errors arising from the use of this method will certainly be greater than those of the methods of Tubis and Roothaan and considerably greater than the errors of the self-consistent-field method. For really quantitative work, one should use the best wave functions one can, namely, the self-consistent-field wave functions. The rules suggested by the author were never intended for anything more than a first orientation, to be improved by later, more accurate work.

The author, in the paper mentioned above, not only gave the rules we have stated for determining Z_{eff} but also gave a much simplified but rather accurate method for finding the energy of the atom or ion in various configurations. This method may be based essentially on the use of the virial theorem. From that theorem, we know that the kinetic energy is numerically equal to the total energy, but of opposite sign. Now the kinetic energy depends on only a single integral for each electron, so that it is much simpler to compute than the potential energy. For a hydrogenic function with effective nuclear charge $Z - s$ and principal quantum number n, the kinetic energy, in Rydbergs, is $(Z - s)^2/n^2$. This formula will be exactly correct for the analytic functions $1s$, $2p$, $3d$ of the type we have been discussing; for $2s$, $3s$, $3p$, which have nodes, it is not exactly correct, since our functions are not exactly hydrogenic, on account of the fact that different exponentials are used for the different terms. Nevertheless even in this case it is not a bad approximation. And the assumption made by the author was that we could get an approximate value for the total energy of an atom or ion by using the formula above, namely,

$$E = -\sum \frac{(Z - s)^2}{n^2} \qquad \text{Rydbergs} \qquad (15\text{-}14)$$

where the s's are to be determined from the rules given earlier in this section. As a matter of fact, those rules were set up by considering the energy for a good many atoms in many states of ionization and by fitting the s's so that Eq. (15-14) would give as good agreement with experiment as possible.

In Table 15-15, we give the energies of the oxygen atom and the ion in various stages of ionization, computed by Eq. (15-14), and for comparison the experimental energies. From these examples we see that this simple method is able to predict the energies of the ions with very good accuracy. The rules apply as well to ions lacking inner electrons, and hence allow one to compute X-ray ionization potentials. Thus, for an oxygen atom lacking one $1s$ electron, but with its six $2s$, p electrons, we have $-8^2 - 6(5.40)^2/4 = -107.74$ Rydbergs. Since we see from Table 8-2 that the ionization potential of the oxygen atom for removal of a $1s$ electron is about 39.9 Rydbergs, and since the experimental energy of the ground state is -150.2 Rydbergs, the experimental energy of $O^+ \, 1s2s^22p^4$ is about -110.3 Rydbergs. Thus the agreement of the simple rule for this case is very nearly as good as for the ions with outer electrons removed.

The accuracy of the rules remains fairly good up through the iron group. Here we need the rule for the $4s$, $4p$ electrons as well as the electrons with $n = 3$, and in the paper quoted above, it was proposed that the shielding constant for these electrons should be computed according to the rules given earlier, but that an effective quantum number of $n^* = 3.7$ should

Table 15-15

Energy of oxygen atom and ions, by method of Eq. (15-14), compared with experimental values E_{av} from Table 15-2, in Rydbergs.

		E_{calc}	E_{exp}
O	$1s^22s^22p^4$	-149.6338	-150.15642
	$1s^22s2p^5$	-149.6338	-148.92983
O^+	$1s^22s^22p^3$	-148.5925	-148.99182
	$1s^22s2p^4$	-148.5925	-147.77676
O^{++}	$1s^22s^22p^2$	-146.1425	-146.55170
	$1s^22s2p^3$	-146.1425	-145.37816
O^{3+}	$1s^22s^22p$	-142.1000	-142.59948
	$1s^22s2p^2$	-142.1000	-141.52694
	$1s^22p^3$	-142.1000	-140.22748
O^{4+}	$1s^22s^2$	-136.28125	-136.91171
	$1s^22s2p$	-136.28125	-135.98666
	$1s^22p^2$	-136.28125	-134.86318
O^{5+}	$1s^22s$	-128.5025	-128.53959
	$1s^22p$	-128.5025	-127.65809
O^{6+}	$1s^2$	-118.5800	-118.38773
O^{7+}	$1s$	$-\ 64.0000$	$-\ 64.04578$

be used instead of the true quantum number $n = 4$. That is, for a $4s$ or $4p$ electron we use a term $-(Z - s)^2/n^{*2}$ in Eq. (15-14). This assumption improves the agreement with the experimental energies. Then we find, for example, for the iron atom, the following results:

Energy of normal atom: $-2(25.70)^2 - 8(21.85/2)^2 - 8(14.75/3)^2$
$-6(6.25/3)^2 - 2(3.75/3.7)^2 = -2,497.2$ Rydbergs.

Atom lacking one $1s$ electron: $-1(26.00)^2 - 8(22.70/2)^2 - 8(15.75/3)^2$
$- 6(7.25/3)^2 - 2(4.75/3.7)^2 = -1,964.6$ Rydbergs.

Difference from energy of normal atom, 532.6 Rydbergs; experimental energy of removal of $1s$ electron, 524.3 Rydbergs.

Atom lacking one $2s$, p electron: $-2(25.70)^2 - 7(22.20/2)^2 - 8(15.60/3)^2$
$- 6(7.25/3)^2 - 2(4.75/3.7)^2 = -2,437.7$ Rydbergs.

Difference from energy of normal atom, 59.5 Rydbergs; experimental energy of removal of $2s$ electron, 63.0 Rydbergs; $2p$, 52.8 Rydbergs.

Atom lacking one $3s$, p electron: $-2,491.1$ Rydbergs. Difference, 6.1 Rydbergs; experimental energy of removal of $3s$ electron, 7.3 Rydbergs; of $3p$, 4.4 Rydbergs.

Atom lacking one $3d$ electron: $-2,496.4$ Rydbergs. Difference, 0.8 Rydberg; experimental energy of removal of $3d$ electron, 0.64 Rydberg.

Atom lacking one $4s$ electron: $-2,496.3$ Rydbergs. Difference, 0.9 Rydberg; experimental energy of removal of $4s$ electron, 0.53 Rydberg.

We see, in other words, that the rules are far from quantitative but that nevertheless they give us good general orientation regarding the absolute values of the energies of the atoms and ions.

PROBLEMS

1. Verify the formulas for $I(1s)$, $I(2p)$, $F^0(1s,1s)$, $F^0(1s,2p)$, $G^1(1s,2p)$ in Table 15-6, by direct evaluation of the integrals from the wave functions of Eq. (15-6).

2. Use Table 15-6 to set up the energy of the ground state of the helium atom, and vary the quantity μa of Eq. (15-6) to minimize the energy. Show that the result agrees with that found in Probs. 1 to 4, Chap. 8, and Prob. 1, Chap. 9.

3. Use Table 15-6 to set up the necessary integrals to compute the energy of the configuration $1s^2 2s^2 2p$ of boron. Using the parameters given for this case in Table 15-7, compute the numerical value of the energy, and check with the value given in Table 15-7.

4. Use the method of Sec. 15-7 to compute $Z_{eff}(1s)$ and $Z_{eff}(2s)$ for the configuration $1s^2 2s$ of the lithium atom. Find the energy of this configuration by the rule of Eq. (15-14), and compare with the experimental value given in Table 15-2.

5. Use the values of $Z_{eff}(1s)$ and $Z_{eff}(2s)$ for lithium, found in Prob. 4, to compute $1s$ and $2s$ wave functions, according to the method of Sec. 15-7. That is, for the $1s$, use a normalized function proportional to $\exp[-Z_{eff}(1s)r]$ and for $2s$ a linear combination of $r \exp[-Z_{eff}(2s)r/2]$ and of $\exp[-Z_{eff}(1s)r]$, with constants chosen so that both functions are normalized and are orthogonal to each other. With the aid of Table 15-6, find the values of the various integrals needed to set up the energy of the lithium atom in the configuration $1s^2 2s$. Find the numerical value of this energy, and compare with experiment and with the value found in Prob. 4 from Eq. (15-14).

6. Proceed, as in Probs. 4 and 5, to find $1s$, $2s$, and $2p$ wave functions for the beryllium atom in the configuration $1s^2 2s 2p$. Compute the values of E_{av}, $G^1(2s,2p)$ and the energies of the $^3P^o$ and $^1P^o$ states. Compare these with the experimental values given in Table 15-2.

7. Proceed as in Probs. 4, 5, and 6, to find the $1s$, $2s$, and $2p$ wave functions for the sodium atom in its ground state. Compute the wave functions, and compare the radii of the outermost maxima of the functions $P = rR$ with the radii tabulated in Table 8-3.

8. Proceed as in Prob. 7 to find the wave function for the $3s$ electron in sodium. Plot this wave function as a function of r. Compare the radius of the outermost maximum of $P = rR$ with the value of Table 8-3. Find how accurately this radius agrees with the value $n^2/(Z - s)$, which would be correct if the wave function were hydrogenic.

9. Use the approximation that the radius of the shell is $n^2/(Z - s)$, mentioned in the preceding problem, where s is to be found by the methods of Sec. 15-7. Compute radii for the atoms with Z up to 20 (compute only enough values to draw the curves). Plot curves of these radii, and compare with the values of Table 8-3.

10. Isoelectronic sequences are sets of ions, all of the same number of electrons, but with different nuclear charges, and hence different degrees of ionization. Compute the ionization potentials $1s^2 2s^2 2p \rightarrow 1s^2 2s^2$, $1s^2 2s^2 3s \rightarrow 1s^2 2s^2$ for the atoms $Z = 5$ to 10, indicating what ions they are (as $Z = 6$, $1s^2 2s^2 2p$ is C$^+$), using the method of Eq. (15-14). Compare these computed values with experiment. Investigate to see whether or not these term values follow Moseley's law that the square root of the term value is a linear function of atomic number.

16

Multiplet Calculations for Iron-group Elements

16-1. Introduction. In the preceding chapter we have been taking up the calculations which have been made on the elements from lithium to neon and their agreement with experiment. Now we shall skip the next period of the periodic table, from sodium to argon, and go on to the iron group, from calcium to copper. The reason is twofold: first, relatively few calculations have been made on the elements from sodium to argon, whereas a great many have been made on the iron group; second, the iron group introduces something new, the partially filled d shell. It is these configurations containing d electrons which will interest us in this chapter. Once we go beyond this period in the periodic table, the next really interesting group, presenting new problems, is that of the rare earths, with the partially filled $4f$ shell. We shall not treat this, because work on it has not gone far enough. The shells of equivalent f electrons are much more complicated than the d shells, both theoretically and experimentally, with the result that both the theoretical and experimental work done on the rare earths is rather fragmentary, in contrast to the iron group, where we have extensive information.

The work which has been done, as with the light elements, is of two sorts. First, efforts have been made to fit the observed multiplets by choosing empirical values of the F and G integrals. A great deal of work has been expended in this direction, which we shall report in Sec. 16-2. In this problem there are far more multiplets for a given configuration than for the light elements with their shells of p electrons, so that the problem of fitting is much more severe and a good agreement between the formulas and experiment is more significant than with the light elements. One finds that integrals can be chosen which lead to agreement with experiment in a broad way; there is approximate agreement between the order in which the terms are found experimentally and the predicted order, though there are many individual discrepancies, and one can get something like quantitative checks with suitably chosen integrals.   One finds that the integrals vary more or less smoothly from element to element.   It is also interesting to study the variation of the experimental value of E_{av} from one configuration to another of each of the atoms, to see the gradual changes in the relative stability of $4s$ and $3d$ electrons as we go through the period.

The second type of work which has been carried out is the determination of the F and G integrals and E_{av}, from direct calculations of self-consistent fields and a study of their agreement with experiment.   Here the major work has been performed very recently; until the last few years, there were hardly any self-consistent fields for elements between calcium and copper, and as a result there were efforts to interpolate between these extreme elements to deduce some of the results for the iron group.   Now we have extensive calculations, largely in unpublished work by Watson.[1] He has used analytic functions, similar to those of Tubis and Roothaan as quoted in the preceding chapter, but containing many more terms, so that there is enough flexibility in the functions to permit of fitting the true Hartree-Fock functions with high accuracy.   In a few cases, Watson has been able to make direct comparison of his results with those of numerical Hartree-Fock calculations, as, for instance, with the very recent work of Worsley[2] on V^{++}.   The agreement is very good, indicating that Watson's analytic functions are probably as correct a description of the true Hartree-Fock functions as one would find by numerical solution of the Hartree-Fock equations, followed by fitting the numerical functions by analytic formulas.

The calculations of Watson have the great advantage over the conventional Hartree-Fock calculations that they were determined by a digital computer, and in the process of calculation, all the F and G integrals concerned in the energy of the atom, as well as the one-electron integrals, were calculated, so that we can make detailed comparisons of theory and experiment at every point.   His calculations have been made for over fifty cases of atoms and ions throughout the iron group, so that we can get a clear picture of the changes of the various integrals with atomic number and with degree of ionization.   We are therefore for the first time really in a position to compare theory with experiment in the iron group.

The results of Watson's calculations and their agreement with experiment will be described in Secs. 16-3 and 16-4.   The conclusion, very briefly, is similar to that which we have already found in discussing the

[1] R. E. Watson, Analytic Hartree-Fock Wave Functions for the Iron Series, MIT thesis, 1959; Iron Series Hartree-Fock Calculations, *MIT Solid-state and Molecular Theory Group, Tech. Rept.* 12, MIT June 15, 1959.

[2] B. J. Worsley, *Proc. Roy. Soc. (London)*, **A247**:390 (1958).

light elements, as far as multiplet separations are concerned. The calculated F integrals determining the separations between the multiplets in the configurations d^n come out very decidedly greater than the empirical integrals found from the observed spectra. We get the impression, in other words, that, just as in the earlier case, the configuration interaction with higher configurations is very important, pushing down the higher multiplets in the low configurations more than the lower multiplets, and thereby squeezing the levels of the observed configurations in comparison with the separations determined by the simple theory. This squeezing can be as much as to half the calculated separations, for some of the neutral atoms, running down to a reduction of perhaps 20 per cent in the ions with higher ionization. It is undoubtedly the different perturbation of the various multiplets by configuration interaction which is responsible for the very appreciable discrepancies between the order of the levels as found experimentally and that predicted by the simple theory. The squeezing of the configurations as a result of configuration interaction, as revealed by Watson's calculations, is a good deal more than has been suspected earlier on the basis of the fairly good agreement between experiment and the calculation of multiplet separation using empirical F and G integrals, and this puts us on our guard against uncritical use of the elementary theory of multiplet separations.

16-2. Experimental Results on Iron-group Multiplets. In the iron group, in contrast to the light elements which we have been discussing in the preceding chapter, the experimental results are too extensive to present in numerical detail. Each configuration leads to many multiplets, often of high multiplicity, so that there would be a great many values to tabulate if we were to try to present the complete data. We shall therefore assemble the experimental results in graphical form, in such a way as to present the essential physical features.

A good deal of work has been done in fitting the observed data with empirical F and G integrals. The leading papers in this field have been by Antunes, Bowman, Brown, Cady, Catalan and associates, Many, Marvin, Merrill, Meshkov, Orgel, Ostrofsky, Racah, Rohrlich, Sack, Schweizer, Stern, Tanabe and Sugano, Trees, and Ufford.[1] They have

[1] M. T. Antunes, *Phys. Rev.*, **62**:362 (1942) [Co I, Ni I].

D. S. Bowman, *Phys. Rev.*, **59**:386 (1941) [V II, Mn II].

D. A. Brown, *J. Chem. Phys.*, **28**:67 (1958) [F and G integrals from hydrogenic functions].

W. M. Cady, *Phys. Rev.*, **43**:322 (1933) [Ca I, Sc II, Ti III, V IV, Cr V, Mn VI, Fe VII, Co VIII, Ni IX].

M. A. Catalan and M. T. Antunes, *Z. Physik*, **102**:432 (1936) [general survey of iron group].

————, F. Rohrlich, and A. G. Shenstone, *Proc. Roy. Soc.* (*London*), **A221**:421 (1954) [average energy of terms of highest multiplicities in iron group].

covered many, though far from all, of the observed multiplets. If there are n electrons in the outer shells of such an atom or ion (that is, outside the $3s$ and $3p$ shells), the most commonly observed configurations are $3d^n$, $3d^{n-1}4s$, $3d^{n-1}4p$, $3d^{n-2}4s^2$, $3d^{n-2}4s4p$, all of which can be computed from the formulas given in Appendix 21. Many of these have been discussed in the papers just quoted, both for neutral atoms and for ions. In most cases F and G integrals, regarded as empirical parameters, have been fitted to the observed spectra, frequently by use of least-squares methods, as described in the preceding chapter, and the positions of the multiplets as computed from these parameters have been compared with the experimental values. The author has recomputed some of the same values and has supplemented these by computing some multiplets not previously considered.

As a typical example of the sort of agreement between theory and experiment which can be reached in this way, we give in Table 16-1 observed and calculated multiplet positions for the configuration $3d^2 4p$ of Sc I, using empirical parameters determined by the author. The calculations put the multiplets in the right general order, though there are exceptions, and we see that with rather few empirical parameters we can fit the data acceptably, though far from exactly. The example we have chosen is a fairly complicated one, involving two and three multiplets of the same type, so that one must solve quadratic and cubic secular equations to get the calculated multiplets. A number of the multiplets have not been observed; this is the case in almost all the more complicated configurations. Calculations were not available, in most cases, when the spectra were analyzed; now that it is more practical to compute the multiplets, it may be anticipated that future workers will

---

A. Many, *Phys. Rev.*, **70**:511 (1946) [Ti I, Ti II, V II, V III].

H. H. Marvin, *Phys. Rev.*, **47**:521 (1935) [Co I].

R. A. Merrill, *Phys. Rev.*, **46**:487 (1934) [Fe I, Cr I, Ni I, Cu I].

S. Meshkov, *Phys. Rev.*, **91**:871 (1953) [Ti II, Ti III]; **93**:270 (1954) [V II, V III].

L. E. Orgel, *J. Chem. Phys.*, **23**:1819 (1955) [estimate of F's for many cases].

M. Ostrofsky, *Phys. Rev.*, **46**:604 (1934) [V II, Cr III].

G. Racah, *Phys. Rev.*, **62**:438 (1942) [Ti II, Ni II].

F. Rohrlich, *Phys. Rev.*, **74**:1381 (1948) [Ti I].

N. Sack, *Phys. Rev.*, **102**:1302 (1956) [Ti II, Ni II].

A. A. Schweizer, *Phys. Rev.*, **80**:1080 (1950) [V I, Cr II].

F. Stern, *Phys. Rev.*, **104**:684 (1956) [Fe I].

Y. Tanabe and S. Sugano, *J. Phys. Soc. Japan*, **9**:753, 766 (1954); **11**:864 (1956) [estimate of F's for many cases].

R. E. Trees, *Phys. Rev.*, **82**:683 (1951) [Fe III]; **83**:756 (1951) [Mn II]; **84**:1089 (1951) [Fe III].

C. W. Ufford, *Phys. Rev.*, **44**:732 (1933) [Ti II].

know more or less where to look for the missing terms and may have a better chance of finding them.

Different workers treating the same configurations have in a number of cases proceeded independently of each other, and each has been able to fit the observed data acceptably with decidedly different values of the parameters. Thus we cannot give too much fundamental significance to them. Furthermore, an attempt to fit the parameters for various atoms

Table 16-1

Calculated and observed values of multiplet positions for configuration $3d^24p$ of Sc I. Calculations are made using empirical parameters as follows: $E_{av} = 0.32499$ Rydberg, $F^2(dd) = 0.27359$, $F^4(dd) = 0.15524$, $F^2(pd) = 0.10046$, $G^1(pd) = 0.05126$, $G^3(pd) = 0.01980$.

Multiplet	Calculated	Observed
$^4G^o$	0.27045	0.28498
$^2F^o$	0.28250	0.30185
$^4F^o$	0.28340	0.28408
$^2D^o$	0.28675	0.30587
$^4D^o$	0.29960	0.29711
$^2G^o$	0.30762	0.30228
$^2S^o$	0.30791	
$^2P^o$	0.33130	0.33179
$^4S^o$	0.33257	0.35156
$^2F^o$	0.33859	
$^4D^o$	0.34154	0.34163
$^2D^o$	0.34157	0.33623
$^4P^o$	0.35115	0.35162
$^2G^o$	0.35135	0.34286
$^2H^o$	0.36056	0.35636
$^2D^o$	0.38460	0.39774
$^2P^o$	0.38742	
$^2F^o$	0.38920	0.36255
$^2P^o$	0.46703	

in various stages of ionization to smooth curves is not very successful. This seems to be a result of the considerable latitude allowed to the individual parameters in the fitting process. Several workers, however, have tried to use such fitting processes to get smoothed values of the parameters; in particular, Orgel, and Tanabe and Sugano, quoted earlier, have used a considerable number of data to arrive at such curves. The author and Watson have used a larger number of data, and in Fig. 16-1 we give smoothed curves showing $F^2(dd)$, for the configurations $3d^n$, for all the atoms and ions of the iron group, in different stages of ionization, with points showing the various estimates of the parameters made by different authors. In spite of the fluctuations from point to point, it seems likely that these curves express adequately the trend of this parameter with atomic number and degree of ionization.

These curves show the qualitative type of behavior which we might reasonably expect: the value of $F^2(dd)$ increases both with atomic number for a constant stage of ionization and with degree of ionization for a given atomic number. Even the simplest theory would indicate that

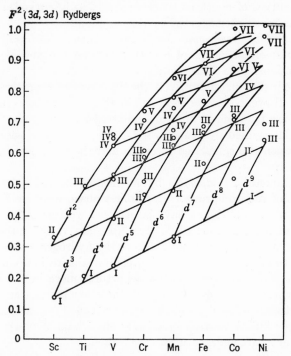

FIG. 16-1. $F^2(3d,3d)$ as a function of atomic number and ionization as determined by least-square fits of the iron series $3d^n$ configuration spectra (from R. E. Watson).

this should be the case. Thus, if we use hydrogenic wave functions, $F^2(dd)$ is proportional to the effective Z. From the simplified treatment of wave functions for light atoms given in Sec. 15-7, the $3d$ electron in an atom or ion of atomic number Z, in the configuration $1s^2 2s^2 2p^6 3s^2 3p^6 3d^n$, would have an effective nuclear charge of

$$Z_{\text{eff}} = Z - 18 - 0.35(n - 1) = Z - 17.65 - 0.35n \qquad (16\text{-}1)$$

If the degree of ionization is p, equal to zero for a neutral atom, 1 for a singly charged ion, and so on, so that $Z = 18 + n + p$, we may rewrite Eq. (16-1) in the form

$$
\begin{aligned}
Z_{\text{eff}} &= Z - 17.65 - 0.35(Z - 18 - p) \\
&= 0.65Z - 11.35 + 0.35p
\end{aligned}
\qquad (16\text{-}2)
$$

From Eq. (16-1) we see that an isoelectronic line, in which Z_{eff} is plotted as a function of Z for constant n, should have a slope of unity, while from Eq. (16-2) we see that for constant p, or constant degree of ionization, the slope of the lines of Z_{eff} against Z should be smaller, equal to 0.65. This is qualitatively in agreement with Fig. 16-1, in that the lines of constant n have a greater slope than those of constant p; but the observed curves of constant n are very decidedly curved, and the ratio of slopes is by no means given by this simple theory.

An attempt has been made by Brown[1] to use the rules of Sec. 15-7 to compute numerical values of $F^2(dd)$, assuming the formulas for hydrogenic functions. He finds the right order of magnitude and of course, as we have just seen, qualitatively the right type of dependence on atomic number. However, as we shall see in the next section, the true wave functions are far from hydrogenic, and when we use correct wave functions, as determined by Watson, we still have a rather serious disagreement between the calculated integrals and the experimental ones given in Fig. 16-1.

The parameter $F^2(3d,3d)$ is by no means the only one met in the multiplets of the iron group. In the first place, we have $F^4(3d,3d)$. In the cases where multiplets have been fitted with empirical parameters, the ratio of the empirical $F^4(dd)$ to $F^2(dd)$ has varied rather erratically but has tended to average not far from the hydrogenic value, which can be shown to be 0.649. The departures from this ratio do not seem to be significant; we shall discuss these departures more in the next section. In smaller numbers of cases values of the other parameters giving interaction between $3d$ and $4s$ electrons or between $3d$ and $4p$ have been determined; but these vary erratically enough so that we cannot draw any very accurate generalizations from them.

In addition to these parameters giving the separations of multiplets, we also have the quantities E_{av}, the weighted mean energy of the configuration. In Fig. 16-2 we give these values for a number of configurations of the atom and ions, for the elements Sc and Ti at the beginning of the iron group and for Fe and Ni toward the end, to show the change. These curves are very interesting and significant, particularly as compared with the simple case shown in Fig. 15-1, where we were discussing the shell of p electrons. Here we show curves giving the energies of configurations with the same total number of electrons, but with varying numbers of d electrons: configurations d^n, $d^{n-1}s$, and $d^{n-2}s^2$, or $d^{n-1}p$, $d^{n-2}sp$, $d^{n-3}s^2p$. Instead of finding straight lines, as we did in Fig. 15-1, where we had configurations p^n, $p^{n-1}s$, $p^{n-2}s^2$, we have curves, with a tendency to have a minimum for a number of d electrons varying from

[1] Brown, *loc. cit.*

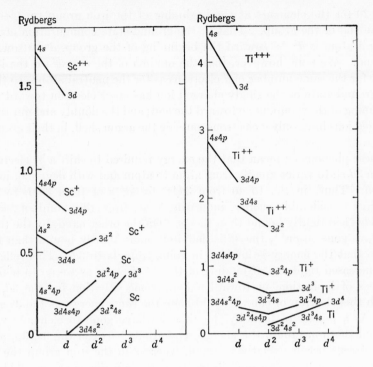

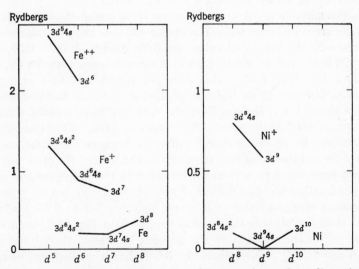

FIG. 16-2. E_{av} for a number of configurations of atoms and ions of scandium, titanium, iron, and nickel, as a function of number of d electrons.

$Z - 20$ for the elements at the beginning of the iron group to $Z - 19$ at the end of the group. That is, the ground-state configuration of the neutral atom is $d^{n-2}s^2$ toward the beginning of the group, $d^{n-1}s$ toward the end. We note, however, that the minima of the curves for the ions come for the same number of d electrons as for the neutral atoms, so that the ground state of the singly charged ion has one s electron toward the beginning of the group, none toward the end; and the doubly and multiply charged ions have only d electrons, outside the argon shell, in their ground states.

These phenomena mean that the energy required to shift a $4s$ electron into a $3d$ state varies greatly from atom to atom and with degree of ionization. Thus, in Sc, to go from $3d4s^2$ to $3d^24s$ or from $3d^24s$ to $3d^3$ requires considerable energy, indicating that, from this point of view, the $3d$ is less tightly bound than the $4s$. On the other hand, by the time we have gone to Sc^{++}, the $3d$ is definitely more tightly bound than the $4s$, so that the energy is lowered in going from $4s$ to $3d$. This reflects the increased tightness of binding of the $3d$ electron as we go to higher degrees of ionization, or toward a hydrogenic situation for the $3d$, in which this electron of course would have the same energy as the $3s$ and $3p$. As a matter of fact, by the time we have gone to elements well beyond the iron group, the energy separations between the $3s$, $3p$, and $3d$ electrons become relatively small, whereas in the iron group the $3d$ has a very much smaller one-electron energy than the $3s$ or $3p$. This is seen in Table 8-2. Here for instance for Sc we have a one-electron energy of 0.59 Rydberg for $3d$, 2.6 for $3p$, and 4.2 for $3s$.

This is a suitable point to comment on these one-electron energies for the $3d$ electrons in Table 8-2. The reader will note that for the elements from Sc to Ni the tabulated values are 0.59, 0.68, 0.74, 0.75, 0.57, 0.64, 0.66, 0.73 Rydbergs, respectively, with a definite break between Cr, with 0.75, and Mn, with 0.57. This does not reflect a sudden change in properties, but merely an incident of the calculation. In the elements from Sc through Cr, in compiling the table we have treated the configuration $3d^{n-2}4s^2$ as the ground-state configuration. Thus the value of 0.59 Rydberg for Sc is the energy difference between the $3d4s^2$ configuration of Sc and the $4s^2$ of Sc^+, as shown in Fig. 16-2. We note that this does not correspond to a vertical transition in the graph, which would correspond rather to the removal of a $4s$ electron, and we see why the one-electron energy of the $4s$ is given in Table 8-2 as 0.55 Rydberg, smaller than for $3d$: it is the vertical transition in Fig. 16-2, from $3d4s^2$ to $3d4s$. This throws light on the paradox by which, though the $4s$ is really more tightly bound than the $3d$, it has a smaller one-electron energy in the table.

In Table 8-2, to take account of the gradual change in the ground-state configuration as we go through the group, we have chosen the $3d^{n-1}4s$ configuration as the ground configuration from Mn on. Thus, in Fe, the $3d$ energy quoted in the table, namely, 0.64 Rydberg, is the energy difference between the $3d^74s$ configuration of Fe and the $3d^64s$ of Fe^+, whereas the $4s$ is the vertical transition between $3d^74s$ and $3d^7$ in Fig. 16-2, equal to 0.53 Rydberg. The jump in one-electron energies between Cr and Mn then merely arises from this different convention regarding the ground state of the atom.

The reader will see from these examples that the question of the relative stability of the $3d$ and $4s$ electrons in the iron group is a very subtle one, best understood by keeping in mind the energies of the various states, as seen in Fig. 16-2. Even in spite of the calculations of Watson, which we present in the next two sections, we do not have enough calculations by the self-consistent-field method to explain the situation from a theoretical point of view. It is clear, as we have mentioned, that we are witnessing the gradual absorption of the $3d$ orbital into the atom, from a definitely excited level in Ca to a definitely internal or X-ray level somewhat beyond Cu. The reason for this behavior can be seen in Fig. 9-4. There we gave the effective potential energy, the actual potential energy plus $l(l + 1)/r^2$, for a d electron, in K^+ and in Cu^+. We see that this effective potential energy has one minimum inside the atom, which is shallow for K^+, deep for Cu^+; and also a very broad minimum outside the inner core of the atom. In K^+, at the beginning of the iron group, the wave function is mainly outside the other electrons and acts not very differently from a hydrogenic $3d$ electron, with an orbital widely extended in space. However, in Cu^+, the inner minimum of effective potential energy is so low that the wave function is drawn almost entirely to the inside of the atom. It is the gradual shift from the one situation to the other which we are witnessing in the iron group.

16-3. Self-consistent-field Calculations for the Iron Group: Multiplet Separations. We have mentioned that Watson has carried out analytic self-consistent-field calculations of the configurations $1s^22s^22p^63s^23p^63d^n$ of a great many atoms and ions of the iron group of elements. In the present section we shall start to describe the results of these calculations and shall compare them with the experimental results on multiplet separations described in the preceding section. In the next section we consider average energies and ionization potentials.

In the first place, Watson has used numerous exponentials to describe his wave functions, in contrast to the small number used in the calculations for light atoms described in Chap. 15. As an example, we shall give the radial wave functions which he finds for the neutral iron atom, in which he has minimized the energy of the average of the configuration. These radial wave functions $R_{nl}(r)$, normalized as in Eq. (9-3), are given

Table 16-2. Watson's Basis Functions u_i for Radial Wave Functions of Iron

$$u_1 = \exp(-27.1431r)$$
$$u_2 = r \exp(-23.7801r)$$
$$u_3 = r \exp(-12.0977r)$$
$$u_4 = r^2 \exp(-11.1832r)$$
$$u_5 = r^2 \exp(-6.5137r)$$
$$u_6 = r^2 \exp(-3.8730r)$$
$$u_7 = r \exp(-16.7957r)$$
$$u_8 = r \exp(-10.0264r)$$
$$u_9 = r^2 \exp(-9.2049r)$$
$$u_{10} = r^2 \exp(-5.3438r)$$
$$u_{11} = r^2 \exp(-3.2876r)$$
$$u_{12} = r^2 \exp(-1.2451r)$$
$$u_{13} = r^2 \exp(-2.5146r)$$
$$u_{14} = r^2 \exp(-4.7614r)$$
$$u_{15} = r^2 \exp(-8.8265r)$$

Table 16-3. Watson's Coefficients C_i for Radial Wave Functions of Iron
(Constants Not Tabulated are Zero)

	$1s$	$2s$	$3s$
C_1	259.9657	− 78.78588	29.12969
C_2	316.8298	−529.7784	163.0930
C_3	−1.555638	431.2606	−141.0783
C_4	3.796725	810.8032	−765.3701
C_5	−0.1257721	8.127969	141.7725
C_6	0.002947797	− 0.04693311	36.34935

	$2p$	$3p$
C_7	206.8481	− 57.62168
C_8	311.7303	−126.9792
C_9	10.23053	− 7.717796
C_{10}	2.895899	84.98016
C_{11}	−0.09352675	15.06950

	$3d$
C_{12}	0.2945930
C_{13}	4.493625
C_{14}	39.88728
C_{15}	72.00112

in the form $\Sigma(i)C_i u_i$, where the u_i's are given in Table 16-2 and the C_i's in Table 16-3.

These numbers are arrived at in the following way. First, a great deal of judgment is required to decide on the best basis functions, as in Table 16-2. Experience regarding the choice of basis functions has been

Table 16-4

One- and two-electron integrals for iron, minimizing the average energy of the configuration $1s^2 2s^2 2p^6 3s^2 3p^6 3d^8$, from results of R. E. Watson. Integrals are given in Rydbergs. The one-electron integrals I represent the sum of the kinetic energy and potential energy in the field of the nucleus.

$I(1s)$	-675.7103
$I(2s)$	-165.3855
$I(2p)$	-164.0499
$I(3s)$	$- 63.27801$
$I(3p)$	$- 59.55344$
$I(3d)$	$- 44.49110$
$F^0(1s,1s)$	31.79529
$F^0(1s,2s)$	9.466773
$G^0(1s,2s)$	0.8661011
$F^0(1s,2p)$	10.60927
$G^1(1s,2p)$	1.779516
$F^0(1s,3s)$	3.179485
$G^0(1s,3s)$	0.1078077
$F^0(1s,3p)$	3.093797
$G^1(1s,3p)$	0.1945056
$F^0(1s,3d)$	2.162650
$G^2(1s,3d)$	0.002548427
$F^0(2s,2s)$	6.378649
$F^0(2s,2p)$	7.129789
$G^1(2s,2p)$	4.112998
$F^0(2s,3s)$	2.855504
$G^0(2s,3s)$	0.1833311
$F^0(2s,3p)$	2.761137
$G^1(2s,3p)$	0.1582516
$F^0(2s,3d)$	2.130620
$G^2(2s,3d)$	0.2270766
$F^0(2p,2p)$	7.735183
$F^2(2p,2p)$	3.652374
$F^0(2p,3s)$	2.897263
$G^1(2p,3s)$	0.2277975
$F^0(2p,3p)$	2.813244
$F^2(2p,3p)$	0.5404704
$G^0(2p,3p)$	0.2053523
$G^2(2p,3p)$	0.2150248
$F^0(2p,3d)$	2.138667
$F^2(2p,3d)$	0.3519028
$G^1(2p,3d)$	0.2454584
$G^3(2p,3d)$	0.1393798
$F^0(3s,3s)$	2.170107
$F^0(3s,3p)$	2.117261
$G^1(3s,3p)$	1.405591
$F^0(3s,3d)$	1.730078
$G^2(3s,3d)$	0.7020999

Table 16-4 (Continued)

$F^0(3p,3p)$	2.068802
$F^2(3p,3p)$	1.037209
$F^0(3p,3d)$	1.696844
$F^2(3p,3d)$	0.7631509
$G^1(3p,3d)$	0.9420055
$G^3(3p,3d)$	0.5623025
$F^0(3d,3d)$	1.439566
$F^2(3d,3d)$	0.6239966
$F^4(3d,3d)$	0.3809839

acquired by numerous workers in attempting to fit analytically the Hartree-Fock wave functions determined by numerical integration. For instance, Löwdin and Appel[1] have fitted the iron-group wave functions with analytic functions similar to those of Watson, though not identical, and their choice of basis functions has been helpful. The author[2] much earlier carried out less accurate fits for the lighter atoms by a choice of functions similar to Watson's, but less extensive. Given a set of basis functions, one sets up the orbitals using undetermined coefficients, calculates the various one- and two-electron integrals necessary to write the complete energy of the atom, and expresses this energy, as in Chap. 14 (for the average energy of a configuration) in terms of the undetermined C's. Then a program is available for a digital computer which starts with these integrals and proceeds to vary the C's until the energy is minimized. This program leads to the C's, to values of the various integrals, and to the total energy.

Having found the energy in this way, one can proceed to improve the choice of basis functions by trying other combinations, going through the whole procedure again, and again finding the minimum energy. If the final result is better than the preceding one, in the sense of giving a lower energy, it is assumed that the basis functions have been improved and further changes are made until one seems to have got the lowest possible energy. It is the final wave functions determined in this way which have been compared with those found by numerical integration of the Hartree-Fock equations in the few cases where that has been carried out and the agreement is good enough so that it is not clear which calculation is the more accurate. In other words, it may be assumed that Watson's results form accurate solutions of the Hartree-Fock equations. When the wave functions have been found in this way, the complete table of one- and two-electron integrals is available. In Table 16-4 we give these integrals for the case of neutral iron, which we are using as an illustration.

[1] P.-O. Löwdin and K. Appel, *Phys. Rev.*, **103**:1746 (1956).
[2] J. C. Slater, *Phys. Rev.*, **42**:33 (1932).

Most of these separate integrals cannot be compared with experiment, but in the preceding section we have seen that $F^2(3d,3d)$ and $F^4(3d,3d)$ are determined by fitting the experimental multiplet separations. In Fig. 16-3 we give a plot of $F^2(3d,3d)$ for all atomic numbers and degrees of ionization, similar to Fig. 16-1 but now showing Watson's computed curves to compare with the smoothed experimental curves of Fig. 16-1.

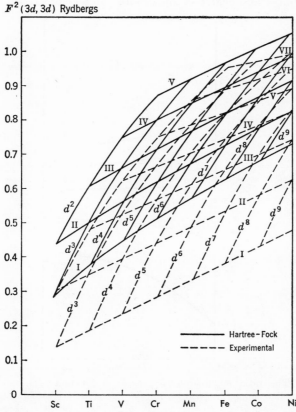

FIG. 16-3. Comparison between experimental and Hartree-Fock average of configuration values for $F^2(3d,3d)$ as a function of atomic number and ionization for the iron series $3d^n$ configurations (from R. E. Watson).

We see, as we have mentioned earlier, that the computed integrals are almost twice the observed ones for the neutral atoms, running down to perhaps 20 per cent more than the observed ones for the highly ionized atoms. As we have discussed earlier, this presumably is an indication of the configuration interaction, which is neglected in the Hartree-Fock calculation, and which would push down the upper multiplets more than the lower ones, compressing the multiplets belonging to a configuration, reducing the empirical $F^2(dd)$, and in some cases interchanging the order of terms.

We have seen that experimentally there is considerable variation in the ratio $F^4(3d,3d)/F^2(3d,3d)$, though the values cluster about the hydrogenic value of 0.649. The calculated curves naturally are smooth, and in Fig. 16-4 we show this ratio, as computed by Watson, as a function of atomic number and degree of ionization. In all cases it lies between 0.60

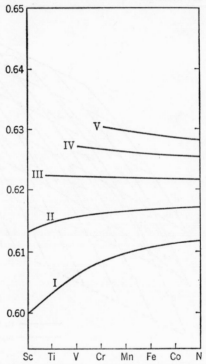

Fig. 16-4. The ratio $F^4(3d,3d)/F^2(3d,3d)$ as a function of atomic number and ionization as determined by Watson for the iron series $3d^n$ configurations.

and 0.63, thus being appreciably less than the hydrogenic value. This difference reflects a very striking difference between the true $3d$ wave function and the hydrogenic functions. This is illustrated in Fig. 16-5, in which we show the computed $3d$ radial wave functions for iron in several stages of ionization and for comparison a hydrogenic $3d$ function of such a scale that its $F^2(3d,3d)$ is equal to that of the actual function for neutral iron. The difference of shape is obvious: the true function has a maximum much farther inside the atom than the hydrogenic function. The maximum, as a matter of fact, falls near the minimum of effective potential energy shown in Fig. 9-4. The true wave function has a much more slowly decreasing tail at large values of r than the hydrogenic function. The change of shape of the true function with increasing degree of ionization is striking: the maximum remains almost exactly at the same place, while the tail shrinks greatly as the ionization increases, in contrast to the hydrogenic case, in which the whole scale would shrink along the axis of abscissas, without change of shape, with of course a compensating stretching along the vertical axis to maintain normalization.

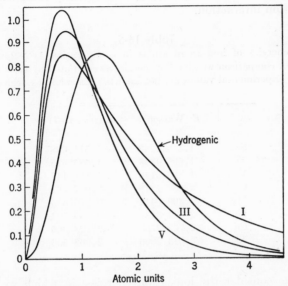

FIG. 16-5. Iron $3d$ wave functions for the $3d^n$ configuration, from R. E. Watson. Functions for Fe I, Fe III, Fe V compared with hydrogenic function which gives same value of $F^2(3d,3d)$ as Fe I function.

16-4. Comparison of Theory and Experiment for Total Energy and Ionization Potentials.

Aside from the integrals $F^2(dd)$ and $F^4(dd)$, as we have said, there are no other individual integrals which can be compared with experiment. We can, however, consider the one-electron energies and the differences of total energy between different stages of ionization, both of which can be compared with observed ionization energies. The total energy of the atom itself, unfortunately, is not known experimentally, but even though the experimental total energies are not known, it is interesting to give the computed values. We do this in Table 16-5, in which the energies quoted are those of the atom in the lowest multiplet of the configuration. It is interesting to compare these computed values with the much cruder values given by the rules of Sec. 15-7 and applied to the case of iron in that section (though for the configuration $3d^{n-2}4s^2$

rather than $3d^n$). For comparison we give the energies computed by this method and see that the difference rapidly increases as we go through the iron group but in no case is greater than about $1\frac{1}{2}$ per cent. We cannot of course estimate the error in Watson's calculation using the self-consistent field, but by analogy with the cases of the lighter atoms treated in Chap. 15, we may surmise that his calculated energies are probably too small numerically by about 1 per cent. This error, as we shall point out in Chap. 18 (Vol. II), arises from disregarding correlation in the Hartree-Fock method and could be removed by a sufficiently elaborate treatment of configuration interaction.

Table 16-5

Computed energies of iron-group atoms in configuration $1s^22s^22p^63s^23p^63d^n$, in Rydbergs. For comparison we give the energies as computed by the simple method of Sec. 15-7. Experimental values are not known. Calculations neglect relativistic correction.

	E (Watson)	E (Sec. 15-7)
Sc	$-1,519.1242$	$-1,511.088$
Ti	$-1,696.4843$	$-1,685.615$
V	$-1,885.5146$	$-1,871.147$
Cr	$-2,086.1818$	$-2,067.967$
Mn	$-2,299.0412$	$-2,276.355$
Fe	$-2,524.3137$	$-2,496.594$
Co	$-2,762.2763$	$-2,728.965$
Ni	$-3,013.2866$	$-2,968.536$

Now let us consider the ionization energies, in which we can make comparisons between theory and experiment in two different ways. First, we can consider the one-electron energies as calculated, which by Sec. 9-6 should agree with the ionization potentials. In fact, we shall show in Sec. 17-6 (Vol. II) that, if we calculate the one-electron energy in the case where we are minimizing the average energy of a configuration, this should agree to the first order with the observed energy difference between the average of the configuration for the atom and for the ion. This allows us to make a comparison between the observed energies of Table 8-2, which are computed in this way, and Watson's one-electron energies, for the cases in which he has carried out calculations involving the average of configurations. In Table 16-6 we give such a comparison. As for the experimental energies, the $3d$ entries differ from those of Table 8-2; as we have remarked earlier, those in Table 8-2 are computed using a configuration $3d^{n-2}4s^2$ or $3d^{n-1}4s$ for the atom, while those in Table 16-6 are recomputed using a configuration $3d^n$ for the atom, to match Watson's calculations.

The agreement between theory and experiment, as given in Table 16-6, seems remarkably good, probably better than one might have anticipated. The largest discrepancies come for the 1s ionization energies,

Table 16-6

Watson's calculated one-electron energies (absolute values), compared with observed ionization energies, in Rydbergs, in both cases dealing with averages of configuration.

	Sc	V	Fe	Co	Ni
1s:					
Calculated..........	331.50	402.55	522.05	565.34	610.46
Experimental........	331.1	402.9	524.3	568.3	614.1
2s:					
Calculated..........	37.80	47.23	63.11	68.88	74.97
Experimental........	37.3	46.9	63.0	69.0	75.3
2p:					
Calculated..........	30.99	39.59	54.08	59.40	65.04
Experimental........	30.0	38.3	52.8	58.2	63.7
3s:					
Calculated..........	4.77	5.85	7.60	8.22	8.91
Experimental........	4.2	5.3	7.3	8.0	8.7
3p:					
Calculated..........	2.82	3.56	4.80	5.24	5.75
Experimental........	2.6	3.2	4.4	4.9	5.4
3d:					
Calculated..........	0.23	0.32	0.42	0.46	0.50
Experimental........	0.23	0.32	0.40	0.40	0.43

and they would have been even larger, but in the opposite direction, if Watson had considered the relativistic correction, which begins to become important for the elements of the iron group. In Appendix 29, Eq. (A29-31), appearing in Vol. II, we give a formula for the relativistic correction to the energy of a hydrogenic level. For a 1s state, this formula reduces to

$$\text{Relativistic correction} = -\frac{\alpha^2 Z^4}{4} \qquad (16\text{-}3)$$

where $\alpha = \frac{1}{137}$, Z is the atomic number, and the correction is in Rydbergs. If we assume that this can be applied to a 1s electron in an atom, using an effective Z equal to $Z - 0.30$, we find relativistic corrections to the 1s levels as given in Table 16-7. We see that, with the relativistic correction, the discrepancies between observed and calculated 1s ionization energies have the opposite sign to what they did in Table 16-6, without this correction, and are somewhat larger. Nevertheless, they are still no more than 1 per cent of the ionization energies. The relativistic corrections are insignificant in the other cases.

We recall that there is another way to compare theory and experiment in the matter of the ionization energies. Since Watson has calculated the energy of the atom and of various ions, we can take the differences of these quantities to find the ionization energies. Thus, he has found the average energy of the configuration for neutral iron and for iron in four stages of ionization. We can compare the differences of these quantities with the one-electron energies and with the experimental ionization energies, as they can be read off Fig. 16-2. The results are given in Table 16-8.

Table 16-7. Relativistic Correction to One-electron Energy of $1s$ Electron, in Rydbergs

	Relativistic correction	Corrected 1-electron energy	Experimental
Sc	2.45	333.95	331.1
V	3.54	406.09	402.9
Fe	5.46	527.51	524.3
Co	6.80	572.14	568.3
Ni	7.85	618.31	614.1

It is clear from the results of Table 16-8 that the one-electron energies agree with the observed ionization energies a good deal more accurately than the differences of energies between one stage of ionization and the next. The reason for this has been mentioned earlier in connection with our discussion of one-electron energies in Sec. 15-6. We may remind the reader again of this reason. In finding the one-electron energies, we use the same one-electron wave functions both for the initial state of the atom or ion and for the state in which one electron is removed; and these wave functions are correct for the initial state, not for the final. Hence by the variation principle the energy which we use for the final state, with the electron removed, will be higher than if we had the correct wave functions for the final state, and hence the one-electron energy will be greater numerically than the numerical value of the energy difference between the two states, as Table 16-8 shows. On the other hand, the error in the calculated energy of a state goes up as the number of electrons in the atom goes up, as we pointed out in Chap. 15. Hence the energy of the initial state in the transition considered will lie above the true value by a greater amount than the energy of the final state, since it has one more electron, and the ionization energy as computed from the difference of energies of the two stages of ionization will be numerically too small, again as shown in Table 16-8. These two effects, one making the computed value too large, the other making it too small, tend to compensate

Table 16-8

Calculated energies of Fe I, Fe II, Fe III, Fe IV, Fe V, in each case found from average of configuration; differences of these values; one-electron energies; and observed ionization energies of $3d$ electron.   In Rydbergs.

	Energy	Energy difference	One-electron energy	Experimental
Fe I	−2,524.2360	0.1335	0.4195	0.3989
Fe II	−2,524.1025	1.1130	1.3545	1.2872
Fe III	−2,522.9895	2.3465	2.5535	2.4687
Fe IV	−2,520.6430	3.7756	3.9507	
Fe V	−2,516.8674		5.5326	

in the one-electron energy, which thus is a very good approximation to the observed ionization energy. This is fortunate, for it means that a simple self-consistent-field calculation in which we use one-electron energies to represent ionization energies can have a very satisfactory reliability. This observation was made empirically by Hartree from the time of his first papers on the self-consistent-field method.

In addition to the comparisons with experiment which we have outlined, there is one additional feature which Watson has calculated. He has in most cases carried through calculations, not only in which he minimizes the energy of the average of a configuration, but also in which he minimizes the energy of a specific multiplet, as was done in some of the calculations reported in Chap. 15. When this is done, he finds, as in that chapter, that the separations between multiplets prove to be reduced slightly, therefore agreeing somewhat better with experiment. But this reduction is small compared with the outstanding discrepancies; the multiplet separations remain too large by a considerable amount. This is again as in Chap. 15, and it lends additional evidence for the point of view presented there, namely, that it is hardly worthwhile using different one-electron wave functions for the different multiplets of a configuration. It seems simpler to proceed, as we have suggested, by minimizing the average energy of the lowest configuration, in which case in addition the one-electron energy has a simple significance. To improve the order of accuracy, one will have somehow to introduce correlation into the wave function, either by extensive configuration interaction, or through the use of a wave function depending explicitly on the interelectronic distances, as we shall discuss in Chap. 18 (Vol. II).

We have now gone about as far as is warranted by existing calculations in comparing self-consistent-field theory and simple multiplet theory with experiment. Much more work is obviously needed, both for handling other atoms in other configurations, and for improving the accuracy of results by means of configuration interaction. We now turn in Chap. 17, the first one in Vol. II, to a consideration of the Hartree-Fock method, which we have so far merely suggested, though really we have been discussing it in the two preceding chapters; then in Chap. 18 to methods of improving the accuracy of atomic calculation. After that we shall be ready to take up more powerful methods of handling multiplet theory, by group theory, the methods of Dirac and Van Vleck, and the methods of Racah. We then pass on to discussions of spin-orbit and other magnetic interactions, using Dirac's theory of the electron; to the intensities of spectral lines; and to hyperfine structure. These topics form the subjects of study in the second volume of this work.

PROBLEMS

1. For iron, set up Z_p by use of the Thomas-Fermi method, using Table A17-1. From this, derive the effective potential energy in which a d electron moves, and compare with the corresponding curves for K^+ and Cu^+ given in Fig. 9-4.

2. Use the effective potential energy found in Prob. 1, and carry out an approximate numerical integration of Schrödinger's equation to get the wave function and eigenvalue of the $3d$ electron in iron. Compare this eigenfunction with Watson's value from Fig. 16-5 and the eigenvalue with Watson's value 0.42 Rydberg given in Table 16-8.

3. Watson's $3d$ radial wave function, from Tables 16-2 and 16-3, can be expressed in the form $r^2[0.2946 \exp(-1.245r) + 4.494 \exp(-2.515r) + 39.89 \exp(-4.761r) + 72.00 \exp(-8.827r)]$. This must be an approximate solution of the radial wave equation

$$\frac{d^2P}{dr^2} + \left[E + \frac{2Z_p}{r} - \frac{l(l+1)}{r^2} \right] P = 0$$

where P is r times the radial wave function. On the other hand, it must be an exact solution of the differential equation above for a slightly incorrect function Z_p, which can be found by solving the equation for Z_p, computing d^2P/dr^2 from the analytic form of the function. Find this function Z_p analytically, and compute its values at several points (as $r = 0, 0.5, 1, 2, 3$). Compare it with the Thomas-Fermi function of Prob. 1.

4. Proceed in the same way as in Prob. 3, using Watson's $1s$ and $2p$ radial wave functions for iron.

5. Use the integrals of Table 16-4 to compute the average energy of the iron atom in the configuration $1s^22s^22p^63s^23p^63d^8$, and verify the value for the energy given in the text.

6. Use the integrals of Table 16-4 to find the calculated energies of the various multiplets arising from the configuration $1s^22s^22p^63s^23p^63d^8$ of iron.

7. Use the integrals of Table 16-4 to find the one-electron energies of the various electrons in the iron atom, and compare with the values given in Table 16-6.

Appendix 1

Bohr's Theory for Motion in a Central Field

Our problem is to investigate the motion and quantization of the system consisting of a nucleus of mass M and charge Z units and an electron of mass m_0, subject to an electrostatic attraction whose potential energy is $-Ze^2/4\pi\epsilon_0 r$, where r is the distance between the particles, e the magnitude of the electronic charge, as in Sec. 1-6. First we shall show how the two-body problem can be reduced to a one-body problem; then we shall solve the one-body problem. We shall base our discussion on the Lagrangian and Hamiltonian methods discussed in Appendix 4, and we suggest that the reader become familiar with that appendix before reading the present one.

First we wish to set up the kinetic energy and Hamiltonian function. Let x_1, y_1, z_1 be the coordinates of the electron, x_2, y_2, z_2 those of the nucleus. The kinetic energy is

$$T = \tfrac{1}{2}m_0(\dot{x}_1^2 + \dot{y}_1^2 + \dot{z}_1^2) + \tfrac{1}{2}M(\dot{x}_2^2 + \dot{y}_2^2 + \dot{z}_2^2) \qquad \text{(A1-1)}$$

where $\dot{x}_1$ stands for the time rate of change of x_1, and similarly for the others. We now make a change of variables, introducing the coordinates X, Y, Z of the center of mass of the two particles and x, y, z, the relative coordinates of the electron referred to the nucleus, according to the equations

$$X = \frac{m_0 x_1 + M x_2}{m_0 + M} \qquad x = x_1 - x_2 \qquad \text{(A1-2)}$$

with corresponding formulas for the y and z coordinates. We solve these for x_1, x_2, etc., finding

$$x_1 = X + \frac{M}{m_0 + M}\, x \qquad x_2 = X - \frac{m_0}{m_0 + M}\, x \qquad \text{(A1-3)}$$

with similar equations for y and z. We use these equations and their time derivatives to convert the kinetic energy to the new coordinates, and we find

$$T = \frac{1}{2}(m_0 + M)(\dot{X}^2 + \dot{Y}^2 + \dot{Z}^2) + \tfrac{1}{2}\mu(\dot{x}^2 + \dot{y}^2 + \dot{z}^2) \qquad \mu = \frac{M m_0}{M + m_0}$$
$$\text{(A1-4)}$$

The quantity μ which we have introduced is the reduced mass; since the nuclear mass M is so much greater than the electronic mass m_0, it is very little different from the electronic mass m_0.

The Hamiltonian function is $T + V$, where T is as given in Eq. (A1-4), and where V is the potential energy $-Ze^2/4\pi\epsilon_0 r$, where

$$r^2 = x^2 + y^2 + z^2 \tag{A1-5}$$

That is,

$$H = \frac{(p_X^2 + p_Y^2 + p_Z^2)}{2(m_0 + M)} + \frac{(p_x^2 + p_y^2 + p_z^2)}{2\mu} + V(r) \tag{A1-6}$$

where the p's are the momenta. Since V does not depend on X, Y, and Z, Hamilton's equations at once lead to the conclusion that p_X, p_Y, p_Z are constant, or the velocity of the center of mass is constant. We do not need to consider this uniform motion of the center of mass further. As for the relative coordinates, we have

$$\frac{dp_x}{dt} = \mu \frac{d^2x}{dt^2} = -\frac{\partial V}{\partial x} \tag{A1-7}$$

with similar equations for y and z. In other words, the motion of the relative coordinates x, y, z is like that of a single particle whose mass equals the reduced mass μ, under the action of the potential energy $V(r)$. This means that, in the treatment of Sec. 1-6, we should really have used the reduced mass μ rather than the electronic mass m_0, which will then make a corresponding change in the formulas of that section. In particular, in the formulas of Eqs. (1-18) and (1-19) for the energy and orbital radius of the hydrogen problem, we should have used μ rather than m_0 in the formula. The quantities defined in Eqs. (1-21) to (1-24), the Rydberg energy and the quantity a_0, are defined in terms of m_0, as we have done, which would be correct for a nucleus of infinite mass, for which $m_0 = \mu$; but this means that the corresponding Rydberg for hydrogen equals μ/m_0 times this Rydberg for infinite mass and a_0 for hydrogen equals m_0/μ times the a_0 for infinite mass. These corrections must be made in accurate numerical work.

Now let us consider the problem of the hydrogen orbits, which as we see from Eq. (A1-7) arise from the motion of a particle of mass μ in the potential V. For the study of the size and shape of the orbits, we may use polar coordinates in the plane of the orbit. The equations of motion are then as given in Eq. (A4-23), in which V is a function of r only. From these equations we see that the angular momentum p_θ is a constant. Sommerfeld's quantum condition then states that $\int_0^{2\pi} p_\theta \, d\theta = kh$, where k is a constant. Since p_θ is constant, this leads to

$$p_\theta = \frac{kh}{2\pi} = k\hbar \tag{A1-8}$$

where $\hbar = h/2\pi$. This quantum number k is called the azimuthal quantum number, as indicated in Sec. 1-7.

We may now use Eq. (A4-22), combined with the fact that the Hamiltonian function H equals the energy E, to give

$$E = \frac{p_r^2}{2\mu} + \frac{k^2\hbar^2}{2\mu r^2} + V$$

$$p_r = \pm \sqrt{-\frac{k^2\hbar^2}{r^2} + \frac{2\mu Ze^2}{4\pi\epsilon_0 r} + 2\mu E} = \pm \sqrt{\frac{R}{r^2}} \tag{A1-9}$$

where $R = a + br + cr^2$, $a = -k^2\hbar^2$, $b = 2\mu Ze^2/4\pi\epsilon_0$, $c = 2\mu E$. Sommerfeld's quantum condition for the variable r is now $\oint p_r\, dr = n_r h$, where the integral is to be taken around a complete cycle, and where n_r is a quantum number, called the radial quantum number.

The radius r varies between two limits r_1 and r_2 at which the radial momentum p_r becomes zero. These limits are given by

$$r_1, r_2 = \frac{-b \pm \sqrt{b^2 - 4ac}}{2c} \tag{A1-10}$$

as we see by solving the quadratic equation arising by setting $p_r = 0$. The motion of p_r and r may be shown graphically in a phase space in which we plot p_r, as given in Eq. (A1-9), as a function of r. This is done in Fig. A1-1. We see that we have a closed curve, around which the representative point, in the sense of Sec. 1-8, revolves in a clockwise direction. The integral $\oint p_r\, dr$ of Sommerfeld's quantum condition is to be taken around this curve. From r_1 to r_2 we use the upper branch of the curve, given by the positive sign in p_r in Eq. (A1-9), and $\int_{r_1}^{r_2} p_r\, dr$ for this half of the complete cycle equals the area of the closed figure above the axis of abscissas. From r_2 back to r_1 we use the negative sign in p_r. This gives the area of the lower half of the figure. Hence we see that $\oint p_r\, dr = 2 \int_{r_1}^{r_2} p_r\, dr$.

We may now compute Sommerfeld's integral. From standard integral tables we find

$$\int \frac{\sqrt{R}}{r}\, dr = \sqrt{R} + \frac{b}{2\sqrt{-c}} \sin^{-1} \frac{-2cr - b}{\sqrt{b^2 - 4ac}}$$
$$- \sqrt{-a} \sin^{-1} \frac{br + 2a}{r\sqrt{b^2 - 4ac}} \tag{A1-11}$$

Here we have chosen the correct form of the integrals for the case we are considering, though there are alternative forms in terms of logarithms and inverse hyperbolic functions. At the upper and lower limits, respectively, the quantities whose inverse sines we are taking are ± 1, so that the differences of the inverse sines at the two limits are π; and the quantity $\sqrt{R}$ vanishes at both limits. Thus we have

$$\oint p_r \, dr = 2\pi \left(\frac{b}{2\sqrt{-c}} - \sqrt{-a} \right) = 2\pi \left(\frac{\mu Z e^2}{4\pi\epsilon_0 \sqrt{-2\mu E}} - k\hbar \right)$$

$$= n_r h \tag{A1-12}$$

We solve this equation for the energy and find

$$E = -\frac{2\pi^2 \mu Z^2 e^4}{(4\pi\epsilon_0)^2 h^2} \frac{1}{(n_r + k)^2} \tag{A1-13}$$

which agrees with Eq. (1-18), if we make the correction we have mentioned earlier for the reduced mass, if we replace the quantum number n by $n_r + k$, and if we note that the energy formula for an atom of nuclear charge Z units is Z^2 as great as for hydrogen.

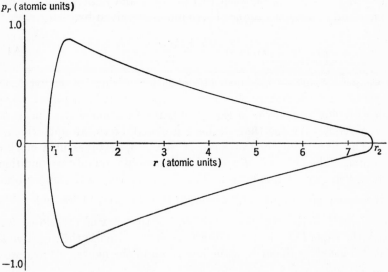

Fig. A1-1. Phase space for p_r versus r, for radial motion in hydrogen, 2s state, Bohr theory.

In a moment we shall consider the shape and size of the orbit and the way in which these quantities are determined by the azimuthal quantum number k and the principal quantum number n, which equals $n_r + k$. First, however, let us consider the space quantization. For this purpose we set up the problem in spherical coordinates, allowing the orbital plane to be arbitrarily oriented in space. We use the Hamiltonian of Eq.

(A4-24).   We find from Hamilton's equations that p_ϕ is a constant, and when we look at the interpretation of this quantity, we find that it is the component of angular momentum along the z axis, in our spherical coordinate system.   Sommerfeld's quantum condition for this variable then leads to the condition that p_ϕ equals an integer times $\hbar$; this integer is defined as m, the magnetic quantum number.   We can proceed from this point to discuss the rest of the motion in spherical coordinates and to arrive at the existence of the azimuthal quantum number in this way; but this is more complicated than the method we have used, of using polar coordinates in the plane of the orbit, and it leads to the same final result.

Now let us return to the study of the shape and size of the orbits. We wish to demonstrate the results stated in Sec. 1-7, namely, that the major axis of the elliptical orbit equals the diameter of the circular orbit of the same energy and the ratio of minor to major axis equals k/n.   As a first step, we shall study the geometrical nature of ellipses and shall prove that an orbit of negative energy, in a problem of motion under an inverse-square force, is an ellipse.   In Fig. A1-2 we show an ellipse

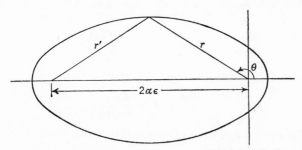

FIG. A1-2. Ellipse, with origin at right-hand focus.

with the origin at the right-hand focus.   Let the radius vector from the origin to a point on the ellipse be r, making an angle of θ with the axis of abscissas, so that r, θ are the polar coordinates of the point.   Let r' be the distance to the other focus.   We recall that the ellipse is defined, in geometry, as the locus of points such that the sum of the distances from two fixed points is constant.   That is, if the fixed points are the foci shown in Fig. A1-2, this condition is that $r + r' = $ constant.   Let the constant be 2α, where we readily see that 2α equals the major axis, α being the semimajor axis.   The distance between foci is called $2\alpha\epsilon$, where ϵ, which must be less than unity for an ellipse, is called the eccentricity.   When we consider the point for which $r = r'$, we find that the semiminor axis is given by $\beta = \alpha \sqrt{1 - \epsilon^2}$.   From the law of cosines we find that

$$r' = \sqrt{r^2 + (2\alpha\epsilon)^2 + 2r(2\alpha\epsilon) \cos \theta} \qquad (\text{A1-14})$$

We write the equation of the ellipse in the form $r + r' = 2\alpha$, use Eq. (A1-14) for r', and eliminate r' to get a relation between r and θ. This is

$$r = \frac{\alpha(1 - \epsilon^2)}{1 + \epsilon \cos \theta} \tag{A1-15}$$

This is the equation of the ellipse, in polar coordinates.

Now we shall prove Kepler's first law, namely, that the orbit of a particle moving according to the inverse-square law is a conic section; in particular, if it moves with negative energy, it is an ellipse. We start with Eq. (A4-23), which in the present case gives

$$\mu \frac{d^2r}{dt^2} = -\frac{Ze^2}{4\pi\epsilon_0 r^2} + \frac{p_\theta^2}{\mu r^3} \tag{A1-16}$$

We wish to derive the equation of the orbit, the relation between r and θ, eliminating the time, to show that this takes the form of Eq. (A1-15). This is most easily done by making the substitution $u = 1/r$. When we make this substitution and use the relation $\dot\theta = p_\theta/\mu r^2$ from Eq. (A4-22), we have

$$\begin{aligned}
\frac{dr}{dt} &= -\frac{1}{u^2}\frac{du}{d\theta}\frac{d\theta}{dt} = -\frac{p_\theta}{\mu}\frac{du}{d\theta} \\
\frac{d^2r}{dt^2} &= -\frac{p_\theta}{\mu}\frac{d^2u}{d\theta^2}\frac{d\theta}{dt} = -\left(\frac{p_\theta}{\mu}\right)^2\frac{d^2u}{d\theta^2}u^2
\end{aligned} \tag{A1-17}$$

We substitute this result into Eq. (A1-16) and find

$$\frac{d^2u}{d\theta^2} + u = \frac{Ze^2\mu}{4\pi\epsilon_0 p_\theta^2} \tag{A1-18}$$

This is a differential equation of elementary form, whose general solution can be written in the form

$$u = \frac{1}{r} = \frac{Ze^2\mu}{4\pi\epsilon_0 p_\theta^2} + A \cos(\theta - \theta_0) \tag{A1-19}$$

where A, θ_0 are arbitrary constants. If we fix $\theta_0 = 0$, it is equivalent to orienting the orbit as in Fig. A1-2. If we write

$$A = \frac{Ze^2\mu}{4\pi\epsilon_0 p_\theta^2}\epsilon \tag{A1-20}$$

we see that Eq. (A1-19) becomes identical with Eq. (A1-15), with

$$\alpha(1 - \epsilon^2) = \frac{4\pi\epsilon_0 p_\theta^2}{Ze^2\mu} \tag{A1-21}$$

Hence we see that the orbit is an ellipse, proving Kepler's first law. In Eq. (A1-21), we must not confuse ϵ, the eccentricity of the ellipse, and ϵ_0, the constant associated with mks units.

From Eq. (A4-23), giving the Hamiltonian function, and Eq. (A1-17), giving dr/dt, we can compute the energy. We find that it is independent of ϵ and that it equals

$$E = -\frac{1}{2\alpha}\frac{Ze^2}{4\pi\epsilon_0} \tag{A1-22}$$

If we combine this with Eq. (A1-13), we find

$$\alpha = (n_r + k)^2 \frac{\hbar^2(4\pi\epsilon_0)}{Ze^2\mu} \tag{A1-23}$$

When we remember that $n_r + k = n$, this is identical with Eq. (A1-19), except that now we are including the general case of nuclear charge Z units, and we find that the orbital dimensions are inversely proportional to Z. The quantity α is the semimajor axis of the ellipse, which equals the radius for circular orbits; this is the reason why we get agreement with Eq. (A1-19). We also have the proof that the semimajor axis of the orbit is equal for all orbits of the same energy, or of the same n. We now recall that the semiminor axis β equals $\alpha\sqrt{1-\epsilon^2}$. Hence from Eq. (A1-21) we have

$$\frac{\beta^2}{\alpha} = k^2\frac{\hbar^2(4\pi\epsilon_0)}{Ze^2\mu} \qquad \frac{\beta}{\alpha} = \frac{k}{n} \tag{A1-24}$$

verifying our earlier statement that the ratio of minor to major axis of the ellipse is k/n.

We now wish to derive Kepler's second law, to get information which we shall need in computing the magnetic moment of the electron's orbit. Kepler's second law states that the area swept out by the radius vector is proportional to the time. This is a direct consequence of the equation $d\theta/dt = p_\theta/\mu r^2$ and holds for any central motion in which the angular momentum is conserved, not merely for motion under the inverse-square law. In time dt, the radius vector will sweep out a small triangle of altitude r, base $r\,d\theta$, in consequence of the increase of θ. This triangle has an area $\frac{1}{2}r^2\,d\theta$. Thus the rate of sweeping out of area is

$$\frac{d(\text{area})}{dt} = \frac{1}{2}r^2\frac{d\theta}{dt} = \frac{p_\theta}{2\mu} \tag{A1-25}$$

From this law, we integrate about a complete period and have

$$\text{Period }\tau = \frac{2\mu}{p_\theta}\,(\text{area}) \tag{A1-26}$$

We can now use this result to find the magnetic moment of the orbit. In mks units, the magnetic moment of a current loop equals the current times the area enclosed by it. In the electron's orbit, the charge $-e$ rotates once in time τ, so that it is equivalent to a current $-e/\tau$. Then we have the magnetic moment equal to $(-e/\tau)(\text{area})$, or the magnetic moment is $-e/2\mu$ times the angular momentum, as indicated in Sec. 1-7.

Appendix 2

The Principle of Least Action

The principle of least action is a standard part of classical mechanics, treated in many texts. We follow the treatment given by E. C. Kemble.[1] We consider only a problem of a single particle, though it is not difficult to extend the discussion to a many-particle problem.

Consider a particle of mass m, moving under the action of a potential energy $V(x,y,z)$. The magnitude of its momentum at any point of space is then determined from the energy equation

$$\frac{p^2}{2m} + V = E \qquad p = \sqrt{2m(E - V)} \qquad \text{(A2-1)}$$

We now consider a path from a point A to a point B and compute S, the line integral of p along the path: $S = \int_A^B p \, ds$, where p is to be found as a function of x, y, z by Eq. (A2-1). The principle of least action then states that, if the path connecting A and B is the actual trajectory of a particle traveling from A to B with the energy E, the integral $\int p \, ds$ will be stationary, or its value along a neighboring path will differ from that along the trajectory by a small quantity of higher order.

As a first step, following Kemble, let us introduce a quantity u, increasing monotonically as we go along the path from A to B, in terms of which we can express the equation of the path parametrically by the relations $x = f_1(u)$, $y = f_2(u)$, $z = f_3(u)$. If dx/du is defined as x', dy/du as y', etc., we then have $ds = (x'^2 + y'^2 + z'^2)^{\frac{1}{2}} \, du$, so that the integral S becomes

$$S = \int_0^1 p(x'^2 + y'^2 + z'^2)^{\frac{1}{2}} \, du \qquad \text{(A2-2)}$$

where we have arranged u in such a way that it takes on the value 0 at the point A, 1 at the point B.

Now we are to construct a slightly different path, such that it is given parametrically by $x = f_1(u) + \delta x(u)$, $y = f_2(u) + \delta y(u)$, etc., where δx,

[1] E. C. Kemble, "Fundamental Principles of Quantum Mechanics," appendix A, McGraw-Hill Book Company, Inc., New York, 1937.

δy, δz are functions of u, and where these new functions are again set up so that u will equal 0 at A, 1 at B. The derivative of this new x with respect to u will then be $x' + d(\delta x)/du$, where x' is as before. We can now construct the change in S, as given by Eq. (A2-2), when we integrate along this slightly different path. In doing this, we are to take account of the fact that p is to be computed at a slightly different point for each value of u and also that $(x'^2 + y'^2 + z'^2)^{\frac{1}{2}}$ is to be found using slightly different values of the derivatives. We then have

$$\delta S = \int_0^1 \left\{ \left(\frac{\partial p}{\partial x} \delta x + \frac{\partial p}{\partial y} \delta y + \frac{\partial p}{\partial z} \delta z \right) (x'^2 + y'^2 + z'^2)^{\frac{1}{2}} \right.$$
$$\left. + \left[p \frac{\partial}{\partial x'} (x'^2 + y'^2 + z'^2)^{\frac{1}{2}} \frac{d(\delta x)}{du} + \cdots \right] \right\} du \quad \text{(A2-3)}$$

The second part of the integral of Eq. (A2-3) can be integrated by parts. The integrated terms vanish, since δx, δy, δz are zero at $u = 0$ and 1, both paths passing through the points A and B. Thus the second part of Eq. (A2-3) can be replaced by

$$- \int_0^1 \left\{ \frac{d}{du} \left[p \frac{\partial}{\partial x'} (x'^2 + y'^2 + z'^2)^{\frac{1}{2}} \right] \delta x + \cdots \right\} du \quad \text{(A2-4)}$$

We carry out the differentiation with respect to x' in Eq. (A2-4) and remember that $ds = (x'^2 + y'^2 + z'^2)^{\frac{1}{2}} du$. Then Eq. (A2-4) becomes

$$- \int_0^1 \left[\frac{d}{ds} \left(p \frac{dx}{ds} \right) \delta x + \cdots \right] (x'^2 + y'^2 + z'^2)^{\frac{1}{2}} du \quad \text{(A2-5)}$$

We now insert this modified term in Eq. (A2-3) and have

$$\delta S = \int_0^1 \left\{ \left[\frac{\partial p}{\partial x} - \frac{d}{ds} \left(p \frac{dx}{ds} \right) \right] \delta x + \cdots \right\} (x'^2 + y'^2 + z'^2)^{\frac{1}{2}} du \quad \text{(A2-6)}$$

We now recall that the quantities $\delta x(u)$, $\delta y(u)$, $\delta z(u)$ were entirely independent and arbitrary functions of u, subject only to the condition that they reduced to zero when $u = 0$ or 1. We can then not have the integral in Eq. (A2-6), representing δS, equal to zero, unless the coefficients of δx, δy, δz inside the integral sign are separately equal to zero. Hence we arrive at the differential equations

$$\frac{\partial p}{\partial x} - \frac{d}{ds} \left(p \frac{dx}{ds} \right) = 0 \quad \text{(A2-7)}$$

representing the path of the particle. Any such problem as the present one, dealing with the variation of an integral, leads in the calculus of variations to such a differential equation, called the Euler equation, and it is in this way, by deriving differential equations, that we can arrive at the equations of motion of a mechanical problem from variation principles.

In the derivative $\partial p/\partial x$, we now use the form of Eq. (A2-1) for p, obtaining

$$\frac{\partial p}{\partial x} = -\left(\frac{m}{p}\right)\frac{\partial V}{\partial x}$$

In the derivative with respect to ds, we recall that $p/m = v = ds/dt$, so that $p/ds = m/dt$. Thus Eq. (A2-7) becomes

$$-\frac{m}{p}\frac{\partial V}{\partial x} - \frac{m}{p}\frac{d}{dt}\left(m\frac{dx}{dt}\right) = 0 \qquad m\frac{d^2x}{dt^2} = -\frac{\partial V}{\partial x} \qquad \cdots$$

or the ordinary Newtonian equations of motion for the particle. The path for which the integral S is stationary, as demanded by the principle of least action, is then the trajectory of a particle obeying Newton's laws, as we wished to prove.

Appendix 3

Wave Packets and Their Motion

We shall first show how a wave packet can be set up, namely, a wave function concentrated in a given small region of space, traveling with a momentum as sharply defined as is allowed by the principle of uncertainty. There are many different ways to set up a wave packet, but the one which we choose is simple and straightforward. We shall assume that, at $t = 0$, the wave function is zero except within a small rectangular volume, limited by $x = x_0 \pm X/2, y = y_0 \pm Y/2, z = z_0 \pm Z/2$. Inside this volume, we assume that it is given by a plane wave, $\exp[i\mathbf{k}_0 \cdot (\mathbf{r} - \mathbf{r}_0)]$, where $\mathbf{k}_0$ is a propagation vector with components k_{0x}, k_{0y}, k_{0z}, $\mathbf{r}$ is the radius vector with components x, y, z, and $\mathbf{r}_0$ is the radius vector to the center of the wave packet, with components x_0, y_0, z_0.

We shall first show that the mere fact of limiting the extension of the wave packet in space results in an uncertainty in the momentum, as the principle of uncertainty demands. To investigate the momentum, we expand the wave function as a linear combination of plane waves. We know that a single plane wave corresponds to a given momentum, given by $\mathbf{k}\hbar$, where $\mathbf{k}$ is the propagation constant, and in such an expansion the square of the amplitude of any plane wave will correspond to the probability of finding the particle with the corresponding momentum. The expansion is based on Fourier's integral theorem, which may be written as

$$f(x_1) = \int_{-\infty}^{\infty} F(w) \exp(iwx_1)\, dw$$

where
$$F(w) = \frac{1}{2\pi} \int_{-\infty}^{\infty} f(x_2) \exp(-iwx_2)\, dx_2$$

(A3-1)

Here we express an arbitrary function $f(x_1)$ as a sum or integral of functions $F(w) \exp(iwx_1)$, where $F(w)$ is an amplitude, $\exp(iwx_1)$ a sinusoidal function of the type expressing a plane wave. It is the square of the amplitude $F(w)$ which we shall use to find the probability of the particle having a given momentum.

In our present case, we may express the wave function $\phi(r)$, for $t = 0$, in the expansion

$$\phi(r) = \int_{-\infty}^{\infty} \int_{-\infty}^{\infty} \int_{-\infty}^{\infty} A_x(k_x) A_y(k_y) A_z(k_z) \exp\left[i\mathbf{k} \cdot (\mathbf{r} - \mathbf{r}_0)\right] dk_x\, dk_y\, dk_z$$

(A3-2)

where $A_x(k_x) = \dfrac{1}{2\pi} \displaystyle\int_{x_0-X/2}^{x_0+X/2} \exp\left[ik_{0x}(x - x_0)\right] \exp\left[-ik_x(x - x_0)\right] dx$

$$= \frac{X}{2\pi} \frac{\sin\left[(k_{0x} - k_x)X/2\right]}{(k_{0x} - k_x)X/2}$$

(A3-3)

with similar expressions for the y and z components; these results follow from use of Eq. (A3-1).   It is well known that the function of Eq. (A3-3) has a sharp peak when $k_x = k_{0x}$ and falls to zero when the argument of the sine equals $\pm\pi$, or when

$$(k_{0x} - k_x)\frac{X}{2\pi} = \pm 1 \qquad (p_x - p_{0x})X = \pm h \qquad \text{3 (A-4)}$$

In the last expression, we have used $k\hbar = p$, where p is the momentum and p_0 the momentum associated with the propagation constant k_0.   We see, then, that the limits of momentum found in the expansion of Eq. (A3-3) are connected with the uncertainty of the coordinate, which is X, by Eq. (2-3), expressing the uncertainty principle.   There are of course similar expressions for the y and z components.

We shall shortly investigate the time dependence of the wave function. We shall find that approximately it will oscillate sinusoidally, according to an expression $\exp(-i\omega_0 t)$, where the angular frequency is related to the energy by Bohr's relation $E_0 = \hbar\omega_0 = h\nu_0$.   We shall also find that the wave packet moves along in space with the group velocity, whose value we shall shortly discuss.   Then the wave packet will pass a given point of space in a finite time interval T.   Hence the wave function, at that particular point of space, will be zero except during this time interval T, during which it will be oscillating like $\exp(-i\omega_0 t)$.   We can then apply Fourier's integral theorem to the time dependence and find

$$\psi(t) = \int_{-\infty}^{\infty} B(\omega) \exp\left[i\omega(t - t_0)\right] d\omega$$

(A3-5)

where $$B(\omega) = \frac{T}{2\pi} \frac{\sin\left[(\omega_0 - \omega)T/2\right]}{(\omega_0 - \omega)T/2}$$

(A3-6)

analogous to Eq. (A3-3); the time t_0 in Eq. (A3-5) is the mean time at which the wave packet passes the point in question.   We have a peak of amplitude, or intensity, at the angular frequency $\omega = \omega_0$, and the intensity falls to zero when

$$(\omega_0 - \omega)\frac{T}{2\pi} = \pm 1 \qquad (E - E_0)T = \pm h$$

(A3-7)

so that there is an uncertainty in frequency or in energy given by the uncertainty principle of Eq. (2-5).

From the uncertainty principle of Eqs. (A3-4) and (A3-7), we see that, if the uncertainty in momentum or energy is to be a small fraction of the whole momentum or energy, there must be many waves in the train; that is, as far as energy is concerned, T must equal many periods of the oscillation, which will be the case if the dimensions of the wave packet are many wavelengths in extent. To see this, we note that the period is $2\pi/\omega_0$, so that the number of waves in the train, which is T divided by the period, is $\omega_0 T/2\pi$. If we let this number be n, we can rewrite Eq. (A3-7) in the form

$$\frac{\omega_0 - \omega}{\omega_0} = \pm \frac{1}{n} \qquad (A3\text{-}8)$$

verifying our statement that n must be large if the uncertainty in frequency is a small fraction of the frequency.

Next we consider the formula for group velocity, which we have given in Eq. (2-2). We wish to show that, if we start a wave packet at $t = 0$ according to the method of the preceding paragraphs, it will move as time goes on with the group velocity. We know from Sec. 4-2 that if we analyze our wave function at $t = 0$, not into plane waves, but into the eigenfunctions of Schrödinger's equation, then a linear combination like that of Eq. (4-8), namely, $\psi = \Sigma(n)C_n u_n \exp(-iE_n t/\hbar)$, will furnish a general solution of Schrödinger's equation, holding at any time. Let us then expand the function we have been considering previously in this way, namely, the function which is a plane wave $\exp[i\mathbf{k}_0 \cdot (\mathbf{r} - \mathbf{r}_0)]$ inside the wave packet, zero outside.

Each of the eigenfunctions u_n will have a character in the neighborhood of the wave packet which is similar to a plane wave. This arises on account of the properties of the WKB approximation, which was discussed in Sec. 3-6, and in which it is shown that u_n resembles a sinusoidal wave with slowly varying amplitude. To produce the expansion of the wave packet, we shall require large amplitudes for those u_n's corresponding to plane waves with propagation constants $\mathbf{k}$ in the neighborhood of $\mathbf{k}_0$; the range of u_n's having large amplitudes C_n will correspond to the range of $\mathbf{k}$'s arising from the uncertainty principle, as in Eq. (A3-4). These will have a corresponding range of energies. We know from the WKB solution that the local propagation constant $\mathbf{k}$ and energy of a solution E are related according to de Broglie's relation,

$$|p| = \sqrt{2m(E - V)} = |k|\hbar$$

Since the magnitudes of the $\mathbf{k}$'s vary by only small amounts, as we see in Eq. (A3-4), the energies will also vary only slightly; this was the basis of our earlier statement that the wave function within the wave packet will vary approximately according to the sinusoidal function $\exp(-iE_0t/\hbar)$, and we now see that E_0 is the energy associated with the propagation constant $\mathbf{k}_0$. But the different u_n's will still have slightly different energies, as well as $\mathbf{k}$'s. It is the interference of these waves with slightly different wavelengths and slightly different frequencies which results in the finite character of the wave packet. If we superpose the waves, with their appropriate $\mathbf{k}$'s and E's, they will be in phase at $t = 0$ in the immediate neighborhood of the wave packet but they will interfere destructively as we go outside the wave packet, which is the way in which we build up a solution which is large within the packet but zero outside.

To investigate the motion of the wave packet, we must now ask how the point of constructive interference moves as time goes on. Let us take two such wave functions, acting like two plane waves of slightly different $\mathbf{k}$ and E. To be specific, let us superpose a wave with propagation constant $\mathbf{k}_0 + \delta\mathbf{k}$, angular frequency $\omega_0 + \delta\omega$, and one with propagation constant $\mathbf{k}_0 - \delta\mathbf{k}$, angular frequency $\omega_0 - \delta\omega$. The sum of the plane waves will be

$$\exp\{i[(\mathbf{k}_0 + \delta\mathbf{k}) \cdot (\mathbf{r} - \mathbf{r}_0) - (\omega_0 + \delta\omega)t]\}$$
$$+ \exp\{i[(\mathbf{k}_0 - \delta\mathbf{k}) \cdot (\mathbf{r} - \mathbf{r}_0) - (\omega_0 - \delta\omega)t]\}$$
$$= 2 \exp\{i[\mathbf{k}_0 \cdot (\mathbf{r} - \mathbf{r}_0) - \omega_0 t]\} \cos[\delta\mathbf{k} \cdot (\mathbf{r} - \mathbf{r}_0) - \delta\omega t] \quad \text{(A3-9)}$$

This takes the form of a plane wave, $\exp\{i[\mathbf{k}_0 \cdot (\mathbf{r} - \mathbf{r}_0) - \omega_0 t]\}$, modulated by an amplitude function, $\cos[\delta\mathbf{k} \cdot (\mathbf{r} - \mathbf{r}_0) - \delta\omega t]$, which is a slowly varying function of position or of time, if $\delta\mathbf{k}$ and $\delta\omega$ are small. Let us find the velocity with which this modulating function moves along. We may, for instance, fix our attention on its maximum, which comes when the argument $\delta\mathbf{k} \cdot (\mathbf{r} - \mathbf{r}_0) - \delta\omega t = 0$, and consider the motion of this point, for short time intervals after $t = 0$, when the wave packet is located at r_0.

The angular frequency ω is functionally related to $\mathbf{k}$, through de Broglie's relation, as we have pointed out earlier. That is, we must have

$$\delta\omega = \frac{\partial\omega}{\partial k_x} \delta k_x + \frac{\partial\omega}{\partial k_y} \delta k_y + \frac{\partial\omega}{\partial k_z} \delta k_z \quad \text{(A3-10)}$$

Let us now take a point moving according to the relation

$$x = x_0 + \frac{\partial\omega}{\partial k_x} t \qquad y = y_0 + \frac{\partial\omega}{\partial k_y} t \qquad z = z_0 + \frac{\partial\omega}{\partial k_z} t \quad \text{(A3-11)}$$

For this point, the quantity

$$\delta\mathbf{k} \cdot (\mathbf{r} - \mathbf{r}_0) = \delta k_x(x - x_0) + \delta k_y(y - y_0) + \delta k_z(z - z_0) = (\delta\omega)t$$

when we use Eq. (A3-10).   Hence we see that $\delta\mathbf{k} \cdot (\mathbf{r} - \mathbf{r}_0) - (\delta\omega)t = 0$ for such a point, so that it moves with the maximum of the modulating function.   The velocity of this point, from Eq. (A3-11), has components

$$v_x = \frac{\partial\omega}{\partial k_x} \qquad v_y = \frac{\partial\omega}{\partial k_y} \qquad v_z = \frac{\partial\omega}{\partial k_z} \tag{A3-12}$$

independent of the value of δk, so long as it is small enough so that the linear approximation of Eq. (A3-10) is valid.   Hence, not only the pair of waves we have been considering but all the waves which are superposed to form the wave packet will produce an interference pattern which will travel along bodily with the velocity given by Eq. (A3-12).   This is the group velocity, as given in Eq. (2-2), when we write the energy E, or H, as $\hbar\omega$ and the momentum p as $\hbar k$ and cancel out $\hbar$ from numerator and denominator.

We have now shown the general form of the wave packet.   For further study, we may examine the motion of its center of gravity, as we do in Sec. 4-7, and as a result we show that its center of gravity moves according to the equations of motion of classical mechanics.   Let us do this, not for the simple Hamiltonian used in Sec. 4-7, but for a general Hamiltonian which merely is Hermitian.   In the many-dimensional case, it is in the first place very simple to extend the arguments of the preceding paragraphs so that we can form a wave packet in which each of the coordinates $x_1 \cdots x_n$ of the problem is limited to a finite region and each of the corresponding momenta is limited as closely as is consistent with the principle of uncertainty, so that we have a wave packet in the many-dimensional space.

We now wish to prove that Hamilton's equations hold for the center of gravity of the wave packet, that is, that

$$\left(\frac{dx}{dt}\right)_{av} = \left(\frac{\partial H}{\partial p}\right)_{av} \qquad \left(\frac{dp}{dt}\right)_{av} = -\left(\frac{\partial H}{\partial x}\right)_{av} \tag{A3-13}$$

where x is one of the coordinates and p its conjugate momentum.   For the first relation, we have

$$\left(\frac{dx}{dt}\right)_{av} = \int \left(\psi^* x \frac{\partial\psi}{\partial t} + \frac{\partial\psi^*}{\partial t} x\psi\right) dv \tag{A3-14}$$

in which we have written $(x)_{av} = \int\psi^* x\psi \, dv$ and have differentiated with respect to time, remembering that x is an independent operator, not involving the time directly.   We use Schrödinger's equation

$$(H)_{op}\psi = i\hbar\frac{\partial\psi}{\partial t} \qquad (H)_{op}^*\psi^* = -i\hbar\frac{\partial\psi^*}{\partial t}$$

and substitute in Eq. (A3-14). We then find

$$\left(\frac{dx}{dt}\right)_{\text{av}} = \frac{1}{i\hbar} \int [\psi^* x(H)_{\text{op}}\psi - \psi x(H)_{\text{op}}^*\psi^*]\, dv \qquad \text{(A3-15)}$$

Since the operators x and $(H)_{\text{op}}$ are both Hermitian and x is real, we can use Eq. (A7-9), applying it to the last term of Eq. (A3-15), and we find that

$$\int \psi x(H)_{\text{op}}^*\psi^*\, dv = \int \psi^*(H)_{\text{op}}x\psi\, dv \qquad \text{(A3-16)}$$

When we substitute this into Eq. (A3-15), that equation becomes

$$\left(\frac{dx}{dt}\right)_{\text{av}} = \frac{1}{i\hbar} \int \psi^*[x(H)_{\text{op}} - (H)_{\text{op}}x]\psi\, dv \qquad \text{(A3-17)}$$

This result could have been derived from Eq. (4-45), but we have preferred to give a very general proof, depending only on the Hermitian nature of $(H)_{\text{op}}$.

Now we must consider the commutator $x(H)_{\text{op}} - (H)_{\text{op}}x$. The most general form of $(H)_{\text{op}}$ which we shall meet can be written as a linear combination of terms, each of the form $f_1(x)p^{n_1}f_2(x)p^{n_2} \cdots$. Here we have not explicitly written the dependence on coordinates and momenta other than x and p, since x commutes with these other coordinates and momenta and we find no terms in the final result from this commutation. Let us now consider $xf_1(x)p^{n_1}f_2(x)p^{n_2} \cdots$. Since x commutes with $f_j(x)$, we first must consider xp^{n_1}. If this operates on a function u, we have

$$xp^{n_1}u = (-i\hbar)^{n_1}x\frac{\partial^{n_1}}{\partial x^{n_1}}u \qquad \text{(A3-18)}$$

On the other hand, we have

$$p^{n_1}(xu) = (-i\hbar)^{n_1}\frac{\partial^{n_1}}{\partial x^{n_1}}(xu) = (-i\hbar)^{n_1}\left(x\frac{\partial^{n_1}u}{\partial x^{n_1}} + n_1\frac{\partial^{n_1-1}u}{\partial x^{n_1-1}}\right) \qquad \text{(A3-19)}$$

Hence we have

$$(xp^{n_1} - p^{n_1}x)_{\text{op}}u = -n_1(-i\hbar)^{n_1}\frac{\partial^{n_1-1}}{\partial x^{n_1-1}}u$$
$$= i\hbar n_1(p^{n_1-1})_{\text{op}}u \qquad \text{(A3-20)}$$

Therefore we see that

$$[xf_1(x)p^{n_1}f_2(x)p^{n_2} \cdots]_{\text{op}} = [f_1(x)p^{n_1}xf_2(x)p^{n_2} \cdots]_{\text{op}}$$
$$+ i\hbar \left[f_1(x)\frac{\partial p^{n_1}}{\partial p}f_2(x)p^{n_2} \cdots\right]_{\text{op}} \qquad \text{(A3-21)}$$

We can now repeat this process, letting x pass beyond p^{n_2}, and adding another term similar to the last term of Eq. (A3-21). When we have continued this the whole way, so that x has appeared at the right side of the complete operator,

$$(F)_{op} = f_1(x) p^{n_1} f_2(x) p^{n_2} \cdots \tag{A3-22}$$

we find

$$x(F)_{op} - (F)_{op} x = i\hbar \left(\frac{\partial F}{\partial p} \right)_{op} \tag{A3-23}$$

This very general relationship holds, as we have shown, for any operator of the form given in Eq. (A3-22) or, obviously, for any linear combination of such operators. As we have mentioned, all Hermitian operators which we meet can be written in this form. We now substitute Eq. (A3-23) into Eq. (A3-17), and find at once that

$$\left(\frac{dx}{dt} \right)_{av} = \int \psi^* \frac{\partial H}{\partial p} \psi \, dv = \left(\frac{\partial H}{\partial p} \right)_{av} \tag{A3-24}$$

which was to be proved.

Hamilton's second equation, from Eq. (A3-13), is more easily proved. We start with $(p)_{av} = \int \psi^* (-i\hbar \, \partial/\partial x) \psi \, dv$ and differentiate with respect to time. We use Schrödinger's equation, as before, for $\partial \psi / \partial t$ and $\partial \psi^* / \partial t$. We then find

$$\left(\frac{dp}{dt} \right)_{av} = \int \left[-\psi^* \left(\frac{\partial H}{\partial x} \right)_{op} \psi - \psi^* (H)_{op} \frac{\partial \psi}{\partial x} + \frac{\partial \psi}{\partial x} (H)_{op}^* \psi^* \right] dv \tag{A3-25}$$

Since $(H)_{op}$ is Hermitian, we have

$$\int \psi^* (H)_{op} \frac{\partial \psi}{\partial x} \, dv = \int \frac{\partial \psi}{\partial x} (H)_{op}^* \psi^* \, dv \tag{A3-26}$$

When we substitute this in Eq. (A3-25), we have

$$\left(\frac{dp}{dt} \right)_{av} = - \int \psi^* \left(\frac{\partial H}{\partial x} \right)_{op} \psi \, dv = - \left(\frac{\partial H}{\partial x} \right)_{av} \tag{A3-27}$$

which was to be proved. Hence we have shown that the center of gravity of a wave packet or of any form of wave function moves according to Hamilton's equations, using any Hermitian Hamiltonian, and therefore including the cases of motion in an electromagnetic field and relativistic motion.

Appendix 4

Lagrangian and Hamiltonian Methods in Classical Mechanics

In classical Newtonian mechanics, Lagrange's and Hamilton's equations are commonly introduced to help in changing variables from rectangular coordinates to what are called generalized coordinates, of which simple examples would be ordinary curvilinear coordinates such as polar or spherical coordinates. We shall first show how these equations are derived in such a case. Let us start with rectangular coordinates $x_1 \cdots x_n$ and introduce n new coordinates, functions of the x's, by the equations

$$x_i = x_i(q_1 \cdots q_n) \qquad i = 1 \cdots n \tag{A4-1}$$

The rectangular velocity components are

$$\dot{x}_i = \sum (j) \frac{\partial x_i}{\partial q_j} \dot{q}_j \tag{A4-2}$$

If F_i is the component of force associated with the coordinate x_i, Newton's equations of motion can be written in the form

$$\frac{d}{dt}(m_i \dot{x}_i) = F_i \tag{A4-3}$$

where m_i is the mass associated with this coordinate. Our problem is to write equations equivalent to Eq. (A4-3) but expressed in terms of the generalized coordinates and their velocity components.

First we consider the kinetic energy, which we shall call T. When we express it in terms of rectangular coordinates, it is

$$T = \Sigma(i) \tfrac{1}{2} m_i \dot{x}_i^2 \tag{A4-4}$$

We note that the component of momentum associated with x_i, in rectangular coordinates, is $m_i \dot{x}_i$, which is equal to $\partial T / \partial \dot{x}_i$. We can introduce a corresponding definition of a generalized momentum associated with, or conjugate to, the generalized coordinate q_i. By using Eq. (A4-2) and substituting into Eq. (A4-4), we can express the kinetic energy as a quadratic function of the generalized velocity components $\dot{q}_j$, with coefficients arising from the partial derivatives $\partial x_i/\partial q_j$, which can be expressed as functions of the q's, by using the defining equations, Eq. (A4-1). Then we define the generalized momentum p_i conjugate to the generalized coordinate q_i as

$$p_i = \frac{\partial T}{\partial \dot{q}_i} \tag{A4-5}$$

where it is understood that T is to be expressed as a function of the q's and the $\dot{q}$'s, in the manner just described, and where these are treated as independent variables in carrying out the partial differentiation of Eq. (A4-5). Since T is a quadratic function of the velocity components $\dot{q}_i$, the generalized momenta p_i will be linear functions of the velocity components; it will not be true in general that p_i depends only on $\dot{q}_i$, but more generally p_i can be a linear combination of the $\dot{q}_j$'s.

Next we must introduce generalized force components, related to the generalized coordinates. The work done in a small displacement, dW, by the forces F_i is

$$dW = \Sigma(i)F_i\, dx_i \tag{A4-6}$$

We now express this in terms of the q's, as follows:

$$dW = \sum (ij)F_i \frac{\partial x_i}{\partial q_j}\, dq_j = \sum (j)Q_j\, dq_j$$

where $\qquad Q_j = \sum (i)F_i \frac{\partial x_i}{\partial q_j}$ $\qquad\qquad$ (A4-7)

where Q_j is the generalized force component associated with the generalized coordinate q_j.

We might now suppose that we should have an equation similar to $dp_i/dt = Q_i$, by analogy with the Newtonian equation, Eq. (A4-3). As a matter of fact, the true equation of motion is more complicated than this, but it is an obvious first step to compute dp_i/dt and see what it is equal to. We use Eq. (A4-2) and find

$$p_i = \frac{\partial T}{\partial \dot{q}_i} = \sum (j)m_j\dot{x}_j \frac{\partial \dot{x}_j}{\partial \dot{q}_i} = \sum (j)m_j\dot{x}_j \frac{\partial x_j}{\partial q_i}$$

$$\frac{dp_i}{dt} = \sum (j)\left(m_j\ddot{x}_j \frac{\partial x_i}{\partial q_i} + m_j\dot{x}_j \frac{d}{dt}\frac{\partial x_j}{\partial q_i}\right) \tag{A4-8}$$

Since $\partial x_j/\partial q_i$ is a function of the q's, which in turn are functions of time, we have

$$\frac{d}{dt}\frac{\partial x_j}{\partial q_i} = \sum (k)\frac{\partial^2 x_j}{\partial q_i\, \partial q_k}\, \dot{q}_k \tag{A4-9}$$

We substitute into Eq. (A4-8), use Eqs. (A4-3) and (A4-7), and find

$$\frac{dp_i}{dt} = Q_i + \sum (jk) m_j \dot{x}_j \frac{\partial^2 x_j}{\partial q_i \, \partial q_k} \dot{q}_k \qquad \text{(A4-10)}$$

The first term on the right side of Eq. (A4-10) would give $dp_i/dt = Q_i$, which we might have expected to be the equation of motion, but the second term remains. To put it in simpler form, let us compute $\partial T/\partial q_i$. This is

$$\frac{\partial T}{\partial q_i} = \sum (j) m_j \dot{x}_j \frac{\partial \dot{x}_j}{\partial q_i} = \sum (j) m_j \dot{x}_j \frac{\partial}{\partial q_i} \left[\sum (k) \frac{\partial x_j}{\partial q_k} \dot{q}_k \right] \qquad \text{(A4-11)}$$

where we have used Eq. (A4-2). But this is just the last term of Eq. (A4-10), so that we have

$$\frac{dp_i}{dt} = Q_i + \frac{\partial T}{\partial q_i} \qquad \text{(A4-12)}$$

which holds in consequence of Newton's law and hence is the generalization of the equation of motion that holds in generalized coordinates. The terms $\partial T/\partial q_i$ are fictitious forces that appear because of the curvature of the generalized coordinates. We see examples of them in Appendix 1, where we treat the motion of a particle in spherical coordinates by means of this method.

If there is a potential function V, then by definition the work done in a small displacement is $-dV$, so that by Eq. (A4-7) we have

$$Q_i = - \frac{\partial V}{\partial q_i} \qquad \text{(A4-13)}$$

We insert this value into Eq. (A4-12), write p_i in terms of Eq. (A4-5), and define a function

$$L = T - V \qquad \text{(A4-14)}$$

called the Lagrangian function, where T is a function of the coordinates q and velocity components $\dot{q}$ and V is a function of the q's. We then find as equations of motion

$$\frac{d}{dt} \left(\frac{\partial L}{\partial \dot{q}_i} \right) - \frac{\partial L}{\partial q_i} = 0 \qquad \text{(A4-15)}$$

In Eq. (A4-15) we have Lagrange's equations. We note that, in place of the definition of p_i given in Eq. (A4-5), we may use

$$p_i = \frac{\partial L}{\partial \dot{q}_i} \qquad \text{(A4-16)}$$

These equations, Eqs. (A4-15) and (A4-16), form the basis for the method of generalized coordinates in mechanics.

The next step in the formulation of the Hamiltonian method, which is an alternative procedure for setting up the equations of motion in generalized coordinates, is to define the Hamiltonian function H by the equation

$$H = \Sigma(i)p_i\dot{q}_i - L \tag{A4-17}$$

Here p_i is given in Eq. (A4-16), L in Eq. (A4-14). The function, as it is written, is a function of the generalized coordinates and the velocity components, $\dot{q}_i$. However, we express the velocity components in terms of the momenta by using Eq. (A4-16), which can be solved inversely for the $\dot{q}$'s as functions of the p's, and rewrite the function H in terms of the coordinates and the momenta. This is implied whenever we speak of the Hamiltonian function.

For the type of problem we have been considering, we can show that the Hamiltonian function is identical with the total energy. From Eqs. (A4-2) and (A4-4), the kinetic energy is

$$T = \tfrac{1}{2} \sum (ijk)m_i \frac{\partial x_i}{\partial q_j} \frac{\partial x_i}{\partial q_k} \dot{q}_j\dot{q}_k$$

a quadratic function of the velocity components. If we differentiate with respect to one of the velocity components to get the corresponding momentum, we note that we get terms both from differentiating the first factor $\dot{q}_j$, when j happens to equal the index in question, and also from differentiating the second $\dot{q}_k$, when k equals the index in question. Thus we have

$$\frac{\partial T}{\partial \dot{q}_s} = p_s = \sum (ij)m_i \frac{\partial x_i}{\partial q_j} \frac{\partial x_i}{\partial q_s} \dot{q}_j$$

We multiply by $\dot{q}_s$, sum over s, and have at once

$$\Sigma(s)p_s\dot{q}_s = 2T \tag{A4-18}$$

Thus we find

$$H = 2T - L = T + V \tag{A4-19}$$

or the Hamiltonian function equals the total energy, expressed as a function of coordinates and momenta.

Now that we have set up the Hamiltonian function, we shall compute $\partial H/\partial q_i$. We have

$$H = \Sigma(j)p_j\dot{q}_j(p_k,q_k) - L[\dot{q}_j(p_k,q_k),q_j]$$

in which we have indicated explicitly that the $\dot{q}$'s are to be expressed as functions of the p's and q's. Then we have

$$\frac{\partial H}{\partial q_i} = \sum (j)p_j\frac{\partial \dot{q}_j}{\partial q_i} - \sum (j)\frac{\partial L}{\partial \dot{q}_j}\frac{\partial \dot{q}_j}{\partial q_i} - \frac{\partial L}{\partial q_i}$$

By Eq. (A4-16), the first two terms cancel, so that by Eq. (A4-15) we have

$$\frac{dp_i}{dt} = -\frac{\partial H}{\partial q_i} \tag{A4-20}$$

We shall next compute $\partial H/\partial p_i$. We have

$$\frac{\partial H}{\partial p_i} = \dot{q}_i + \sum (j)p_j \frac{\partial \dot{q}_j}{\partial p_i} - \sum (j) \frac{\partial L}{\partial \dot{q}_j} \frac{\partial \dot{q}_j}{\partial p_i}$$

The last two terms cancel as a result of Eq. (A4-16), leaving

$$\frac{dq_i}{dt} = \frac{\partial H}{\partial p_i} \tag{A4-21}$$

Equations (A4-20) and (A4-21) are Hamilton's equations.

We have stated that the commonest use of Lagrangian and Hamiltonian methods in classical mechanics is to introduce curvilinear coordinates. Simple examples are found in the case of polar coordinates in a plane or spherical coordinates in three-dimensional space. For polar coordinates we have $x = r \cos \theta$, $y = r \sin \theta$. When we substitute into Eqs. (A4-2), (A4-4), etc., we have

$$L = \frac{m}{2} (\dot{r}^2 + r^2\dot{\theta}^2) - V$$

from which

$$p_r = m\dot{r} \qquad p_\theta = mr^2\dot{\theta} \qquad H = \frac{p_r^2}{2m} + \frac{p_\theta^2}{2mr^2} + V \tag{A4-22}$$

Hamilton's equations are

$$\frac{dp_r}{dt} = -\frac{\partial V}{\partial r} + \frac{p_\theta^2}{mr^3} \qquad \frac{dp_\theta}{dt} = -\frac{\partial V}{\partial \theta} \tag{A4-23}$$

Here p_r is the ordinary radial momentum and p_θ is the angular momentum. The term p_θ^2/mr^3, which is equal to $mr\dot{\theta}^2$, is the centrifugal force, that is, the fictitious outward force which must be included in the radial equation of motion, on account of the rotation. In a case where the torque, which is $-\partial V/\partial \theta$, is zero, the angular momentum remains constant.

In spherical coordinates, we have $x = r \sin \theta \cos \phi$, $y = r \sin \theta \sin \phi$, $z = r \cos \theta$, and we find

$$L = \frac{m}{2} (\dot{r}^2 + r^2\dot{\theta}^2 + r^2 \sin^2 \theta \, \dot{\phi}^2) - V$$

$$p_r = m\dot{r} \qquad p_\theta = mr^2\dot{\theta} \qquad p_\phi = mr^2 \sin^2 \theta \, \dot{\phi} \tag{A4-24}$$

$$H = \frac{p_r^2}{2m} + \frac{p_\theta^2}{2mr^2} + \frac{p_\phi^2}{2mr^2 \sin^2 \theta} + V$$

We discuss this case in Appendix 1, in connection with the Bohr theory of the hydrogen atom.

These applications of the Hamiltonian method to curvilinear coordinates are not, as a matter of fact, useful in wave mechanics. In Eq. (3-8) we have given a rule for converting a classical Hamiltonian into a wave-mechanical operator. We might suppose that this could be done directly in curvilinear coordinates, but as a matter of fact it cannot. We can see why this is the case from the example of spherical coordinates, which we have just mentioned. The kinetic-energy operator in spherical coordinates is

$$- \frac{\hbar^2}{2m} \left[\frac{1}{r^2} \frac{\partial}{\partial r} \left(r^2 \frac{\partial}{\partial r} \right) + \frac{1}{r^2 \sin \theta} \frac{\partial}{\partial \theta} \left(\sin \theta \frac{\partial}{\partial \theta} \right) + \frac{1}{r^2 \sin^2 \theta} \frac{\partial^2}{\partial \phi^2} \right] \quad (A4\text{-}25)$$

If we wish to use Eq. (3-8), stating that to set up the Hamiltonian operator we replace each p_j by $-i\hbar\, \partial/\partial q_j$, we should suppose that this method could be used in curvilinear coordinates as well as in rectangular coordinates. But the Hamiltonian which would lead to the operator of Eq. (A4-25) would be

$$H = \frac{1}{2m} \left(\frac{1}{r^2} p_r r^2 p_r + \frac{1}{r^2 \sin \theta} p_\theta \sin \theta\, p_\theta + \frac{1}{r^2 \sin^2 \theta} p_\phi^2 \right) \quad (A4\text{-}26)$$

In classical mechanics, where we can interchange the order of momenta and coordinates, this is identical with the kinetic-energy part of the Hamiltonian of Eq. (A4-24). But in the wave-mechanical case the order of terms, as given in Eq. (A4-26), is essential, and this cannot be predicted in the inverse direction from the classical Hamiltonian of Eq. (A4-24). Hence we cannot use these classical Hamiltonians as the starting point for setting up a Hamiltonian operator in wave mechanics. The case of rectangular coordinates is exceptional: there no ambiguity arises, and it is for this reason that in wave mechanics one always starts in rectangular coordinates, sets up Schrödinger's equation in those coordinates, and then if necessary makes a change of variables in Schrödinger's equation, as in Appendix 13.

The cases in which the complete Hamiltonian method is particularly necessary in wave mechanics are problems of quite a different sort: problems in which we have external electromagnetic fields, or problems of relativistic dynamics, in which the derivation as we have carried it out is not applicable. In these cases, we do not have the expression of Eq. (A4-4) for the kinetic energy and cannot use the derivation of Lagrange's equations which we have given. Nevertheless, in each of these cases, it is possible to set up a Lagrangian such that Lagrange's equations give the correct equations of motion. For a particle of charge e, mass m, in an external electric field E, and a magnetic induction B, expressed in terms of a scalar potential ϕ and a vector potential $\mathbf{A}$ by the equation

$$E = -\nabla\phi - \dot{\mathbf{A}} \qquad \mathbf{B} = \nabla \times \mathbf{A}$$

we can use a Lagrangian function

$$L = \frac{mv^2}{2} + e(\mathbf{v} \cdot \mathbf{A}) - e\phi \tag{A4-27}$$

where $\mathbf{v}$ is the velocity of the particle. This leads to the correct equations of motion for the particle, in the presence of the electric and magnetic forces. Let us see why this is the case.

First, we notice that when we find the momentum components from Eq. (A4-27), using Eq. (A4-16), we find

$$p_x = m\dot{x} + eA_x \tag{A4-28}$$

with corresponding equations for the y and z components. We then find that Lagrange's equations are

$$\frac{d}{dt}(m\dot{x} + eA_x) = e\left(\dot{x}\frac{\partial A_x}{\partial x} + \dot{y}\frac{\partial A_y}{\partial x} + \dot{z}\frac{\partial A_z}{\partial x}\right) - e\frac{\partial\phi}{\partial x} \tag{A4-29}$$

and corresponding equations for the y and z components. The quantity A_x is the value of the vector potential at the position of the particle. Consequently we have

$$\frac{dA_x}{dt} = \frac{\partial A_x}{\partial t} + \frac{\partial A_x}{\partial x}\dot{x} + \frac{\partial A_x}{\partial y}\dot{y} + \frac{\partial A_x}{\partial z}\dot{z} \tag{A4-30}$$

When we insert Eq. (A4-30) into Eq. (A4-29) and take account of the definitions of the electric and magnetic fields, we find

$$\frac{d}{dt}(m\dot{x}) = e[E_x + (\mathbf{v} \times \mathbf{B})_x] \tag{A4-31}$$

This is the correct equation of motion for a particle of mass m, under the action of the electric force $e\mathbf{E}$ and the magnetic force $e(\mathbf{v} \times \mathbf{B})$, which are the ordinary Lorentz expressions for the forces on a charged particle moving with velocity $\mathbf{v}$, whose components are $\dot{x}$, $\dot{y}$, $\dot{z}$.

In other words, the Lagrangian of Eq. (A4-27) correctly describes the motion of a charged particle; and yet it is not of the form considered in our derivation of Lagrange's equations. For it is not obvious whether the term $e(\mathbf{v} \cdot \mathbf{A})$ in Eq. (A4-27) should be regarded as kinetic energy, potential energy, or neither. Quite aside from this fact, however, Eqs. (A4-15) and (A4-16) hold in this case, as we have demonstrated above. Now, if we examine the derivation of the Hamiltonian equations, Eqs. (A4-17), (A4-20), and (A4-21), we see that they rest only on Eqs. (A4-15) and (A4-16), and not on any of the preliminary discussion leading up to Lagrange's equations. Hence, in such a case as this, the Hamiltonian function is still given by Eq. (A4-17), and Hamilton's equations still hold. When we use the expressions of Eq. (A4-28) for the momenta, Eq. (A4-27) for the Lagrangian, and set up the Hamiltonian according to the prescription of Eq. (A4-17), we find that

$$H = \frac{(p - eA)^2}{2m} + e\phi \qquad (A4\text{-}32)$$

Hamilton's equations, using this Hamiltonian, lead to the same equations of motion, Eq. (A4-31), which we have derived from Lagrange's equations. It is this Hamiltonian of Eq. (A4-32) which we have used, in the many-electron case, in Eq. (6-27), as the basis of our study of the interaction of atomic systems and a radiation field. It is clear that in such a case we need the complete Lagrangian and Hamiltonian formalism, as discussed in this appendix, in order to handle the problem.

In the case of a relativistic particle moving in the same electromagnetic field as before, we find that we can use the Lagrangian

$$L = -m_0 c^2 \sqrt{1 - v^2/c^2} + e(\mathbf{v} \cdot \mathbf{A}) - e\phi \qquad (A4\text{-}33)$$

Here m_0 is the rest mass of the particle, c is the velocity of light. We then find that

$$p_x = \frac{m_0 \dot{x}}{\sqrt{1 - v^2/c^2}} + eA_x \qquad (A4\text{-}34)$$

differing from Eq. (A4-28), the corresponding classical expression, by the replacement of the mass m by the relativistic mass $m_0(1 - v^2/c^2)^{-\frac{1}{2}}$. The equation of motion, arising from Lagrange's equations, is

$$\frac{d}{dt} \left(\frac{m_0 \dot{x}}{\sqrt{1 - v^2/c^2}} \right) = e[E_x + (\mathbf{v} \times \mathbf{B})_x] \qquad (A4\text{-}35)$$

This equation of motion, involving the relativistic momentum rather than the Newtonian value, is the correct equation of motion of the particle according to relativistic mechanics, so that we have demonstrated in this case as well that we can use Lagrange's equations, though the Lagrangian of Eq. (A4-33) is not at all in the same form as the classical value.

Now, as before, we can use Eq. (A4-17) to derive the Hamiltonian. We find that

$$H = \sqrt{m_0^2 c^4 + (p - eA)^2 c^2} + e\phi \qquad (A4\text{-}36)$$

a Hamiltonian such that Hamilton's equations will lead to the same equation of motion given in Eq. (A4-35). This, then, is to be used as the basis of the wave-mechanical treatment of a relativistic particle in the presence of an electromagnetic field, and it is identical with Eq. (23-11), which we have used for this purpose, when we recall that Eq. (23-11) is written for an electron of charge $-e$, while e in Eq. (A4-36) stands for the charge of the particle.

Appendix 5
The WKB Method

In setting up the solution of Eq. (3-47) of Schrödinger's equation according to the WKB method, it seems almost intuitive that the sinusoidal function should be as written there. Let us then assume that $u = f(x) \sin [(1/\hbar)\int p \, dx + \alpha]$, where $f(x)$ is an amplitude function to be determined, and substitute this into Schrödinger's equation, which we can write in the form

$$\frac{d^2u}{dx^2} + \frac{p^2}{\hbar^2} u = 0 \tag{A5-1}$$

to see what differential equation f would have to satisfy. We remember, of course, that p is a function of x. When we carry out the differentiation and make the substitution, we find that the term $(p^2/\hbar^2)u$ is canceled, and the remaining part of the differential equation proves to be

$$\frac{d^2f}{dx^2} \sin \left(\frac{1}{\hbar} \int p \, dx + \alpha \right) + \left(2p \frac{df}{dx} + f \frac{dp}{dx} \right) \left(\frac{1}{\hbar} \right) \cos \left(\frac{1}{\hbar} \int p \, dx + \alpha \right) = 0 \tag{A5-2}$$

We shall now show that the first term can be neglected compared with the second, provided p varies slowly enough with position. Consider the comparison of the quantity d^2f/dx^2 occurring in the first term with the quantity $(p/\hbar) \, df/dx$ occurring in the second. The ratio of the first to the second is

$$\frac{\hbar}{p} \frac{d}{dx} \ln \frac{df}{dx} \tag{A5-3}$$

Since h/p is a wavelength, this is the proportional change in df/dx in $(2\pi)^{-1}$ wavelengths. If p varies by only a small fraction of itself in a wavelength, we may reasonably assume that the same thing will be true of df/dx (and we can verify this as soon as we get a solution for f in terms of p). Thus the ratio of these two terms will be small, and the first can be neglected compared with the second.

We are then justified in setting only the second term equal to zero,

420

which leads to the differential equation

$$2p \frac{df}{dx} + f \frac{dp}{dx} = 0 \qquad d \ln f = -\frac{1}{2} d \ln p$$
$$\ln f = -\frac{1}{2} \ln p + \text{constant} \qquad \text{(A5-4)}$$
$$f = \text{constant} \times p^{-\frac{1}{2}}$$

agreeing with the solution of Eq. (3-47). Once we see that this expresses the relation between f and p, we can find df/dx and its variation in a wavelength and verify that this is in fact small if the fractional variation of p in a wavelength is small. We also see that the term $f\, dp/dx$ is numerically equal to $2p\, df/dx$, but of opposite sign, so that, in proving that the term in d^2f/dx^2 is small compared with the term in $2p\, df/dx$, we have also shown that it is small compared with the term in $f\, dp/dx$. We thus justify the correctness of our solution.

Appendix 6

Properties of the Solution of the Linear-oscillator Problem

In Sec. 3-7 we have shown that the wave function u_n of the linear-oscillator problem can be written in the form $\exp{(-y^2/2)}v$, where $y = 2\pi \sqrt{m\nu/h}\, x$, and where v is a polynomial in y, of the form $A_0 + A_1 y + A_2 y^2 + \cdots$, where the coefficients are related by the recursion formula of Eq. (3-56). If we write this recursion formula for the nth state, whose energy is $(n + \frac{1}{2})h\nu$, it is

$$(k + 2)(k + 1)A_{k+2} + 2(n - k)A_k = 0 \qquad (A6\text{-}1)$$

For even n, we have only even terms in the polynomial and for odd n only odd terms.

It is now customary to denote these polynomials, when written in a suitable way, as Hermite polynomials, $H_n(y)$. These are defined as

$$H_n(y) = (2y)^n - \frac{n(n - 1)}{1!}(2y)^{n-2} + \frac{n(n - 1)(n - 2)(n - 3)}{2!}(2y)^{n-4}$$

$$- \cdots + (-1)^{(n-m)/2}\frac{n(n - 1)\,\cdots\,(m + 2)(m + 1)}{[(n - m)/2]!}(2y)^m$$

$$+ \cdots \qquad (A6\text{-}2)$$

When we substitute

$$A_k = (-1)^{(n-k)/2}\frac{n(n - 1)\,\cdots\,(k + 2)(k + 1)}{[(n - k)/2]!}2^k \qquad (A6\text{-}3)$$

from Eq. (A6-2) into the recursion formula of Eq. (A6-1), we find that it is satisfied, so that $\exp{(-y^2/2)}H_n(y)$ forms a solution of the linear-oscillator problem, though it is not normalized.

We wish to determine the normalization constant of these functions and to find the matrix components of the operator x between the various eigenfunctions, to use in Sec. 4-6. This is most conveniently done by writing H_n in the form

$$H_n(y) = (-1)^n \exp{(y^2)}\frac{d^n \exp{(-y^2)}}{dy^n} \qquad (A6\text{-}4)$$

We shall next prove this relation. We can prove that

$$\frac{d^{n+2}\exp(-y^2)}{dy^{n+2}} = -2y\frac{d^{n+1}\exp(-y^2)}{dy^{n+1}} - 2(n+1)\frac{d^n\exp(-y^2)}{dy^n} \quad (A6-5)$$

To do so, we proceed by induction. We assume that it is true for a given value of n, then differentiate again with respect to y, and show that it then must be true if n is greater by unity. We can prove immediately that it holds for $n = 0$, and hence it holds for all values of n. But now from Eq. (A6-4) we have

$$(-1)^n\frac{d^n\exp(-y^2)}{dy^n} = \exp(-y^2)H_n(y) \quad (A6-6)$$

where $H_n(y)$ is being defined by Eq. (A6-4). We differentiate Eq. (A6-6) and have

$$(-1)^n\frac{d^{n+1}\exp(-y^2)}{dy^{n+1}} = \exp(-y^2)\left(\frac{dH_n}{dy} - 2yH_n\right)$$
$$(-1)^n\frac{d^{n+2}\exp(-y^2)}{dy^{n+2}} = \exp(-y^2)\left[\frac{d^2H_n}{dy^2} - 4y\frac{dH_n}{dy} + (4y^2 - 2)H_n\right]$$
$$(A6-7)$$

When we substitute these expressions into Eq. (A6-5), we find that H_n satisfies Eq. (3-55), so that it is the solution of the problem. To prove the identification of H_n from Eq. (A6-4) with the series of Eq. (A6-2), we need only check the coefficient of the first term of the series; the other coefficients will all follow from the recursion relation which must hold. This is easily done: in Eq. (A6-4), each time we differentiate $\exp(-y^2)$ we multiply by $-2y$, and it is the product of n such terms which appears in the first term of Eq. (A6-2), verifying the coefficient of that term.

Next we consider the normalization. We define the normalized function as $N_n\exp(-y^2/2)H_n(y)$, where N_n is a normalization constant to be determined. If this function is denoted as u_n, we have

$$\int_{-\infty}^{\infty} u_n^2\, dx = \frac{1}{2\pi}\sqrt{\frac{h}{m\nu}}N_n^2\int_{-\infty}^{\infty}\exp(-y^2)H_n^2(y)\, dy$$
$$= \frac{1}{2\pi}\sqrt{\frac{h}{m\nu}}N_n^2(-1)^n\int_{-\infty}^{\infty}\frac{d^n\exp(-y^2)}{dy^n}H_n(y)\, dy \quad (A6-8)$$

We now integrate by parts repeatedly. The integrated terms drop out at the limits, and we are left with

$$\int_{-\infty}^{\infty} u_n^2\, dx = \frac{1}{2\pi}\sqrt{\frac{h}{m\nu}}N_n^2\int_{-\infty}^{\infty}\exp(-y^2)\frac{d^nH_n(y)}{dy^n}\, dy \quad (A6-9)$$

From the expansion of $H_n(y)$ given in Eq. (A6-2), we see that

$$\frac{d^n H_n}{dy^n} = 2^n n!$$

Thus we have

$$\int_{-\infty}^{\infty} u_n^2 \, dx = \frac{1}{2\pi} \sqrt{\frac{h}{m\nu}} N_n^2 2^n n! \sqrt{\pi} \tag{A6-10}$$

But for a normalized function this must equal 1, so that we find that

$$N_n = \left(\frac{\pi m\nu}{h}\right)^{\frac{1}{4}} (2^{n-1}n!)^{-\frac{1}{2}}$$

$$u_n = \left(\frac{\pi m\nu}{h}\right)^{\frac{1}{4}} (2^{n-1}n!)^{-\frac{1}{2}} \exp \frac{-y^2}{2} H_n(y) \tag{A6-11}$$

The orthogonality of the u_n's can of course be proved by the general theorem giving orthogonality of eigenfunctions of Schrödinger's equation, though it can also be proved directly.

Next we consider the matrix components of x. Let us find the matrix component $x_{n,n'}$. This can be rewritten in the form

$$x_{n,n'} = \int_{-\infty}^{\infty} x u_n(y) u_{n'}(y) \, dx$$

$$= \frac{h}{4\pi^2 m\nu} \int_{-\infty}^{\infty} y u_n(y) u_{n'}(y) \, dy \tag{A6-12}$$

We take the case where $n < n'$. Then $y u_n(y)$ will equal $\exp(-y^2/2)$ times a polynomial whose highest term is in y^{n+1}. This polynomial can be written as a linear combination of H_{n+1}, H_n, H_{n-1}, ... , H_0. That is, $y u_n(y)$ can be written as a linear combination of u_{n+1}, u_n, u_{n-1}, ... If $u_{n'}$ corresponds to n' greater than $n + 1$, the orthogonality properties of the u's will result in the integral of Eq. (A6-12) vanishing. The only nonvanishing matrix component for $n < n'$ is then that for which $n' = n + 1$. Let us take that case.

To carry out the argument sketched above, we must know the coefficient of H_{n+1} in the expansion of $y u_n(y)$. From Eq. (A6-2), the first term in $y H_n(y)$ is $2^n y^{n+1}$, which is one-half the first term in $H_{n+1}(y)$. Thus we have

$$y H_n = \frac{1}{2} H_{n+1} + \text{terms in } H_n, H_{n-1}, \ldots \tag{A6-13}$$

These other terms all integrate to zero when multiplied by $u_{n+1}(y)$, on account of orthogonality. Hence, when we substitute from Eq. (A6-11), we are left with

$$x_{n,n+1} = \frac{h}{4\pi^2 m\nu} \left(\frac{\pi m\nu}{h}\right)^{\frac{1}{2}} (2^{n-1}n!)^{-\frac{1}{2}}[2^n(n+1)!]^{-\frac{1}{2}}$$

$$\frac{1}{2} \int_{-\infty}^{\infty} \exp(-y^2) H_{n+1}^2(y) \, dy \tag{A6-14}$$

From the derivation of Eq. (A6-10) we find that

$$\int_{-\infty}^{\infty} \exp\left(-y^2\right) H_{n+1}^2(y)\, dy = 2^{n+1}(n+1)!\,\sqrt{\pi} \qquad \text{(A6-15)}$$

When we substitute this in Eq. (A6-14) and combine terms, we find

$$x_{n,n+1} = \sqrt{\frac{h(n+1)}{8\pi^2 m\nu}} \qquad \text{(A6-16)}$$

in agreement with Eq. (4-46). We can proceed similarly and show that $x_{n+1,n} = x_{n,n+1}$, and furthermore $x_{n+1,n}$ is the only nonvanishing component for which $n' < n$.

Appendix 7

The Hermitian Character of Matrices

We have given two definitions of the Hermitian character of operators or of the matrices derived from them. In Eq. (4-11), we have stated that an operator $(F)_{op}$ is Hermitian provided we have

$$\int u_n^*(F)_{op} u_m \, dv = \int u_m (F)_{op}^* u_n^* \, dv \qquad (A7-1)$$

In Eq. (4-31), we have stated that a matrix F_{nm} is Hermitian provided

$$F_{mn}^* = F_{nm} \qquad (A7-2)$$

The second statement follows obviously from the first; the left side of Eq. (A7-1) expresses F_{nm}, according to the standard definition, and the right side is the complex conjugate of F_{mn}.

First we shall prove that the ordinary operators which we habitually meet are Hermitian. For a function of the coordinates only, such as the potential energy or the displacement x, it is obvious. The interchange of the order of operations in Eq. (A7-1) is immaterial for such an operator, and since we are interested only in real functions of coordinates, $(F)_{op} = (F)_{op}^*$. The other operators which we generally meet are the momentum and the kinetic energy, which is proportional to the square of the momentum. We can include both these cases if we prove that the operator p^k is Hermitian. We shall prove this for a one-dimensional problem; if our problem is really many-dimensional, the extension is made in an obvious way.

We have

$$(p^k)_{nm} = \int u_n^* \left(-i\hbar \frac{\partial}{\partial x} \right)^k u_m \, dx \qquad (A7-3)$$

We integrate Eq. (A7-3) by parts repeatedly. With each integration, the integrated terms vanish, if we assume that the u's and their derivatives vanish sufficiently strongly at the limits of integration. With each integration, we transfer one differentiation $\partial/\partial x$ to a differentiation of u_n^* rather than of u_m, and we introduce a minus sign. Then, after the k

integrations by parts, we find that

$$(p^k)_{nm} = (-1)^k \int \left[\left(-i\hbar \frac{\partial}{\partial x} \right)^k u_n^* \right] u_m \, dx \qquad \text{(A7-4)}$$

in which the differentiations apply only to u_n^*. This can be rewritten in the form

$$(p^k)_{nm} = \int u_m \left(i\hbar \frac{\partial}{\partial x} \right)^k u_n^* \, dx = (p^k)_{mn}^* \qquad \text{(A7-5)}$$

as was to be proved.

In the electromagnetic and relativistic Hamiltonians we meet more complicated cases than these, for example the term $\mathbf{p} \cdot \mathbf{A}$, where $\mathbf{A}$ is the vector potential, which we find in the presence of a magnetic field. Here we have an operator which is the product of a function of momenta and a function of coordinates. Let us examine more generally the behavior of an operator which can be written as the product of two operators each of which is Hermitian. Thus, let $(F)_{op}$ and $(G)_{op}$ both satisfy conditions like Eq. (A7-1), and let us inquire about the relations satisfied by the product operator, $(F)_{op}(G)_{op}$. We have

$$\int u_n^*(F)_{op}(G)_{op}u_m \, dv = \int [(G)_{op}u_m](F)_{op}^* u_n^* \, dv \qquad \text{(A7-6)}$$

in which we have used a relation like Eq. (A7-1) and the place of u_m is taken by $(G)_{op}u_m$; we note that, if $(F)_{op}$ is Hermitian, Eq. (A7-1) will hold for any functions u_n^* and u_m satisfying the proper behavior at the limits of integration. In Eq. (A7-6), the operator $(G)_{op}$ is to operate only on u_m. We may then replace this equation by

$$\int [(G)_{op}u_m](F)_{op}^* u_n^* \, dv = \int [(F)_{op}^* u_n^*][(G)_{op}u_m] \, dv \qquad \text{(A7-7)}$$

where it is understood that $(F)_{op}^*$ operates only on u_n^*. Now we can use Eq. (A7-1) again and find

$$\int [(F)_{op}^* u_n^*][(G)_{op}u_m \, dv] = \int u_m(G)_{op}^*(F)_{op}^* u_n^* \, dv \qquad \text{(A7-8)}$$

Thus finally we find that

$$\int u_n^*(F)_{op}(G)_{op}u_m \, dv = \int u_m(G)_{op}^*(F)_{op}^* u_n^* \, dv \qquad \text{(A7-9)}$$

where $(F)_{op}$ and $(G)_{op}$ are Hermitian.

If the operators $(F)_{op}$ and $(G)_{op}$ do not commute with each other, the right side of Eq. (A7-9) will not equal $\int u_m(F)_{op}^*(G)_{op}^* u_n^* \, dv$, which it must do if the operator $(F)_{op}(G)_{op}$ is to be Hermitian. In our special case of the operator $\mathbf{p} \cdot \mathbf{A}$, which we encountered in the electromagnetic theory, these operators $\mathbf{p}$ and $\mathbf{A}$ do commute with each other, provided we choose the vector potential so that $\nabla \cdot \mathbf{A} = 0$, which we are free to do, and which we discuss in Appendix 12. In general, we must be on our guard against constructing operators by multiplying functions of coordinates by functions of momenta, or more generally by multiplying noncommuting operators. We note from the derivation of the preceding paragraph that an operator $(F)_{op}(G)_{op} + (G)_{op}(F)_{op}$ will always be Hermitian, provided $(F)_{op}$ and $(G)_{op}$ are Hermitian. We must carry out an investigation, according to the principles just described, to find whether any given complicated operator is Hermitian or not; we find, however, that the relativistic Hamiltonian, including the electromagnetic term, is Hermitian, so that we do not run into trouble in the cases which we are dealing with in this volume.

Appendix 8

Solution of a Cubic Secular Equation

Let us have a secular equation

$$\begin{vmatrix} H_{11} - E & H_{12} & H_{13} \\ H_{21} & H_{22} - E & H_{23} \\ H_{31} & H_{32} & H_{33} - E \end{vmatrix} = 0 \qquad \text{(A8-1)}$$

We shall assume that the matrix components of H are all real; since $(H)_{op}$ is Hermitian, this implies that $H_{12} = H_{21}$, etc. We furthermore choose the zero of energy so that the diagonal sum $H_{11} + H_{22} + H_{33} = 0$. This amounts to removing the quadratic term in the cubic secular equation, which is the first step in the solution of the cubic.

Then the standard formula for the solution of a cubic equation results in the following values for the energy:

$$E = 2(3)^{-1/2}(H_{12}^2 + H_{23}^2 + H_{31}^2 - H_{11}H_{22} - H_{22}H_{33}$$
$$- H_{33}H_{11})^{1/2} \cos \frac{\phi + 2\pi n}{3} \qquad \text{(A8-2)}$$

where $n = 0, 1, 2$, and where

$$\cos \phi = \tfrac{1}{2}(3)^{3/2} \begin{vmatrix} H_{11} & H_{12} & H_{13} \\ H_{21} & H_{22} & H_{23} \\ H_{31} & H_{32} & H_{33} \end{vmatrix}$$
$$\times (H_{12}^2 + H_{23}^2 + H_{31}^2 - H_{11}H_{22} - H_{22}H_{33} - H_{33}H_{11})^{-3/2} \qquad \text{(A8-3)}$$

This solution can be verified by writing the three roots as E_1, E_2, E_3 and expanding the quantity $(E - E_1)(E - E_2)(E - E_3)$. This will prove to be the negative of the determinant of Eq. (A8-1), as it should be if we have the correct solutions.

Appendix 9

Orthogonality of Solutions of a Secular Problem

We assume that we are building up wave functions u_m as linear combinations of M orthonormal unperturbed functions u_k^0, according to Eq. (5-10), which is

$$u_m = \Sigma(k)C_{km}u_k^0 \tag{A9-1}$$

The coefficients C_{km} which make the energy stationary will be given by Eq. (5-12), which is

$$\Sigma(k)C_{km}(H_{nk}^0 - E_m\delta_{nk}) = 0 \tag{A9-2}$$

where the matrix H_{nk}^0 of the Hamiltonian is Hermitian. We wish to prove that the u_m's are orthogonal to each other. If this is the case, we shall have

$$\int u_p^* u_q \, dv = \Sigma(kl)C_{kp}^* C_{lq}\int u_k^{0*}u_l^0 \, dv$$
$$= \Sigma(k)C_{kp}^* C_{kq} \tag{A9-3}$$

where the last step follows from the orthogonality of the u^0's. We must therefore prove Eq. (A9-3).

We rewrite Eq. (A9-2), using different indices, in the form

$$\Sigma(s)C_{sq}(H_{ks}^0 - E_q\delta_{ks}) = 0 \tag{A9-4}$$

multiply by C_{kp}^*, and sum over k. We then have

$$\Sigma(k,s)C_{kp}^* C_{sq}H_{ks}^0 = E_q\Sigma(k)C_{kp}^* C_{kq} \tag{A9-5}$$

Again, we rewrite the complex conjugate of Eq. (A9-2) in the form

$$\Sigma(k)C_{kp}^*(H_{sk}^{0*} - E_p\delta_{sk}) = 0 \tag{A9-6}$$

multiply by C_{sq}, and sum over s. We then have

$$\Sigma(k,s)C_{kp}^* C_{sq}H_{sk}^{0*} = E_p\Sigma(k)C_{kp}^* C_{kq} \tag{A9-7}$$

Since H^0 is Hermitian, we have $H_{sk}^{0*} = H_{ks}^0$, so that the summation on the left side of Eq. (A9-7) equals that on the left side of Eq. (A9-5). We may then equate the right sides of these two equations, and we find

$$(E_p - E_q)\Sigma(k)C_{kp}^*C_{kq} = 0 \tag{A9-8}$$

As in the proof of the orthogonality of solutions of Schrödinger's equation, Eq. (A9-8) tells us that, if states p and q are not degenerate, the wave functions are orthogonal. If they are degenerate, we can make linear combinations of the functions to bring about orthogonality.

Appendix 10

The Correspondence Principle

The correspondence principle was a method suggested by Bohr[1] before the development of wave mechanics, for estimating the intensities of quantum transitions by correlating them with the amplitudes of Fourier components in the Fourier analysis of classical periodic motions. As a preliminary to studying or even stating it, we must consider the periodicity properties of motion in classical mechanics. This is best done by treating the motion in the phase space, in which we have as variables all the coordinates and all the momenta of the problem. A single point in this phase space, called the representative point, gives complete information about the instantaneous behavior of the system, and the motion of the representative point tells us how the system changes with time. Hamilton's equations, $dq_i/dt = \partial H/\partial p_i$, $dp_i/dt = -\partial H/\partial q_i$, give us the time rates of change of each of the variables in the phase space. We have met the phase space already in Sec. 1-8, where we discussed the problem of the linear oscillator.

We first notice that, if the Hamiltonian does not involve the time explicitly, we shall have conservation of energy, or H remains constant. To see this, we have

$$\frac{dH}{dt} = \sum (i) \left(\frac{\partial H}{\partial q_i} \frac{dq_i}{dt} + \frac{\partial H}{\partial p_i} \frac{dp_i}{dt} \right)$$

which vanishes on account of Hamilton's equations. Hence the path of the representative point, in such a case, which is the only one that we consider, must lie on what is called the energy surface, that is, the locus of points on which $H = E$, where H is the Hamiltonian function, a function of the q_i's and p_i's, while E, the energy, is constant. If there are n variables and $2n$ q's and p's, this single equation will determine a $(2n - 1)$-dimensional manifold, which is what is called the energy surface.

In a one-dimensional problem, $2n - 1 = 1$, and the energy surface

[1] N. Bohr, "The Theory of Spectra and Atomic Constitution," Cambridge University Press, New York, 1922.

degenerates to a curve in the phase space. For instance, for the linear oscillator we have seen in Fig. 1-2 that this curve is an ellipse. If the curve is closed, which it will be if the motion does not go to infinity, the motion then must be periodic. Hamilton's equations predict the velocity of the representative point at each point of the curve $H = E$, so that it takes a definite time for the point to move once around the path, and once it does this it proceeds to do it again and again, exactly repeating its motion each time.

If we have more than one coordinate in our problem, however, we no longer have any requirement that the motion be periodic. In some cases it is true that we have periodic motions, even in two or three dimensions. Thus the motion of a particle under the action of an inverse-square field is periodic, as we showed in Appendix 1. Let us consider this case further, using polar coordinates r, θ in a plane, as we did for most of our discussion in Appendix 1. We know that the angular momentum stays constant, as well as the energy. The angular momentum, like the energy, is a function of the q's and p's; thus the representative point, instead of being able to reach every point of the three-dimensional $(2n - 1 = 3$, if $n = 2)$ energy surface, can reach only every point of a two-dimensional region determined simultaneously by the two equations, energy = constant, angular momentum = constant.

We can go further than this, however. We can take advantage of the constancy of the angular momentum and set up an equation for the radial motion only, as we did in Eq. (A4-23), where we set p_θ = constant. Hence the motion of r is periodic, like a one-dimensional motion. Then we can expand r, like any one-dimensional periodic motion, in a Fourier series in the time:

$$r = \Sigma(k)A_k \exp(ik\omega t) \qquad \text{(A10-1)}$$

where ω is the angular frequency. We then use the relation $p_\theta = mr^2\dot{\theta}$, from Eq. (A4-23), where p_θ is the constant angular momentum, and note that $\dot{\theta} = p_\theta/mr^2$. Since r is periodic in time with angular frequency ω, the same must be true of p_θ/mr^2. We integrate with respect to time and find that θ similarly is periodic with the same angular frequency, aside from a term proportional to the time, coming from the integration of the constant term in $\dot{\theta}$ [that is, the term arising from A_0 in Eq. (A10-1)]. If we denote this term proportional to time by $\omega_0 t$, we then have

$$\theta = \omega_0 t + \Sigma(k)B_k \exp(ik\omega t) \qquad \text{(A10-2)}$$

We now investigate the x and y coordinates and their time dependence; Bohr assumed in the correspondence principle that it was the Fourier expansion of the electric dipole moment which determined the radiation, just as we have found in wave mechanics in Chap. 6. We examine

$x + iy = r \exp (i\theta)$. We know that r is periodic with angular frequency ω, and so is the last term of θ. If we take $\exp [i\Sigma(k)B_k \exp (ik\omega t)]$, since the quantity whose exponential is taken is periodic with this same frequency, the same must be true of the exponential. Thus finally we can expand $x + iy$ in the form

$$x + iy = [\exp (i\omega_0 t)]\Sigma(k)C_k \exp (ik\omega t) \qquad \text{(A10-3)}$$

But this is a summation of periodic terms, each having an angular frequency $\omega_0 + k\omega$. This is a special case of what is called a doubly periodic motion. Such a motion is one in which the coordinates can be expanded as a sum of periodic terms, having angular frequencies $k_1\omega_1 + k_2\omega_2$, where k_1, k_2 are integers and ω_1, ω_2 fundamental angular frequencies. Our special case is that in which one of the k's takes on only the value unity.

So far we have used only the properties of a general central field, for which the angular momentum p_θ is constant, without using the specific properties of the inverse-square field. We see, then, that in the general central field the motion is doubly periodic, though of the special type where k_1 takes on only the value unity (or, if we were instead expanding $x - iy$, the value -1). In the special case of the inverse-square field, the angular frequency ω_0 is equal to ω. Thus every term of $x + iy$ has the form of a periodic term of angular frequency $k\omega$, and the whole motion is periodic. Let us see what are the implications of having a periodic or a doubly periodic motion when we interpret them in the phase space. If the motion is periodic, as with the inverse-square field, the representative point traces out a single closed curve in the phase space, just as it does in a periodic motion in a one-dimensional problem. This curve, a one-dimensional path, is determined by three separate equations between the q's and p's: the energy is constant, the angular momentum is constant, and the phase difference between the oscillations in r and in θ (when properly defined) is constant. On the other hand, in the doubly periodic motion, though the energy and angular momentum stay constant, the phase difference between these oscillations does not stay constant; the frequencies ω_0 and ω are different and, we assume, incommensurable with each other. The representative point, then, in the course of time fills up the two-dimensional region determined by the constancy of the energy and angular momentum. The way in which a point in the course of its travels can fill up a surface is familiar from the well-known Lissajous figures in mechanics.

Let us now consider a motion in two dimensions in which the force is not central. Then not even the angular momentum stays constant, and the representative point in the course of time fills up the whole energy surface or comes arbitrarily close to any point of this energy surface. Such a motion is called quasi-ergodic. We can see that, if we start with the inverse-square periodic motion and introduce a small perturbation in the form of a central field which does not follow the inverse-square law, the phase difference between the two oscillations, in r and θ, will gradually change, so that the representative point will gradually fill the two-dimensional region characteristic of the doubly periodic motion; the smaller the perturbation, the more slowly the point fills up the region. Similarly, if we introduce a small perturbation which is not central, the angular momentum will gradually change, and the representative point will eventually fill up the energy surface, but it will take longer to get around, the smaller the perturbation.

Situations similar to the ones we have described occur in many dimensions. There are a few problems in three dimensions in which we can separate variables, reducing the problem to three one-dimensional problems, and hence leading to triply periodic motions. The three-dimensional central field and the field of two centers attracting according to the inverse-square law are two of the very limited number of such problems. In such a triply (or, more generally, a multiply) periodic problem, there are n quantities, including the energy, which stay constant during the motion; these quantities have properties similar to angular momenta. There remain $(n - 1)$ phase differences between the oscillations of the various coordinates, and in very special cases some or all of these phase differences can also be constant; if they are all constant, we have a periodic problem. All of these multiply periodic cases are very exceptional, however; the general case is the quasi-ergodic motion, in which the representative point, in the course of time, comes arbitrarily close to every point of the energy surface. This quasi-ergodic motion is the basis of the ordinary treatment of statistical mechanics.

The older quantum theory, in the form used by Bohr and Sommerfeld, could be applied only to cases in which the classical motion was multiply periodic; this was perhaps its greatest limitation and the clearest indication that it was inadequate. Each of the n quantities which stayed constant during the motion was quantized by an appropriate Sommerfeld quantum condition, so that it could take on only certain discrete values. The way of setting up these quantum conditions can be stated most generally by a change of variables, called a contact transformation, which can usefully be made in the case of a classical multiply periodic motion. These contact transformations are changes of coordinates of a particular type, so called because they transform two curves which are in contact with each other in the original space into curves in contact in the new space.

In the Lagrangian and Hamiltonian methods, which we have discussed in Appendix 4, we know that if we introduce new coordinates q'_i, which are functions of the original coordinates $q_1 \cdots q_n$, we can still use

Lagrange's and Hamilton's equations in the new coordinates.   The new Lagrangian and Hamiltonian functions are defined in terms of the old ones by simple rules, and the new momenta p_i' are functions of the old coordinates and momenta: $p_i' = p_i'(q_1 \cdots q_n, \ p_1 \cdots p_n)$.   Such a transformation is called a point transformation.   But in a contact transformation, the new coordinates as well as the new momenta are functions of both the old coordinates and momenta:

$$q_i' = q_i'(q_1 \cdots q_n, p_1 \cdots p_n)$$
$$p_i' = p_i'(q_1 \cdots q_n, p_1 \cdots p_n)$$

There must naturally be restrictions on the functions, just as in ordinary point transformations we require that the new momenta be derived from the new Lagrangian function.[1]   When these restrictions are applied, however, it proves to be the case that Hamilton's equations are still satisfied in the new coordinates, though Lagrange's equations are not.   Such contact transformations can often be very useful in complicated problems, reducing them to forms which can be handled mathematically.

A contact transformation can be most easily visualized simply as a change of variables in the phase space.   For instance, suppose we have the phase space for a linear oscillator, as in Fig. 1-2.   We can easily choose the scale so that the line of constant energy is a circle, rather than an ellipse.   Then it is often useful to introduce polar coordinates in the phase space, so that the motion is represented by a constant value of r and a value of θ increasing uniformly with time.   The angle θ, or rather $\theta/2\pi$ in this case, is often called the angle variable and is used as the coordinate.   This is from analogy with the rotation of a body acted on by no torques, where the angular momentum stays constant and the angle increases linearly with the time.   The momentum conjugate to the angle variable, which stays constant with time, is not simply the radius, as we should expect from the simple use of polar coordinates, but proves to be proportional to the square of r; in fact, it is just πr^2, or the area of the circle.   This momentum is called the action variable, or phase integral, denoted by J, and the angle variable is denoted by w.

Since Hamilton's equations hold in the transformed coordinates, and since evidently the energy H depends only on J, being independent of w, Hamilton's equations become

$$-\frac{\partial H}{\partial w} = 0 = \frac{dJ}{dt}$$

[1] For further details about contact transformations, as well as more discussion of various matters taken up in this appendix, see H. Goldstein, "Classical Mechanics," chaps. 8 and 9, Addison-Wesley Publishing Company, Reading, Mass., 1950.

verifying the fact that J is a constant of the motion, and

$$\frac{\partial H}{\partial J} = \frac{dw}{dt}$$

a quantity independent of time, verifying the fact that w increases uniformly with time.   Now since $w = \theta/2\pi$, it increases by unity in one period, so that dw/dt is just $1/T$, where T is the period, or is ν, the frequency of motion.   Hence we have the important relation that

$$\nu = \frac{\partial H}{\partial J} \qquad\qquad (A10\text{-}4)$$

giving the frequency of motion in terms of the derivative of the energy with respect to the action variable J.

It can be shown in a similar way that action and angle variables can be introduced, in general, in one-dimensional periodic motions.   In every case the w's increase uniformly with time, the frequency being given by Eq. (A10-4).   It also proves to be true, in general, that the action variable J is given by the area of the path of the representative point in phase space, which is the reason why it is called a phase integral.   This area can be written $\oint p\, dq$, which proves to be equal to J.   Connected with this is the criterion which a transformation of the p's and q's must satisfy if it is to be a contact transformation: it can be proved that it is a transformation in which areas in the phase space are preserved, or are not affected by the transformation, though the shape of an area in the new coordinates may be very different from what it was in the old.   An immediate result of this is that the J's are the same no matter what coordinates we may use for computing them.

Angle variables can also be introduced in cases with several degrees of freedom, provided the motion is multiply periodic, by using a separate angle variable for each coordinate.   It is evident that the method could not be used with motions which are not multiply periodic, for we have seen that it is only in the multiply periodic motions that there are quantities, as, for example, angular momenta, which stay constant.   Yet the action variables, or J's, must stay constant and consequently cannot be introduced, for example, in quasi-ergodic motions, where by hypothesis constants of the motion of this sort do not exist.

Since the action variables J are equal to the integrals $\oint p\, dq$, and these are the quantities concerned in Sommerfeld's quantum condition, it is clear that the quantum conditions can be stated in the form that each J must be an integral multiple of Planck's constant h; this is the most general form of the Bohr-Sommerfeld quantum condition.   We can now make a very interesting connection between Eq. (A10-4) and Bohr's frequency condition.   We first consider the case of only one degree of freedom. The emitted energy, according to Bohr's condition, when a system jumps between the states of energy E_2 and E_1, is $(E_2 - E_1)/h$. If we choose two states whose quantum numbers differ by unity, we have $\Delta H = E_2 - E_1$, $\Delta J = h$, so that the frequency given by Bohr's condition is

$$\nu = \frac{\Delta H}{\Delta J}$$

similar to Eq. (A10-4), but with finite differences instead of derivatives. Hence we have the following relation: The derivative $\partial H/\partial J$ gives the classical frequency of motion of a system; the difference ratio $\Delta H/\Delta J$, where the difference of J is one unit, gives the frequency of emitted light according to the quantum theory. We shall consider later the significance of transitions of more than one unit in J.

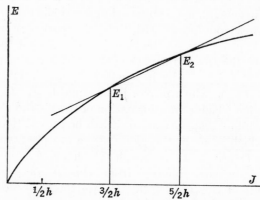

FIG. A10-1. Energy curve for anharmonic oscillator. Slope of curve gives classical frequency; slope of straight line connecting E_2 and E_1 gives quantum frequency.

For the oscillator, as one can immediately see from the fact that its energy in the nth state is $(n + \frac{1}{2})h\nu$, the classical and quantum frequencies are exactly equal, the derivative equaling the difference. This is plain from the fact that here $E = J\nu$, so that the curve of E against J is a straight line and the ratio of a finite increment in ordinate to a finite increment in abscissa equals the slope or derivative. But for any other case the curve of E against J is really curved, so that the derivative and difference ratio are different and classical and quantum frequencies do not agree. Thus in Fig. A10-1 we show an energy curve for an anharmonic oscillator, in which the tightness of binding decreases with increasing amplitude, the frequency decreases, and therefore the slope decreases with large quantum numbers. Here the classical frequency, as given by the slope of the curve, does not agree with the quantum frequency connected with the transition indicated. We may assume, however, that if we go to a very high quantum number, so that we are far out on the axis of abscissas, any ordinary energy curve will become asymptotically fairly smooth and straight, so that the chord and tangent to the curve will more and more nearly coincide. This certainly happens in the important physical applications. In these cases Bohr's correspondence principle states that, in the limit of high quantum numbers, the classical and quantum frequencies become equal. This is essentially simply a special case of the general result that in the limit of high quantum numbers the classical and quantum theories become essentially equivalent.

In classical mechanics, certain problems, such as the central-field motion, are separable, so that they can be broken up into several one-dimensional motions. Since each of these motions was periodic, the whole motion is multiply periodic in these cases. In these particular problems, separation of variables can also be carried out in the quantum theory. In phase space we can pick out the two-dimensional space representing one coordinate and its conjugate momentum, and the projection of the representative point on this plane will trace out a closed curve. There is a quantum condition associated with this coordinate, the area enclosed by the curved path in the two-dimensional space being an integer times h. Thus we have a quantum number associated with each degree of freedom in such a problem. Further, we can introduce angle and action variables connected with each of the coordinates, just as if each formed a problem of one degree of freedom. The various frequencies of the multiple periodicity can be found by differentiating the energy with respect to the various J's, and the correspondence principle can be applied to connect these classical frequencies with the quantum frequencies associated with various possible transitions.

We have seen that a coordinate of, say, a doubly periodic motion can be analyzed in a series of harmonic terms, in which we have oscillations of angular frequency $k_1\omega_1 + k_2\omega_2$, or of frequency $k_1\nu_1 + k_2\nu_2$, where k_1 and k_2 are arbitrary integers. Now we can carry out a general correspondence between any one of these overtone or combination frequencies and a corresponding transition. Thus let us consider the transition in which J_1 changes by k_1 units, J_2 by k_2 units, and where J_1 and J_2 are the two action variables. The quantum frequency emitted will be

$$\frac{E(J_1, J_2) - E(J_1 - k_1 h, J_2 - k_2 h)}{h}$$

where E is the energy, written as function of the J's. But if we are allowed to replace differences by derivatives, as we assume we are in the correspondence principle, this becomes

$$\frac{1}{h}\left(\frac{\partial E}{\partial J_1} k_1 h + \frac{\partial E}{\partial J_2} k_2 h\right) = k_1 \nu_1 + k_2 \nu_2$$

agreeing with the classical value, if $\nu_1 = \partial E/\partial J_1$, $\nu_2 = \partial E/\partial J_2$. Thus we have a one-to-one correspondence between all possible overtone vibrations of the classical motion and all possible quantum transitions.

We are now ready to see how it was that Bohr's correspondence principle could lead to predictions about the intensity of spectral lines. If we carry out the expansion of the electric dipole moment of the atom, as a series of sinusoidal terms in the time, we see that we shall have a sum of terms of frequencies $k_1\nu_1 + k_2\nu_2$ for a doubly periodic system or a sum of such terms for a multiply periodic system and we have just seen how each of these sinusoidal terms can be correlated with a quantum transition. Each of these sinusoidal terms will have a definite amplitude, and this amplitude will be the quantity whose square is proportional to the intensity of the corresponding radiation, if we assume classical mechanics. Bohr assumed that these amplitudes gave at least an indication of the radiated intensity, in the quantum theory. Now that we have the wave mechanics, we can see the exact nature of the correspondence: we find that in the limit of high quantum numbers the amplitudes of the classical sinusoidal terms approach the matrix components of the corresponding quantum transitions. For small quantum numbers, we expect the quantum matrix component to be in some sense an average of the classical amplitude, averaged between the initial and final state. We shall not go further into the details of this correspondence but shall call attention to the case of selection rules. If a classical amplitude is zero, we can reasonably expect that the quantum amplitude, or the matrix component, of the corresponding transition will also be zero.

By use of this rule, many selection rules were proved before the availability of wave mechanics. Thus, with the linear oscillator, the classical motion is purely sinusoidal, without any harmonics. In other words, the amplitudes of all terms of frequency $k_1\nu$ are zero, except for $k_1 = 1$. We infer then that all transitions of the linear oscillator are forbidden, except those for which the quantum number changes by unity. This, of course, is the result found by wave mechanics. Again, in the central-field motion in two dimensions, we found earlier in this appendix that in the analysis of the displacement in sinusoidal terms we had all integral multiples of the radial frequency ω, but the frequency ω_0 of angular motion appeared only with a coefficient of unity. This angular frequency can be shown to be that associated with the J leading to the azimuthal quantum number. Thus we see the proof, from the correspondence principle, that the azimuthal quantum number can change only by a single unit in a transition, a selection rule which also follows from wave mechanics.

Appendix 11

The Sum Rule for Oscillator
Strengths

We wish to prove that the sum of the oscillator strengths f_{mn}, given in Eq. (6-58), equals N, the number of electrons in the atom. Here $f_{mn} = 8\pi^2 m_0 \nu_{nm} (M_x)^2_{nm}/e^2 h$, where $h\nu_{nm} = E_n - E_m$ and $(M_x)_{nm}$ is the x component of the matrix component of the electric moment between the two states, given by $(M_x)_{nm} = -\int u_n^* \Sigma(j) e x_j u_m \, dv$. In these expressions the electronic charge is $-e$, and its mass is m_0.

The proof is based on the commutation rule of Eq. (4-33), which states that $p_x x - x p_x = -i\hbar$. This commutation rule holds for a single coordinate and its conjugate momentum. If we write a commutation rule for the sum of the x's of all electrons, we have

$$[\Sigma(i)p_{xi}][\Sigma(j)x_j] - [\Sigma(j)x_j][\Sigma(i)p_{xi}] = -i\hbar N \qquad \text{(A11-1)}$$

where the sums are over all N electrons. The reason for this is that the commutator of each coordinate with its momentum is $-i\hbar$, but that of one coordinate and another momentum is zero.

Next we use Eq. (4-52), relating the matrix of momentum to that of the velocity, and Eq. (4-43), relating the matrix of the time derivative of a quantity to the matrix of the quantity itself. We thus find that

$$\left[\sum (i)p_{xi} \right]_{nm} = m_0 \frac{i}{\hbar} (E_n - E_m) \left[\sum (i)x_i \right]_{nm} \qquad \text{(A11-2)}$$

We note furthermore that $(M_x)_{nm} = -e[\Sigma(i)x_i]_{nm}$. We put these pieces of information together, insert them in Eq. (A11-1), and take the diagonal m, m component of that equation. We then use the law of matrix multiplication and find

$$\sum (n) \frac{m_0}{e^2} \frac{i}{\hbar} [(E_m - E_n)(M_x)_{mn}(M_x)_{nm} - (E_n - E_m)(M_x)_{mn}(M_x)_{nm}]$$
$$= -i\hbar N$$

or
$$\frac{8\pi^2 m_0}{e^2 h} \sum (n) \nu_{nm} |(M_x)_{nm}|^2 = N \qquad \text{(A11-3)}$$

which is the desired sum rule.   It is to be noticed that we have proved this sum rule separately for the x component of dipole moment; it holds similarly for the y and z components, a result which we use in Eq. (25-13) appearing in Vol. II.   The sum rule for the oscillator strength of Eq. (6-62) follows at once from this result.

Appendix 12

The Quantum Theory of the Electromagnetic Field

In Eq. (6-27) we have a Hamiltonian which leads to the correct equations of motion of a system of electrons in an electromagnetic field; but it does not lead to equations of motion of the field itself, which rather must be handled classically. Our first task will be to express Maxwell's equations, the equations of the field, in Hamiltonian language, so that we can use this Hamiltonian as the starting point of a quantum-theoretical treatment of the field. We shall start by treating an electromagnetic field in a hollow cavity with perfectly reflecting walls, such as we considered in Sec. 6-1, with no electrons or atoms within the cavity.

We start our discussion by setting up an infinite set of orthogonal functions within the cavity, in terms of which we can expand the vector potential as a sort of Fourier expansion. For a rectangular cavity such as we took up in Sec. 6-1, these functions can be modeled after the solutions of Eq. (6-1) for the electric field within the cavity. Thus, for the ath function, which we shall call $\mathbf{E}_a$, a vector function of position, let us assume

$$
\begin{aligned}
E_{ax} &= E_{ax}^0 \cos \frac{n_x \pi x}{X} \sin \frac{n_y \pi y}{Y} \sin \frac{n_z \pi z}{Z} \\
E_{ay} &= E_{ay}^0 \sin \frac{n_x \pi x}{X} \cos \frac{n_y \pi y}{Y} \sin \frac{n_z \pi z}{Z} \qquad \text{(A12-1)} \\
E_{az} &= E_{az}^0 \sin \frac{n_x \pi x}{X} \sin \frac{n_y \pi y}{Y} \cos \frac{n_z \pi z}{Z}
\end{aligned}
$$

For each set of integers n_x, n_y, n_z, we have two independent modes, with two vectors $\mathbf{E}_a^0$; as in Sec. 6-1, each of these $\mathbf{E}_a^0$'s is perpendicular to the propagation vector of components $n_x \pi / X$, $n_y \pi / Y$, $n_z \pi / Z$, and the two $\mathbf{E}_a^0$'s are at right angles to each other.

We can at once prove that any two of these functions are orthogonal, in the sense that the scalar product $\mathbf{E}_a \cdot \mathbf{E}_{a'}$ integrates to zero, when we integrate over the cavity. For two modes which differ in any one of the three integers n_x, n_y, n_z, this follows from the properties of the sines and cosines, and for the two modes with the same n_x, n_y, n_z it follows because their $\mathbf{E}_a^0$'s are at right angles to each other. We now determine the magnitudes of the vectors $\mathbf{E}_a^0$ by a normalization condition: the square of $\mathbf{E}_a$, integrated over the cavity, is to give unity. Then this infinite set of functions $\mathbf{E}_a$ proves to be a suitable set in terms of which we can expand the vector potential of a radiation field. We note that the divergence of each of the $\mathbf{E}_a$'s is zero, but we shall assume that $\nabla \cdot \mathbf{A} = 0$, where $\mathbf{A}$ is the vector potential, so that it is appropriate to expand it in terms of functions with zero divergence. We can then expand the vector potential of a radiation field within the cavity in the form

$$\mathbf{A} = \Sigma(a)Q_a\mathbf{E}_a \qquad (A12\text{-}2)$$

where the Q_a's are functions of time, to be determined. Let us find the differential equations satisfied classically by the Q_a's, in order that the field arising from the vector potential may satisfy Maxwell's equations.

Maxwell's equations in empty space are

$$\nabla \times \mathbf{E} + \frac{\partial \mathbf{B}}{\partial t} = 0 \qquad \nabla \cdot \mathbf{B} = 0$$
$$\nabla \times \mathbf{H} - \frac{\partial \mathbf{D}}{\partial t} = 0 \qquad \nabla \cdot \mathbf{D} = 0 \qquad (A12\text{-}3)$$

when expressed in mks units, coupled with the equations

$$\mathbf{D} = \epsilon_0\mathbf{E} \qquad \mathbf{B} = \mu_0\mathbf{H} \qquad (A12\text{-}4)$$

where the velocity of light c is given by the equation $c^2 = 1/\epsilon_0\mu_0$. We assume that $\mathbf{E}$ and $\mathbf{B}$ are given by a vector potential $\mathbf{A}$, by the equations

$$\mathbf{E} = -\frac{\partial \mathbf{A}}{\partial t} \qquad B = \nabla \times \mathbf{A} \qquad (A12\text{-}5)$$

In empty space in the absence of charges, we assume no scalar potential. We then find, when we substitute Eqs. (A12-4) and (A12-5) into Maxwell's equations, that the first two equations are satisfied automatically and the last two require that

$$\nabla \cdot \mathbf{A} = 0 \qquad \nabla^2\mathbf{A} - \frac{1}{c^2}\frac{\partial^2 \mathbf{A}}{\partial t^2} = 0 \qquad (A12\text{-}6)$$

Our expansion of $\mathbf{A}$ is chosen so that its divergence is zero, so that we need merely require that each term $Q_a\mathbf{E}_a$ of Eq. (A12-2) satisfy the wave equation in order that the field determined from $\mathbf{A}$ may satisfy Maxwell's equations.

In the function $Q_a\mathbf{E}_a$, the first factor is a function of time, the second of the coordinates. In Eq. (A12-6), we require the Laplacian of this function. We find from Eq. (A12-1) that

$$\nabla^2 \mathbf{E}_a = -k_a^2 \mathbf{E}_a \qquad (A12\text{-}7)$$

where k_a is the vector of components $n_x\pi/X$, $n_y\pi/Y$, $n_z\pi/Z$. Then, when we insert the function $Q_a\mathbf{E}_a$ into the wave equation of Eq. (A12-6), we find

$$\left(-k_a^2 Q_a - \frac{1}{c^2}\frac{d^2 Q_a}{dt^2}\right)\mathbf{E}_a = 0 \qquad (A12\text{-}8)$$

from which we see that Q_a satisfies the differential equation

$$\frac{d^2 Q_a}{dt^2} = -k_a^2 c^2 Q_a = -\omega_a^2 Q_a \qquad (A12\text{-}9)$$

where we have introduced $\omega_a = k_a c$, ω_a being the angular frequency of the oscillatory mode of the cavity which we are considering, as we saw in Sec. 6-1.

In Eq. (A12-9) we have the differential equation leading to a sinusoidal oscillation of Q_a, with angular frequency ω_a and arbitrary phase and amplitude; this represents the classical oscillation in this mode, and the linear combination of all modes, given in Eq. (A12-2), represents the general classical solution for the field in the cavity, in the absence of charges. We now wish to express the equations of motion in Hamiltonian form. It is natural to use the Q_a's as generalized coordinates. We wish to set up a Hamiltonian function leading to Eq. (A12-9). There is no unique way to do this, but the natural way is to demand that the Hamiltonian function represent the ordinary electromagnetic energy in the cavity. This, in the mks system, is the integral over the cavity of the quantity $(\epsilon_0/2)E^2 + (1/2\mu_0)B^2$.

First we determine the electric field $\mathbf{E}$ from Eq. (A12-5), using Eq. (A12-2) for the vector potential. We integrate over the cavity and take account of the orthonormal properties of the $\mathbf{E}_a$'s. We then find

$$\text{Electric energy} = \frac{\epsilon_0}{2}\sum (a)\dot{Q}_a^2 \qquad (A12\text{-}10)$$

For the magnetic energy, we need the curl of $\mathbf{A}$, which requires the curl of the function $\mathbf{E}_a$, given in Eq. (A12-1). We find

$$(\nabla \times \mathbf{E}_a)_x = (\mathbf{k}_a \times \mathbf{E}_a^0)_x \sin\frac{n_x\pi x}{X}\cos\frac{n_y\pi y}{Y}\cos\frac{n_z\pi z}{Z}$$

$$(\nabla \times \mathbf{E}_a)_y = (\mathbf{k}_a \times \mathbf{E}_a^0)_y \cos\frac{n_x\pi x}{X}\sin\frac{n_y\pi y}{Y}\cos\frac{n_z\pi z}{Z} \qquad (A12\text{-}11)$$

$$(\nabla \times \mathbf{E}_a)_z = (\mathbf{k}_a \times \mathbf{E}_a^0)_z \cos\frac{n_x\pi x}{X}\cos\frac{n_y\pi y}{Y}\sin\frac{n_z\pi z}{Z}$$

We readily prove that any two of these functions ($\nabla \times \mathbf{E}_a$) are orthogonal, in the sense that the integral of their scalar product over the cavity is zero. As for their normalization, we take the scalar product of the function with itself, integrate over the cavity, and use the vector identity

$$(\mathbf{k}_a \times \mathbf{E}_a^0)^2 = \mathbf{k}_a^2 E_a^{02} - (\mathbf{k}_a \cdot \mathbf{E}_a^0)^2 \qquad (A12\text{-}12)$$

which holds for any two vectors. In the present case, since $\mathbf{E}_a^0$ is perpendicular to $\mathbf{k}_a$, we have only the first term of Eq. (A12-12). Then we can show that

$$\int (\nabla \times \mathbf{E}_a)^2 \, dv = k_a^2 \qquad (A12\text{-}13)$$

when we remember the normalization of the $\mathbf{E}_a$'s. We then find that the magnetic energy is given by

$$\begin{aligned} \text{Magnetic energy} &= \frac{1}{2\mu_0} \sum (a) k_a^2 Q_a^2 \\ &= \frac{\epsilon_0}{2} \sum (a) \omega_a^2 Q_a^2 \end{aligned} \qquad (A12\text{-}14)$$

where we have used the relation $\omega_a = k_a c$, and $c^2 = 1/\epsilon_0\mu_0$.

We see from Eq. (A12-10) that, when we express the electromagnetic field in this way, the electric energy has an analogy to the kinetic energy and from Eq. (A12-14) that the magnetic energy has an analogy to the potential energy. It is then natural to introduce a generalized momentum conjugate to the coordinate Q_a, which from Eq. (A4-5) should be given by the derivative of the electric energy with respect to $\dot{Q}_a$. That is, we have

$$P_a = \epsilon_0 \dot{Q}_a \qquad (A12\text{-}15)$$

If we use this definition and express $\dot{Q}_a$ in terms of P_a, we can set up a Hamiltonian function H_1 as the sum of the electric and magnetic energies, in the form

$$H_1 = \sum (a) \left(\frac{P_a^2}{2\epsilon_0} + \frac{\epsilon_0 \omega_a^2}{2} Q_a^2 \right) \qquad (A12\text{-}16)$$

We verify that Hamilton's equations for this Hamiltonian lead to Eqs. (A12-15) and (A12-9), so that this Hamiltonian correctly leads to the equations of motion of the electromagnetic field in an empty cavity.

Before we go on to treat the case where charges are present in the cavity, let us see how we should apply wave mechanics to the radiation field in empty space in the cavity. The problem is exactly like a mechanical problem with the infinite set of coordinates Q_a. We should handle this by introducing a wave function varying sinusoidally with time and with a space part equal to a function $u(Q_1, Q_2, \ldots)$. This wave function would then satisfy the Schrödinger equation

$$\sum_{(a)} \left(-\frac{\hbar^2}{2\epsilon_0} \frac{\partial^2}{\partial Q_a^2} + \frac{\epsilon_0 \omega_a^2}{2} Q_a^2 \right) u = Eu \qquad \text{(A12-17)}$$

Since the Hamiltonian function is a sum of terms, one depending on each of the Q's, we can at once separate variables, writing

$$u = u_1(Q_1)u_2(Q_2) \cdots$$

and find that u_a satisfies the equation

$$-\frac{\hbar^2}{2\epsilon_0} \frac{d^2 u_a}{dQ_a^2} + \frac{\epsilon_0 \omega_a^2}{2} Q_a^2 u_a = \epsilon_a u_a \qquad \text{(A12-18)}$$

where ϵ_a is the energy of the ath mode, and where E is the sum of the ϵ_a's. But Eq. (A12-18) is just like the Schrödinger equation for a linear oscillator, which we have solved in Sec. 3-7, so that we know its wave functions and energy levels, and, in particular, we know that

$$\epsilon_a = (n_a + \tfrac{1}{2})h\nu_a \qquad \text{(A12-19)}$$

where $\nu_a = \omega_a/2\pi$. Thus we have verified that the energy of a normal mode of frequency ν can take on only certain discrete energies, differing by the amount $h\nu$. As we have stated in Chap. 6, this can be regarded as one of the bases for the photon hypothesis, according to which the energy of the radiation field can change only by an amount $h\nu$.

We also have the justification for the remarks made in Sec. 6-6 about the limiting case of large electromagnetic energy, in which the quantum numbers n_a are all large, so that we can approach the case of classical electromagnetic theory, in which Q_a would be a definitely determined function of time, instead of being described only statistically by a wave function. By the methods of Appendix 3, we can show that in the classical limit the average Q_a's, averaged over a wave packet set up in the space in which Q_a is a coordinate, will satisfy Eq. (A12-9), or Hamilton's equation, which is equivalent in this case to Maxwell's equations. The principle of uncertainty, however, requires that in all cases the wave packet have a certain width; that is, a certain fluctuation in Q_a, or in the field strength associated with the ath mode, is present in wave mechanics, whereas in classical electromagnetic theory the amplitude of each mode is a definitely determined function of time.

There is one interesting aspect of the uncertainty principle, related to the question as to whether one can or cannot observe the phase of an electromagnetic oscillation. At low radio frequencies, of course, this is possible, and in the frequency range of the visible spectrum it is impossible. We can understand this difference in terms of the phase space for a linear oscillator, as given in Fig. 1-2. The principle of uncertainty implies that a wave packet must cover an area in such a phase space equal at least to h, that is, equal to the complete area of the range of this space from the origin out to the line of constant energy associated with the first quantum state. In case we are dealing with systems in a very low quantum number, then, the wave packet must cover all possible phases, so that we are equally likely to find systems in any phase. On the other hand, if we are dealing with systems mostly in the nth stationary state, where n is large, then, as indicated in Fig. A12-1, we can have a wave

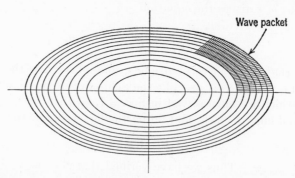

Fig. A12-1. Phase space for linear oscillator, showing range covered by a wave packet in which phase is localized as much as possible. In case shown, wave packet extends over six units of quantum number and over phase $2\pi/6$.

packet which extends over a range of phases of the order of magnitude of $2\pi/n$. Thus, if we are dealing with large quantum numbers, the phase can be fairly well determined, and in the frequency range used in electrical engineering, this can be done as accurately as we please.

We have now considered the electromagnetic field in empty space and are ready to take up the question as to the field in the presence of electronic charges. First we shall put Maxwell's equations for this case in Hamiltonian form. In the presence of a charge density ρ and current density $\mathbf{J}$, the first two of Maxwell's equations, Eq. (A12-3), are unaltered, but the last two are changed to

$$\nabla \times \mathbf{H} - \frac{\partial \mathbf{D}}{\partial t} = \mathbf{J} \qquad \nabla \cdot \mathbf{D} = \rho \qquad \text{(A12-20)}$$

We now need a scalar potential ϕ, as well as the vector potential $\mathbf{A}$, and assume that the fields are determined from them by the equations

$$\mathbf{E} = -\nabla \phi - \frac{\partial \mathbf{A}}{\partial t} \qquad \mathbf{B} = \nabla \times \mathbf{A} \qquad \text{(A12-21)}$$

in place of Eq. (A12-5). We continue to assume that the divergence of $\mathbf{A}$ is zero. If we now substitute from Eq. (A12-21) into Maxwell's equations, we find

$$\nabla^2 \phi = -\frac{\rho}{\epsilon_0}$$

$$\nabla^2 \mathbf{A} - \frac{1}{c^2}\frac{\partial^2 \mathbf{A}}{\partial t^2} = -\mu_0 \mathbf{J} + \frac{1}{c^2}\frac{\partial}{\partial t}(\nabla \phi) \qquad \text{(A12-22)}$$

The first equation of Eq. (A12-22) tells us that the scalar potential is determined from the charge density by Poisson's equation. Therefore, by well-known methods of electrostatics, the potential is to be determined by Coulomb's law, as

$$\phi = \int \frac{\rho}{4\pi\epsilon_0 r}\, dv + \phi_0 \qquad \text{(A12-23)}$$

Here we are determining the scalar potential at a point within the cavity. We take the charge $\rho\, dv$ located in a volume element dv, divide by the distance r between the volume element and the point where the potential is being computed, and sum over all volume elements in the cavity. The additional term ϕ_0 is a solution of Laplace's equation, therefore corresponding to an electrostatic potential which can exist in the absence of charge. It is necessary to include such a term, so as to satisfy the boundary conditions on the surface of the cavity. Since the walls are perfect reflectors, they must be perfect conductors and therefore equipotentials. Consequently ϕ_0 is such a solution of Laplace's equation that, superposed on the first term of Eq. (A12-23), it reduces the potential on the walls to a constant value, which we may take to be zero.

Next we consider the second equation of Eq. (A12-22), determining the vector potential. As before, we expand $\mathbf{A}$ as a linear combination of the $\mathbf{E}_a$'s, according to Eq. (A12-2). We find

$$\sum (a) \left(-k_a^2 Q_a - \frac{1}{c^2}\frac{\partial^2 Q_a}{\partial t^2} \right) \mathbf{E}_a = -\mu_0 \mathbf{J} + \frac{1}{c^2}\frac{\partial}{\partial t}(\nabla\phi) \qquad \text{(A12-24)}$$

To find the differential equation satisfied by Q_a, we multiply Eq. (A12-24) by one of the $\mathbf{E}_a$'s, integrate over the cavity, and use the orthonormal properties of the $\mathbf{E}_a$'s. When we do so, we find that the term arising from the scalar potential drops out. Let us first inquire why this is the case. We have to compute $\int \mathbf{E}_a \cdot \nabla\phi\, dv$. In doing this, we use the vector identity $\nabla \cdot (\phi \mathbf{E}_a) = \phi \nabla \cdot \mathbf{E}_a + \mathbf{E}_a \cdot \nabla\phi$, coupled with the fact that $\nabla \cdot \mathbf{E}_a = 0$. We then have

$$\int \mathbf{E}_a \cdot \nabla\phi\, dv = \int \nabla \cdot (\phi \mathbf{E}_a)\, dv = \int (\phi \mathbf{E}_a)_n\, dS \qquad \text{(A12-25)}$$

where in the last step of Eq. (A12-25) we have used the divergence theorem, and where $\int (\phi \mathbf{E}_a)_n\, dS$ indicates a surface integral of ϕ times the normal component of $\mathbf{E}_a$, over the surface of the cavity. Since ϕ is zero over the surface, this integral is zero. Thus we are led to the vanishing of the contribution of the scalar potential to our result.

We then find that

$$-k_a^2 Q_a^2 - \frac{1}{c^2} \frac{d^2 Q_a}{dt^2} = -\mu_0 \int \mathbf{J} \cdot \mathbf{E}_a \, dv$$

$$\frac{d^2 Q_a}{dt^2} + \omega_a^2 Q_a = \frac{1}{\epsilon_0} \int \mathbf{J} \cdot \mathbf{E}_a \, dv$$

(A12-26)

as the differential equation satisfied by Q_a. This is like the equation of a classical oscillator with an external force, varying as a function of time (since $\mathbf{J}$ is a function of time). We can solve the problem classically by well-known methods, and in this way we find the Q_a's, and hence the vector potential and field, set up by external currents. Equation (A12-26), then, along with Eq. (A12-23) for the scalar potential, provides the equivalent of Maxwell's equations.

If the charge distribution consists of a number of point charges, of charge e_i, located at points with vector position $\mathbf{r}_i$, moving with velocities $\dot{\mathbf{r}}_i$, we can rewrite the right side of Eq. (A12-26) in an alternative form. To do this, we note that the integral will have contributions only from the places where the charges are. The ith charge will have a current density which is infinite if it is really a point charge or which is very large, equal to the charge density times the velocity if the charge density is large but not infinite. If we integrate the current density of this charge over the volume, the result will be the charge e_i times the velocity vector $\dot{\mathbf{r}}_i$. The value of $\mathbf{E}_a$ will have to be computed at the position $\mathbf{r}_i$ of the charge. Thus we may rewrite Eq. (A12-26) in the form

$$\frac{d^2 Q_a}{dt^2} + \omega_a^2 Q_a = \frac{1}{\epsilon_0} \sum (i) e_i \dot{\mathbf{r}}_i \cdot \mathbf{E}_a(\mathbf{r}_i)$$

(A12-27)

It is this equation of motion which we wish to derive from Hamiltonian methods.

We shall now show that the desired Hamiltonian can be set up in a very simple way. In Eq. (A12-16) we have found a Hamiltonian which describes the electromagnetic field in the empty cavity, and in Eq. (6-27) we have found a Hamiltonian for the particles, in the presence of the field. We need only add these two functions, with a few obvious modifications, to get the Hamiltonian for the whole system. The modifications which we must make are in Eq. (6-27). First, the vector potential $\mathbf{A}(\mathbf{r}_j)$ appears in that equation; we replace it by its expression in terms of the normal modes of the cavity, namely, $\Sigma(a) Q_a \mathbf{E}_a(\mathbf{r}_j)$. We shall disregard any additional vector potential arising from currents outside the cavity, though it is easy to include the effect of a constant magnetic field imposed from outside by keeping an external term in the vector potential, not expandable in terms of the normal modes. Second, the potential energy $V(x_1 \cdots z_N)$ arising from Coulomb interactions between particles can be rewritten explicitly as $\Sigma(\text{pairs } i,j) e_i e_j / 4\pi\epsilon_0 r_{ij}$, where r_{ij} is the distance from the ith to the jth particle. We can include the effect of the scalar potential ϕ_0, of Eq. (A12-23), arising from the boundary conditions, in a term $e_j \phi_0(r_j)$. Aside from this, we assume no external scalar potential.

When we make these modifications, we have for the Hamiltonian

$$
H = \sum (a) \left(\frac{P_a^2}{2\epsilon_0} + \frac{\epsilon_0 \omega_a^2}{2} Q_a^2 \right)
$$
$$
+ \sum (i) \left\{ \frac{[\mathbf{p}_i - e_i \Sigma(a) Q_a \mathbf{E}_a(\mathbf{r}_i)]^2}{2m_i} + e_i \phi_0(\mathbf{r}_i) \right\}
$$
$$
+ \sum (\text{pairs } i,j) \frac{e_i e_j}{4\pi\epsilon_0 r_{ij}} \quad (\text{A12-28})
$$

We must now show that this Hamiltonian leads to the correct equations of motion. As far as the motion of the charges is concerned, this proof is no different from that given in Sec. 6-7 and Appendix 4. When we find the equations of motion of the Q_a's, however, we find new terms, arising from the presence of Q_a in the part of the Hamiltonian of Eq. (A12-28) arising from the particles. We compute these terms, make use of Eq. (6-28), which gives the relation between the momentum and the velocity of a particle, and find that we are led exactly to Eq. (A12-27). Hence we find that Eq. (A12-28) is a classical Hamiltonian which leads both to Newton's laws of motion for the particles, under the action of the electromagnetic forces, and to Maxwell's equations for the field. It is this Hamiltonian which we shall use as a basis of the formulation of Schrödinger's equation for this problem.

Before we proceed with this quantum-mechanical formulation, it is well to qualify a little the statement of the preceding paragraph that we have formulated our problem completely according to classical mechanics. It is well known that, if we try to set up a complete classical theory of a point electron, we find an infinite electrostatic self-energy, for there is an infinite amount of electrostatic energy in the field immediately around a given charge. We have avoided this term in our Hamiltonian by including in V only the interactions between pairs of particles, excluding the interaction of a charge with itself. This is legitimate here, but it does not entirely get rid of self-energy troubles. The reason is that, in addition, a moving point charge produces an infinite magnetic field in its neighborhood, which exerts infinite magnetic forces on it, and we have not eliminated these magnetic interactions in our formulation. If we used Eq. (A12-27) in a straightforward way to investigate the magnetic fields produced by a moving point charge, we should find just the infinite contributions to the field which we have just mentioned and these, in turn, would produce infinite forces. Fortunately these terms will not concern us in the use which we shall make of the method, which is the study of the effect of radiation fields emitted by one atom in causing quantum transitions of another atom. They should be enough to show the reader, however, that the subject of quantum electrodynamics is one with difficulties, in the way of infinite terms, which are fundamental and not easy to avoid.

The difficulties we have been mentioning fortunately do not come in in the problems we are considering in this appendix. Let us then take our Hamiltonian H of Eq. (A12-28) and set up the related Schrödinger equation. We shall set it up in the form involving the time, for we wish to investigate nonstationary states by the method of variation of constants. We then have a wave function ψ which is a function of the Q_a's and the $\mathbf{r}_i$'s. The Schrödinger equation is

$$
\begin{aligned}
\Bigg(\sum (a) \left(- \frac{\hbar^2}{2\epsilon_0} \frac{\partial^2}{\partial Q_a^2} + \frac{\epsilon_0 \omega_a^2}{2} Q_a^2 \right) \\
+ \sum (j) \Bigg\{ - \frac{\hbar^2}{2m_j} \nabla_j^2 + \frac{ie_j\hbar}{m_j} [\Sigma(a) Q_a \mathbf{E}_a(\mathbf{r}_j)] \cdot \nabla_j \\
+ \frac{e_j^2}{2m_j} [\Sigma(a) Q_a \mathbf{E}_a(\mathbf{r}_j)]^2 + e_j \phi_0(\mathbf{r}_j) \Bigg\} \\
+ \sum (\text{pairs } i,j) \frac{e_i e_j}{4\pi\epsilon_0 r_{ij}} \Bigg) \psi = i\hbar \frac{\partial \psi}{\partial t} \quad (A12\text{-}29)
\end{aligned}
$$

We note, as has been mentioned elsewhere, that in the term involving ∇_j it is immaterial whether the operator is written before or after the function $\mathbf{E}_a(r_j)$, since the two quantities commute on account of the fact that the divergence of $\mathbf{E}_a$ is zero.

Equation (A12-29) is now the one which we must solve; but it is much too complicated to handle directly, even in the simplest cases. Hence all discussions of it proceed by perturbation theory. There are two terms involving both the coordinates of the radiation field and of the particles: those involving $\Sigma(a) Q_a \mathbf{E}_a(\mathbf{r}_j)$, one of the first power in the field, the other of the second power. If these terms were omitted, the Hamiltonian would be a sum of terms depending only on the radiation field and terms depending only on the particles. Then the problem could be separated, ψ being written as a product of a function of the field and a function of the particles. The function of the field can be set up as described earlier, as a product of solutions of linear-oscillator-like problems, one for each normal mode of the cavity, each characterized by a quantum number n_a, indicating the number of photons in the corresponding mode of oscillation. The function of the particles can be solved like all the problems of interaction of particles which we consider in this volume, neglecting radiation. Thus, at least in principle, we can set up a wave function of the particles corresponding to the quantum numbers of the particles. The unperturbed problem then is that of separated radiation field and particles, and the energy is the sum of the energies of radiation field and particles.

We then introduce the remaining terms in the Hamiltonian as perturbations and proceed by perturbation theory. In the ordinary case we use the method of variation of constants. The essential quantity to compute in this method is the matrix component of the Hamiltonian between unperturbed wave functions. We may denote an unperturbed wave function by giving the quantum numbers n_1, n_2, . . . of the various oscillators representing the radiation field and the quantum numbers describing the atomic system, which we may symbolize by p (but which may include a number of quantum numbers). We are then interested in the nondiagonal matrix component of energy between states with quantum numbers n_1, n_2, . . . , p and n'_1, n'_2, . . . , p'. The only terms of the Hamiltonian of Eq. (A12-29) which can lead to such non-diagonal terms are those involving $Q_a E_a(\mathbf{r}_j)$; and a more careful examination, which we shall not give, shows that only the linear terms in these quantities need be retained for the present purposes. The quadratic terms, being of a smaller order of magnitude if the external fields are small, can be neglected.

We wish then to find the nondiagonal matrix component of the energy

$$\sum (j) \sum (a) \frac{ie_j\hbar}{m_j} Q_a E_a(\mathbf{r}_j) \cdot \nabla_j \qquad \text{(A12-30)}$$

between two states of the system. Let us find the component of one term of this summation, $(ie_j\hbar/m_j)Q_a E_{ax}(\mathbf{r}_j)\partial/\partial x_j$. We write the unperturbed wave functions in the form $u_{n1}(Q_1)u_{n2}(Q_2) \cdots w_p(\mathbf{r}_1 \cdots \mathbf{r}_n)$, where w represents the wave function of the particles. The u's are the wave functions of the oscillators representing the field. On account of their orthogonality and the form of the energy operator, which involves the quantity Q_a, it is clear that the nondiagonal matrix component will be zero if any n'''s differ from the corresponding n's, except for n_a. And on account of normalization of the u's, we have

$$\int u_{n1}^*(Q_1) \cdots w_p^*(\mathbf{r}_1 \cdots)Q_a E_{ax}(\mathbf{r}_j) \frac{\partial}{\partial x_j}$$
$$\times u_{n1}(Q_1) \cdots u_{na'}(Q_a) \cdots w_{p'}(\mathbf{r}_1 \cdots) \, dQ_1 \cdots d\mathbf{r}_1 \cdots$$
$$= \int u_{na}^*(Q_a) Q_a u_{na'}(Q_a) \, dQ_a \int w_p^*(\mathbf{r}_1 \cdots)E_{ax}(\mathbf{r}_j) \frac{\partial}{\partial x_j} w_{p'}(\mathbf{r}_1 \cdots) \, d\mathbf{r}_1 \cdots$$
$$\text{(A12-31)}$$

The first factor in Eq. (A12-31) is the matrix component of the coordinate Q_a between two wave functions of a harmonic oscillator, characterized by quantum numbers n_a and n'_a. We have derived these matrix components in Eq. (4-46) and Eq. (A6-16) and have found that the matrix component is zero unless the quantum number increases or decreases by just one unit: n_a' must equal $n_a \pm 1$ in order to have a nonvanishing matrix component. We shall see presently that this has a simple physical significance in our problem of radiation or absorption: in every such act only one photon is emitted or absorbed by the radiating system. It is simple to get the actual values of the matrix components, as in Eq. (A6-16). We see that we have

$$\int u_{na}^*(Q_a) Q_a u_{n_a\pm 1} \, dQ_a = \begin{cases} \sqrt{\dfrac{h(n_a+1)}{8\pi^2\epsilon_0\nu_a}} & \text{for plus sign} \\ \sqrt{\dfrac{hn_a}{8\pi^2\epsilon_0\nu_a}} & \text{for minus sign} \end{cases} \tag{A12-32}$$

The remaining factor in the matrix component of the Hamiltonian is like that given in Eq. (6-33), except for the replacement of the vector potential $\mathbf{A}(\mathbf{r}_j)$ by $\mathbf{E}_a(\mathbf{r}_j)$. We can then make the same transformation which we have done in deriving Eq. (6-36).

We are now ready to put our information together and evaluate the nondiagonal matrix component of the operator of Eq. (A12-30). We have a matrix component connected with each transition from the original state in which one particular oscillator has its quantum number change by ± 1 unit and in which the atom has its quantum numbers change from p to p'. If it is the ath oscillator which has a transition, the matrix component is

$$H_{n_a,n_a\pm 1} = \begin{cases} \sqrt{\dfrac{h(n_a+1)}{8\pi^2\epsilon_0\nu_a}} \dfrac{i}{\hbar} (E_{p'} - E_p)\mathbf{E}_a(\mathbf{r})_{\text{av}} \cdot \mathbf{M}_{pp'} & \text{for plus sign} \\ \sqrt{\dfrac{hn_a}{8\pi^2\epsilon_0\nu_a}} \dfrac{i}{\hbar} (E_{p'} - E_p)\mathbf{E}_a(\mathbf{r})_{\text{av}} \cdot \mathbf{M}_{pp'} & \text{for minus sign} \end{cases}$$
$$\tag{A12-33}$$

In Eq. (A12-33), we have written $\mathbf{E}_a(\mathbf{r})_{\text{av}}$ for the average value of $\mathbf{E}_a(\mathbf{r}_j)$ over the atomic system; from the derivation of Eq. (6-36), we see that this expression is not valid unless we are dealing with modes of such long wavelength that $\mathbf{E}_a$ does not vary appreciably from one part of the atomic system to another. Our results then agree with those of Eq. (6-63), in which the quantity written as $\mathbf{A}$ is really our quantity $\mathbf{E}_a(\mathbf{r})_{\text{av}}$.

We are now ready to proceed by the method of variation of constants. This is sufficiently similar to the calculation of Sec. 6-8 and is sufficiently well described in Sec. 6-10 so that it is not necessary to reproduce the discussion here. The result is easily found to be that of Eq. (6-64), and the remaining discussion of the problem is given in Chap. 6.

Appendix 13

Schrödinger's Equation for the Central-field Problem

Schrödinger's equation for the central-field problem is

$$(-\nabla^2 + V)u = Eu$$

where V, the potential energy, is a function of r, which is equal to $-2Z/r$ in atomic units for the Coulomb field as given in Eq. (7-5). We express this equation in spherical polar coordinates, in which the equation becomes

$$\frac{1}{r^2}\frac{\partial}{\partial r}\left(r^2\frac{\partial u}{\partial r}\right) + \frac{1}{r^2\sin\theta}\frac{\partial}{\partial\theta}\left(\sin\theta\frac{\partial u}{\partial\theta}\right) + \frac{1}{r^2\sin^2\theta}\frac{\partial^2 u}{\partial\phi^2}$$
$$= (V - E)u \quad \text{(A13-1)}$$

We now assume, as in Sec. 7-1, that u can be written as a product of functions R, Θ, Φ, which are functions, respectively, of r, θ, ϕ. We substitute this expression for u into Eq. (A13-1) and divide by the product $R\Theta\Phi$. We multiply by r^2; and then, rearranging terms, we can rewrite Eq. (A13-1) in the form

$$\frac{1}{R}\frac{d}{dr}\left(r^2\frac{dR}{dr}\right) - r^2(V - E) = -\frac{1}{\Theta}\frac{1}{\sin\theta}\frac{d}{d\theta}\left(\sin\theta\frac{d\Theta}{d\theta}\right)$$
$$- \frac{1}{\Phi}\frac{1}{\sin^2\theta}\frac{d^2\Phi}{d\phi^2} \quad \text{(A13-2)}$$

In this equation the left side is a function of r alone, the right side a function of the angles alone. These quantities cannot be equal, for all values of r, θ, and ϕ, unless each side is a constant. Let this constant be called $l(l + 1)$. Setting the left side of Eq. (A13-2) equal to this constant, we arrive at the first equation of Eq. (7-7). Setting the right side of Eq. (A13-2) equal to this constant, we may then multiply by $\sin^2\theta$, rearrange terms, and find

$$\frac{1}{\Phi}\frac{d^2\Phi}{d\phi^2} = \left[-\frac{1}{\Theta}\frac{1}{\sin\theta}\frac{d}{d\theta}\left(\sin\theta\frac{d\Theta}{d\theta}\right) - l(l + 1)\right]\sin^2\theta \quad \text{(A13-3)}$$

Here the left side is a function of ϕ alone, the right side a function of θ alone; by the same argument used above, each side must then be a constant, and we let this constant be called $-m^2$. When we set the left side of Eq. (A13-3) equal to this constant, we arrive at the third equation of Eq. (7-7), and when we set the right side equal to the same constant, we find the second equation of Eq. (7-7).

Appendix 14

Properties of the Associated Legendre Functions

In Eq. (7-7) we have given the differential equation satisfied by the associated Legendre functions. For analytical purposes, it is convenient to write these functions as $P_l^m(x)$, where $x = \cos \theta$. In this case, the differential equation becomes

$$(1 - x^2) \frac{d^2 P_l^m}{dx^2} - 2x \frac{dP_l^m}{dx} + \left[l(l + 1) - \frac{m^2}{1 - x^2} \right] P_l^m = 0 \quad \text{(A14-1)}$$

The important theorems regarding these functions are proved from a form of the function which we have not used in the text, namely,

$$P_l^m(x) = \frac{1}{2^l l!} (1 - x^2)^{m/2} \frac{d^{l+m}(x^2 - 1)^l}{dx^{l+m}} \quad \text{(A14-2)}$$

In Eq. (7-10) we have an expansion for $P_l^m(\cos \theta)$. If we rewrite this in terms of x, it is

$$P_l^m(x) = \frac{1}{2^l l!} (1 - x^2)^{m/2} \frac{(2l)!}{(l - m)!} \left[x^{l-m} \right.$$
$$\left. - \frac{(l - m)(l - m - 1)}{2(2l - 1)} x^{l-m-2} + \cdots \right] \quad \text{(A14-3)}$$

We may write Eq. (A14-2) or Eq. (A14-3) in the form

$$P_l^m(x) = \frac{1}{2^l l!} (1 - x^2)^{m/2} v(x) \quad \text{(A14-4)}$$

where $v(x)$ is given alternatively as a derivative in Eq. (A14-2) or as a polynomial in Eq. (A14-3). If we substitute Eq. (A14-4) in Eq. (A14-1), we find that the differential equation satisfied by v must be

$$(1 - x^2) \frac{d^2 v}{dx^2} - 2(m + 1)x \frac{dv}{dx} + [l(l + 1) - m(m + 1)]v = 0 \quad \text{(A14-5)}$$

From our discussion in the text, it is clear that the polynomial of Eq. (A14-3) will satisfy this differential equation. We must now prove that

457

the derivative of Eq. (A14-2) also satisfies it and that the constant factor in the polynomial is so chosen as to agree with the polynomial. Then we shall have proved that the expression of Eq. (A14-2) is equivalent to that of Eq. (A14-3).

We can prove at once that

$$(1 - x^2) \frac{d^{n+2}(x^2 - 1)^l}{dx^{n+2}} - 2(n + 1 - l)x \frac{d^{n+1}(x^2 - 1)^l}{dx^{n+1}}$$

$$+ (2l - n)(n + 1) \frac{d^n(x^2 - 1)^l}{dx^n} = 0 \quad \text{(A14-6)}$$

This is most easily proved by induction. If we substitute $n = 0$, we can verify very easily, by direct differentiation of $(x^2 - 1)^l$, that it holds. But if it holds for any n value, we can then prove that it holds for $n + 1$, by differentiating Eq. (A14-6) with respect to x; the result can be put in the form of an identical expression, but with $n + 1$ in place of n. Hence Eq. (A14-6) must be true in general. If now we let $n = l + m$ and assume that $v = d^{l+m}(x^2 - 1)^l/dx^{l+m}$, as in Eq. (A14-2), then we find at once that v satisfies Eq. (A14-5). Since this is a linear differential equation, it does not determine the constant factor but aside from this we have in this way a proof that Eq. (A14-2) gives a solution of Eq. (A14-1).

Next we must prove that the function of Eq. (A14-2) agrees with Eq. (A14-3), even as far as the multiplicative constant is concerned. To do this, we need show only that the term of highest power in the polynomial, namely, $[(2l)!/(l - m)!]x^{l-m}$, agrees with the corresponding term in Eq. (A14-2); since both functions satisfy the same differential equation, and hence the same recursion formula, this will guarantee that all the other terms agree. But the term of highest power in x comes from the term x^{2l} in the expression $(x^2 - 1)^l$. That is, it is $d^{l+m}(x^{2l})/dx^{l+m}$, which can easily be shown to have the required value.

The factor $2^l l!$ in the denominator of Eq. (A14-2) is chosen so that the value of $P_l(x)$, which is the ordinary notation for $P_l^0(x)$, should go to unity when $x = 1$, or when $\theta = 0$. Let us verify this fact. From Eq. (A14-2) we have

$$P_l(x) = \frac{1}{2^l l!} \frac{d^l}{dx^l} [(x - 1)^l(x + 1)^l] \quad \text{(A14-7)}$$

When $x = 1$, the factor $x - 1$ and all its powers go to zero. Therefore the only terms remaining under these circumstances are those in which the differentiations all apply to $(x - 1)^l$, leaving $(x + 1)^l$ untouched. We then have

$$P_l(x) \bigg|_{x=1} = \frac{1}{2^l l!} (x + 1)^l \frac{d^l(x - 1)^l}{dx^l} \bigg|_{x=1} = 1 \quad \text{(A14-8)}$$

since when $x = 1$, $(x + 1)^l = 2^l$ and $d^l(x - 1)^l/dx^l = l!$.

Next we shall prove various relations between the functions, which have been quoted in the text. In particular, we have Eqs. (11-5) and (11-6) and Eqs. (25-2) and (25-4) (appearing in Vol. II), which can be written in the form

$$(1 - x^2) \frac{d}{dx} P_l^m = -mx P_l^m + \sqrt{1 - x^2}\, P_l^{m+1} \tag{11-5}$$

$$\sqrt{1 - x^2}\, P_l^m = 2(m - 1)x P_l^{m-1} \\ - (l + m - 1)(l - m + 2)\sqrt{1 - x^2}\, P_l^{m-2} \tag{11-6}$$

$$(2l + 1)\sqrt{1 - x^2}\, P_l^m = P_{l+1}^{m+1} - P_{l-1}^{m+1} \tag{25-2}$$

$$(l + m)P_{l-1}^m = (2l + 1)x P_l^m - (l - m + 1)P_{l+1}^m \tag{25-4}$$

We shall prove these relations from relations like Eq. (A14-6). From Eq. (A14-6) directly, we substitute $n = l + m - 2$, multiply by $(1 - x^2)^{m/2}/2^l l!$, and are led directly to Eq. (11-6).

For the other relations, we need the equations

$$\frac{d^{n+2}(x^2 - 1)^l}{dx^{n+2}} - 2lx \frac{d^{n+1}(x^2 - 1)^{l-1}}{dx^{n+1}} \\ - 2l(n + 1)\frac{d^n(x^2 - 1)^{l-1}}{dx^n} = 0 \tag{A14-9}$$

and

$$\frac{d^{n+2}(x^2 - 1)^l}{dx^{n+2}} - 2l(2l - 1)\frac{d^n(x^2 - 1)^{l-1}}{dx^n} \\ - 4l(l - 1)\frac{d^n(x^2 - 1)^{l-2}}{dx^n} = 0 \tag{A14-10}$$

These, like Eq. (A14-6), can be proved by induction. If we now start with Eq. (A14-9), let $n = l + m - 1$ and multiply by $(1 - x^2)^{(m+1)/2}/2^l l!$, the equation is converted into

$$P_l^{m+1} = x P_{l-1}^{m+1} + (l + m)\sqrt{1 - x^2}\, P_{l-1}^m \tag{A14-11}$$

If we take Eq. (A14-10), let $n = l + m - 2$, and multiply by $(1 - x^2)^{m/2}/2^l l!$, we find

$$P_l^m = (2l - 1)\sqrt{1 - x^2}\, P_{l-1}^{m-1} + P_{l-2}^m \tag{A14-12}$$

In Eq. (A14-12), if we replace m by $m + 1$, l by $l + 1$, we find Eq. (25-2).
Let us now take Eq. (A14-11) and replace l by $l + 1$. We find

$$(l + m + 1)\sqrt{1 - x^2}\, P_l^m = P_{l+1}^{m+1} - x P_l^{m+1} \tag{A14-13}$$

Let us subtract this from Eq. (25-2). We have

$$(l - m)\sqrt{1 - x^2}\, P_l^m = x P_l^{m+1} - P_{l-1}^{m+1} \tag{A14-14}$$

Let us now multiply Eq. (A14-13) by $l - m$, Eq. (A14-14) by $l + m + 1$, and subtract, so that the terms on the left cancel. We find

$$(l + m + 1)P_{l-1}^{m+1} = (2l + 1)xP_l^{m+1} - (l - m)P_{l+1}^{m+1} \quad (A14\text{-}15)$$

If we replace $m + 1$ by m, this is Eq. (25-4). We have, then, proved Eqs. (11-6), (25-2), and (25-4). To prove Eq. (11-5), we take Eq. (A14-2), differentiate once with respect to x, and the result follows immediately. There are a good many other relations similar to the ones we have given, obtained by combining expressions which we have already found. Many of these are given by Kemble.[1]

We still have not proved the relation

$$\int_{-1}^{1} (P_l^m)^2 \, dx = \frac{2}{2l + 1} \frac{(l + m)!}{(l - m)!} \quad (A14\text{-}16)$$

of Eq. (7-11), used in normalizing the wave functions in the central-field problem. This relation is rather tedious to prove, though one starts with Eq. (A14-2) and proceeds fairly straightforwardly. We shall not give the proof, but it can be found, for instance, in Sommerfeld's book.[2]

[1] E. C. Kemble, "Fundamental Principles of Quantum Mechanics," p. 584, McGraw-Hill Book Company, Inc., New York, 1937.

[2] A. Sommerfeld, "Atombau und Spektrallinien," p. 71, Vieweg-Verlag, Brunswick, Germany, 1939.

Appendix 15

Solutions of the Hydrogen Radial Equation

In Eqs. (7-7) and (7-12) we have given two forms of the radial wave equation for hydrogen. If we make the change of variables $x = 2Zr/n$ and $E = -Z^2/n^2$, of Eqs. (7-21) and (7-22), the wave equation for the function P, which is r times the radial wave function, takes the form

$$\frac{d^2P}{dx^2} + \left[-\frac{1}{4} + \frac{n}{x} - \frac{l(l+1)}{x^2} \right] P = 0 \qquad \text{(A15-1)}$$

In Eq. (7-23) we give a normalized radial wave function, a solution of Eq. (A15-1), in the form

$$P_{nl}(x) = \sqrt{\frac{(n-l-1)!Z}{n^2[(n+l)!]^3}}\, x^{l+1} \exp \frac{-x}{2} L_{n+l}^{2l+1}(x) \qquad \text{(A15-2)}$$

where
$$L_{n+l}^{2l+1}(x) = B_0 + B_1 x + \cdots + B_{n-l-1}x^{n-l-1} \qquad \text{(A15-3)}$$

where the B's satisfy a recursion relation given in Eq. (7-24), and where

$$B_{n-l-1} = (-1)^{n+l}\frac{(n+l)!}{(n-l-1)!} \qquad \text{(A15-4)}$$

The function of Eq. (A15-2) is normalized in the sense that

$$\int_0^\infty P_{nl}^2(x)\, dr = 1 \qquad \text{(A15-5)}$$

where r is measured in atomic units and $P_{nl}(x)$ is expressed in terms of r.

We now substitute the expression of Eq. (A15-2) into Eq. (A15-1), to find the differential equation satisfied by L_{n+l}^{2l+1}. We find

$$x\frac{d^2L_q^p}{dx^2} + (p+1-x)\frac{dL_q^p}{dx} + (q-p)\, L_q^p = 0 \qquad \text{(A15-6)}$$

where we have used upper and lower indices p and q on the function L, in place of the specialized values $2l+1$ and $n+l$ found in Eq. (A15-2). The function $L_q^p(x)$ is called an associated Laguerre polynomial. We

461

shall now show that it can be written in the form

$$L_q^p(x) = \frac{d^p}{dx^p} L_q(x) \qquad \text{(A15-7)}$$

where
$$L_q(x) = e^x \frac{d^q}{dx^q} (x^q e^{-x}) \qquad \text{(A15-8)}$$

The functions $L_q(x)$ are called Laguerre polynomials.

Let us verify that Eq. (A15-6) is satisfied by the functions of Eq. (A15-7). We may rewrite Eq. (A15-6) in the form

$$x \frac{d^{p+2}}{dx^{p+2}} L_q + (p + 1 - x) \frac{d^{p+1}}{dx^{p+1}} L_q + (q - p) \frac{d^p}{dx^p} L_q = 0 \quad \text{(A15-9)}$$

We can now prove this equation by induction. If the equation is satisfied for one value of p, we can prove that it is satisfied for $p + 1$, by differentiating Eq. (A15-9) with respect to x and combining terms; we are led immediately to the same equation, with $p + 1$ substituted for p. In other words, Eq. (A15-6) is satisfied by Eq. (A15-7), for all values of p, provided it is satisfied for one value such as zero. For $p = 0$, Eq. (A15-6) reduces to

$$x \frac{d^2 L_q}{dx^2} + (1 - x) \frac{dL_q}{dx} + qL_q = 0 \qquad \text{(A15-10)}$$

If we can show that L_q, as defined in Eq. (A15-8), satisfies Eq. (A15-10), then we shall have proved that L_{n+l}^{2l+1}, defined by Eq. (A15-7), at least is proportional to the function given in Eq. (A15-3), since it satisfies the same differential equation. We shall have to investigate the multiplicative constant factor later.

To prove Eq. (A15-10), we substitute Eq. (A15-8) into Eq. (A15-10) and find

$$x \frac{d^{q+2}}{dx^{q+2}} (x^q e^{-x}) + (1 + x) \frac{d^{q+1}}{dx^{q+1}} (x^q e^{-x}) + (q + 1) \frac{d^q}{dx^q} (x^q e^{-x}) = 0$$
$$\text{(A15-11)}$$

In other words, if we can prove Eq. (A15-11), we shall have demonstrated Eq. (A15-10), which is what we wish to do.

To carry through this proof, we next show that

$$\frac{d^n}{dx^n} (x^q e^{-x}) = q! e^{-x} \sum_{s=0}^{n} \frac{(-1)^s n! x^{q-n+s}}{s!(n - s)!(q - n + s)!} \qquad \text{(A15-12)}$$

where n is any integer. This can be proved directly by differentiating the product $x^q e^{-x}$, or it can be proved by induction. To carry out the latter proof, we differentiate once with respect to x, combine terms, and can show that the result is the same as Eq. (A15-12), but with $n + 1$ in place of n. Hence, if Eq. (A15-12) holds for one value of n, it holds for all larger values. But it obviously holds for $n = 0$, so that the equation is satisfied.

We now use Eq. (A15-12) to compute the derivatives occurring in Eq. (A15-11). When we substitute these into Eq. (A15-11), we can combine terms and we find that it is satisfied. Hence we have completed our demonstration, which we have described in a reverse order, working backward from the answer which we wished to prove. We have shown from Eq. (A15-12), which is straightforwardly proved, that Eq. (A15-11) holds. This is equivalent to Eq. (A15-10), provided L_q is defined by Eq. (A15-8). But then we have shown that Eq. (A15-6) is satisfied by the function of Eq. (A15-7), provided Eq. (A15-10) holds, which we have now proved. Consequently, working still one step along, we have shown that the function of Eq. (A15-2), in which the associated Laguerre function is defined by Eqs. (15-7) and (15-8), satisfies Schrödinger's equation, Eq. (A15-1).

There is only one solution of Eq. (A15-1) in polynomial form for a given eigenvalue; the other solution of the equation is the one which goes exponentially infinite. Hence the function of Eq. (A15-7) must differ from the function of Eq. (A15-3) at most by a constant factor. Let us show that this factor is unity. To do so, we compare the terms of highest power in x in the two expressions and prove that they agree; since the functions must satisfy the same recursion formulas, on account of satisfying the same differential equations, this guarantees that the functions are identical. The term of highest power in x in Eq. (A15-3), using Eq. (A15-4), is found to be

$$(-1)^{n+l} \frac{(n + l)!}{(n - l - 1)!} x^{n-l-1} \tag{A15-13}$$

We have

$$L_{n+l}^{2l+1}(x) = \frac{d^{2l+1}}{dx^{2l+1}} \left[e^x \frac{d^{n+l}}{dx^{n+l}} \left(x^{n+l} e^{-x} \right) \right] \tag{A15-14}$$

The term of highest power in x, in the differentiation of $x^{n+l} e^{-x}$, will arise from differentiating e^{-x} each time, introducing merely a factor -1 for each differentiation, and resulting then in $(-1)^{n+l} x^{n+l} e^{-x}$. As far as the term of highest power in x is concerned, we then have

$$L_{n+l}^{2l+1}(x) = (-1)^{n+l} \frac{d^{2l+1}}{dx^{2l+1}} x^{n+l} + \text{terms of lower powers}$$

$$= (-1)^{n+l} \frac{(n + l)!}{(n - l - 1)!} x^{n-l-1} + \text{terms of lower powers}$$

$$\tag{A15-15}$$

This agrees with Eq. (A15-13) and completes the proof of the identity of the expressions of Eqs. (A15-3) and (A15-14).

Next let us check the normalization of the function of Eq. (A15-2). Since $dr = (n/2Z) \, dx$, we shall find that Eq. (A15-5) is satisfied provided

$$\frac{2n[(n + l)!]^2}{(n - l - 1)!} = \int_0^\infty x^{2l+2} e^{-x} [L_{n+l}^{2l+1}(x)]^2 \, dx \qquad \text{(A15-16)}$$

We shall now show that this equation holds. If we wrote $L_{n+l}^{2l+2}(x)$ in the form given in Eq. (A15-3), we should have to square the polynomial and integrate each term separately. This could be done, but it would involve many terms, and it would be hard to simplify the result. It proves to be simpler to write one of the two factors $L_{n+l}^{2l+1}(x)$ in the form of Eq. (A15-3) and the other in the form of Eq. (A15-14). When we do this, we have

$$\int_0^\infty x^{2l+2} e^{-x} [L_{n+l}^{2l+1}(x)]^2 \, dx$$

$$= \sum_{s=0}^{n-l-1} B_s \int_0^\infty x^{2l+2+s} e^{-x} \frac{d^{2l+1}}{dx^{2l+1}} \left[e^x \frac{d^{n+l}}{dx^{n+l}} (x^{n+l} e^{-x}) \right] dx \qquad \text{(A15-17)}$$

Here B_s is given by the recursion formula of Eq. (7-24), in combination with Eq. (A15-4).

We next integrate by parts $2l + 1$ times in Eq. (A15-17). The integrated terms drop out, and the expression above becomes equal to

$$- \sum_{s=0}^{n-l-1} B_s \int_0^\infty \frac{d^{2l+1}}{dx^{2l+1}} (x^{2l+2+s} e^{-x}) e^x \frac{d^{n+l}}{dx^{n+l}} (x^{n+l} e^{-x}) \, dx \qquad \text{(A15-18)}$$

We now use Eq. (A15-12) to rewrite the expression

$$\frac{d^{2l+1}}{dx^{2l+1}} (x^{2l+2+s} e^{-x})$$

using $n = 2l + 1$, $q = 2l + 2 + s$, and we find

$$\frac{d^{2l+1}}{dx^{2l+1}} (x^{2l+2+s} e^{-x}) = (2l + 2 + s)! e^{-x} \sum_{t=0}^{2l+1} \frac{(-1)^t (2l + 1)! x^{s+1+t}}{t!(2l + 1 - t)!(s + 1 + t)!}$$

$$\text{(A15-19)}$$

in which we have introduced t as an index of summation. When we insert this expression into Eq. (A15-18), that expression becomes equal to

$$-\sum_{s=0}^{n-l-1} B_s \sum_{t=0}^{2l+1} \frac{(2l+2+s)!(2l+1)!(-1)^t}{t!(2l+1-t)!(s+1+t)!} \int_0^\infty x^{s+1+t} \frac{d^{n+l}}{dx^{n+l}} (x^{n+l}e^{-x})\, dx$$

$$(A15\text{-}20)$$

We now integrate by parts $n+l$ times in the integral of Eq. (A15-20). Again the integrated terms drop out, and we are left with

$$\int_0^\infty x^{s+1+t} \frac{d^{n+l}}{dx^{n+l}} (x^{n+l}e^{-x})\, dx$$

$$= (-1)^{n+l} \int_0^\infty \frac{d^{n+l}}{dx^{n+l}} (x^{s+1+t}) x^{n+l}e^{-x}\, dx$$

$$= (-1)^{n+l} \int_0^\infty \frac{(s+1+t)!}{(s+1+t-n-l)!} x^{s+1+t}e^{-x}\, dx$$

$$= (-1)^{n+l} \frac{[(s+1+t)!]^2}{(s+1+t-n-l)!} \qquad \text{if } s+1+t-n-l \ge 0$$

$$= 0 \qquad \text{if } s+1+t-n-l < 0 \quad (A15\text{-}21)$$

The case where $s+1+t-n-l < 0$ is that in which the differentiations of x^{s+1+t} reduce the integrand to zero.

Hence the integral which we are computing, from Eq. (A15-20), reduces to

$$\sum_{s=0}^{n-l-1} B_s \sum_{t=0}^{2l+1} \frac{(2l+2+s)!(2l+1)!(s+1+t)!(-1)^{n+l+t+1}}{t!(2l+1-t)!(s+1+t-n-l)!} \quad (A15\text{-}22)$$

where the summation is to extend only over those values of s and t for which $s+1+t-n-l \ge 0$. When we examine the situation, we find that the only terms in the double summation which contribute to the result are, for $s = n-l-1$, $t = 2l$ and $2l+1$ and, for $s = n-l-2$, $t = 2l+1$. These three terms are simple to compute, and we see the advantage of this procedure, in that we have reduced the problem to a sum of only three terms, instead of many terms as we should have had if we had proceeded directly. We get B_{n-l-1} from Eq. (A15-4), B_{n-l-2} from the recursion relation, Eq. (7-24), substitute into Eq. (A15-22), and the terms simplify without trouble, leading to the result of Eq. (A15-16).

This method, then, leads straightforwardly to the normalization integral. Ordinarily a more involved proof is used, based on what is called a generating function,[1] but, as we have seen, this is unnecessary, though

---

[1] For such a proof, see, for instance, A. Sommerfeld, "Atombau und Spektrallinien," Vieweg-Verlag, Brunswick, Germany, 1939.

the proof by means of the generating function is rather more elegant than the one we have given.   We now readily see that the same method we have used can be adapted for finding the diagonal matrix component of any power of r or of x: we insert an extra factor x^k, where k is the desired power, into the integrand of Eq. (A15-17) and from that point proceed by the same general method we have used.   We shall not give the steps, which are derived from Waller,[1] but in Table A15-1 we give the average

Table A15-1. Diagonal Matrix Components of r^k, for $k = 2, 1, -1, -2,$ $-3, -4,$ for the Hydrogenlike Wave Functions

$$(r^2)_{av} = \frac{a_0^2 n^4}{Z^2}\left\{1 + \frac{3}{2}\left[1 - \frac{l(l+1) - \frac{1}{3}}{n^2}\right]\right\}$$

$$r_{av} = \frac{a_0 n^2}{Z}\left\{1 + \frac{1}{2}\left[1 - \frac{l(l+1)}{n^2}\right]\right\}$$

$$\left(\frac{1}{r}\right)_{av} = \frac{Z}{a_0 n^2}$$

$$\left(\frac{1}{r^2}\right)_{av} = \frac{Z^2}{a_0^2 n^3 (l + \frac{1}{2})}$$

$$\left(\frac{1}{r^3}\right)_{av} = \frac{Z^3}{a_0^3 n^3 l(l + \frac{1}{2})(l + 1)}$$

$$\left(\frac{1}{r^4}\right)_{av} = \frac{\frac{3}{2} Z^4 [1 - l(l+1)/3n^2]}{a_0^4 n^3 (l + \frac{3}{2})(l + 1)(l + \frac{1}{2}) l(l - \frac{1}{2})}$$

values of r^k, for $k = 2, 1, -1, -2, -3, -4$, for the hydrogen wave functions, computed in this way.   The case $k = 2$ is needed for study of diamagnetism; $k = -1$ for the potential energy; $k = -3$ for the spin-orbit interaction.   The same type of argument can be used for calculating various other quantities: kinetic energy, nondiagonal matrix components of the dipole moment (needed for finding transition probabilities), and for demonstrating the orthogonality of the functions.

In Sec. 18-3 (Vol. II), we have mentioned that the functions $r^l e^{-ar}$ provide a set from which one can construct an infinite number of orthogonal functions forming a complete set, in terms of which it is convenient to expand the helium problem.   These functions, all of which have the same exponential, are to be contrasted with the ordinary hydrogenic functions, which have the exponential $e^{-x/2}$, where $x = 2Zr/n$, different for each value of n.   The functions which we are now describing are related to the hydrogenic ones, however, and can also be expressed in terms of the Laguerre functions.   Thus, one can prove that, if x is now defined as

[1] I. Waller, Z. Physik, **38**:635 (1926).

$x = 2ar$, these functions can be expressed in the form

$$u_{nl} = \frac{1}{(n + l + 1)!} \frac{1}{\sqrt{(n + l + 1)(n + l)(n + l - 1) \cdots (n - l)}}$$
$$\times e^{-x/2} x^l L_{n+l+1}^{2l+2}(x) \quad \text{(A15-23)}$$

These functions are normalized in the sense that

$$\int_0^\infty u_{nl}^2(x) x^2 \, dx = 1$$

One can use the same general methods just employed to prove the orthogonality and normalization of these functions; that is, all that is required to show that the functions of Eq. (A15-23) are in fact those described in the text. The proofs follow, as in our previous discussion, by expressing one of the functions in the form of Eq. (A15-3), the other in the form of Eq. (A15-14). After one has set up the function in the form of Eq. (A15-23), one finds that the integrals of the kinetic- and potential-energy operators over the wave function can be expressed in simple analytic forms, the derivations using the same type of argument already employed.

Appendix 16

Bibliography of the Hartree and Hartree-Fock Methods

In this appendix we give a bibliography of papers dealing with the Hartree and Hartree-Fock methods or, more broadly, with methods of atomic calculations based on the variation principle. We include not only those giving calculations by the methods but also those going into the general principles. For convenience in following the development of the subject, the bibliography is arranged chronologically and alphabetically within each year. In cases where the title is not sufficiently descriptive, we give a few additional comments as to the contents of the paper.

1928

Gaunt, J. A.: A Theory of Hartree's Atomic Fields, *Proc. Cambridge Phil. Soc.*, **24**:328 (1928).

Hartree, D. R.: The Wave Mechanics of an Atom with a Noncoulomb Central Field. Part I. Theory and Methods. Part II. Some Results and Discussions, *Proc. Cambridge Phil. Soc.*, **24**:89, 111 (1928). [Calculations on He, Rb+, Rb, Na+, Cl−.]

———: The Wave Mechanics of an Atom with a Noncoulomb Central Field. Part III. Term Values and Intensities in Series in Optical Spectra, *Proc. Cambridge Phil. Soc.*, **24**:426 (1928).

Hylleraas, E. A.: Über den Grundzustand des Heliumatoms, *Z. Physik*, **48**:469 (1928).

Slater, J. C.: The Self Consistent Field and the Structure of Atoms, *Phys. Rev.*, **32**:339 (1928).

1929

Gaunt, J. A.: The Triplets of Helium, *Proc. Roy. Soc. (London)*, **A122**:513 (1929); *Phil. Trans. Roy. Soc. (London)*, **A228**:151 (1929).

———: Relativistic Theory of an Atom with Many Electrons, *Proc. Roy. Soc. (London)*, **A124**:163 (1929).

Hargreaves, J.: Dispersion Electrons of Li, *Proc. Cambridge Phil. Soc.*, **25**:75 (1929).

Hartree, D. R.: The Wave Mechanics of an Atom with a Noncoulomb Central Field. IV. Further Results Relating to Terms of the Optical Spectra, *Proc. Cambridge Phil. Soc.*, **25**:310 (1929).

Hylleraas, E.: Die Energie des Heliumatoms im Grundzustande, *Physik. Z.*, **30**:249 (1929).

———: Neue Berechnung der Energie des Heliums im Grundzustande, sowie des tiefsten Terms von Orthohelium, *Z. Physik*, **54**:347 (1929).

1930

Eckart, C.: Theory and Calculation of Screening Constants, *Phys. Rev.*, **36**:878 (1930).

Fock, V.: Näherungsmethode zur Lösung des quantenmechanischen Mehrkörperproblems, *Z. Physik*, **61**:126 (1930).

———: "Self-consistent Field" mit Austausch für Natrium, *Z. Physik*, **62**:795 (1930).

Guillemin, Jr., V., and C. Zener: Über eine einfache Eigenfunktion für den Grundzustand des Li-atoms und der Ionen mit drei Elektronen, *Z. Physik*, **61**:199 (1930).

Hylleraas, E.: Die Elektronenaffinität des Wasserstoffatoms nach der Wellenmechanik, *Z. Physik*, **60**:624 (1930); **63**:291 (1930).

———: Über den Grundterm der Zweielektronenprobleme von H⁻, He, Li⁺, Be⁺⁺ usw., *Z. Physik*, **65**:209 (1930).

——— and B. Undheim: Numerische Berechnung der 2S-terme von Ortho- und Parhelium, *Z. Physik*, **65**:759 (1930).

———: Die Para-orthoaufspaltung und der Mittelwert der S-terme von Helium bei hohen Quantenzahlen, *Z. Physik*, **66**:453 (1930).

Slater, J. C.: Note on Hartree's Method, *Phys. Rev.*, **35**:210 (1930).

———: Atomic Shielding Constants, *Phys. Rev.*, **36**:57 (1930).

Zener, C.: Analytic Atomic Wave Functions, *Phys. Rev.*, **36**:51 (1930).

1931

Lennard-Jones, J. E.: Wave Functions of Many-electron Atoms, *Proc. Cambridge Phil. Soc.*, **27**:469 (1931).

1932

Brillouin, L.: Les Problèmes de perturbations et les champs self-consistents, *J. phys. radium*, **7**(3):373 (1932).

McDougall, J.: Calculation of the Terms of the Optical Spectrum of an Atom with One Series Electron, *Proc. Roy. Soc. (London)*, **A138**:550 (1932). [Calculations for Si³⁺, Si⁴⁺, by Hartree-Fock method.]

Slater, J. C.: Analytic Atomic Wave Functions, *Phys. Rev.*, **42**:33 (1932).

Weinstein, D. H.: Lower Limit for the Ground State of the Helium Atom, *Phys. Rev.*, **40**:797 (1932).

1933

Bartlett, Jr., J. H., and J. J. Gibbons, Jr.: Isotope Shift in Neon, *Phys. Rev.*, **44**:538 (1933). [Includes wave functions for neon.]

Brillouin, L.: La Méthode du champ self-consistent, *Actualités sci. ind.*, vol. 71 (1933).

Brown, F. W.: Charge Distributions in Fluorine and Neon, *Phys. Rev.*, **44**:214 (1933). [Calculations for F, F⁻, Ne.]

———, J. H. Bartlett, Jr., and C. G. Dunn: Charge Distributions for the Normal Atoms from Boron to Neon, *Phys. Rev.*, **44**:296 (1933). [Calculations for B, interpolation for C, N.]

Hartree, D. R., and M. M. Black: A Theoretical Investigation of the Oxygen Atom in

Various States of Ionization, *Proc. Roy. Soc.* (*London*), **A139**:311 (1933). [Calculations for O, O$^+$, O^{++}, O^{3+}.]

————: Results of Calculations of Atomic Wave Functions I. Survey, and Self-consistent Fields for Cl$^-$ and Cu$^+$, *Proc. Roy. Soc.* (*London*), **A141**:282 (1933).

Hylleraas, E.: Wellenmechanische Berechnung der Rydbergkorrektion der Heliumterme, *Z. Physik*, **83**:739 (1933).

Koopmans, T. A.: Über die Zuordnung von Wellenfunktionen und Eigenwerten zu den einzelnen Elektronen eines Atoms, *Physica*, **1**:104 (1933).

Vinti, J. P., and P. M. Morse: Variable Scale Atomic Wave functions, *Phys. Rev.*, **43**:337 (1933).

Wilson, Jr., E. B.: Wave Functions for the Ground State of Lithium and Three-electron Ions, *J. Chem. Phys.*, **1**:210 (1933).

1934

Black, M. M.: Approximate Numerical Values of the Atomic Field and Radial Wave Functions of the Silver Ion Ag$^+$, *Mem. Proc. Manchester Lit. & Phil. Soc.*, **79**:29 (1934–1935).

Brillouin, L.: Les Champs "self-consistents" de Hartree et de Fock, *Actualités sci. ind.*, vol. 159 (1934).

————: L'Atome de Thomas-Fermi et la méthode du champ "self-consistent," *Actualités sci. ind.*, vol. 160 (1934).

————: Le modéle d'atomes de Fock-Dirac et l'existence des potentials d'ionisation, *J. phys. radium*, **5**:185 (1934).

Fock, V., and M. Petrashen: On the Numerical Solution of Generalized Equations of the Self-consistent Field, *Physik. Z. Sowjetunion*, **6**:368 (1934).

Hartree, D. R.: Results of Calculations of Atomic Wave Functions II. Results for K$^+$ and Cs$^+$, *Proc. Roy. Soc.* (*London*), **A143**:506 (1934).

————: Approximate Wave Functions and Atomic Fields for Mercury, *Phys. Rev.*, **46**:783 (1934).

Hylleraas, E.: Polarisationseffekt der Helium-D-terme, Dipol und Quadrupoleffekt, *Z. Physik*, **88**:108 (1934).

Kennard, E. H., and E. Ramberg: Self-consistent Field and Some X-ray Terms of the Sodium Atom, *Phys. Rev.*, **46**:1034 (1934).

Møller, C., and M. S. Plesset: Approximate Treatment for Many-electron Systems, *Phys. Rev.*, **46**:618 (1934).

Porter, A.: Approximate Determination of the Atomic Wave Function of Chromium, *Mem. Proc. Manchester Lit. & Phil. Soc.*, **79**:75 (1934–35). [Calculations for Cr, Cr^{++}.]

Torrance, C. C.: Hartree Fields for Carbon, *Phys. Rev.*, **46**:388 (1934).

1935

Bartlett, Jr., J. H., J. J. Gibbons, and C. G. Dunn: Normal Helium Atom, *Phys. Rev.*, **47**:679 (1935).

Fock, V., and Mary J. Petrashen: Analytical Wave Functions for Beryllium-like Atoms, *Physik. Z. Sowjetunion*, **8**:359 (1935). [Calculations for Be, B$^+$, C^{++}, N^{3+}, O^{4+}, by Hartree-Fock.]

———— and ————: Self-consistent Field with Exchange for Lithium, *Physik. Z. Sowjetunion*, **8**:547 (1935).

Gibbons, J. J., and J. H. Bartlett, Jr.: Magnetic Moment of the K^{39} Nucleus, *Phys. Rev.*, **47**:692 (1935). [Includes calculation of K valence electron.]

Hartree, D. R., and W. Hartree: Results of Calculations of Atomic Wave Functions

III. Results for Be, Ca, and Hg, *Proc. Roy. Soc. (London)*, **A149**:210 (1935). [Calculations for Be, Be++, Ca, Ca++, Hg, Hg++.]

—— and ——: Self-consistent Field with Exchange for Beryllium, *Proc. Roy. Soc. (London)*, **A150**:9 (1935).

——: Results of Calculations of Atomic Wave Functions IV. Results for F⁻, Al+3, and Rb+, *Proc. Roy. Soc. (London)*, **A151**:96 (1935).

Morse, P. M., L. A. Young, and Eva S. Haurwitz: Tables for Determining Atomic Wave Functions and Energies, *Phys. Rev.*, **48**:948 (1935).

Romberg, W.: Lower Limit of the Helium Ground-state Calculated by the Ritz Method, *Physik. Z. Sowjetunion*, **8**:516 (1935).

Swirles, B.: Relativistic Self-consistent Field, *Proc. Roy. Soc. (London)*, **A152**:625 (1935).

Wilson, W. S., and R. B. Lindsay: Atomic Wave Functions for Excited States of Helium, *Phys. Rev.*, **47**:681 (1935).

——: Atomic Energy States for Excited Helium, *Phys. Rev.*, **48**:536 (1935).

1936

Coolidge, A. S., and H. M. James: Wave Functions for 1s2s ¹S Helium, *Phys. Rev.*, **49**:676 (1936).

Donley, H. L.: Atomic Wave Functions for Two Stages of Ionization of Silicon, *Phys. Rev.*, **50**:1012 (1936). [Calculations for Si++, Si3+.]

Hartree, D. R., and W. Hartree: Self-consistent Field with Exchange for Beryllium II. The 2s2p ³P and ¹P excited states, *Proc. Roy. Soc. (London)*, **A154**:588 (1936).

—— and ——: Self-consistent Field, with Exchange, for Cl⁻, *Proc. Roy. Soc. (London)*, **A156**:45 (1936).

—— and ——: Self-consistent Field, with Exchange, for Cu+, *Proc. Roy. Soc. (London)*, **A157**:490 (1936).

James, H. M., and A. S. Coolidge: Ground State of Lithium, *Phys. Rev.*, **49**:688 (1936).

Manning, M. F., and J. Millman: Self-consistent Field for Tungsten, *Phys. Rev.*, **49**:848 (1936).

Swirles, Bertha: Relativistic Interaction of Two Electrons in the Self-consistent Field Method, *Proc. Roy. Soc. (London)*, **A157**:680 (1936).

Wu, T.-Y., and S. T. Ma: Variational Wave Functions of Doubly Excited States of Helium, *J. Chinese Chem. Soc.*, **4**:344 (1936).

1937

Bartlett, Jr., J. H.: Helium Wave Equation, *Phys. Rev.*, **51**:661 (1937).

Gronwall, T. H.: Helium Wave Equation, *Phys. Rev.*, **51**:655 (1937).

Hartree, D. R., and Bertha Swirles: Effect of Configuration Interaction on the Low Terms of the Spectra of Oxygen, *Proc. Cambridge Phil. Soc.*, **33**:240 (1937).

Stevenson, A. F.: Spherical Symmetry of Self-consistent Fields, *Phys. Rev.*, **51**:285 (1937).

——: Generalization of the Equations of the Self-consistent Field for Two-electron Configurations, *Proc. Roy. Soc. (London)*, **A160**:588 (1937).

1938

Hartree, D. R., and W. Hartree: Self-consistent Field with Exchange for Calcium, *Proc. Roy. Soc. (London)*, **A164**:167 (1938). [Calculations for Ca, Ca+, Ca++.]

—— and ——: Self-consistent Field with Exchange for Potassium and Argon, *Proc. Roy. Soc. (London)*, **A166**:450 (1938).

—— and ——: Wave Functions for Negative Ions of Sodium and Potassium, *Proc. Cambridge Phil. Soc.*, **34**:550 (1938).

Kritschagina, A., and M. Petrashen: Self-consistent Field with Exchange for Al^{++}, *J. Exptl. Theoret. Phys.* (*U.S.S.R.*), **8**:507 (1938).

Manning, M. F., and L. Goldberg: Self-consistent Field for Iron, *Phys. Rev.*, **53**:662 (1938).

Stevenson, A. F., and M. F. Crawford: Lower Limit for Theoretical Energy of Normal State of Helium, *Phys. Rev.*, **54**:375 (1938).

Swirles, B.: Construction of Zero-order Wave Functions for Complex Atoms, *Mem. Proc. Manchester Lit. & Phil. Soc.*, **82**:21 (1938).

Ufford, C. W.: Term Values in Carbon, *Phys. Rev.*, **53**:568 (1938).

1939

Goldberg, L., and A. M. Clogston: Variational Atomic Wave Functions, *Phys. Rev.*, **56**:696 (1939).

Hartree, D. R., W. Hartree, and B. Swirles: Self-consistent Field, Including Exchange and Superposition of Configurations, with Some Results for Oxygen, *Phil. Trans. Roy. Soc.* (*London*), **A238**:229 (1939). [Results for O, O$^+$, O^{++}, O^{3+}.]

Jucys, A.: Self-consistent Field with Exchange for Carbon, *Proc. Roy. Soc.* (*London*), **A173**:59 (1939). [Results for C, C^{++}, C^{4+}.]

Mooney, R. L.: Self-consistent Field for Doubly-ionized Chromium, *Phys. Rev.*, **55**:557 (1939).

Stevenson, A. F.: Method for Improved Calculation of Energies of Two-electron Configurations from Hartree Functions: Application to $2p^2$ Terms of O III, *Phys. Rev.*, **56**:586 (1939).

Thatcher, W. A.: Calculated Wave Functions and Energy Values for X-ray Terms of Potassium, *Proc. Roy. Soc.* (*London*), **A172**:242 (1939).

1940

Williams, A. O.: Relativistic Self-consistent Field for Cu$^+$, *Phys. Rev.*, **58**:723 (1940).

Yost, W. J.: Self-consistent Field for Doubly Ionized Magnesium, *Phys. Rev.*, **57**:557 (1940).

————: Self-consistent Fields and Diamagnetic Susceptibility for Magnesium III, *Phys. Rev.*, **58**:557 (1940).

1941

Gray, R. B., and M. F. Manning: Self-consistent Field Calculation for Nickel, *Phys. Rev.*, **59**:475 (1941).

Hartree, D. R., W. Hartree, and M. F. Manning: Self-consistent Field, with Exchange, for Si IV and Si V, *Phys. Rev.*, **60**:857 (1941).

Hartree, W., D. R. Hartree, and M. F. Manning: Self-consistent Field Calculations for Zn, Ga, Ga$^+$, Ga^{+3}, Ge, Ge^{+2}, As, As$^+$, As^{+2}, As^{+3}, *Phys. Rev.*, **59**:299, 306 (1941).

1942

Peter, G.: Berechnung der Energie des ($4s$-$5s$)-triplett-S-zustandes des Ca-atoms, *Z. Physik.*, **119**:713 (1942).

Wheeler, T. S.: The Energy of the $1s2s$ ^3S State of the Helium Atom and Related Two-electron Ions, *Proc. Roy. Irish Acad.*, **48**:43 (1942).

Williamson, R. E.: The Wave Function for the Negative Hydrogen Ion, *Phys. Rev.*, **62**:538 (1942).

1943

Chandrasekhar, S., and M. K. Klogdahl: On the Negative Hydrogen Ion and Its Absorption Coefficient, *Astrophys. J.*, **98**:205 (1943).

1944

Chandrasekhar, S.: The Negative Ions of Hydrogen and Oxygen in Stellar Atmospheres, *Revs. Modern Phys.*, **16**:301 (1944).

Duncanson, W. E., and C. A. Coulson: Atomic Wave Functions for Ground States of Elements Li to Ne, *Proc. Roy. Soc. Edinburgh*, **62**:37 (1944).

Wu, T.-Y., and S. T. Shen: Variational Energies of Anomalous States of 2- and 3-electron Configurations of Light Atoms, *Chinese J. Phys.*, **5**:150 (1944).

1945

Kou, T. J., and T.-Y. Wu: Hylleraasian Wave Function of $2s^2$ ^1S State of Helium, *Chinese J. Phys.*, **6**:50 (1945).

Ku, T. Z.: Separable Wave Functions of the Ground State of Helium, Constructed from Hylleraas's Wave Function, *Chinese J. Phys.*, **6**:21 (1945).

1946

Biermann, L.: Normierte Wellenfunktionen verschiedener Zustände des Leuchtelektrons und Oszillatorenstärken der Übergängen zwischen ihnen für Na, K, Mg+, Si+, Al, *Nachr. Akad. Wiss. Göttingen*, (2):116 (1946).

Hartree, D. R.: The Calculation of Atomic Structures, *Repts. Progr. Phys.*, **11**:113 (1946).

Huang, K.: Wave Function for the Ground State of Lithium, *Phys. Rev.*, **70**:197 (1946).

1947

Jucys, A.: Self-consistent Field with Exchange for the Configurations $1s^22s2p^3$ and $1s^22p^4$ of carbon, *J. Phys. (U.S.S.R.)*, **11**:49 (1947).

1948

Conwell, E.: Non-product Wave Function for a Negative Ion, *Phys. Rev.*, **74**:268 (1948).

———: Wave Functions for H⁻ Obtained by Variation Method, *Phys. Rev.*, **74**:277 (1948).

Hartree, D. R., and W. Hartree: Self-consistent Field, with Exchange, for Nitrogen and Sodium, *Proc. Roy. Soc. (London)*, **A193**:299 (1948). [Results for N, N⁻, Na, Na⁺.]

Tutihasi, J.: Analytical Expression of Self-consistent Wave Functions for Lithium, Boron, Carbon, and Oxygen, *J. Phys. Soc. Japan*, **3**:135 (1948).

1949

Biermann, L., and E. Trefftz: Wellenfunktionen und Übergangswahrscheinlichkeiten der Leuchtelektronen des Atoms Mg I, *Z. Astrophys.*, **26**:240 (1949).

Gold, M. T.: Wave Functions for Fe XIV, *Monthly Notices Roy. Astron. Soc.*, **109**:471 (1949).

Trefftz, E.: Wellenfunktionen und Übergangswahrscheinlichkeiten der Leuchtelektronen des Atoms Mg I, II, *Z. Astrophys.*, **26**:240 (1949).

Wataki, W.: Analytical Expression of Self-consistent Functions and Doublet Intervals for FI, Ne II, Mg IV, and Al IV, *Progr. Theoret. Phys. (Kyoto)*, **4**:42 (1949).

Yutsis, A. P.: Interaction of Configurations in the Carbon Atom, *J. Exptl. Theoret. Phys. (U.S.S.R.)*, **19**:565 (1949).

1950

Boys, S. F.: Electronic Wave Functions II. A Calculation for the Ground State of the Beryllium Atom, *Proc. Roy. Soc. (London)*, **A201**:125 (1950).

Dickinson, W. C.: Hartree Computation of the Internal Diamagnetic Field for Atoms, *Phys. Rev.*, **80**:563 (1950).

Hylleraas, E. A.: A New Stable State of the Negative Hydrogen Ion, *Astrophys. J.*, **111**:209 (1950).

——— and S. Skavlem: On the Magnetic Shielding in He and H₂, *Phys. Rev.*, **79**:117 (1950).

Majumdar, S. D., and D. C. Chowdhury: Wave Function for the Ground State of Lithium, *Z. Physik*, **128**:455 (1950).

Pluvinage, P.: Fonction d'onde approchée à un paramètre pour l'état fondamental des atomes à deux électrons, *Ann. phys.*, **5**:145 (1950).

Trefftz, E.: Wellenfunktionen und Übergangswahrscheinlichkeiten beim Atom Mg I, III. Der Einfluss der Polarisation, *Z. Astrophys.*, **28**:67 (1950).

1951

Garstang, R. H.: Self-consistent Field, with Exchange, for Ne III, *Proc. Cambridge Phil. Soc.*, **47**:243 (1951).

Kato, T.: On the Existence of Solutions of the Helium Wave Equation, *Trans. Am. Math. Soc.*, **70**:212 (1951).

Luke, P. J., R. E. Meyerott, and W. W. Clendenin: Wave Function of Ionized Lithium, *Phys. Rev.*, **83**:847 (1951).

Meyerott, R. E., and W. W. Clendenin: Wave Function of Ionized Lithium, *Phys. Rev.*, **83**:847 (1951).

Pluvinage, P.: A New Family of Approximate Solutions for Certain Non-separable Schrödinger Equations. Application to the Ground State of Helium, *J. phys. radium*, **12**:789 (1951).

Slater, J. C.: A Simplification of the Hartree-Fock Method, *Phys. Rev.*, **81**:385 (1951).

———: Magnetic Effects and the Hartree-Fock Equation, *Phys. Rev.*, **82**:538 (1951).

Trefftz, E.: Wellenfunktionen des neutralen Calciumatoms, *Z. Astrophys.*, **29**:287 (1951).

Yutsis, A. P., and V. J. Kavetskis: Interaction of Configurations in Atoms of Beryllium Type, *J. Exptl. Theoret. Phys. (U.S.S.R.)*, **21**:1139 (1951).

1952

Bartlett, Jr., J. H.: Iterative Procedures and the Helium Wave Equation, *Phys. Rev.*, **88**:525 (1952).

Bernal, M. J., and S. F. Boys: Electronic Wave Functions VIII. A Calculation of the Ground States of Na⁺, Ne, and F⁻, *Phil. Trans. Roy. Soc. (London)*, **A245**:139 (1952).

Green, L. C., M. M. Mulder, C. W. Ufford, E. Slaymaker, E. Krawitz, and R. T. Mertz: Superposition of Configurations in the Ground State of He I, *Phys. Rev.*, **85**:65 (1952).

Lennard-Jones, J. E., and J. A. Pople: The Spatial Correlation of Electrons in Atoms and Molecules I. Helium and Similar Two-electron Systems in Their Ground States, *Phil. Mag.*, **43**:581 (1952).

Luke, P. J., R. E. Meyerott, and W. W. Clendenin: Wave Function of Ionized Lithium, *Phys. Rev.*, **85**:401 (1952).

Mishra, B.: Wave Functions for Excited States of Mercury and Potassium, *Proc. Cambridge Phil. Soc.*, **48**:511 (1952).

Pratt, Jr., G. W.: Wave Functions and Energy Levels for Cu^+ as Found by the Slater Approximation to the Hartree-Fock Equations, *Phys. Rev.*, **88**:1217 (1952).

Taylor, R. G., and R. G. Parr: Superposition of Configurations: The Helium Atom, *Proc. Natl. Acad. Sci. (U.S.)*, **38**:154 (1952).

Trefftz, E., and L. Biermann: Wellenfunktionen und Oszillatorenstärken des Calciumions Ca II; die Zustände $4s$, $4p$, und $3d$, *Z. Astrophys.*, **30**:275 (1952).

Yutsis, A. P.: Fock Equations in Many-configuration Approximation, *J. Exptl. Theoret. Phys. (U.S.S.R.)*, **23**:129 (1952).

———: The Application of the Method of the Partial Separation of Variables to Two Equivalent p-electrons, *J. Exptl. Theoret. Phys. (U.S.S.R.)*, **23**:357 (1952).

———: The Generalization of the Theory of the Partial Separation of Variables to the Case of Polyvalent Atoms, *J. Exptl. Theoret. Phys. (U.S.S.R.)*, **23**:371 (1952).

———: The Fock Self-consistent Field for the Configuration $1s^2 2p^2$ of the Beryllium Atom, *J. Exptl. Theoret. Phys. (U.S.S.R.)*, **23**:512 (1952).

1953

Boys, S. F.: Electronic Wave Functions IX. Calculation for the Three Lowest States of the Beryllium Atom, *Proc. Roy. Soc. (London)*, **A217**:136 (1953).

———: Electronic Wave Functions X. A Calculation of Eight Variational Poly-Deter Wave Functions for Boron and Carbon, *Proc. Roy. Soc. (London)*, **A217**:235 (1953).

Chandrasekhar, S., D. Elbert, and G. Herzberg: Shift of the 1 ^1S State of Helium, *Phys. Rev.*, **91**:1172 (1953).

Freeman, A. J.: Effective Nuclear Charges for Atoms from Self-consistent Field Calculations, *Phys. Rev.*, **91**:1410 (1953).

Green, L. C., M. M. Mulder, and P. C. Milner: Correlation Energy in the Ground State of He I, *Phys. Rev.*, **91**:35 (1953).

Katterbach, K.: Die Wellenfunktionen des Al III und Al IV, *Z. Astrophys.*, **32**:165 (1953).

Löwdin, P.-O.: Studies of Atomic Self-consistent Fields I. Calculation of Slater Functions, *Phys. Rev.*, **90**:120 (1953).

Slater, J. C.: A Generalized Self-consistent Field Method, *Phys. Rev.*, **91**:528 (1953).

Williams, Jr., A. O.: Two-electron Self-consistent Field, *Phys. Rev.*, **90**:803 (1953).

Wu, T.-Y.: The Spectrum of Discrete Eigenvalues in a Negative Atomic Ion, *Phys. Rev.*, **89**:629 (1953).

1954

Boys, S. F., and V. E. Price: Electronic Wave Functions XI. A Calculation of Eight Variational Wave Functions for Cl, Cl$^-$, S, and S$^-$, *Phil. Trans. Roy. Soc. (London)*, **A246**:451 (1954).

Green, L. C., M. N. Lewis, M. M. Mulder, C. W. Wyeth, and J. W. Woll, Jr.: Correlation Energies and Angular Components of the Wave Functions of the Ground States of H$^-$, He, and Li II, *Phys. Rev.*, **93**:273 (1954).

———, M. M. Mulder, M. N. Lewis, and J. W. Woll, Jr.: A Discussion of Analytic and Hartree-Fock Wave Functions for $1s^2$ Configurations from H$^-$ to C V, *Phys. Rev.*, **93**:757 (1954).

———, ———, P. C. Milner, M. N. Lewis, J. W. Woll, Jr., E. K. Kokhin, and D. Mace: Analysis of the Three Parameter Wave Function of Hylleraas for the

He I Ground State in Terms of Central Field Wave Functions, *Phys. Rev.*, **96**:319 (1954).

Henry, W. G.: The Self-consistent Field for Au$^+$, *Proc. Phys. Soc. (London)*, **A67**:789 (1954).

Löwdin, P.-O.: Studies of Atomic Self-consistent Fields II. Interpolation Problems, *Phys. Rev.*, **94**:1600 (1954).

Meyerott, R. E.: Approximate Hartree-type Wave Functions and Matrix Elements for the K and L Shells of Atoms and Ions, *Phys. Rev.*, **95**:72 (1954).

Morrow, J. C.: Hartree-Fock-Slater Self-consistent Field, and the Calculation of Some Properties of the Cu$^+$ Ion, *J. Chem. Phys.*, **58**:245 (1954).

Munschy, G., and P. Pluvinage: Fonctions d'onde approchées à un paramètre pour les états 2s de He I, *J. phys. radium*, **15**:122 (1954).

1955

Altmann, S. L.: The Self-consistent Field for Zr^{+4}, *Proc. Phys. Soc. (London)*, **A68**:987 (1955).

Bartlett, Jr., J. H.: Helium Wave Equation, *Phys. Rev.*, **98**:1067 (1955).

Bolotin, A. B., I. B. Levinson, and L. I. Levin: The Two-configurational Approximation in the Case of Atoms of the Type of Carbon, *J. Exptl. Theoret. Phys. (U.S.S.R.)*, **29**:449 (1955).

Chandrasekhar, S., and G. Herzberg: Energies of the Ground State of He, Li$^+$, and O^{+6}, *Phys. Rev.*, **98**:1050 (1955).

Douglas, A. S., D. R. Hartree, and W. A. Runciman: Atomic Wave Functions for Gold and Thallium, *Proc. Cambridge Phil. Soc.*, **51**:486 (1955).

Glembotskii, I. I., V. V. Kibartas, and A. P. Yutsis: Self-consistent Field of Fock in the Two-configurational Approximation for Boron, *J. Exptl. Theoret. Phys. (U.S.S.R.)*, **29**:617 (1955).

Hartree, D. R.: Approximate Wave Functions, with Exchange, for Mn^{+2}, *Proc. Cambridge Phil. Soc.*, **51**:126 (1955).

————: The Interpolation of Atomic Wave Functions, *Proc. Cambridge Phil. Soc.*, **51**:684 (1955).

Holøien, E.: Note on a Search for Simple Analytic Wave Functions for Configurations $1s^2 2s$ and $1s^2 2s^2$ in Atoms and Ions from He to C, *Proc. Phys. Soc. (London)*, **A68**:297 (1955).

Kibartas, V. V., V. I. Kavetskis, and A. P. Yutsis: Self-consistent Field of Fock in the Three-configurational Approximation for Beryllium, *J. Exptl. Theoret. Phys. (U.S.S.R.)*, **29**:623 (1955).

Löwdin, P.-O.: Quantum Theory of Many-particle Systems, I, II, III, *Phys. Rev.*, **97**:1474, 1490, 1509 (1955).

Mitler, H.: Correlation Energy of Helium, *Phys. Rev.*, **99**:1835 (1955).

Pluvinage, P.: Approximations systématiques dans la résolution de l'équation de Schrödinger des atomes à deux électrons I. Principe de la méthode. États S symétriques, *J. phys. radium*, **16**:675 (1955).

Ridley, E. C.: The Interpolation of Atomic Fields, *Proc. Cambridge Phil. Soc.*, **51**:693 (1955).

————: The Self-consistent Field for Mo$^+$, *Proc. Cambridge Phil. Soc.*, **51**:702 (1955).

Shull, H., and P.-O. Löwdin: Correlation Effects in Two-electron Systems, *Svensk. Kem. Tidskr.*, **67**:370 (1955).

————: On the Selection of Orthogonal Sets in the Method of Superposition of Configurations, *Svensk. Kem. Tidskr.*, **67**:373 (1955).

———— and P.-O. Löwdin: Concerning the Pauli Exclusion Principle, *Svensk. Kem. Tidskr.*, **67**:375 (1955).

Shull, H., and P.-O.Löwdin: Role of the Continuum in Superposition of Configurations, *J. Chem. Phys.*, **23**:1362 (1955).

—— and ——: Natural Spin-Orbitals for Helium, *J. Chem. Phys.*, **23**:1565 (1955).

Yilmaz, H.: Wave Functions and Transition Probabilities for Light Atoms, *Phys. Rev.*, **100**:1148 (1955).

Zirin, H.: Wave Functions, Spin-Orbit and Spin-Spin Parameters for the $1s^22s^22p^4$ Isoelectronic Sequence, *Astrophys. J.*, **122**:52 (1955).

1956

Douglas, A. S.: A Method of Improving Energy-level Calculations for "Series" Electrons, *Proc. Cambridge Phil. Soc.*, **52**:687 (1956).

Hartree, D. R.: Approximate Wave Functions for Some Atoms of the First Long Period, *J. Opt. Soc. Am.*, **46**:350 (1956). [Approximate $3d$ and $4s$ wave functions for Ti+, V++, Mn, Mn+, Zn++.]

Holøien, E.: Further Remarks on Atomic Component Orbitals for the Configurations $1s^22s$ and $1s^22s^2$, *Ark. Math. Naturvidenskab.*, **53** (5): (1956).

Hylleraas, E. A., and J. Midtdal: Ground-state Energy of Two-electron Atoms, *Phys. Rev.*, **103**:829 (1956).

Löwdin, P.-O., and H. Shull: Natural Orbitals in the Quantum Theory of the Two-electron System, *Phys. Rev.*, **101**:1730 (1956).

—— and K. Appel: Studies of Atomic Self-consistent Fields. Analytic Wave Functions for the Argon-like Ions and for the First Row of the Transition Metals, *Phys. Rev.*, **103**:1746 (1956).

Morse, P. M., and H. Yilmaz: "Tables for the Variational Calculation of Atomic Wave Functions," Technology Press, Cambridge, Mass., 1956.

Piper, W. W.: A Digital Computer Program for Determining Atomic Wave Functions, *Trans. AIEE*, (I) 75:152 (1956); *Communs. Electronics*, no. 24 (1956).

Pluvinage, P.: On the Rigorous Solution of Schrödinger's Equation for Atoms with Two Electrons, *Compt. rend.*, **242**:2109 (1956).

Pratt, Jr., G. W.: Unrestricted Hartree-Fock Method, *Phys. Rev.*, **102**:1303 (1956).

Ridley, E. C.: Approximate Self-consistent Fields for In+3 and Sb+3, *Proc. Cambridge Phil. Soc.*, **52**:698 (1956).

Shull, H., and P.-O. Löwdin: Natural Orbitals in the Quantum Theory of Two-electron Systems, *Phys. Rev.*, **101**:1730 (1956).

—— and ——: Correlation Splitting in Helium-like Ions, *J. Chem. Phys.*, **25**:1035 (1956).

Stern, F.: Self-consistent Field Calculation for Three Configurations of Atomic Iron, *Phys. Rev.*, **104**:684 (1956).

Tsyunaitis, G. K., V. V. Kibartas, and A. P. Yutsis: The Self-consistent Field for the Basic Configuration of Atoms of Helium Type, *Optika i Spektroskopiya*, **1**:5 (1956).

Tubis, A.: Tables of Atomic Wave Functions and Energies for Light Elements, *Phys. Rev.*, **102**:1049 (1956).

Vizbaraite, Ya. I., A. I. Kantserevichyus, and A. P. Yutsis: Self-consistent Fock Field for the Excited Helium Atom, *Optika i Spektroskopiya*, **1**:9 (1956).

Wilets, I., and I. J. Cherry: Lower Bound to the Ground-state Energy and Mass Polarization in Helium-like Atoms, *Phys. Rev.*, **103**:112 (1956).

1957

Brigman, G. H., and F. A. Matsen: Open Configuration Calculations for Lithium, *J. Chem. Phys.*, **27**:829 (1957).

Froese, C.: The Self-consistent Field with Exchange for Some 10 and 12 Electron Systems, *Proc. Cambridge Phil. Soc.*, **53**:206 (1957).

—— and D. R. Hartree: Wave Functions for the Normal States of Ne^{+3} and Ne^{+4}, *Proc. Cambridge Phil. Soc.*, **53**:663 (1957).

——: The Limiting Behavior of Atomic Wave Functions for Large Atomic Number, *Proc. Roy. Soc. (London)*, **A239**:311 (1957).

Hart, J. F., and G. Herzberg: Twenty-parameter Eigenfunctions and Energy Values of the Ground States of He and He-like Ions, *Phys. Rev.*, **106**:79 (1957).

Kinoshita, T.: Ground State of the Helium Atom, *Phys. Rev.*, **105**:1490 (1957).

Mayers, D. F.: Relativistic Self-consistent Field Calculation for Mercury, *Proc. Roy. Soc. (London)*, **A241**:93 (1957).

Munschy, G., and P. Pluvinage: Résolution de l'équation de Schrödinger des atomes à deux électrons II.   Méthode rigoreuse, états S symétriques, *J. phys. radium*, **18**:157 (1957).

Pluvinage, P.: Sur la valeur théorique de l'énergie de l'état fondamental de He I, *J. phys. radium*, **18**:474 (1957).

Stewart, A. L.: Wave Functions for Helium and Similar Atomic Systems, *Proc. Phys. Soc. (London)*, **A70**:756 (1957).

Vainshtein, L. A.: The Calculation of Atomic Wave Functions and Oscillator Strengths with an Electronic Computer, *Optika i Spektroskopiya*, **3**:313 (1957).

Wood, J. H., and G. W. Pratt, Jr.: Wave Functions and Energy Levels for Fe as Found by the Unrestricted Hartree-Fock Method, *Phys. Rev.*, **107**:995 (1957).

1958

Breene, Jr., R. G.: Analytic Wave Functions I.   Atoms with 1s, 2s, and 2p Electrons, *Phys. Rev.*, **111**:1111 (1958).

——: Analytic Wave Functions II.   Atoms with 1s, 2s, 2p, 3s, and 3p Electrons, *Phys. Rev.*, **113**:809 (1959).

Brigman, G. H., R. P. Hurst, J. D. Gran, and F. A. Matsen: Open Configuration Calculations for Beryllium, *J. Chem. Phys.*, **29**:251 (1958).

Burke, E. A., and J. F. Mulligan: Open-shell Energies of Lithium-type Ions, *J. Chem. Phys.*, **28**:995 (1958).

Froese, C.: The Limiting Behavior of Atomic Wave Functions for Large Atomic Number II, *Proc. Roy. Soc. (London)*, **A244**:390 (1958).

Gold, A., and R. S. Knox: Excited State Wave Functions, Excitation Energies, and Oscillator Strengths for Ne $2p^53s$, *Phys. Rev.*, **113**:834 (1959).

Green, L. C., S. Matsuchima, C. Stephens, E. K. Kolchin, M. M. Kohler, Y. Wang, B. B. Baldwin, and R. J. Wisner: Effect on the Energy of Increased Flexibility in the Separable Factor of Hylleraas-type Atomic Wave Functions from H$^-$ to O VII, *Phys. Rev.*, **112**:1187 (1958).

Günther, M.: Two-quantum Interaction Correction for the Ground-state Energy of the Helium atom, *Phys. Rev.*, **111**:182 (1958).

Gupta, B. K., and V. S. R. Rao: Configuration Interaction in the Ground State and Two Excited States 1s2s ^1S and 1s3s ^1S of He Atom, *Proc. Phys. Soc. (London)*, **71**:1015 (1958).

Hartree, D. R.: Variation of Atomic Wave Functions with Atomic Number, *Revs. Modern Phys.*, **30**:63 (1958).

——: Representation of the Exchange Terms in Fock's Equations by a Quasi-potential, *Phys. Rev.*, **109**:840 (1958).

Holøien, E.: The $2s^2$ ^1S State Solution of the Nonrelativistic Schrödinger Equation for Helium and the Negative Hydrogen Ion, *Proc. Phys. Soc. (London)*, **71**:357 (1958).

Holøien, E.: On the $2p^2$ State Solution of the Nonrelativistic Schrödinger Helium Equation, *Proc. Phys. Soc. (London)*, **72**:141 (1958).

Horak, Z.: Calculations of the Excited States of Atoms, *Czechoslov. J. Phys.*, **8**:271 (1958).

Hurst, R. P., J. D. Gray, G. H. Brigman, and F. A. Matsen: Open Shell Calculations for the Two- and Three-electron Ions, *Molecular Phys.*, **1**:189 (1958).

Hylleraas, E. A., and J. Midtdal: Ground State Energy of Two-electron Atoms, *Phys. Rev.*, **109**:1013 (1958).

Knox, R. S.: Excited-state Wave Functions, Excitation Energies, and Oscillator Strengths for Argon $3p^5rs$, *Phys. Rev.*, **110**:375 (1958).

Nesbet, R. K., and R. E. Watson: Approximate Wave Functions for the Ground State of Helium, *Phys. Rev.*, **110**:1073 (1958).

Nicklas, J. P., and C. E. Treanor: Hartree-Fock Functions and Spectral Isotope Shift for Excited States of Carbon and Oxygen, *Phys. Rev.*, **110**:370 (1958).

Pekeris, C. L.: Ground State of Two-electron Atoms, *Phys. Rev.*, **112**:1649 (1958).

Ridley, E. C.: Self-consistent Field without Exchange for U^{+6}, *Proc. Roy. Soc. (London)*, **A243**:422 (1958).

Saturno, A. F., and R. G. Parr: Improved Simple Analytical Wave Functions for Atoms, *J. Chem. Phys.*, **29**:490 (1958).

Snyder, L. C., and R. G. Parr: Some Extraordinary Functions for Improving Calculations of Electronic Energies, *J. Chem. Phys.*, **28**:1250 (1958).

Traub, J., and H. M. Foley: Variational Calculations of the 2 ^3S State of Helium, *Phys. Rev.*, **111**:1098 (1958).

Tycko, D. H., L. H. Thomas, and K. M. King: Numerical Calculation of the Wave Functions and Energies of the 1 ^1S and 2 ^3S States of Helium, *Phys. Rev.*, **109**:369 (1958).

Watson, R. E.: Analytic Hartree-Fock Solutions for O^-, *Phys. Rev.*, **111**:1108 (1958).

Worsley, B. H.: The Self-consistent Field with Exchange for Neon by FERUT Program, *Can. J. Phys.*, **36**:280 (1958).

———: Radial Wave Functions with Exchange for V^{++}, Kr, and Ag^+, *Proc. Roy. Soc. (London)*, **A247**:390 (1958).

Appendix 17

The Thomas-Fermi Method for Atoms

The Thomas-Fermi method is based on the Fermi-Dirac[1] theory of a free-electron gas. Let us therefore first consider that theory. We consider a gas consisting of free electrons, acted on by no forces, moving in a cubical box bounded by infinitely high potential barriers at $x = 0$, $x = A$, $y = 0$, $y = A$, $z = 0$, $z = A$. Since actually these electrons will exert repulsive forces on each other, we may assume that they are to be handled by a self-consistent-field method and that we are to have a uniform density of positively charged material, throughout the box, of density just enough to balance the average negative charge density of the electrons. The ordinary Fermi-Dirac theory neglects exchange effects and assumes that under these circumstances the electrons can be considered to move as if they had no potential energy. We shall consider the exchange effects later, in Appendix 22 (Vol. II).

The wave function for a free electron moving in such a box is

$$u = \sin \frac{n_x \pi x}{A} \sin \frac{n_y \pi y}{A} \sin \frac{n_z \pi z}{A} \tag{A17-1}$$

This is not normalized, but we shall not have to use the normalization. The kinetic energy of the electron with this wave function is

$$E = \frac{h^2}{8mA^2} (n_x^2 + n_y^2 + n_z^2) \tag{A17-2}$$

Here n_x, n_y, n_z are positive integers. The wave function for the completed electronic system will be a product of functions of the type of Eq. (A17-1) or, more properly, an antisymmetrized product or determinantal function. We shall take account of the antisymmetry only to the extent of assuming the exclusion principle, according to which no more than one electron of each spin can have a given set of n's.

We wish to find how many electrons have energy less than a particular value, E_0. Let us take a space in which n_x, n_y, n_z are plotted as rec-

[1] E. Fermi, *Z. Physik*, **36**:902 (1926); P. A. M. Dirac, *Proc. Roy. Soc. (London)*, **A112**:661 (1926).

tangular coordinates. One wave function and hence two electrons, one of each spin, are associated with each set of positive n's, or with each unit volume in the first octant of this space. The surface of constant energy is a sphere, as we see from Eq. (A17-2), with radius $(8mA^2E_0/h^2)^{1/2}$. The volume enclosed by the sphere is $4\pi/3$ times the cube of the radius. The volume in the first octant is one-eighth of this, and since we have two electrons for each set of n's, we find that the number of electrons with energy less than E_0 is

$$\frac{\pi}{3}\left(\frac{8mA^2E_0}{h^2}\right)^{3/2} = \frac{8\pi}{3}\,V\,\frac{(2mE_0)^{3/2}}{h^3} \qquad (A17\text{-}3)$$

where V, the volume, equals A^3. If, then, all energy states with energy up to E_0 are filled, the number of electrons per unit volume will be $(8\pi/3)(2mE_0)^{3/2}/h^3$ and the electronic charge density is $-e$ times this quantity. The continuous distribution of positive charge must then have the same magnitude but opposite sign.

Now we are ready to consider the Thomas-Fermi assumptions. Let the electrostatic potential at a point within the atom be $V(r)$, a function of r. The potential energy of an electron at a point r will be $-eV(r)$. Let us suppose that we have electrons at this point with all values of kinetic energy from zero up to $eV(r)$, such that the electrons of maximum kinetic energy have zero total energy and are just prevented from escaping from the atom [we assume that $V(r)$ goes to zero as r becomes infinite]. Then Thomas and Fermi assumed that the charge density of electrons at distance r from the nucleus would be determined from this maximum kinetic energy just as it would be in a free electron gas with the same maximum kinetic energy. In other words, they assumed that the charge density ρ of electronic charge was

$$\rho = -e\,\frac{8\pi}{3}\,\frac{[2meV(r)]^{3/2}}{h^3} \qquad (A17\text{-}4)$$

In an atom, however, there is no uniformly distributed positive charge; the positive charge is concentrated at the nucleus and is of amount Ze.

We can now apply essentially the condition of self-consistency: the electrostatic potential $V(r)$ must be determined by Poisson's equation from the charge density ρ of the electrons, as given in Eq. (A17-4), and from the nuclear charge. Poisson's equation is

$$\nabla^2 V = -\frac{\rho}{\epsilon_0} = \frac{8\pi e}{3\epsilon_0}\,\frac{[2meV(r)]^{3/2}}{h^3} \qquad (A17\text{-}5)$$

In Eq. (A17-5) we have the fundamental form of the Thomas-Fermi equation determining the potential V. It is more convenient, however, to put it in a different form.

Let us write the potential $V(r)$ in the form

$$V(r) = \frac{Z_p(r)e}{4\pi\epsilon_0 r} \tag{A17-6}$$

where Z_p is the same effective Z for potential which we have used in the text. Let us write

$$\phi = \frac{Z_p(r)}{Z} \qquad x = \frac{r}{(a_0/4)(9\pi^2/2Z)^{\frac{1}{3}}} \tag{A17-7}$$

where Z is the atomic number, a_0 the Bohr hydrogen radius. Then we find that Eq. (A17-5) takes the form

$$\frac{d^2\phi}{dx^2} = \phi^{\frac{3}{2}}x^{-\frac{1}{2}} \tag{A17-8}$$

Equation (17-8) is the standard form of the Thomas-Fermi equation. It cannot be solved analytically, but numerical solutions have been given. We wish a solution which goes to unity when $x = 0$, since Z_p must equal Z at the origin, and which goes to zero at infinite x. This solution, as determined numerically, is given in Table A17-1.

Table A17-1

Thomas-Fermi function ϕ, as function of x, from Eqs. (A17-7) and (A17-8). Taken from P. Gombas, "Die Statistische Theorie des Atoms und ihre Anwendungen," p. 45, Springer-Verlag, Vienna, 1949.

x	ϕ	x	ϕ
0.000	1.000	1.2	0.375
0.010	0.985	1.4	0.333
0.020	0.972	1.6	0.297
0.030	0.959	1.8	0.268
0.040	0.947	2.0	0.244
0.050	0.935	2.2	0.221
0.060	0.924	2.4	0.202
0.080	0.902	2.6	0.185
0.100	0.882	2.8	0.170
0.150	0.835	3.0	0.157
0.200	0.793	3.5	0.130
0.300	0.721	4.0	0.108
0.400	0.660	5.0	0.0788
0.500	0.607	7.5	0.0408
0.600	0.562	10.0	0.0244
0.700	0.521	20.0	0.0058
0.800	0.485	30.0	0.0022
0.900	0.453	40.0	0.0011
1.000	0.425	50.0	0.00061

The function $\phi(x)$, as tabulated in Table 17-1, gives a universal curve of Z_p as a function of r, to the approximation to which the Thomas-Fermi method is applicable. The quantity ϕ, as we see from Eq. (A17-7), is Z_p/Z. The quantity x is the distance, expressed in multiples of a unit which numerically is $0.8853a_0/Z^{1/3}$. The simple curve for Z_p given in this way represents with remarkable accuracy the general trend of the curves derived by the method of the self-consistent field.

Appendix 18

Commutation Properties of Angular Momenta for Complex Atoms

In Eq. (11-15) we have given the commutation relations which hold for the orbital angular-momentum operator of a single electron. The orbital angular-momentum operator of a complex atom equals the sum of the operators for the various electrons. If we denote its x, y, and z components by $\Sigma(L_x)_{op}$, etc., then we wish to prove that

$$\Sigma(L_y)_{op}\Sigma(L_z)_{op} - \Sigma(L_z)_{op}\Sigma(L_y)_{op} = i\Sigma(L_x)_{op} \qquad \text{(A18-1)}$$

etc. In the double sums, we have terms in which both operators, such as $(L_y)_{op}$ and $(L_z)_{op}$, refer to the same electron and other terms in which they refer to different electrons. In the latter case, they automatically commute, for the coordinates and momenta of one particle commute with those of another. Hence the only nonvanishing terms on the left side of Eq. (A18-1) come from the single sum of terms $(L_y)_{op}(L_z)_{op} - (L_z)_{op}(L_y)_{op}$ in which both operators refer to the same electron. In this case, Eq. (11-15) holds for the operators of each electron, and when we sum over electrons, we are led to Eq. (A18-1). A similar proof will hold for the spin operators.

We wish next to show that neither the total orbital angular momentum nor the total spin will commute with the term $\gamma(\mathbf{L} \cdot \mathbf{S})$ in the Hamiltonian but that the total angular momentum, orbital plus spin, will commute with this term, as well as with all other terms in the Hamiltonian. Let us first consider a one-electron case. We find that the components of $(L)_{op}$ do not commute with $(\mathbf{L} \cdot \mathbf{S})_{op}$. For example, from Eq. (11-15), we can show that

$$(L_x)_{op}[(L_x)_{op}(S_x)_{op} + (L_y)_{op}(S_y)_{op} + (L_z)_{op}(S_z)_{op}]$$
$$- [(L_x)_{op}(S_x)_{op} + (L_y)_{op}(S_y)_{op} + (L_z)_{op}(S_z)_{op}](L_x)_{op}$$
$$= [(L_x)_{op}(L_y)_{op} - (L_y)_{op}(L_x)_{op}](S_y)_{op}$$
$$+ [(L_x)_{op}(L_z)_{op} - (L_z)_{op}(L_x)_{op}](S_z)_{op}$$
$$= i[(L_z)_{op}(S_y)_{op} - (L_y)_{op}(S_z)_{op}] \qquad \text{(A18-2)}$$

There is no reason why this should vanish.   However, if we compute the commutator of $(S_x)_{op}$ with $(\mathbf{L} \cdot \mathbf{S})_{op}$ in the same way, we find a result which is the negative of that given in Eq. (A18-2).   Hence we see that $(L_x + S_x)_{op}$ commutes with $(\mathbf{L} \cdot \mathbf{S})_{op}$, which was to be shown.   The fact that the total angular momentum commutes with the other terms in the Hamiltonian can be proved very easily by direct calculation.   The extension to the many-electron case follows as in the preceding paragraph.

Appendix 19

Positive Nature of Exchange Integrals

We wish to show that an exchange integral, such as

$$\int u_1^*(r_1)u_2^*(r_2)g_{12}u_2(r_1)u_1(r_2)\, dv_1\, dv_2$$

is necessarily positive, where r_1, etc., symbolize x_1, y_1, z_1. If we write $u_1^*(r_1)u_2(r_1) = F(r_1)$, the exchange integral may be rewritten in the form

$$\text{Exchange integral} = 2\int F(r_1)F^*(r_2)\frac{1}{r_{12}}\, dv_1\, dv_2 \qquad \text{(A19-1)}$$

in which we have written $g_{12} = 2/r_{12}$. We may now define a potential, as

$$\phi(r_1) = \int F^*(r_2)\frac{1}{r_{12}}\, dv_2 \qquad \text{(A19-2)}$$

By Green's theorem, we know that, for any function ϕ, we must have

$$\phi(r_1) = -\frac{1}{4\pi}\int \frac{\nabla^2\phi(r_2)}{r_{12}}\, dv_2 \qquad \text{(A19-3)}$$

where the integration is over all space, and where it is assumed that ϕ vanishes sufficiently rapidly at infinity to avoid surface integrals. Hence we must have

$$F^*(r_2) = -\frac{1}{4\pi}\nabla^2\phi(r_2) \qquad \text{(A19-4)}$$

from which

$$F(r_1) = -\frac{1}{4\pi}\nabla^2\phi^*(r_1) \qquad \text{(A19-5)}$$

We may now use these results to rewrite the exchange integral in the form

$$\text{Exchange integral} = -\frac{2}{4\pi}\int \phi(r_1)\nabla^2\phi^*(r_1)\, dv_1 \qquad \text{(A19-6)}$$

We now use the vector identity

$$\nabla(\phi\nabla\phi^*) = \phi\nabla^2\phi^* + \nabla\phi\cdot\nabla\phi^* \qquad \text{(A19-7)}$$

486

which holds for any pair of functions ϕ, ϕ^*. We integrate this equation over all space. The divergence on the left side, by the divergence theorem, integrates to a surface integral over the volume enclosing the space, and in the case we are assuming, the functions will vanish rapidly enough at infinity so that these integrated terms vanish. Hence we are left with the result that

$$\int \phi \nabla^2 \phi^* \, dv = -\int \nabla \phi \cdot \nabla \phi^* \, dv \tag{A19-8}$$

That is, we have

$$\text{Exchange integral} = \frac{2}{4\pi} \int |\nabla \phi|^2 \, dv \tag{A19-9}$$

Since this is the integral of a square, it is necessarily positive, which was to be proved.

Appendix 20a

Tabulation of c's and a's for Multiplet Theory for s, p, and d Electrons

In this appendix we give the values of $c^k(l_i m_{li}; l_j m_{lj})$ and of $a^k(l_i m_{li}; l_j m_{lj})$, as defined in Eqs. (13-17) and (13-21), respectively, for s, p, and d electrons. Values for higher l's are given in Appendix 20, in Vol. II. Note that $c^k(l_j m_{lj}; l_i m_{li}) = (-1)^{(m_{li}-m_{lj})} c^k(l_i m_{li}; l_j m_{lj})$. The values of l_i and l_j are given by the symbols s, p, d of the electrons. We now give values of c^k in Table A20a-1 and of a^k in Table A20a-2.

Table A20a-1. $c^k(l_i m_{li}; l_j, m_{lj})$ for s, p, d Electrons

	m_{li}	m_{lj}	k				
			0	1	2	3	4
ss	0	0	1	0	0	0	0
sp	0	± 1	0	$-\sqrt{1/3}$	0	0	0
	0	0	0	$\sqrt{1/3}$	0	0	0
pp	± 1	± 1	1	0	$-\sqrt{1/25}$	0	0
	± 1	0	0	0	$\sqrt{3/25}$	0	0
	± 1	∓ 1	0	0	$-\sqrt{6/25}$	0	0
	0	0	1	,0	$\sqrt{4/25}$	0	0
sd	0	± 2	0	0	$\sqrt{1/5}$	0	0
	0	± 1	0	0	$-\sqrt{1/5}$	0	0
	0	0	0	0	$\sqrt{1/5}$	0	0
pd	± 1	± 2	0	$-\sqrt{6/15}$	0	$\sqrt{3/245}$	0
	± 1	± 1	0	$\sqrt{3/15}$	0	$-\sqrt{9/245}$	0
	± 1	0	0	$-\sqrt{1/15}$	0	$\sqrt{18/245}$	0
	± 1	∓ 1	0	0	0	$-\sqrt{30/245}$	0
	± 1	∓ 2	0	0	0	$\sqrt{45/245}$	0
	0	± 2	0	0	0	$\sqrt{15/245}$	0
	0	± 1	0	$-\sqrt{3/15}$	0	$-\sqrt{24/245}$	0
	0	0	0	$\sqrt{4/15}$	0	$\sqrt{27/245}$	0
dd	± 2	± 2	1	0	$-\sqrt{4/49}$	0	$\sqrt{1/441}$
	± 2	± 1	0	0	$\sqrt{6/49}$	0	$-\sqrt{5/441}$
	± 2	0	0	0	$-\sqrt{4/49}$	0	$\sqrt{15/441}$
	± 2	∓ 1	0	0	0	0	$-\sqrt{35/441}$
	± 2	∓ 2	0	0	0	0	$\sqrt{70/441}$
	± 1	± 1	1	0	$\sqrt{1/49}$	0	$-\sqrt{16/441}$
	± 1	0	0	0	$\sqrt{1/49}$	0	$\sqrt{30/441}$
	± 1	∓ 1	0	0	$-\sqrt{6/49}$	0	$-\sqrt{40/441}$
	0	0	1	0	$\sqrt{4/49}$	0	$\sqrt{36/441}$

Note: In cases where there are two $\pm$ signs, the two upper or the two lower signs must be taken together.

Table A20a-2. $a^k(l_i m_{li}; l_j m_{lj})$ for s, p, d Electrons

	m_{li}	m_{lj}	k		
			0	2	4
ss	0	0	1	0	0
sp	0	± 1	1	0	0
	0	0	1	0	0
pp	± 1	± 1	1	$\frac{1}{25}$	0
	± 1	0	1	$-\frac{2}{25}$	0
	0	0	1	$\frac{4}{25}$	0
sd	0	± 2	1	0	0
	0	± 1	1	0	0
	0	0	1	0	0
pd	± 1	± 2	1	$\frac{2}{35}$	0
	± 1	± 1	1	$-\frac{1}{35}$	0
	± 1	0	1	$-\frac{2}{35}$	0
	0	± 2	1	$-\frac{4}{35}$	0
	0	± 1	1	$\frac{2}{35}$	0
	0	0	1	$\frac{4}{35}$	0
dd	± 2	± 2	1	$\frac{4}{49}$	$\frac{1}{441}$
	± 2	± 1	1	$-\frac{2}{49}$	$-\frac{4}{441}$
	± 2	0	1	$-\frac{4}{49}$	$\frac{6}{441}$
	± 1	± 1	1	$\frac{1}{49}$	$\frac{19}{441}$
	± 1	0	1	$\frac{2}{49}$	$-\frac{24}{441}$
	0	0	1	$\frac{4}{49}$	$\frac{36}{441}$

Note: In cases with two $\pm$ signs, the signs can be combined in any of the four possible ways.

Appendix 21a

Tabulation of Energies of Multiplets

In this appendix we list the energies of the multiplets p^n and d^n and give Van Vleck's rule for getting the multiplets of $p^n s$ or $d^n s$ from those of p^n or d^n. A much more complete tabulation of the energies of multiplets is given in Appendix 21, contained in Vol. II. We first give the configurations p^2 and p^3, already discussed in the text; we recall that the multiplets for p^4 are identical with those of p^2. The energies are

$$p^2 \; {}^3P : E_{av} - \tfrac{3}{25}F^2(pp)$$
$$ {}^1D : E_{av} + \tfrac{3}{25}F^2(pp)$$
$$ {}^1S : E_{av} + 1\tfrac{2}{25}F^2(pp)$$
$$p^3 \; {}^4S^0 : E_{av} - \tfrac{9}{25}F^2(pp)$$
$$ {}^2D^0 : E_{av}$$
$$ {}^2P^0 : E_{av} + \tfrac{6}{25}F^2(pp)$$

Next we give, in Table A21a-1, the energies for the configurations d^2, d^3, d^4, d^5. We recall that d^6 is identical with d^4, d^7 with d^3, and d^8 with d^2. In this case, unlike that of p^n, we find more than one multiplet with the same value of S and L, the first case being that of two ${}^2D$'s in d^3. We have denoted these by subscripts, such as 1 and 2. In such cases we give the nondiagonal matrix components of the Hamiltonian between states with the same S and L values, as well as the diagonal components. To save writing, we omit the term E_{av} in writing the energies and present the results in the form of tables: the quantities tabulated are in each case to be multiplied by the integrals, such as $F^2(dd)$, standing at the head of the column.

We next give Van Vleck's[1] rule for writing the energy of a configuration $l^n s$ (that is, $p^n s$ for $l = 1$, $d^n s$ for $l = 2$), in case we know the energies of l^n. By Van Vleck's theorem, we can write the energy of each multiplet of this configuration as the sum of the energy of the parent multiplet and a diagonal term to be added to the diagonal matrix components of the energy. We give the term to be added in each case, in Table A21a-2.

[1] J. H. Van Vleck, *Phys. Rev.*, **46**:405 (1934); see also Vol. II, Eq. (21-52).

Table A21a-1

Diagonal and nondiagonal matrix components for multiplets of configurations d^n. The quantities tabulated are in each case to be multiplied by the integrals, such as $F^2(dd)$, standing at the head of the column.   In each case E_{av} is to be added to diagonal components.

	$F^2(dd)$	$F^4(dd)$
d^2 diagonal matrix components		
^3F	$-58/441$	$5/441$
^3P	$77/441$	$-70/441$
^1G	$50/441$	$15/441$
^1D	$-13/441$	$50/441$
^1S	$140/441$	$140/441$
d^3 diagonal matrix components		
^4F	$-93/441$	$-30/441$
^4P	$42/441$	$-105/441$
^2H	$-12/441$	$30/441$
^2G	$-57/441$	$55/441$
^2F	$123/441$	$-45/441$
$^2D_1$	$105/441$	$105/441$
$^2D_2$	$69/441$	$-15/441$
^2P	$-12/441$	$30/441$
d^3 nondiagonal matrix component		
$^2D_1$—$^2D_2$	$27\sqrt{21}/441$	$-15\sqrt{21}/441$
d^4 diagonal matrix components		
^5D	$-105/441$	$-105/441$
^3H	$-69/441$	$15/441$
^3G	$-24/441$	$-10/441$
$^3F_1$	$66/441$	$45/441$
$^3F_2$	$12/441$	$-30/441$
^3D	$39/441$	$-45/441$
$^3P_1$	$21/441$	$70/441$
$^3P_2$	$57/441$	$-55/441$
^1I	$-51/441$	$75/441$
$^1G_1$	$30/441$	$135/441$
$^1G_2$	$48/441$	$20/441$
^1F	$84/441$	0
$^1D_1$	$219/441$	$30/441$
$^1D_2$	$111/441$	$-15/441$
$^1S_1$	$210/441$	$210/441$
$^1S_2$	$138/441$	$-30/441$

Table A21a-1 (Continued)

	$F^2(dd)$	$F^4(dd)$
d^4 nondiagonal matrix components		
$^3F_1$—$^3F_2$	$108/441$	$-60/441$
$^3P_1$—$^3P_2$	$36\sqrt{14}/441$	$-20\sqrt{14}/441$
$^1G_1$—$^1G_2$	$36\sqrt{11}/441$	$-20\sqrt{11}/441$
$^1D_1$—$^1D_2$	$108\sqrt{2}/441$	$-60\sqrt{2}/441$
$^1S_1$—$^1S_2$	$54\sqrt{21}/441$	$-30\sqrt{21}/441$
d^5 diagonal matrix components		
^6S	$-175/441$	$-175/441$
^4G	$-85/441$	$-50/441$
^4F	$23/441$	$-40/441$
^4D	$-22/441$	$-85/441$
^4P	$-112/441$	$35/441$
^2I	$-76/441$	$50/441$
^2H	$-58/441$	$110/441$
$^2G_1$	$167/441$	$-15/441$
$^2G_2$	$23/441$	$-5/441$
$^2F_1$	$-85/441$	$125/441$
$^2F_2$	$59/441$	$-25/441$
$^2D_1$	$140/441$	$140/441$
$^2D_2$	$104/441$	$20/441$
$^2D_3$	$86/441$	$-40/441$
^2P	$320/441$	$-100/441$
^2S	$113/441$	$-55/441$
d^5 nondiagonal matrix component†		
$^2D_1$—$^2D_2$	$54\sqrt{14}/441$	$-30\sqrt{14}/441$

† All other nondiagonal matrix components vanish.

Table A21a-2

Terms to be added to diagonal matrix components of configuration l^n, to get diagonal matrix components of $l^n s$, according to Van Vleck's theorem.

Parent	Multiplet	Added term in energy
Singlet	Doublet	Zero
Doublet	Triplet	$-\dfrac{1}{2}\dfrac{G^l(sl)}{2l+1}$
	Singlet	$\dfrac{3}{2}\dfrac{G^l(sl)}{2l+1}$
Triplet	Quartet	$-\dfrac{G^l(sl)}{2l+1}$
	Doublet	$2\dfrac{G^l(sl)}{2l+1}$
Quartet	Quintet	$-\dfrac{3}{2}\dfrac{G^l(sl)}{2l+1}$
	Triplet	$\dfrac{5}{2}\dfrac{G^l(sl)}{2l+1}$
Quintet	Sextet	$-2\dfrac{G^l(sl)}{2l+1}$
	Quartet	$3\dfrac{G^l(sl)}{2l+1}$
Sextet	Septet	$-\dfrac{5}{2}\dfrac{G^l(sl)}{2l+1}$
	Quintet	$\dfrac{7}{2}\dfrac{G^l(sl)}{2l+1}$

Index